Voices from the Past

The Cycle of Life
in Indo-European Folktales

D. L. Ashliman

Third Edition, Expanded and Revised

For Patricia

Contents

Prologue

Once upon a time a holy man told tales of beasts that talk and ghosts that live in trees. His people heard, and understood. An old seafarer pointed out the creatures in the sky and remembered times before the sea had salt. And a deformed, hunchbacked slave, some say, told fables so filled with beauty, wisdom and wit, that his master set him free. Then a clever woman stayed her husband's murderous hand for a thousand and one nights with as many well wrought tales. A carpenter from Nazareth taught with stories of prodigal sons and good Samaritans, and a new religion was born. Refugees eased the pain of exile with stories, some recalled from happier times, others made up on demand. Pilgrims shortened their hard and dangerous road with accounts of strength and faith, and yes of greed and guile and lust. And a mother comforts her child with fantasies of make believe and far away and long ago and once upon a time.

Voices from the Past

Origins

Giants in Denmark

Saxo Grammaticus

That the country of Denmark was once cultivated and worked by giants, is attested by the enormous stones attached to the barrows and caves of the ancients. Should any man question that this is accomplished by superhuman force, let him look up at the tops of certain mountains and say, if he knows, what man has carried such immense boulders up to their crests. For anyone considering this marvel will mark that it is inconceivable how a mass, hardly at all or but with difficulty movable upon a level, could have been raised to so mighty a peak of so lofty a mountain by mere human effort, or by the ordinary exertion of human strength. But as to whether, after the deluge[1] went forth, there existed giants who could do such deeds, or men endowed beyond others with bodily force, there is scant tradition to tell us.

But, as our countrymen assert, even today there are those who dwell in that rugged and inaccessible region to the north who, by the transformable nature of their bodies, are granted the power of being near or distant, and of appearing and vanishing in turn. The approach to this region, whose position and name are unknown, and which lacks all civilization, but teems with peoples of monstrous strangeness, is beset with perils of a fearful kind, and has seldom granted to those who attempted it an unscathed return.[2]

---

[1]Early Christian theologians often theorized that the flood of Noah had killed off the giants and similar creatures who previously inhabited the earth.

[2]Source: The First Nine Books of the Danish History of Saxo Grammaticus [Gesta Danorum], translated by Oliver Elton (London, 1894), pp. 12-14. Slightly revised. Saxo's Gesta Danorum (The Deeds of the Danes) was written ca. 1208.

The Frau Holle Stone

Germany

In the forest near Fulda there is a stone with many furrows. It was there that Frau Holle cried such bitter tears over her husband that it softened the hard stone.[3]

Druidical Circles and Monoliths

Scotland

Druidical circles and monoliths were looked upon with awe; and there were few that would have dared to remove them. Here is a tradition of a monolith on the farm of Achorrachin in Glenlivet. The farmer was building a steading, and took the stone as a lintel to a byre door. Disease fell upon the cattle, and most unearthly noises were heard during the night all round the steading. There was no peace for man or beast. By the advice of a friend, the stone was taken from the wall and thrown into the river that ran past the farm. Still there was no peace. The stone was at last put into its old place in the middle of a field. Things then returned to their usual course. The stone stands to the present day in the middle of the field, and in some of its crevices were seen, not many years ago, small pieces of mortar.[4]

---

[3]Source: J. W. Wolf, *Hessische Sagen* (Göttingen and Leipzig, 1853), p. 10.

[4]Source: Walter Gregor, *Notes on the Folk-Lore of the North-East of Scotland* (London, 1881), p. 115.

Bomere Pool

England

Many years ago a village stood in the hollow which is now filled up by the mere.[5] But the inhabitants were a wicked race, who mocked at God and his priest. They turned back to the idolatrous practices of their fathers, and worshipped Thor and Woden; they scorned to bend the knee, save in mockery, to the White Christ who had died to save their souls. The old priest earnestly warned them that God would punish such wickedness as theirs by some sudden judgment, but they laughed him to scorn. They fastened fish bones to the skirt of his cassock, and set the children to pelt him with mud and stones. The holy man was not dismayed at this; nay, he renewed his entreaties and warnings, so that some few turned from their evil ways and worshipped with him in the little chapel which stood on the bank of a rivulet that flowed down from the mere on the hillside.

The rains fell that December in immense quantities. The mere was swollen beyond its usual limits, and all the hollows in the hills were filled to overflowing. One day when the old priest was on the hillside gathering fuel he noticed that the barrier of peat, earth, and stones, which prevented the mere from flowing into the valley, was apparently giving way before the mass of water above. He hurried down to the village and besought the men to come up and cut a channel for the discharge of the superfluous waters of the mere. They only greeted his proposal with shouts of derision, and told him to go and mind his prayers, and not spoil their feast with his croaking and his killjoy presence.

These heathen were then keeping their winter festival with great revelry. It fell on Christmas Eve. The same night the aged priest summoned his few faithful ones to attend at the midnight mass, which ushered in the feast of our Savior's nativity. The night was stormy, and the rain fell in torrents, yet this did not prevent the little flock from coming to the chapel. The old servant of God had already begun the holy sacrifice, when a roar was heard in the upper part of the valley. The server was just ringing the Sanctus bell which hung in the bell cot, when a flood of water dashed into the church, and rapidly rose till it put out the altar lights. In a few moments more the whole building was washed away, and the mere, which had burst its mountain barrier, occupied the hollow in which the village had stood. Men say that if you sail over the mere on Christmas Eve, just after midnight, you may hear the Sanctus bell tolling.[6]

---

[5]The word *mere* (akin to the German *Meer*, sea) can refer to a sea, an inlet, or a lake.

[6]Source: Edwin Sidney Hartland, *English Fairy and Other Folk Tales* (London, ca. 1890), pp. 83-84. Hartland's source is Charlotte S. Burne, *Shropshire Folk-Lore* (London, 1883).

4

The Origin of Tis Lake

Denmark

A troll had once taken up his abode near the village of Kund, in the high bank on which the church now stands; but when the people about there had become pious, and went constantly to church, the troll was dreadfully annoyed by their almost incessant ringing of bells in the steeple of the church. He was at last obliged, in consequence of it, to take his departure; for nothing has more contributed to the emigration of the troll folk out of the country than the increasing piety of the people, and their taking to bell ringing. The troll of Kund accordingly quitted the country, and went over to Funen, where he lived for some time in peace and quiet.

Now it chanced that a man who had lately settled in the town of Kund, coming to Funen on business, met on the road with this same troll. "Where do you live?" said the troll to him.

Now there was nothing whatever about the troll unlike a man, so he answered him, as was the truth, "I am from the town of Kund."

"So?" said the troll. "I don't know you then! And yet I think I know every man in Kund. Will you, however," continued he, "just be so kind to take a letter from me back with you to Kund?" The man said, of course, he had no objection. The troll then thrust the letter into his pocket, and charged him strictly not to take it out till he came to Kund church, and then to throw it over the churchyard wall, and the person for whom it was intended would get it.

The troll then went away in great haste, and with him the letter went entirely out of the man's mind. But when he was come back to Zealand he sat down by the meadow where Tis Lake now is, and suddenly recollected the troll's letter. He felt a great desire to look at it at least. So he took it out of his pocket, and sat a while with it in his hands, when suddenly there began to dribble a little water out of the seal. The letter now unfolded itself, and the water came out faster and faster, and it was with the utmost difficulty that the poor man was enabled to save his life; for the malicious troll had enclosed an entire lake in the letter. The troll, it is plain, had thought to avenge himself on Kund church by destroying it in this manner; but God ordered it so that the lake chanced to run out in the great meadow where it now flows.[7]

---

[7]Source: Thomas Keightley, *The Fairy Mythology* (London, 1850), pp. 111-112.

The Origin of the Wrekin

England

Once upon a time there was a wicked old giant in Wales who, for some reason or other, had a very great spite against the Mayor of Shrewsbury and all his people, and he made up his mind to dam up the Severn, and by that means cause such a flood that the town would be drowned.

So off he set, carrying a spadeful of earth, and tramped along mile after mile trying to find the way to Shrewsbury. And how he missed it I cannot tell, but he must have gone wrong somewhere, for at last he got close to Wellington, and by that time he was puffing and blowing under his heavy load, and wishing he was at the end of his journey. By and by there came a cobbler along the road with a sack of old boots and shoes on his back, for he lived at Wellington, and went once a fortnight to Shrewsbury to collect his customers' old boots and shoes, and take them home with him to mend.

And the giant called out to him. "I say," he said, "how far is it to Shrewsbury?"

"Shrewsbury?" said the cobbler; "what do you want at Shrewsbury?"

"Why," said the giant, "to fill up the Severn with this lump of earth I've got here. I've an old grudge against the mayor and the folks at Shrewsbury, and now I mean to drown them out, and get rid of them all at once."

"My word!" thought the cobbler, "this'll never do! I can't afford to lose my customers!" and he spoke up again. "Eh!" he said, "you'll never get to Shrewsbury—not today *nor* tomorrow. Why look at me! I'm just come from Shrewsbury, and I've had time to wear out all these old boots and shoes on the road since I started." And he showed him his sack.

"Oh! said the giant, with a great groan, "then it's no use! I'm fairly tired out already, and I can't carry this load of mine any farther. I shall just drop it here and go back home."

So he dropped the earth on the ground just where he stood, and scraped his boots on the spade, and off he went home again to Wales, and nobody ever heard anything of him in Shropshire after. But where he put down his load, there stands the Wrekin to this day; and even the earth that he scraped off his boots was such a pile that it made the little Ercall by the Wrekin's side.[8]

---

[8]Source: Edwin Sidney Hartland, *English Fairy and Other Folk Tales* (London, ca. 1890), pp. 85-86. Hartland's source: Charlotte S. Burne, *Shropshire Folk-Lore* (London, 1883). The Wrekin is a prominent peak (1334 feet high) just south of Wellington and Shrewsbury in western England.

Miracles

Moses and El Khudr

Palestine

The great Lawgiver was much perplexed and troubled when he thought about the apparently confused and strange dealings of Divine Providence, and besought Allah to enlighten him. He was told, in answer to her prayer, to go on a certain day to a certain place where he would meet a servant of the Merciful, who would instruct him. Moses did as he was told and found at the rendezvous a venerable dervish, who, to start with, made him promise not to make remarks or ask questions concerning anything he might see him do while they journeyed together. Moses promised, and the pair set out on their travels.

At sunset they reached a village, and went to the house of the sheik, a man rich and kindly, who bade them welcome and ordered a sheep to be killed in their honor. When bedtime came they were conducted to a large, well furnished room. The *tusht* and *ibrik*,[9] which in most houses are of tinned copper, were here of silver plate set with jewels.

Moses, being tired out, soon fell asleep; but long ere daylight his companion woke him, saying they must start at once. Moses objected, finding the bed comfortable. He declared it ungrateful to leave so early while their host was still abed and they could not thank him.

"Remember the terms of our compact," said the dervish sternly, while to Moses' amazement he coolly slipped the silver *tusht* or wash-hand-basin into the bosom of his robe. Moses then rose in silence and they left the house.

That evening, quite worn out, they reached another village, and were once more guests of the sheik, who proved the very opposite of their host of the previous night. He grumbled at the necessity he was under of harboring vagrants, and bade a servant take them to a cave behind the stable where they could sleep on a heap of chopped straw. For supper he sent them scraps of moldy bread and a few bad olives. Moses could not touch the stuff, though he was starving, but his companion made a good meal.

Next morning, Moses awoke very early, feeling hungry and miserable. He roused his guide and suggested that it was time to rise and start. But the dervish said, "No, we must not sneak away like thieves," and went to sleep again.

---

[9]Vessels for ceremonial ablution.

7

Some two hours later the ascetic rose, bade Moses put the fragments of the night's meal into his bosom, and said, "Now we must bid our host farewell." In the presence of the sheik, the dervish made a low reverence, thanking him for his hospitality towards them, and begging him to accept a slight token of their esteem. To the amazement of the sheik, as well as Moses, he produced the stolen basin, and laid it at the sheik's feet. Moses, mindful of his promise, said no word.

The third day's journey was through a barren region, where Moses was glad of the scraps which, but for the dervish, he would have thrown away. Towards evening they came to a river, which the dervish decided not to attempt to cross till next morning, preferring to spend the night in a miserable reed-built hut, where the widow of a ferryman dwelt with her orphan nephew, a boy of thirteen. The poor woman did all in her power to make them comfortable, and in the morning made them breakfast before starting. She sent her nephew with them to show the way to a ruinous bridge further down the river. She shouted instructions to the boy to guide their honors safely over it ere he returned. The guide led the way, the dervish followed him and Moses brought up the rear.

When they got to the middle of the bridge, the dervish seized the boy by the neck and flung him into the water, and so drowned him.

"Monster! Murderer!" cried Moses, beside himself.

The dervish turned upon his disciple, and the Prophet knew him for El Khudr. "You once more forget the terms of our agreement," he said sternly, "and this time we must part. All that I have done was predestined by Divine mercy. Our first host, though a man of the best intentions, was too confiding and ostentatious. The loss of his silver basin will be a lesson to him. Our second host was a skinflint. He will now begin to be hospitable in the hope of gain; but the habit will grow upon him, and gradually change his nature. As for the boy whose death so angers you, he is gone to Paradise, whereas, had he lived but two years longer, he would have killed his benefactress, and in the year following he would have killed you."[10]

---

[10]Type 934D. Source: J. E. Hanauer, *Folk-Lore of the Holy Land: Moslem, Christian, and Jewish* (London, 1935), pp. 51-53. First published 1907. Similar stories are included in *The Koran*, 18:60-82, and in chapter 18 of François-Marie Voltaire's short oriental novel *Zadig* (1747). El Khudr, the "Evergreen One," as the Moslems call him, is one of the Holy Land's most enduring folklore heroes. He is said to have successfully discovered the Fountain of Youth somewhere near the confluence of the Mediterranean Sea and the Red Sea. Christians call him "Saint George" or "Mar Jiryis." Jews attribute his exploits variously to Phinehas, the son of Eleazar, or to Elijah the prophet.

For more information on the classification of folktales by type numbers, see Antti Aarne and Stith Thompson, *The Types of the Folktale: A Classification and Bibliography* (Helsinki, 1961); and D. L. Ashliman, *A Guide to Folktales* (Westport, Connecticut, 1987).

Mar Jiryis [St. George] and the Dragon

Palestine

There was once a great city that depended for its water supply upon a fountain without the walls. A great dragon, possessed and moved by Satan himself, took possession of the fountain and refused to allow water to be taken unless, whenever people came to the spring, a youth or maiden was given to him to devour. The people tried again and again to destroy the monster; but though the flower of the city cheerfully went forth against it, its breath was so pestilential that they used to drop down dead before they came within bowshot.

The terrorized inhabitants were thus obliged to sacrifice their offspring, or die of thirst; till at last all the youth of the place had perished except the king's daughter. So great was the distress of their subjects for want of water that her heart-broken parents could no longer withhold her, and amid the tears of the populace she went out towards the spring, where the dragon lay awaiting her. But just as the noisome monster was going to leap on her, Mar Jiryis appeared, in golden panoply, upon a fine white steed, and spear in hand. Riding full tilt at the dragon, he struck it fair between the eyes and laid it dead. The king, out of gratitude for this unlooked-for succor, gave Mar Jiryis his daughter and half of his kingdom.[11]

As Many Children as There Are Days in the Year

Jacob and Wilhelm Grimm

Loosduynen (Leusden) is a small village one mile from The Hague. In the church there they still point out two baptismal fonts with the inscription, "In deze twee beckens zyn alle deze kinderen ghedoopt."[12] A plaque hanging nearby, inscribed with Latin and Dutch verses, commemorates the event described in the following popular legend:

---

[11]Type 300. Source: J. E. Hanauer, *Folk-Lore of the Holy Land: Moslem, Christian, and Jewish* (London, 1935), pp. 51-53. First published 1907. Saint George is one of the most durable legendary heroes in the western world. According to tradition, he was born in England in the fourth century and served in the imperial army in Asia Minor. He has been the patron saint of England since the middle ages and is among the greatest saints for the Eastern Orthodox Christian Churches. His famous duel with the dragon is set in various Holy Land locations plus Egypt, Libya, and even Greece.

[12]"All the children were baptized in these two fonts." The Grimms, by giving the inscription in Dutch, add credibility to their story.

9

Many years ago there lived in the village a Countess Margaretha (according to others her name was Mathilde), wife of Count Hermann of Henneberg. Sometimes she is referred to simply as the Countess of Holland. One day a poor woman carrying twins in her arms approached her and asked for charity. The countess scolded her, saying, "Get away, you shameless beggar! It is impossible for a woman to have two children at once from just one father!"

The poor woman replied, "Then may God let you have as many children as there are days in the year!" Some time later the countess became pregnant and on one day gave birth to 365 children. This happened in the year 1270 (1276), in the countess's forty-third year. These children were all baptized alive by Guido, the Bishop of Utrecht, in two bronze fonts. All the boys were named Johannes and the girls Elizabeth. However, within one day they all died, together with their mother, and all lie buried in one grave in the village church.

It is said that there is also a monument to this event in the church at Delft.[13]

The Woman Who Had No Shadow

Scandinavia

Once there was a pastor's wife who was afraid to have children. Other women are concerned when they have no children; but she was constantly afraid that she could have children.

One day she went to a wise woman, a wicked witch, and asked her what to do to avoid having children. The wise woman gave her seven stones and told her if she would throw them into the well she would be spared from having children.

The pastor's wife threw the stones into the well. As each stone splashed below, she thought that she heard the cry of a child, but still she felt a great sense of relief.

Some time later the pastor and his were walking across the churchyard by the light of a full moon, when the pastor suddenly noticed that his wife did not have a shadow. This frightened him, and he asked her for an explanation, stating that she must have committed a dreadful sin, a sin that she would have to confess to him.

He continued to press her for a confession, until finally she admitted what she had done. Upon hearing her story, he angrily proclaimed, "Cursed woman! Flowers will grow from our slate roof before God forgives you of this sinful deed!" With that he sent her away, telling her to never again step across his threshold.

---

[13]Type 762. Source: *Deutsche Sagen* (Berlin, 1816/1818), no. 584.

One night, many years later, a wretched and tattered beggar woman approached the parsonage and asked for shelter. The housekeeper gave the poor woman a bit to eat and made a bed for her next to the kitchen stove.

The next morning the pastor found the beggar woman dead on the kitchen floor. In spite of her rags, he recognized her immediately as the woman he had cursed and disowned. As he stood there contemplating her lifeless, but serene face, his housekeeper burst into the room. "Pastor!" she exclaimed. "Come outside! A miracle has happened during the night!" The pastor followed her outside and saw that his slate roof was covered with blossoming flowers.[14]

The Flourishing Staff

Jewish

One day a man who had left the faith of his fathers came to Rabbi Jehuda Ha-Chassid and intimated his ardent wish to do penance, but Rabbi Jehuda grew angry and sent him away.

"As little," he said, "as this staff in my hand will blossom and produce green leaves, can you hope to obtain pardon and forgiveness for your sins." And lo! a few days after this scene the staff in the rabbi's hand began to blossom and produced green leaves! Greatly astonished at this miracle, the pious rabbi sent for the repentant sinner and informed him of the miracle that had happened in his favor.

"Now tell me," continued Rabbi Jehuda, "have you ever rendered any service to your brethren in faith?" The sinner could not recall to his memory any such deed.

"Once only," he added; "I came to a town inhabited by a great number of Jews. They were all in great distress, for they were being accused of a ritual murder, of having assassinated a Christian child with the object of using its blood for ritual purposes. As I was no longer a Jew, but nevertheless acquainted with the religious

---

[14]Type 755. Retold from Scandinavian sources, including: Sven Grundtvig, *Gamle danske Minder i Folkemunde* (Copenhagen, 1854-1861), v. 3, no. 6; and Ella Ohlson, *Sagor från Ångermanland* (Stockholm, 1931), no. 30.

The opera *Die Frau ohne Schatten* (1919), with text by Hugo von Hofmannsthal and music by Richard Strauss is related to this folktale. Further, the motif of flowers growing from a stone roof as a sign of God's reconciliation is reminiscent of the German legend of Tannhäuser, in which leaves sprout from a staff as a sign that God has forgiven the German knight for his affair with Venus, in spite of the Pope Urban's curse to the contrary. See Jacob and Wilhelm Grimm, *Deutsche Sagen* (Berlin, 1816/1818), no. 171. Richard Wagner used this legend as a foundation for his opera *Tannhäuser und der Sängerkrieg auf Wartburg* (1842-1845). As the following tale illustrates, this motif is not limited to Christian legendry.

customs of the Jews, I was chosen as an expert in the matter and was called upon to express my opinion before the court of justice. I could not in honor do otherwise than tell the truth and assure the judges that the use of human blood by the Jews was absolutely impossible and diametrically opposed to all the tenets of their creed, and that the ritual murder was an absurd myth unworthy of credence. Thanks to my arguments and evidence, the persecution of the Jews was stopped." Thus spoke the repentant sinner, and Rabbi Jehuda no longer wondered at the miracle which had been wrought in his favor.[15]

The Testimony of the Dead

Jewish

In the days of Rabbi Kalonymos a wonderful incident occurred in the holy city of Jerusalem. The enemies of Israel were constantly planning and devising ways and means how to hurt and destroy the Jews. Daily did they invent new lies and raise accusations against the community. The governor of the city, however, paid but little heed to their calumnies and falsehoods and refused to harm the Jews. One night the miscreants foregathered and discussed how they could convince the governor of the city of Jewish wickedness and induce him to destroy the hateful community. They decided to kidnap the son of the governor and kill him and then accuse the Jews of the murder. Having seized the boy, they murdered him, drained his blood into a vessel and carried the corpse into the synagogue, pouring out the blood in the vestibule.

The governor of the city, greatly distressed at the disappearance of his beloved son, issued a proclamation and called upon the inhabitants to bring him any information they might have been able to gather concerning his child. The city was in a state of great excitement, but no trace of the missing boy could be found. In the meantime the servants of the governor discovered the body of the murdered boy in the synagogue and brought it to the sorrowing father. "The Jews," they triumphantly exclaimed, "have murdered your child and we have found his mutilated body in their place of worship."

When the governor of the city saw the mutilated body of his beloved son and heard the words of his servants, his wrath knew no bounds and he cursed the Jews to whom he had shown so many favors but who had returned evil for good.

The elders of the community were immediately summoned into his presence and the governor of the city thus addressed them, "I command you to deliver into my

---

[15]Type 756. Source: Angelo S. Rappoport, *The Folklore of the Jews* (London, 1937), pp. 206-207.

power the monster who has committed the atrocious deed so that I may wreak vengeance on him. Should you refuse to obey my command, I swear to you that I will destroy the whole Jewish community in this city."

When the elders of the community heard these words, they were terribly frightened and unable to utter a word of protest against the atrocious accusation.

"Grant us a short time," they stammered at last, "that we may search for the culprit." Thereupon they called together all the members of the community and fasted and prayed to God to save the children of Israel. When Rabbi Kalonymos heard of the terrible danger that was threatening the Jewish community in Jerusalem, he at once betook himself to the governor of the city and thus addressed him, "My Lord! My grief at your terrible loss is great, but I assure you that the God of Israel will work a miracle and help me to discover the murderer on whom you will be able to wreak your vengeance."

The rabbi then went home, purified his body, changed his garments and betook himself to the synagogue where he fervently prayed to his God. "Lord of the Universe!" he cried, "for thy sake we have suffered and been slaughtered like sheep! Have pity upon our community in this hour of need and help me to find out the murderer who has committed this atrocious deed in order to destroy thy children." From the place of worship the rabbi went straight to the house of the governor where the high officials of the city had assembled and were discussing the punishment to be meted out to the Jews. Rabbi Kalonymos asked for a sheet of paper on which he wrote the Ineffable Name. He then stuck it on the forehead of the murdered child, and lo! the boy at once came to life, rose up and stood on his feet.

"My son," now cried the rabbi, "tell your father and all the people here present what has happened and who are your murderers."

In answer to the rabbi's request the dead boy pointed out three men and related how they had kidnapped and murdered him. Having completed his speech, he fell down dead.[16]

The Story of the Grateful Dead

Jewish

Once upon a time there lived a very wealthy man in the city of Jerusalem to whom a son was born in his old age. When the boy had attained the age of six and was old enough to grasp the meaning of things and to distinguish between good and evil, his fond father, noticing his gifts, decided to keep him away from the idle ways of the world, from frivolous things, dreams and illusions,

---

[16]Source: Angelo S. Rappoport, *The Folklore of the Jews* (London, 1937), pp. 136-138.

and to bring him up in the study of the Divine Law which alone vouchsafes happiness to the pious, both in this world and in the next. "My offspring," thought the fond and God-fearing father, "shall be the joy and honor of my old age." Thereupon the old man locked up the boy in a special apartment which he shared with a famous and learned master whom he had engaged as a teacher to his only son.

Day and night master and pupil studied the Holy Law. And in order to prevent the boy from being attracted by the world outside, all the splendors of the world were gathered in the sumptuous apartment to gladden the youngster's heart. Nor was the master forgotten, for all his wishes were promptly fulfilled. And thus master and pupil remained in seclusion for ten years, studying all the time the Holy Law, in which the pupil made rapid progress. He soon acquired vast knowledge and knew all the books of Scripture by heart.

Years passed; the father had reached an advanced age, whilst the son had become a mature youth. And one day the old man said to himself, "My end is near and soon the day will come when I shall be called upon to return to my Maker the pledge that I have received; what shall I do with all my possessions that will be left after my demise? Should all the toil of my hands be lost? My only son is quite ignorant of the ways of the world and unacquainted with the intricacies of commerce, of mart and exchange of goods. Should my wealth be lost and one day my dear son be driven to the necessity of stretching out his hands, begging for alms and living on charity?"

These thoughts greatly troubled the old man, and he now began to enlighten his son on worldly affairs, told him the exact amount of his possessions and acquainted him with the ways of commerce. Accompanied by his son, the father visited places of business and markets and initiated his heir into the knowledge of commerce, so as to enable him to take care of his possessions.

"Be circumspect, my son," said the father, "and thus you will gladden my heart. Abandon not, however, the Law of God, for happy is he who is able to combine the ways of life with the ways of the Law." Thus spoke the father, and the boy proved a receptive pupil, intelligent and docile even in these things. Shortly afterwards the rich man died and went the way of all flesh.

As soon as the days of mourning were over, the son collected all the treasures and money which his father had left and went forth to see the world. Many cities and countries did he visit where he gathered knowledge and experience, until he finally reached the capital of Turkey. One day, when he was walking through the streets and market places of the capital, he suddenly found himself in an open square and was surprised to behold an iron coffin suspended from an iron chain between two pillars and guarded by a soldier. The traveler's curiosity was aroused and he tried to elicit some information from the guard, but the latter only told him to mind his own business.

"Get hence," he shouted, "and do not meddle with forbidden things that do not concern you."

14

The youth, however, was not to be shaken off so easily and by bribing the soldier with a handful of silver, he at last succeeded in obtaining the explanation he desired.

"This coffin," said the now friendly guard, "contains the body of a Jew who in his lifetime was the financial adviser of the sultan and manager of his treasury. The sultan trusted and respected him highly, but one day the enemies of the Jew, and they were many who were envious of his success, calumniated him and finally convinced the ruler that his financial adviser had been guilty of maladministration and malversation. They said the Jew had robbed his royal employer of vast sums and thus enriched himself, and the slanderers succeeded in poisoning the mind of the sultan, who had lent a willing ear to their words. Summoning the Jew into his presence, he commanded him to produce a detailed account of all the sums that had passed through his hands in the course of the twenty years that he had been in his master's service.

"A great fright now seized the Jewish banker, for how could he remember all the sums that had passed through his hands in the course of two decades? In vain did he assure the sultan of his honesty, in vain did he plead innocence, the irate ruler would not listen to his words, his prayers and supplications. Convinced that the Jewish banker had robbed him of vast sums, the sultan condemned his former adviser to death and decreed that the body of the culprit should be embalmed, placed in an iron coffin and deprived of decent burial until his co-religionists should have paid the sum of which the unhappy banker had defrauded and robbed him.

"And thus," concluded the soldier, "this coffin remains here in the square until such time as the Jews shall have collected the money due from the executed man only then will the sultan permit the body of his former banker to be buried according to their custom and ritual."

The youth was greatly affected by this story and learning from the soldier the amount of money the sultan was claiming, he betook himself to the royal palace where he craved an audience from the ruler on a very urgent matter. Admitted to the presence of the sultan, he acquainted him with his request in humble words which greatly pleased the potentate.

"I have come from a distant land," he said, "and if it please your majesty I am ready to pay the sum claimed as ransom for the body of the poor banker so that his body may be set free and buried according to the custom of the Jews."

Well pleased with the words of the stranger and glad, too, to receive the money, the sultan at once set the body free and gave instructions that it should be buried. But the generous youth was not yet content and asked for a further favor from the well disposed sultan.

"If it please your majesty," he pleaded, "may it be decreed that all the inhabitants of the city, old and young, be present at the funeral of your former treasurer." The sultan graciously granted the request and issued such a decree, and thus a great concourse of people accompanied the body of the unhappy banker to his last resting place.

On the following day the sultan summoned the stranger into his presence and offered to return his money in exchange for the celestial reward awaiting him in the next world for his noble deed.

But the young Jew refused the bargain and thus he spoke, "My lord and master, I am your slave and owe you obedience, but this I cannot do. What is man and what good to him were his life upon earth if he did not use all his endeavors to fulfill the commandments of the Lord? All my life I have been craving for an opportunity when I should be allowed to perform such a deed, and shall I now bargain away the reward that is awaiting me in the world to come?"

The sultan admitted that the stranger was right, and having shown him all his treasures he let him go in peace. The young man left the capital of Turkey and after visiting many foreign cities, he finally boarded a ship that was to bring him back to his home. But lo! as soon as the vessel had reached the open sea a terrific storm arose and sunk the ship so that all the passengers were thrown into the sea and drowned with the exception of the young man, who was the only survivor. Perceiving a plank, he seized it and was safely carried to the shore. Here he sat down and burst into tears, for deprived of all his possessions, poor, destitute, and far away from his home, he despaired of ever reaching it.

Suddenly a white eagle swooped down from on high and seemed to address the traveler in the language of the birds. The poor boy, although he could not understand the eagle's instructions, guessed that the bird was a messenger sent by God to save him, and as the eagle had spread out its wings, he mounted on its back. It brought him to Jerusalem in the twinkling of an eye—and disappeared. In the darkness of the night the returned traveler, beholding a man wrapped in a white shroud, was greatly frightened, but the apparition spoke in the language of man and told him to be comforted.

"Fear not," said the man in the white shroud, "I am the dead banker for whom you did perform a noble and generous deed. It was I who appeared to you as a plank and as an eagle and saved you from certain death. And now be of good cheer, for you will be happy in this world and a glorious reward awaits you in the next."

And indeed the honest boy was happy until the end of his days; he never gave up or neglected the study of the Law of Moses and performed good actions all his days.[17]

---

[17]Type 505. Source: Angelo S. Rappoport, *The Folklore of the Jews* (London, 1937), pp. 132-136.

16

The Golem

European Jewish

In the town of Worms[18] there once lived a pious man of the name of Bezalel to whom a son was born on the first night of Passover. This happened in the year five thousand two hundred and seventy-three after the creation of the world,[19] at a time when the Jews all over Europe were suffering from cruel persecutions.

The nations in whose midst the children of Israel were dwelling constantly accused them of ritual murder. The Jews, their enemies pretended, used the blood of Christian children in the preparation of their Passover bread; but the arrival of the son of Rabbi Bezalel soon proved to be the occasion of frustrating the evil intentions of two miscreants who sought to show to Christendom that the Jews were actually guilty of ritual murder.

In the night, when the wife of Rabbi Bezalel was seized with labor pains, the servants who had rushed out of the house in search of a midwife luckily prevented two men, who were just going to throw a sack containing the body of a dead child into the Jew-street, with a view to proving the murderous practice of the Jews, from carrying out their evil intention. Rabbi Bezalel then prophesied that his newborn son was destined to bring consolation to Israel and to save his people from the accusation of ritual murder.

"The name of my son in Israel," said Rabbi Bezalel "shall be Judah Arya, even as the Patriarch Jacob said when he blessed his children: 'Judah is a lion's whelp; from the prey, my son, thou art gone up.'" (Genesis 49:9)

Rabbi Bezalel's son grew up and increased in strength and knowledge; he became a great scholar, well versed in the Holy Law, but also a master of all branches of knowledge and familiar with many foreign languages. In time he was elected Rabbi of Posen,[20] but later received a call to the city of Prague, where he was appointed chief judge of the Jewish community.

All his thoughts and actions were devoted to the welfare of his suffering people and his great aim in life was to clear Israel of the monstrous accusation of ritual murder which like a sword of Damocles was perpetually suspended over the head of the unhappy race. Fervently did the rabbi pray to Heaven to teach him in a vision by what means he could best bring to naught the false accusations of the miscreant priests who were spreading the cruel rumors.

And one night he heard a mysterious voice calling to him, "Make a human image of clay and thus you will succeed in frustrating the evil intentions of the enemies of Israel."

---

[18]An ancient German city on the Rhine River.

[19]1512 AD.

[20]In Poland.

On the following morning the master called his son-in-law and his favorite pupil and acquainted them with the instruction he had received from Heaven. He also asked the two to help him in the work he was about to undertake.

"Four elements," he said, "are required for the creation of the golem or homunculus, namely, earth, water, fire and air."

"I myself," thought the holy man, "possess the power of the wind; my son-in-law embodies fire, while my favorite pupil is the symbol of water, and between the three of us we are bound to succeed in our work." He urged on his companions the necessity of great secrecy and asked them to spend seven days in preparing for the work.

On the twentieth day of the month of Adar, in the year five thousand three hundred and forty after the creation of the world,[21] in the fourth hour after midnight, the three men betook themselves to a river on the outskirts of the city on the banks of which they found a loam pit. Here they kneaded the soft clay and fashioned the figure of a man three ells[22] high. They fashioned the features, hands and feet, and then placed the figure of clay on its back upon the ground.

The three learned men then stood at the feet of the image which they had created and the rabbi commanded his son-in-law to walk round the figure seven times, while reciting a cabalistic formula he had himself composed. And as soon as the son-in-law had completed the seven rounds and recited the formula, the figure of clay grew red like a gleaming coal. Thereupon the rabbi commanded his pupil to perform the same action, namely, walk round the lifeless figure seven times while reciting another formula. The effect of the performance was this time an abatement of the heat. The figure grew moist and vapors emanated from it, while nails sprouted on the tips of its fingers and its head was suddenly covered with hair. The face of the figure of clay looked like that of a man of about thirty.

At last the rabbi himself walked seven times round the figure, and the three men recited the following sentence from the history of creation in Genesis: "And the Lord God formed man of the dust of the ground, and breathed into his nostrils the breath of life; and man became a living soul." (Genesis 2:7)

As soon as the three pious men had spoken these words, the eyes of the Golem opened and he gazed upon the rabbi and his pupils with eyes full of wonder. Rabbi Loew thereupon spoke aloud to the man of clay and commanded him to rise from the ground. The Golem at once obeyed and stood erect on his feet. The three men then arrayed the figure in the clothes they had brought with them, clothes worn by the beadles of the synagogues, and put shoes on his feet.

And the rabbi once more addressed the newly fashioned image of clay and thus he spoke, "Know you, clod of clay, that we have fashioned you from the dust of the earth that you may protect the people of Israel against its enemies and shelter it from the misery and suffering to which our nation is subjected. Your name shall be Joseph, and you shall dwell in my courtroom and perform the work of a servant.

---

[21] 1579 AD.

[22] An ell, depending on time and place, was between two and four feet in length.

18

You shall obey my commands and do all that I may require of you, go through fire, jump into water or throw yourself down from a high tower."

The Golem only nodded his head as if to give his consent to the words spoken by the rabbi. His conduct was in every respect that of a human being; he could hear and understand all that was said to him, but he lacked the power of speech. And thus it happened on that memorable night that while only three men had left the house of the rabbi, four returned home in the sixth hour after midnight.

The rabbi kept the matter secret, informing his household that on his way in the morning to the ritual bathing establishment he had met a beggar, and, finding him honest and innocent, had brought him home. He had the intention of engaging him as a servant to attend to the work in his schoolroom, but he forbade his household to make the man perform any other domestic work.

And the Golem thenceforth remained in a corner of the schoolroom, his head upon his two hands, sitting motionless. He gave the impression of a creature bereft of reason, neither understanding nor taking any notice of what was happening around him. Rabbi Loew said of him that neither fire nor water had the power of harming him, nor could any sword wound him. He had called the man of clay Joseph, in memory of Joseph Sheda mentioned in the Talmud who is said to have been half human and half spirit, and who had served the rabbis and frequently saved them from great trouble.

Rabbi Loew, the miracle worker, availed himself of the services of the Golem only on occasions when it was a question of defending his people against the blood accusations from which the Jews of Prague had to suffer greatly in those days.

Whenever the miracle-working Rabbi Loew sent out the Golem and was anxious that he should not be seen, he used to suspend on his neck an amulet written on the skin of a hart, a talisman which rendered the man of clay invisible, while he himself was able to see everything. During the week preceding the feast of Passover the Golem wandered about in the streets of the city stopping everybody who happened to be carrying some burden on his back. It frequently occurred that the bundle contained a dead child which the miscreant intended to deposit in the Jew-street; the Golem at once tied up the man and the body with a rope which he carried in his pocket, and, leading the mischief maker to the town hall, handed him over to the authorities. The Golem's power was quite supernatural and he performed many good deeds.

A day came when a law was finally promulgated declaring the blood accusation to be groundless, and the Jews breathed a sigh of relief when all further persecutions on account of alleged ritual murder were forbidden. Rabbi Loew now decided to take away the breath of life from the Golem, the figure of clay which his hands had once fashioned. He placed Joseph upon a bed and commanded his disciples once more to walk round the Golem seven times and repeat the words they had spoken when the figure was created, but this time in reverse order. When the seventh round was finished, the Golem was once more a lifeless piece of clay. They divested him of his clothes, and wrapping him in two old praying shawls, hid the clod of clay under a heap of old books in the rabbi's garret.

Rabbi Loew afterwards related many incidents connected with the creation of the Golem. When he was on the point of blowing the breath of life into the nostrils of the figure of clay he had created, two spirits had appeared to him; that of Joseph the demon and that of Jonathan the demon. He chose the former, the spirit of Joseph, because he had already revealed himself as the protector of the rabbis of the Talmud, but he could not endow the figure of clay with the power of speech because the living spirit inhabiting the Golem was only a sort of animal vitality and not a soul. He possessed only small powers of discernment, being unable to grasp anything belonging to the domain of real intelligence and higher wisdom.

And yet, although the Golem was not possessed of a soul, one could not fail to notice that on the Sabbath there was something peculiar in his bearing, for his face bore a friendlier and more amiable expression than it did on weekdays. It was afterwards related that every Friday Rabbi Loew used to remove the tablet on which he had written the Ineffable Name from under the Golem's tongue, as he was afraid lest the Sabbath should make the Golem immortal and men might be induced to worship him as an idol. The Golem had no inclinations, either good or bad. Whatever action he performed he did under compulsion and out of fear lest he should be turned again into dust and reduced to naught once more. Whatever was situated within ten ells above the ground or under it he could reach easily and nothing would stop him in the execution of anything that he had undertaken.[23]

Friday

Russia

There was once a certain woman who did not pay due reverence to Mother Friday, but set to work on a distaff full of flax, combing and whirling it. She span away till dinner time, then suddenly sleep fell upon her—such a deep sleep! And when she had gone to sleep, suddenly the door opened and in came Mother Friday, before the eyes of all who were there, clad in a white dress, and in such a rage! And she went straight up to the woman who had been spinning, scooped up from the floor a handful of the dust that had fallen out of the flax, and began stuffing and stuffing that woman's eyes full of it! And when she had stuffed them full, she went off in a rage—disappeared without saying a word.

When the woman awoke, she began squalling at the top of her voice about her eyes, but couldn't tell what was the matter with them. The other women, who had been terribly frightened, began to cry out, "Oh, you wretch, you! You've brought a terrible punishment on yourself from Mother Friday."

---

[23]Source: Angelo S. Rappoport, *The Folklore of the Jews* (London, 1937), pp. 195-203.

Then they told her all that had taken place. She listened to it all, and then began imploring, "Mother Friday, forgive me! Pardon me, the guilty one! I'll offer you a taper, and I'll never let friend or foe dishonor you, Mother!"

Well, what do you think? During the night, back came Mother Friday and took the dust out of that woman's eyes, so that she was able to get about again. It's a great sin to dishonor Mother Friday——combing and spinning flax, forsooth![24]

Frau Holle and the Distaff

Germany

In Clausthal there once lived two girls who had neither father nor mother and hence had to provide for themselves with their own hands. Spinning was their only source of income. One of the girls span very industriously, but the other one liked to spend her time chatting, and furthermore, when evening came she was the first one who began to nod and to sleep. When the industrious one quit work for the night at eleven o'clock, the lazy one had already slept a few hours. For this reason the lazy sister caused the industrious girl much grief.

It was Easter time, and on Easter Eve the industrious girl sat spinning while the other one had gone out to see the Easter celebration and to amuse herself. Liese was spinning when the clock struck eleven. The door opened and in walked a beautiful woman wearing a long white silken dress. She had beautiful long golden yellow hair and carried in her hand a beautiful distaff, white as silver and fine as silk. With a friendly voice she greeted the good girl, who was just letting the last flax run onto the reel as thread.

Feeling the thread, she said:

> Industrious Liese,
> Empty is your distaff,
> Fine is your thread,
> You have done well.

[24]Source: W. R. S. Ralston, *Russian Folk-Tales* (London, 1873), p. 200. Ralston's source: Aleksandr Afanasyev. Note by Ralston: "The Russian name for that day, *Pyatnitsa* (from *pyat* = five, Friday being the fifth working day), has no such mythological significance as have our own Friday and the French *Vendredi*. But the day was undoubtedly consecrated by the old Slavonians to some goddess akin to Venus or Freyja, and her worship in ancient times accounts for the superstitions now connected with the name of Friday." (p. 198)

Aleksandr Afanasyev (the transliteration Afanas'ev as well as other spellings are also used) was the Slavic counterpart to the brothers Grimm. Between the years 1855 and 1873 he published some 640 Russian and Ukrainian folktales.

Then she touched the girl's spinning wheel with her golden distaff, and with a friendly smile she disappeared. And who was she? She was Frau Holle.

Following this appearance, industrious Liese went to bed. Her sister came home later and went to bed as well. On Easter morning when the two girls got up, in the place of Liese's wooden spinning wheel there stood one of shining gold. It sparkled and glistened magnificently, and the thread that Liese had spun was as fine and white as silk. And as she unreeled it, she discovered that however much thread she removed, the reel remained full. Liese was delighted!

However, when the lazy girl looked at her spinning wheel, she was startled to discover that her distaff was covered with straw instead of flax. And her chest was now filled with chopped straw instead of the beautiful linen cloth that had been there.

And that is why even today they say that the distaff must be spun empty on the Holy Evening, or Frau Holle will come and bring chopped straw.[25]

Frau Holla and the Peasant

Germany

Once when Frau Holla was traveling about she came upon a peasant carrying an ax. She asked him to cut some wedges and tighten up the boards in her carriage, which he did. When the work was finished, she said, "Gather up the shavings and take them along as your reward," and then drove away. The man thought that the shavings were worthless, so he left most of them lying there, taking only a few pieces along on a whim. When he arrived home he reached into his bag, and found that the shavings had turned into pure gold. He immediately returned to get the ones that he had left lying about, but it was too late, and however much he searched, he could find nothing.[26]

---

[25]Source: August Ey, *Harzmärchenbuch; oder, Sagen und Märchen aus dem Oberharze* (Stade, 1862), pp. 193-194.

[26]Source: Jacob and Wilhelm Grimm, *Deutsche Sagen* (Berlin, 1816/1818), no. 8. Legends 4-7 also deal with Frau Holla, (or "Holle," as her name is variously spelled). This being is also known as Frau Berta and Frau Perchta. See *Deutsche Sagen*, nos. 268, 269.

Frau Holle

Jacob and Wilhelm Grimm

A widow had two daughters; the one was beautiful and industrious, the other ugly and lazy. The mother greatly favored the ugly, lazy girl. The other one had to do all the work, and was truly a Cinderella. One day while pulling a bucket of water from the well she leaned over too far and fell in.[27] Recovering, she found herself in a beautiful meadow. The sun was shining, and there were thousands of flowers. She walked along and soon came to an oven full of bread. The bread called out, "Take me out, or I'll burn! I've been thoroughly baked for a long time!" The girl took the bread from the oven and walked further until she came to a tree laden with ripe apples.

"Shake me! Shake me! We apples are all ripe!" cried the tree, and the girl shook the tree until the apples fell as though it were raining apples. When none were left in the tree, she continued on her way.

Finally she came to a small house. An old woman was peering out from inside. She had very large teeth, which frightened the girl, and she wanted to run away. But the old woman called out to her, "Don't be afraid, dear child. Stay here with me, and if you do my housework in an orderly fashion, it will go well with you. Only you must take care to make my bed well and shake it until the feathers fly, then it will snow in the world.[28] I am Frau Holle."

Because the old woman spoke so kindly to her, the girl agreed, and started in her service. She took care of everything to her satisfaction and always shook her featherbed vigorously. Therefore she had a good life with her: no angry words, and cooked meals every day. Now after she had been with Frau Holle for a time, her heart saddened. Even though she was many thousands of times better off here than at home, still she had a yearning for home. Finally she said to the old woman, "I

---

[27]In the second edition of their tales (1819), the Grimms changed the nature of the accident that caused the heroine to fall into the underground realm. The relevant passage follows:

Every day the poor girl had to take a seat on the road by a well and had to spin so much that the blood sprang from her fingers. Now it happened once that the spool was entirely bloody, and she leaned over into the well and wanted to wash it off; but it jumped from her hand and fell down. She cried, ran to her stepmother and told her of the misfortune. She scolded her severely and was so uncompassionate that she said, "You let the spool fall, so go get it back." Then the girl went back to the well and didn't know what she should do; and in her great fear she jumped into the well, in order to get the spool.

[28]The Grimms add the following footnote: "For this reason, in Hesse when it snows they say that Frau Holle is making her bed." They might also have mentioned, but did not, that in some areas of Europe Frau Holle's snow making abilities were transferred, in the Christian era, either to Saint Peter or to Jesus himself, both of whom, like their pagan counterpart, caused it to snow by shaking their beds. Bed-making in European folklore is thus not entirely dominated by females.

have such a longing for home, and even though I am very well off here, I cannot stay longer."

Frau Holle said, "You are right, and because you have served me so faithfully, I will take you back myself." With that she took her by the hand and led her to a large gate. The gate was opened, and while the girl was standing under it, an immense rain of gold fell, and all the gold stuck to her, so that she was completely covered with it. "This is yours because you have been so industrious," said Frau Holle. With that the gate was closed and the girl found herself above in the world. She went home to her mother, and because she arrived all covered with gold, she was well received.[29]

When the mother heard how she had come to the great wealth, she wanted to achieve the same fortune for the other, the ugly and lazy daughter. She made her go and jump into the well. Like the other one, she too awoke in a beautiful meadow, and she walked along the same path. When she came to the oven, the bread cried again, "Oh, take me out, take me out, or else I'll burn! I've been thoroughly baked for a long time!" But the lazy one answered, "As if I would want to get all dirty," and walked away. Soon she came to the apple tree. It cried out, "Oh, shake me, shake me, we apples are all ripe." But she answered, "Oh yes, one could fall on my head," and with that she walked on.

When she came to Frau Holle's house, she was not afraid, because she had already heard about her large teeth, and she immediately began to work for her. On the first day she forced herself, was industrious and obeyed Frau Holle, when she said something to her, because she was thinking about all the Gold that she would give her. But on the second day she already began to be lazy, on the third day even more so, then she didn't even want to get up in the morning. She did not make the bed for Frau Holle, the way she was supposed to, and she did not shake it until the feathers flew.

Frau Holle soon became tired of this and dismissed her of her duties. This is just what the lazy girl wanted, for she thought that she would now get the rain of gold. Frau Holle lead her too to the gate. She stood beneath it, but instead of gold, a large kettle full of pitch spilled over her. "That is the reward for your services," said Frau Holle, and closed the gate. Then the lazy girl returned home, entirely covered with pitch, and it would not come off as long as she lived.[30]

---

[29]In the second edition, the Grimms added a rooster to the heroine's welcoming committee. He sings out his greeting and approval with the verse (which rhymes in the original German):

> Cock-a-doodle-doo,
> our golden maid is here again.

[30]Type 480. Source: *Kinder- und Hausmärchen*, 1st ed. (Berlin, 1812/1815), v. 1, no. 24.

24

Fairies

Prilling and Pralling Is Dead

Germany

The servant of Landholder Gireck (whose residence in Plau was on Elden Street where Master Mason Büttner's house now stands) was once hauling a load of manure to a field abutting Gall Mountain. He had just unloaded the manure and was about to put the sideboards back onto the wagon when he heard his name being called from the mountain, together with the words, "When you get home say that Prilling and Pralling is dead." Back at home, he had scarcely related this experience and repeated the words, when they heard groaning and crying coming from the house's cellar. They investigated, but found nothing but a pewter mug, of a kind that had never before been seen in Plau. The master of the house kept the mug, and when he later moved to Hamburg he took it with him. About seventy years ago someone from Plau saw it there.[31]

Mally Dixon

England

Stories of fairies appearing in the shape of cats are common in the North of England. Mr. Longstaffe relates that a farmer of Staindrop, in Durham, was one night crossing a bridge, when a cat jumped out, stood before him, and looking him full in the face, said:

> Johnny Reed! Johnny Reed!
> Tell Madam Momfort
> That Mally Dixon's dead.

The farmer returned home, and in mickle wonder recited this awfu' stanza to his wife, when up started their black cat, saying, "Is she?" and disappeared for ever. It

---

[31]Migratory legend type 6070A; related to folktale type 113A. Source: Karl Bartsch, *Sagen, Märchen und Gebräuche aus Meklenburg* (Vienna, 1879), v. 1, pp. 42-43.

was supposed she was a fairy in disguise, who thus went to attend a sister's funeral, for in the North fairies do die, and green shady spots are pointed out by the country folks as the cemeteries of the tiny people.[32]

Demons

The Demon in the Tree

Jewish

A demon once fixed his abode under a tree that stood in a field belonging to a pious man. The owner of the field planted vegetables there, but as the passers-by were in the habit of sitting down in the shade of the tree they destroyed all his vegetables.

One day therefore he said to his wife, "I will cut down the tree in order to preserve our vegetables," and his wife consented. Hardly, however, had he lifted his ax to cut down the tree when the demon suddenly appeared and implored him to desist.

"I will give you a golden dinar every day, if you will spare the tree," he said, but the pious man refused. The demon now offered him three golden dinars daily, and tempted by this bribe, the owner of the field consented. On the following morning he betook himself to the tree and found the promised three golden dinars. This went on for many days until the man grew very rich. He bought houses, vineyards and slaves, but never knew whence all the golden pieces really came. One day, however, his two sons died and a short time afterwards he lost his slaves.

"I must have committed a heavy sin," said the man, "to have been punished so heavily." And one day, when he went to the tree to fetch his three dinars he found none. He now realized that he had committed the sin of idol worship. "I will now cut down this tree," he said, but hardly had he raised his ax, when the demon again appeared threatening to kill him if he touched the tree which he had chosen for his abode. Greatly frightened, the man went and told his case to the Sanhedrin, and the members of the Supreme Court advised him to sell all his possessions, return the money to the demon and then cut down the tree. This he did, but when he raised

---

[32]Type 113A. Source: James Halliwell-Phillipps, *Popular Rhymes and Nursery Tales* (London, 1849), p. 51.

his ax the demon once more appeared and offered him a daily reward of six golden dinars if he consented to leave the tree in its place. This time, however, the man refused to be tempted. "Even if you did offer me all the money in the world, I would not accept it," he declared. On hearing these words the demon fled. The man now sowed his field, and when the time of harvest came, he obtained one hundred measures of barley which he sold for eight hundred golden dinars. The next year, while laboring his field, he found a treasure on the very spot where the tree once stood.[33]

Water Demons

Scotland

In many of the deep pools of the streams and rivers guardian-demons were believed to reside, and it was dangerous to bathe in them.

Sometimes, when a castle or mansion was being sacked, a faithful servant or two contrived to rescue the plate chest, and to cast it into a deep pool in the nearest stream. On one occasion a diver was got to got to the bottom of such a pool to fetch up the plate of the neighboring castle. He dived, saw the plate chest, and was preparing to lift it, when the demon ordered him to go to the surface at once, and not to come back. At the same time the demon warned him that, if he did come back, he would forfeit his life. The diver obeyed. When he reached the bank he told what he had seen, and what he had heard. By dint of threats and promises of large reward, he dived again. In a moment or two afterwards his heart and lungs rose and floated on the surface of the water. They had been torn out by the demon of the pool.[34]

---

[33]Source: Angelo S. Rappoport, *The Folklore of the Jews* (London, 1937), pp. 234-235.

[34]Source: Walter Gregor, *Notes on the Folk-Lore of the North-East of Scotland* (London, 1881), p. 67.

Wod, the Wild Huntsman

Germany

The dogs of the air often bark on a dark night on the heath, in the woods, or at a crossroads. Country dwellers know their leader Wod[35] and pity the traveler who has not yet reached home, for Wod is often malicious, seldom kind. The rough huntsman spares only those who remain in the middle of the path. Therefore he often calls out to travelers, "In the middle of the path!"

One night a drunk peasant was returning home from town. His path led him through the woods. There he heard the wild hunt with the huntsman shouting at his noisy dogs high in the air.

A voice called out, "In the middle of the path! In the middle of the path!" But the peasant paid no attention to it.

Suddenly a tall man on a white horse bolted from the clouds and approached him. "How strong are you?" he said. "Let's have a contest. Here is a chain. Take hold of it. Who can pull the hardest?"

Undaunted, the peasant took hold of the heavy chain, and the huntsman remounted. Meanwhile the peasant wrapped his end of the chain around a nearby oak tree, and the huntsman pulled in vain.

"You wrapped your end around the oak tree," said Wod, dismounting.

"No," responded the peasant, quickly undoing the chain. "See, here it is in my hands."

"I'll have you in the clouds!" cried the huntsman and remounted. The peasant quickly wrapped the chain around the oak tree once again, and once again Wod pulled in vain. Up above the dogs barked, the wagons rolled, and the horses neighed. The oak tree creaked at its roots and seemed to twist itself sideways. The peasant was terrified, but the oak tree stood.

"You have pulled well!" said the huntsman. "Many men have become mine. You are the first who has withstood me. I will reward you."

The hunt proceeded noisily, "Halloo! Halloo!" The peasant crept along his way. Then suddenly, from unseen heights, a groaning stag fell before him. Wod appeared and jumped from his white horse. He hurriedly cut up the game.

"The blood is yours," he said to the peasant, "and a hind quarter as well."

"My lord," said the peasant, "your servant has neither a bucket nor a pot."

"Pull off your boot!" cried Wod. He did it.

"Now take the blood and the meat to your wife and child."

At first his fear lightened the burden, but gradually it became heavier and heavier until he was barely able to carry it. With a crooked back and dripping with sweat

---

[35]Wod, both in name and in description, is apparently a survival of the chief pre-Christian Germanic deity, known variously as Wodan, Wotan, Oden, or Odin. His name lives on in place names (for example Odense, Denmark) and in the name "Wednesday." As the above story illustrates, it is also possible that his name is etymologically connected to the English word "wood" and the German word "Wut" (fury).

28

he finally reached his hut, and behold, his boot was filled with gold, and the hind quarter was a leather bag filled with silver coins.[36]

The Night Huntsman at the Udarser Mill

Germany

It is said that the Night Huntsman haunts the vicinity of the Udarser Mill. Once a mill worker who had spent the night at the mill heard the Night Huntsman passing by with great commotion, shouting "Halloo!" The worker had heard a lot about the Night Huntsman's sinister deeds, and he wanted to know more about him, so he went out onto the mill platform and heartily added his voice to the wild noise. Suddenly he heard a voice calling out:

> If you want to hunt,
> You can join the ride!

At the same time someone threw a woman's leg at the worker, a woman's leg wearing a red shoe. The worker quickly retreated into the mill. It is said that the next morning he buried the leg beneath the mill platform.[37]

Two Eyes Too Many

Germany

In Hiddestorf[38], not too long ago, there lived a widow who every Sunday was miraculously able to cook the most delicious meals. By the time that the servant girls had gone to church in the morning, she had not yet made a fire, had not cleaned the vegetables, and had not even fetched any meat. But by the time church was finished, the best meal was on the table. Because that was not possible with ordinary powers, one Sunday a servant hid himself behind a large barrel in the

---

[36]Source: Carl and Theodor Colshorn, *Märchen und Sagen aus Hannover* (Hannover, 1854), pp. 192-193. Slightly abridged.

[37]Source: A. Haas, *Rügensche Sagen und Märchen* (Stettin, 1903), p. 24.

[38]A village south of Hannover.

kitchen in order to spy on the woman. Just about the time the sermon was beginning there was a commotion in the chimney, and the devil came down and began to caress the woman. Afterward he started to fill the pots for her, but he suddenly stood still and said, "Woman, there are two eyes too many in here!" She denied it. "There are two eyes too many in here!" he said again, but when the woman began to make fun of him, he filled the pots and disappeared up the chimney.

At noon when everyone was seated at the table, the servant said, "I don't want to eat, because I know that it came from the devil!"

He had scarcely spoken when the Black One came in through the window, grabbed the woman by her braid, wrung her neck, and flew out the window with her.[39]

Witches, Warlocks, and Werewolves

The Witch of Treva

England

Once on a time, long ago, there lived at Treva, a hamlet in Zennor, a wonderful old lady deeply skilled in necromancy. Her charms, spells, and dark incantations made her the terror of the neighborhood. However, this old lady failed to impress her husband with any belief in her supernatural powers, nor did he fail to proclaim his unbelief aloud.

One day this skeptic came home to dinner, and found, being exceedingly hungry, to his bitter disappointment, that not only was there no dinner to eat, but that there was no meat in the house. His rage was great, but all he could get from his wife was, "I couldn't get meat out of the stones, could I?" It was in vain to give the reins to passion, the old woman told him, and he must know "that hard words buttered no parsnips."

Well, at length he resolved to put his wife's powers to the proof, and he quietly but determinedly told her that he would be the death of her if she did not get him some dinner; but if in half an hour she gave him some good cooked meat, he would believe all she had boasted of her power, and be submissive to her forever. St.

---

[39]Source: Carl and Theodor Colshorn, *Märchen und Sagen aus Hannover* (Hannover, 1854), p. 160.

Ives, the nearest market town, was five miles off; but nothing doubting, the witch put on her bonnet and cloak, and started. Her husband watched her from their cottage door, down the hill; and at the bottom of the hill, he saw his wife quietly place herself on the ground and disappear. In her place a fine hare ran on at its full speed.

He was not a little startled, but he waited, and within the half hour in walked his wife with "good flesh and taties all ready for aiting." There was no longer any doubt, and the poor husband lived in fear of the witch of Treva to the day of her death.

This event took place after a few years, and it is said the room was full of evil spirits, and that the old woman's shrieks were awful to hear. Howbeit, peace in the shape of pale-faced death came to her at last, and then a black cloud rested over the house when all the heavens were clear and blue.

She was borne to the grave by six aged men, carried, as is the custom, underhand. When they were about half way between the house and the church, a hare started from the roadside and leaped over the coffin. The terrified bearers let the corpse fall to the ground, and ran away. Another lot of men took up the coffin and proceeded. They had not gone far when puss was suddenly seen seated on the coffin, and again the coffin was abandoned. After long consultation, and being persuaded by the parson to carry the old woman very quickly into the churchyard, while he walked before, six others made the attempt, and as the parson never ceased to repeat the Lord's Prayer, all went on quietly. Arrived at the church stile, they rested the corpse, the parson paused to commence the ordinary burial service, and there stood the hare, which, as soon as the clergyman began "I am the resurrection and the life," uttered a diabolical howl, changed into a black, unshapen creature, and disappeared.[40]

The Girl Who Transformed Herself into a Hare

Germany

In Trent[41] there formerly lived a girl who had inherited a witch's thong from her grandmother. Whenever she tied the thong around herself she would turn into a hare. In this form she often heckled a forester who lived in the vicinity.

[40]Source: Robert Hunt, *Popular Romances of the West of England; or, The Drolls, Traditions, and Superstitions of Old Cornwall* (London, 1871), pp. 335-336.

[41]Trent (Germany) is a town on the island of Rügen in the Baltic Sea.

Whenever he would shoot at her, his bullets just glanced off her pelt. When he came to realize that there was something uncanny going on here, he loaded his flintlock with a coffin nail that he had somehow acquired.

The next time he saw the hare, he shot it as it was running away. In an instant the hare disappeared, and the girl stood before him in its place. With tears she asked him for help, for she had a serious wound on her foot. In order to gain his sympathy, she confessed her evil power to the forester, promising never again to make use of it.

For a time she kept her promise, but no sooner had her foot healed than she fell back into her old vices. Now her fiancé worked as a herdsman at a nearby estate, and she frequently made use of her thong in order to visit him often and undisturbed. Her fiancé knew nothing of her powers, and one day when she appeared before him as a hare—for she had not yet had time to assume her human form—he struck her with a water carrier. As a result she started to bleed profusely, and with tears she confessed to her fiancé what her situation was.

He broke off his relationship with her. She remained lame for the rest of her life. It is said that the witch's thong was later buried in the grandmother's grave.[42]

Ridden by a Witch

Germany

A miner was always making fun of people who claimed that witches ride to the Brocken on Walpurgis Night.[43] He often said, "If such an old creature ever crosses my path, I will throw her down. What chance would such an old skeleton of a hag made up of nothing but skin and bones have against the likes of me?"

"Now, now," an old neighbor woman who lived nearby would say. "It wouldn't be all that easy to throw down such a rider. You should be careful what you say!"

"Tomfoolery! Tomfoolery!" he said. "I'd make her forget about riding." To that the old woman said nothing.

Walpurgis Night arrived. There was shooting everywhere, as though the enemy were attacking. They were shooting off firecrackers, flintlocks, rifles, and pistols.

---

[42]Migratory legend type 3055. Source: A. Haas, *Rügensche Sagen und Märchen* (Stettin, 1903), pp. 92-93.

[43]The Brocken is the highest summit (elevation 3747 feet) in the Harz Mountains of central Germany. Witches are said to assemble there for their yearly "Sabbath" on Walpurgis Night, the eve of May 1st.

On that evening everyone was firing his shooting iron, and the louder the noise, the better everyone liked it.

About nine o'clock the miner learned that something had gone wrong in the shaft, and he was called upon to report for duty. He got as far as Bremen Hill when he was approached by a swarm of old hags flying through the air. There was such commotion and uproar as though all the devils were on the loose.

One of the hags came down, turned the miner over, whether he wanted to or not, and mounted him. Then away they went through the air, following the others to the Brocken. He could barely breathe, and the old hag was so heavy that she nearly broke his bones. She finally climbed off him, and he fell to the ground half dead. The other witches then surrounded him and danced around him, and the devil himself was there with them. Finally they picked him up and asked him if he could remain silent, or if he would like to be boiled in oil. Now no one wants to be boiled in oil, so he said that he would never say anything about the witches. Then the devil said to him that he would be a child of death if he ever uttered a single word. And then the witches did unspeakable things up there on the mountain.

As midnight approached, they all gathered together, and one of the witches again took our miner and mounted him, and they swarmed through the air until they reached Bremen Hill near Clausthal. They released him at the same spot where the witch had captured him. He lay there for a few hours recovering his strength; then he slowly crept homeward. When he arrived home, his wife was already up and was preparing to go into the woods for a load of wood.

"Wife," he said, "stay here. I have had a bad night. Go into the kitchen and put a little wood into the stove. I have been sweating, and I need to change my clothes." She did what he said. He then told the stove what had happened. His wife overheard it all, but said nothing.

A half hour later the old neighbor woman came by and said that it was a good thing he had spoken to the stove and not to a person, or he would see how things would go with him.

And thus they knew that she was a witch. The wife reported her, and the wicked witch was burned to death, just as she deserved.[44]

---

[44]Source: August Ey, *Harzmärchenbuch; oder, Sagen und Märchen aus dem Oberharze* (Stade, 1862), pp. 46-48.

The Werewolf of Jarnitz

Germany

In the vicinity of Jarnitz[45] there lived a werewolf who had the ability to transform himself into all kinds of different shapes. This werewolf spent the nights stealing sheep from their enclosures, for in those days the sheep were kept at night in enclosures in the open fields. For several nights in a row the shepherd, armed with a loaded gun, had kept watch for the night robber. He had already hit the werewolf several times, as he had clearly seen, but the bullets seemed to have done him no harm, and he had escaped with his booty every time. Then the shepherd loaded his gun with bullets made of inherited silver—which never fail—and thus that this time he would be successful.

Following his custom, the werewolf appeared again that night. But as he was approaching the enclosure, he immediately sensed that this time the shepherd might do him in. Therefore he quickly turned himself into a human, walked up to the shepherd, and said to him in a familiar tone, "You don't have to shoot me dead!" That so unsettled the shepherd that he lowered his gun, which he had been aiming at the intruder.

The werewolf never again dared to steel sheep from the Jarnitz enclosures.[46]

Vampires and Ghosts

The Shroud

Russia

In a certain village there was a girl who was lazy and slothful, hated working, but would gossip and chatter away like anything! Well, she took it into her head to invite the other girls to a spinning party. For in the villages, as every one knows, it is the lazybones who gives the spinning feast, and the sweet-toothed are those who go to it.

---

[45]Jarnitz (Germany) is a town on the island of Rügen in the Baltic Sea.

[46]Source: A. Haas, *Rügensche Sagen und Märchen* (Stettin, 1903), pp. 98-99.

Well, on the appointed night she got her spinners together. They span for her, and she fed them and feasted them. Among other things they chatted about was this—which of them all was the boldest?

Says the lazybones, "I'm not afraid of anything!"

"Well then," say the spinners, "if you're not afraid, go past the graveyard to the church, take down the holy picture from the door, and bring it here."

"Good, I'll bring it; only each of you must spin me a distaff-full."

That was just her sort of notion: to do nothing herself, but to get others to do it for her. Well, she went, took down the picture, and brought it home with her. Her friends all saw that sure enough it was the picture from the church. But the picture had to be taken back again, and it was now the midnight hour. Who was to take it? At length the lazybones said, "You girls go on spinning. I'll take it back myself. I'm not afraid of anything!"

So she went and put the picture back in its place. As she was passing the graveyard on her return, she saw a corpse in a white shroud, seated on a tomb. It was a moonlight night; everything was visible. She went up to the corpse, and drew away its shroud from it. The corpse held its peace, not uttering a word; no doubt the time for it to speak had not come yet. Well, she took the shroud and went home.

"There!" says she, "I've taken back the picture and put it in its place; and, what's more, here's a shroud I took away from a corpse." Some of the girls were horrified; others didn't believe what she said, and laughed at her.

But after they had supped and lain down to sleep, all of a sudden the corpse tapped at the window and said, "Give me my shroud! Give me my shroud!"

The girls were so frightened they didn't know whether they were alive or dead. But the lazybones took the shroud, went to the window, opened it, and said, "There, take it."

"No," replied the corpse, "restore it to the place you took it from." Just then the cocks suddenly began to crow. The corpse disappeared.

Next night, when the spinners had all gone home to their own houses, at the very same hour as before, the corpse came, tapped at the window, and cried, "Give me my shroud!"

Well, the girl's father and mother opened the window and offered him his shroud. "No," says he, "let her take it back to the place she took it from."

"Really now, how could one go to a graveyard with a corpse? What a horrible idea!" she replied. Just then the cocks crew. The corpse disappeared.

Next day the girl's father and mother sent for the priest, told him the whole story, and entreated him to help them in their trouble. "Couldn't a service be performed?" they said.

The priest reflected awhile; then he replied, "Please tell her to come to church tomorrow."

Next day the lazybones went to church. The service began, numbers of people came to it. But just as they were going to sing the cherubim song, there suddenly arose, goodness knows whence, so terrible a whirlwind that all the congregation fell flat on their faces. And it caught up that girl, and then flung her down on the

35

ground. The girl disappeared from sight; nothing was left of her but her back hair.[47]

The Coffin Lid

Russia

A moujik was driving along one night with a load of pots. His horse grew tired, and all of a sudden it came to a standstill alongside of a graveyard. The moujik unharnessed his horse and set it free to graze; meanwhile he laid himself down on one of the graves. But somehow he didn't go to sleep.

He remained lying there some time. Suddenly the grave began to open beneath him. He felt the movement and sprang to his feet. The grave opened, and out of it came a corpse—wrapped in a white shroud, and holding a coffin lid—came out and ran to the church, laid the coffin lid at the door, and then set off for the village.

The moujik was a daring fellow. He picked up the coffin lid and remained standing beside his cart, waiting to see what would happen. After a short delay the dead man came back, and was going to snatch up his coffin lid—but it was not to be seen. Then the corpse began to track it out, traced it up to the moujik, and said, "Give me my lid: if you don't, I'll tear you to bits!"

"And my hatchet, how about that?" answers the moujik. "Why, it's I who'll be chopping you into small pieces!"

"Do give it back to me, good man!" begs the corpse.

"I'll give it when you tell me where you've been and what you've done."

"Well, I've been in the village, and there I've killed a couple of youngsters."

"Well then, now tell me how they can be brought back to life."

The corpse reluctantly made answer, "Cut off the left skirt of my shroud, and take it with you. When you come into the house where the youngsters were killed, pour some live coals into a pot and put the piece of the shroud in with them, and then lock the door. The lads will be revived by the smoke immediately."

The moujik cut off the left skirt of the shroud, and gave up the coffin lid. The corpse went to its grave—the grave opened. But just as the dead man was descending into it, all of a sudden the cocks began to crow, and he hadn't time to get properly covered over. One end of the coffin lid remained sticking out of the ground.

---

[47]Type 366. Source: W. R. S. Ralston, *Russian Folk-Tales* (London, 1873), pp. 307-309. Ralston's source: Aleksandr Afanasyev. Ralston's footnote concerning "her back hair": "The *kosa* or single braid in which Russian girls wear their hair."

36

The moujik saw all this and made a note of it. The day began to dawn; he harnessed his horse and drove into the village. In one of the houses he heard cries and wailing. In he went. There lay two dead lads.

"Don't cry," says he, "I can bring them to life!"

"Do bring them to life, kinsman," say their relatives. "We'll give you half of all we possess."

The moujik did everything as the corpse had instructed him, and the lads came back to life. Their relatives were delighted, but they immediately seized the moujik and bound him with cords, saying, "No, no, trickster! We'll hand you over to the authorities. Since you knew how to bring them back to life, maybe it was you who killed them!"

"What are you thinking about, true believers! Have the fear of God before your eyes!" cried the moujik.

Then he told them everything that had happened during the night. Well, they spread the news through the village; the whole population assembled and swarmed into the graveyard. They found out the grave from which the dead man had come out, they tore it open, and they drove an aspen stake right into the heart of the corpse, so that it might no more rise up and slay. But they rewarded the moujik richly, and sent him away home with great honor.[48]

The Two Corpses

Russia

A soldier had obtained leave to go home on furlough—to pray to the holy images, and to bow down before his parents. And as he was going his way, at a time when the sun had long set, and all was dark around, it chanced that he had to pass by a graveyard. Just then he heard that someone was running after him, and crying, "Stop! You can't escape!"

He looked back and there was a corpse running and gnashing its teeth. The soldier sprang on one side with all his might to get away from it, caught sight of a little chapel, and bolted straight into it.

There wasn't a soul in the chapel, but stretched out on a table there lay another corpse, with tapers burning in front of it. The soldier hid himself in a corner, and remained there hardly knowing whether he was alive or dead, but waiting to see what would happen. Presently up ran the first corpse—the one that had chased the

[48]Source: W. R. S. Ralston, *Russian Folk-Tales* (London, 1873), pp. 309-311. Ralston's source: Aleksandr Afanasyev.

soldier—and dashed into the chapel. Thereupon one that was lying on the table jumped up, and cried to it, "What have you come here for?"

"I've chased a soldier in here, so I'm going to eat him."

"Come now, brother! He's run into my house. I shall eat him myself."

"No, I shall!"

"No, I shall!"

And they set to work fighting; the dust flew like anything. They'd have gone on fighting ever so much longer, only the cocks began to crow. Then both the corpses fell lifeless to the ground, and the soldier went on his way homeward in peace, saying, "Glory be to Thee, O Lord! I am saved from the wizards!"[49]

The Dog and the Corpse

Russia

A moujik went out in pursuit of game one day, and took a favorite dog with him. He walked and walked through woods and bogs, but got nothing for his pains. At last the darkness of night surprised him. At an uncanny hour he passed by a graveyard, and there, at a place where two roads met, he saw standing a corpse in a white shroud. The moujik was horrified, and knew not which way to go—whether to keep on or to turn back.

"Well, whatever happens, I'll go on," he thought; and on he went, his dog running at his heels. When the corpse perceived him, it came to meet him; not touching the earth with its feet, but keeping about a foot above it—the shroud fluttering after it. When it had come up with the sportsman, it made a rush at him; but the dog seized hold of it by its bare calves, and began a tussle with it. When the moujik saw his dog and the corpse grappling with each other, he was delighted that things had turned out so well for himself, and he set off running home with all his might. The dog kept up the struggle until cock-crow, when the corpse fell motionless to the ground. Then the dog ran off in pursuit of its master, caught him up just as he reached home, and rushed at him, furiously trying to bite and to rend him. So savage was it, and so persistent, that it was as much as the people of the house could do to beat it off.

"Whatever has come over the dog?" asked the moujik's old mother. "Why should it hate its master so?"

The moujik told her all that had happened.

---

[49]Source: W. R. S. Ralston, *Russian Folk-Tales* (London, 1873), p. 312. Ralston's source: Aleksandr Afanasyev.

38

"A bad piece of work, my son!" said the old woman. "The dog was disgusted at your not helping it. There it was fighting with the corpse—and you deserted it, and thought only of saving yourself! Now it will owe you a grudge for ever so long."

Next morning, while the family were going about the farmyard, the dog was perfectly quiet. But the moment its master made his appearance, it began to growl like anything.

They fastened it to a chain; for a whole year they kept it chained up. But in spite of that, it never forgot how its master had offended it. One day it got loose, flew straight at him, and began trying to throttle him. So they had to kill it.[50]

The Soldier and the Vampire

Russia

A certain soldier was allowed to go home on furlough. Well, he walked and walked, and after a time he began to draw near to his native village. Not far off from that village lived a miller in his mill. In old times the soldier had been very intimate with him. Why shouldn't he go and see his friend? He went. The miller received him cordially, and at once brought out liquor; and the two began drinking, and chattering about their ways and doings. All this took place towards nightfall, and the soldier stopped so long at the miller's that it grew quite dark.

When he proposed to start for his village, his host exclaimed, "Spend the night here, trooper! It's very late now, and perhaps you might run into mischief."

"How so?"

"God is punishing us! A terrible warlock has died among us, and by night he rises from his grave, wanders through the village, and does such things as bring fear upon the very boldest! How could even you help being afraid of him?"

"Not a bit of it! A soldier is a man who belongs to the crown, and 'crown property cannot be drowned in water nor burnt in fire.' I'll be off. I'm tremendously anxious to see my people as soon as possible."

Off he set. His road lay in front of a graveyard. On one of the graves he saw a great fire blazing. "What's that?" thinks he. "Let's have a look." When he drew near, he saw that the warlock was sitting by the fire, sewing boots.

"Hail, brother!" calls out the soldier.

The warlock looked up and said, "What have you come here for?"

"Why, I wanted to see what you're doing."

The warlock threw his work aside and invited the soldier to a wedding.

---

[50]Source: W. R. S. Ralston, *Russian Folk-Tales* (London, 1873), pp. 313-314. Ralston's source: Aleksandr Afanasyev.

"Come along, brother," says he, "let's enjoy ourselves. There's a wedding going on in the village."

"Come along!" says the soldier.

They came to where the wedding was; there they were given drink, and treated with the utmost hospitality. The warlock drank and drank, reveled and reveled, and then grew angry. He chased all the guests and relatives out of the house, threw the wedded pair into a slumber, took out two vials and an awl, pierced the hands of the bride and bridegroom with the awl, and began drawing off their blood. Having done this, he said to the soldier, "Now let's be off."

Well, they went off. On the way the soldier said, "Tell me; why did you draw off their blood in those vials?"

"Why, in order that the bride and bridegroom might die. Tomorrow morning no one will be able to wake them. I alone know how to bring them back to life."

"How's that managed?"

"The bride and bridegroom must have cuts made in their heels, and some of their own blood must then be poured back into those wounds. I've got the bridegroom's blood stowed away in my right-hand pocket, and the bride's in my left."

The soldier listened to this without letting a single word escape him. Then the warlock began boasting again. "Whatever I wish," says he, "That I can do!"

"I suppose it's quite impossible to get the better of you?" says the soldier.

"Why impossible? If anyone were to make a pyre of aspen boughs, a hundred loads of them, and were to burn me on that pyre, then he'd be able to get the better of me. Only he'd have to look out sharp in burning me; for snakes and worms and different kinds of reptiles would creep out of my inside, and crows and magpies and jackdaws would come flying up. All these must be caught and flung on the pyre. If so much as a single maggot were to escape, then there'd be no help for it; in that maggot I should slip away!"

The soldier listened to all this and did not forget it. He and the warlock talked and talked, and at last they arrived at the grave. "Well, brother," said the warlock, "now I'll tear you to pieces. Otherwise you'd be telling all this."

"What are you talking about? Don't you deceive yourself; I serve God and the Emperor."

The warlock gnashed his teeth, howled aloud, and sprang at the soldier—who drew his sword and began laying about him with sweeping blows. They struggled and struggled; the soldier was all but at the end of his strength. "Ah!" thinks he, "I'm a lost man—and all for nothing!" Suddenly the cocks began to crow. The warlock fell lifeless to the ground.

The soldier took the vials of blood out of the warlock's pockets, and went on to the house of his own people. When he had got there, and had exchanged greetings with his relatives, they said, "Did you see any disturbance, soldier?"

"No, I saw none."

"There now! Why we've a terrible piece of work going on in the village. A warlock has taken to haunting it!"

After talking awhile, they lay down to sleep. Next morning the soldier awoke, and began asking, "I'm told you've got a wedding going on somewhere here?"

"There was a wedding in the house of a rich moujik," replied his relative, "but the bride and bridegroom have died this very night—what from, nobody knows."

They showed him the house. He went there without speaking a word. When he got there, he found the whole family in tears.

"What are you mourning about?" says he.

"Such and such is the state of things, soldier," say they.

"I can bring your young people to life again. What will you give me if I do?"

"Take what you like, even were it half of what we've got!"

The soldier did as the warlock had instructed him, and brought the young people back to life. Instead of weeping, there began to be happiness and rejoicing; the soldier was hospitably treated and well rewarded. Then left about face! off he marched to the Starosta, and told him to call the peasants together and to get ready a hundred loads of aspen wood. Well, they took the wood into the graveyard, dragged the warlock out of his grave, placed him on the pyre, and set it alight—the people all standing round in a circle with brooms, shovels, and fire irons. The pyre became wrapped in flames, the warlock began to burn. His corpse burst, and out of it crept snakes, worms, and all sorts of reptiles, and up came flying crows, magpies, and jackdaws. The peasants knocked them down and flung them into the fire, not allowing so much as a single maggot to creep away! And so the warlock was thoroughly consumed, and the soldier collected his ashes and strewed them to the winds. From that time forth there was peace in the village.

The soldier received the thanks of the whole community. He stayed at home some time, enjoying himself thoroughly. Then he want back to the czar's service with money in his pocket. When he had served his time, he retired from the army, and began to live at his ease.[51]

The Specter Bridegroom

England

Long, long ago a farmer named Lenine lived in Boscean. He had but one son, Frank Lenine, who was indulged into waywardness by both his parents. In addition to the farm servants, there was one, a young girl, Nancy Trenoweth, who especially assisted Mrs. Lenine in all the various duties of a small farmhouse.

Nancy Trenoweth was very pretty, and although perfectly uneducated, in the sense in which we now employ the term education, she possessed many native

[51]Source: W. R. S. Ralston, *Russian Folk-Tales* (London, 1873), pp. 314-318. Ralston's source: Aleksandr Afanasyev.

graces, and she had acquired much knowledge, really useful to one whose aspirations would probably never rise higher than to be mistress of a farm of a few acres.

Frank Lenine and Nancy were thrown as much together as if they had been brother and sister. Although it was evident to all the parish that Frank and Nancy were seriously devoted to each other, the young man's parents were blind to it, and were taken by surprise when one day Frank asked his father and mother to consent to his marrying Nancy. The old man felt it would be a degradation for a Lenine to marry a Trenoweth, and, in the most unreasoning manner, he resolved it should never be.

The first act was to send Nancy home to Alsia Mill, where her parents resided; the next was an imperious command to his son never again to see the girl. The commands of the old are generally powerless upon the young where the affairs of the heart are concerned. So were they upon Frank. He, who was rarely seen of an evening beyond the garden of his father's cottage, was now as constantly absent from his home.

Rarely an evening passed that did not find Nancy and Frank together in some retired nook. The Holy Well was a favorite meeting place, and here the most solemn vows were made. Locks of hair were exchanged; a wedding ring, taken from the finger of a corpse, was broken, when they vowed that they would be united either dead or alive; and they even climbed at night the granite pile at Treryn, and swore by the Logan Rock the same strong vow.

Time passed onward thus unhappily, and, as the result of the endeavors to quench out the passion by force, it grew stronger under the repressing power, and, like imprisoned steam, eventually burst through all restraint. Nancy's parents discovered at length that moonlight meetings between two untrained, impulsive youths, had a natural result, and they were now doubly earnest in their endeavors to compel Frank to marry their daughter.

The elder Lenine could not be brought to consent to this, and he firmly resolved to remove his son entirely from what he considered the hateful influences of the Trenoweths. He resolved to send him away to sea, hoping thus to wean him from this love madness. Frank, poor fellow, with the best intentions, was not capable of any sustained effort, and consequently he at length succumbed to his father; and, to escape his persecution, he entered a ship bound for India, and bade adieu to his native land.

Frank could not write, and this happened in days when letters could be forwarded only with extreme difficulty, consequently Nancy never heard from her lover.

A baby had been born into a troublesome world, and the infant became a real solace to the young mother. Young Nancy lived for her child, and on the memory of its father. She felt that no distance could separate their souls, that no time could be long enough to destroy the bond between them.

The winter was coming on, and nearly three years had passed away since Frank Lenine left his country. It was Allhallows Eve, and two of Nancy's companions persuaded her—no very difficult task—to go with them and sow hemp seed.

42

At midnight the three maidens stole out unperceived into Kimyall town place to perform their incantation. Nancy was the first to sow, the others being less bold than she.

Boldly she advanced, saying, as she scattered the seed:

> Hemp seed I sow thee,
> Hemp seed grow thee;
> And he who will my true love be,
> Come after me
> And shaw thee.

This was repeated three times, when looking back over her left shoulder, she saw Lenine; but he looked so angry that she shrieked with fear, and broke the spell. One of the other girls, however, resolved now to make trial of the spell, and the result of her labors was the vision of a white coffin. Fear now fell on all, and they went home sorrowful, to spend each one a sleepless night.

November came with its storms, and during one terrific night a large vessel was thrown upon the rocks in Bernowhall Cliff, and, beaten by the impetuous waves, she was soon in pieces. Amongst the bodies of the crew washed ashore, nearly all of whom had perished, was Frank Lenine. He was not dead when found, but the only words he lived to speak were begging the people to send for Nancy Trenoweth, that he might make her his wife before he died.

Rapidly sinking, Frank was borne by his friends on a litter to Boscean, but he died as he reached the town place. His parents, overwhelmed in their own sorrows, thought nothing of Nancy, and without her knowing that Lenine had returned, the poor fellow was laid in his last bed, in Burian Churchyard.

On the night of the funeral, Nancy went, as was her custom, to lock the door of the house, and as was her custom too, she looked out into the night. At this instant a horseman rode up in hot haste, called her by name, and hailed her in a voice that made her blood boil.

The voice was the voice of Lenine. She could never forget that; and the horse she now saw was her sweetheart's favorite colt, on which he had often ridden at night to Alsia. The rider was imperfectly seen; but he looked very sorrowful, and deadly pale, still Nancy knew him to be Frank Lenine.

He told her that he had just arrived home, and that the first moment he was at liberty he had taken horse to fetch his loved one, and to make her his bride. Nancy's excitement was so great, that she was easily persuaded to spring on the horse behind him, that they might reach his home before the morning.

When she took Lenine's hand a cold shiver passed through her, and as she grasped his waist to secure herself in her seat, her arm became as stiff as ice. She lost all power of speech, and suffered deep fear, yet she know not why. The moon had arisen, and now burst out in a full flood of light, through the heavy clouds which had obscured it. The horse pursued its journey with great rapidity, and whenever in weariness it slackened its speed, the peculiar voice of the rider aroused its drooping energies. Beyond this no word was spoken since Nancy had mounted behind her lover. They now came to Trove Bottom, where there was no bridge at that time; they dashed into the river. The moon shone full in their faces. Nancy looked into the stream, and saw that the rider was in a shroud and other grave clothes. She now knew that she was being carried away by a spirit, yet she had no power to save herself; indeed, the inclination to do so did not exist.

On went the horse at a furious pace, until they came to the blacksmith's shop near Burian Church-town, when she knew by the light from the forge fire thrown across the road that the smith was still at his labors. She now recovered speech. "Save me! Save me! Save me!" she cried with all her might. The smith sprang from the door of the smithy, with a red-hot iron in his hand, and as the horse rushed by, caught the woman's dress and pulled her to the ground. The spirit, however, also seized Nancy's dress in one hand, and his grasp was like that of a vice. The horse passed like the wind, and Nancy and the smith were pulled down as far as the old Almshouses, near the churchyard. Here the horse for a moment stopped. The smith seized that moment, and with his hot iron burned off the dress from the rider's hand, thus saving Nancy, more dead than alive; while the rider passed over the wall of the churchyard, and vanished on the grave in which Lenine had been laid but a few hours before.

The smith took Nancy into his shop, and he soon aroused some of his neighbors, who took the poor girl back to Alsia. Her parents laid her on her bed. She spoke no word, but to ask for her child, to request her mother to give up her child to Lenine's parents, and her desire to be buried in his grave. Before the morning light fell on the world, Nancy had breathed her last breath.

A horse was seen that night to pass through the Church-town like a ball from a musket, and in the morning Lenine's colt was found dead in Bernowhall Cliff, covered with foam, its eyes forced from its head, and its swollen tongue hanging out of its mouth. On Lenine's grave was found the piece of Nancy's dress which was left in the spirit's hand when the smith burnt her from his grasp.

It is said that one or two of the sailors who survived the wreck related after the funeral, how, on the 30th of October, at night, Lenine was like one mad; they could scarcely keep him in the ship. He seemed more asleep than awake, and, after great excitement, he fell as if dead upon the deck, and lay so for hours. When he came to himself, he told them that he had been taken to the village of Kimyall, and that if he ever married the woman who had cast the spell, he would make her suffer the longest day she had to live for drawing his soul out of his body.

Poor Nancy was buried in Lenine's grave, and her companion in sowing hemp seed, who saw the white coffin, slept beside her within the year.[52]

---

[52]Type 365. Source: Robert Hunt, *Popular Romances of the West of England; or, The Drolls, Traditions, and Superstitions of Old Cornwall* (London, 1871), pp. 233-239. Slightly abridged.

Give Me My Teeth

England

An old lady had been to the church in the sands of Perranzabuloe. She found, amidst the numerous remains of mortality, some very good teeth. She pocketed these, and at night placed them on her dressing table before getting into bed. She slept, but was at length disturbed by someone calling out, "Give me my teeth. Give me my teeth." At first, the lady took no notice of this, but the cry, "Give me my teeth," was so constantly repeated, that she, at last, in terror, jumped out of bed, took the teeth from the dressing table, and, opening the window, flung them out, exclaiming, "Drat the teeth, take 'em!" They no sooner fell into the darkness on the road than hasty retreating footsteps were heard, and there were no more demands for the teeth.[53]

---

[53]Type 366. Source: Robert Hunt, *Popular Romances of the West of England; or, The Drolls, Traditions, and Superstitions of Old Cornwall* (London, 1871), pp. 452-453.

Roots

Family

The Girl with White Hands

D. L. Ashliman

In midsummer of 1814 in the village of Hørby on the island of Sjælland in the Kingdom of Denmark, a handsome carriage stopped at the cottage where the wheelwright Anders Olsen lived with his wife Anne Katrine. A fine lady, with the help of her footman, stepped from the carriage and approached the cottage. She was carrying a newborn child. Saying that she had errands in the vicinity, the lady engaged the wheelwright's wife to watch the baby for a few hours. Anne Katrine gladly accepted, not only because the promised pay was generous, but also because Anders and Anne Katrine had no children of their own, and her maternal instincts were strong. With the pride and awe of a new mother, Anne Katrine uncovered the baby and admired her face, her arms, and her hands. She was perfect in every way, except—except for her hands. They had no color. They were totally white.

June days are long in Denmark, so the wheelwright and his wife were not concerned when evening came without the fine lady's return. Finally the gray of a northern summer night fell over their cottage, bringing with it anxious feelings, first of fear, and then of hope, and again of fear.

The fine lady did not return for the girl with white hands.

On June 29, 1814, in a simple ceremony held in the wheelwright's cottage, the girl with white hands was christened Kirstine Andersdatter: Kirstine, the daughter of Anders. On October 9, 1814, the christening was formalized in the Hørby church. Friends from neighboring villages served as witnesses. In 1818 the wheelwright and his family moved to the city of Kalundborg, halfway across the island.

Kirstine Andersdatter was my great-great grandmother. My cousin Duane Dalley, who knows his way around archives and libraries, discovered the place names and the dates, but the heart of the story comes from my mother. She vouches for its truth, because she heard it from her aunt, Josepha Clinger. Anyone who knew Aunt Seph, as we called her, remembers well that she could always tell a good story, but never a lie. Aunt Seph, while still a young girl, learned the story of the abandoned child from her grandmother, a small blond woman from the Old Country, a woman with glistening white hands.[54]

The Eagle and the Owl

Aesop

The eagle and the owl entered into a treaty with one another, each taking a solemn oath that neither would ever harm the chicks of the other. "But do you know what my chicks look like?" asked the mother owl, fearing that the eagle might attack them by mistake.

"No," said the eagle. "Describe them, so that I will know to spare them."

"They cannot be mistaken for any other bird," returned the proud mother owl. "They are small and ever so beautiful, by far the prettiest of any baby bird."

One evening, while scouting for food, the eagle came upon a nest filled with screeching baby birds. "Surely these do not belong to my friend, the owl," said the eagle. "No, for hers are things of great beauty, but these are hideous, ugly creatures." And he swept down and devoured them every one.

Returning to her nest, the mother owl found only the feet of her offspring. "How can the eagle have violated our bond?" she asked herself in grief. Did he not hear me describe my little ones as the most beautiful chicks of all?

> Moral: Every mother thinks that her own children are the prettiest of all.[55]

---

[54]Source: Personal recollection. Another girl with white hands from folklore is Tristan's wife in the Celtic legend of *Tristan and Isolde*.

[55]Type 247. Retold from a fable in verse by Jean de La Fontaine (1621-1695). Variations of this tale are found in India and throughout Europe. Sometimes the contract is between a hunter and a snipe.

The Mother, the Child, and the Wolf

Aesop

A mother said to her crying child, "Be quiet now, or I will throw you to the wolf."

Now a wolf happened to pass beneath the window as this was being said. "This is my lucky day," he thought. "Surely the child will cry again soon, and what a dainty morsel it will be." And he crouched down and waited.

Later the child did cry, and the wolf advanced toward the window for his expected treat. The mother, however, instead of throwing out the child, set the dogs on the brazen wolf. They cornered the unsuspecting beast at a bound, and men from the house quickly killed him.

Moral: Enemies' promises were made to be broken.[56]

Solomon and the Two Women

The First Book of Kings, Chapter Three

Then came there two women, that were harlots, unto King Solomon, and stood before him.

17. And the one woman said, "Oh my lord, I and this woman dwell in one house; and I was delivered of a child with her in the house.

18. And it came to pass the third day after that I was delivered, that this woman was delivered also: and we were together; there was no stranger with us in the house, save we two in the house.

19. And this woman's child died in the night; because she overlaid it.

20. And she arose at midnight, and took my son from beside me, while thine handmaid slept, and laid it in her bosom, and laid her dead child in my bosom.

21. And when I rose in the morning to give my child suck, behold, it was dead: but when I had considered it in the morning, behold, it was not my son, which I did bear."

22. And the other woman said, "Nay; but the living is my son, and the dead is thy son." And this said, "No; but the dead is thy son, and the living is my son." Thus they spake before the king.

---

[56]Type 75*. Retold from a fable in verse by Jean de La Fontaine (1621-1695), with reference to Joseph Jacobs, *The Fables of Aesop* (London, 1894), no. 46.

23.   Then said the king, "The one saith, 'This is my son that liveth, and thy son is the dead'; and the other saith, 'Nay; but thy son is the dead, and my son is the living.'"

24.   And the king said, "Bring me a sword." And they brought a sword before the king.

25.   And the king said, "Divide the living child in two, and give half to the one, and half to the other."

26.   Then spake the woman whose the living child was unto the king, for her bowels yearned upon her son, and she said, "Oh my lord, give her the living child, and in no wise slay it." But the other said, "Let it be neither mine nor thine, but divide it."

27.   Then the king answered and said, "Give her the living child, and in no wise slay it: she is the mother thereof."

28.   And all Israel heard of the judgment which the king had judged; and they feared the king: for they saw that the wisdom of God was in him, to do judgment.[57]

The Future Buddha as Judge

The Jataka Tales

A woman, carrying her child, went to the future Buddha's tank to wash. And having first bathed the child, she put on her upper garment and descended into the water to bathe herself.

Then a Yaksha, seeing the child, had a craving to eat it. And taking the form of a woman, she drew near, and asked the mother, "Friend, this is a very pretty child. Is it one of yours?" And when she was told it was, she asked if she might nurse it. And this being allowed, she nursed it a little, and then carried it off.

But when the mother saw this, she ran after her, and cried out, "Where are you taking my child to?" and caught hold of her.

The Yaksha boldly said, "Where did you get the child from? It is mine!" And so quarreling, they passed the door of the future Buddha's Judgment Hall.

He heard the noise, sent for them, inquired into the matter, and asked them whether they would abide by his decision. And they agreed. Then he had a line drawn on the ground; and told the Yaksha to take hold of the child's arms, and the mother to take hold of its legs; and said, "The child shall be hers who drags him over the line."

---

[57]Type 926. Solomon's wise judgments (including many that are not recorded in the Bible) are featured in many Middle Eastern and European folktales.

49

But as soon as they pulled at him, the mother, seeing how he suffered, grieved as if her heart would break. And letting him go, she stood there weeping.

Then the future Buddha asked the bystanders, "Whose hearts are tender to babes? Those who have borne children, or those who have not?"

And they answered, "Oh sire! The hearts of mothers are tender."

Then he said, "Who, think you, is the mother? She who has the child in her arms, or she who has let go?"

And they answered, "She who has let go is the mother."

And he said, "Then do you all think that the other was the thief?"

And they answered, "Sire! We cannot tell."

And he said, "Verily, this is a Yaksha, who took the child to eat it."

And he replied, "Because her eyes winked not, and were red, and she knew no fear, and had no pity, I knew it."

And so saying, he demanded of the thief, "Who are you?"

And she said, "Lord! I am a Yaksha."

And he asked, "Why did you take away this child?"

And she said, "I thought to eat him, Oh my Lord!"

And he rebuked her, saying, "Oh foolish woman! For your former sins you have been born a Yaksha, and now do you still sin!" And he laid a vow upon her to keep the Five Commandments, and let her go.

But the mother of the child exalted the future Buddha, and said, "Oh my Lord! Oh great physician! May your life be long!" And she went away, with her babe clasped to her bosom.[58]

The King's Son

Georgia

A certain king had a son, and sent him out to be nursed by a smith's wife. This crafty woman put the king's child in a common cradle, and her own son in the gorgeous royal cradle. Some years afterwards, the king took the changeling to court, and brought his foster brother with him. One fine day, the king set out for his favorite forest to hunt, and took his pretended son with him. When they arrived, the king asked, "How do you like this place, my son? Is it not a magnificent wood?"

The boy replied, "Oh father, if we could only burn it all somehow, what a fine lot of charcoal we should have!"

---

[58]Type 926. Source: *Buddhist Birth-Stories; or, Jataka Tales*, edited by V. Fausbøll and translated by T. W. Rhys Davids (London, 1880), pp. xiv-xvi.

Then the king sent for the other boy, and asked him the same question. "There could not be a better forest, your majesty!"

"But what would you do with it if it were yours?"

"Nothing, your majesty. I would double the guards, so that it should not be injured."

Then the king saw how the smith's wife had tried to cheat him, and put her in prison.[59]

Thumbthick

Jacob and Wilhelm Grimm

Once there was a poor peasant who would sit at the hearth poking the fire every evening, while his wife sat nearby spinning. Once he said, "It is sad that we have no children. It is so quiet here, while it is so loud and cheerful in other houses."

"Yes," answered the wife with a sigh, and said, "I would be satisfied even if there were just one, and even if it were ever so small—no larger than a thumb. We would still love it."

And then it happened that the wife took ill, and seven months later she gave birth to a child. All of his parts were perfectly formed, but he was no larger than a thumb. Then they said, "Yes, he is what we asked for. He will be our dear child." And because of his size they named him Thumbthick. They gave him good things to eat, but the child still did not grow any larger, remaining just as he had been in his first hour. But he had an intelligent look in his eyes, and he soon proved to be a clever and quick little thing, succeeding in everything that he undertook.

One day while the peasant was making preparations to go into the forest to cut wood, he said to himself, "I wish that I had someone to follow me up with the wagon."

"Oh, father," shouted Thumbthick, "I'll take care of that. The wagon will be in the forest whenever you say."

The man laughed and said, "How can that be? You are much too small to guide the horse with the reigns."

"That doesn't matter, father. If mother will hitch up the horse, I'll sit in his ear and tell him which way to go."

"Well," said the father, "we can try it once."

When the time came, the mother hitched the horse to the wagon and set Thumbthick in his ear. The little one shouted which way the horse was to go,

---

[59]Source: Marjory Wardrop, *Georgian Folk Tales*, (London, 1894), pp. 162-163.

51

"Gee! Haw! Giddap! Whoa!" Everything went as it should, and they followed the right trail into the forest.

Now it happened that just as they were rounding a bend, with the little one shouting, "Haw! Haw!," two strange men came by.

"What is that?" said the one. "There is a wagon with a driver calling to the horse, but there is no one to be seen!"

"That can't be," said the other. "Let's follow the cart and see where it stops."

The wagon continued on into the forest to the place where the wood was being cut. When Thumbthick saw his father, he called out, "See, father, I'm here with the wagon. Lift me down." The father held the horse with his left arm, and with his right arm lifted his little son down from the ear, who then cheerfully sat down on a piece of straw.

When the two strangers saw Thumbthick, they were so amazed that they didn't know what to say. The one took the other one aside and said, "Listen, that little fellow could be our fortune, if we could just get him to a big city where there is money. Let's buy him."

They went to the peasant and said, "Sell us the little man. He'll be well off with us."

"No," answered the father. "My pride and joy is not for sale at any price."

However, when Thumbthick heard what was going on, he climbed up the crease in his father's jacket and onto his shoulder, then said into his ear, "Father, let me go. I'll come right back to you." So, for a pretty piece of money, the father let the two men have him.

"Where do you want to sit?" they asked him.

"Oh, put me on the brim of your hat so I can walk back and forth like on a balcony and observe the scenery."

They did as he asked, and as soon as Thumbthick had taken leave from his father, they set forth with him. They walked on until evening, and as it was getting dark the little one said, "Put me down. I have to go."

"Just stay up there," said the man whose head he was sitting on. "It doesn't matter to me. The birds let things drop on me from time to time too."

"No," said Thumbthick. "I know what's proper. Lift me down right now."

The man took off his hat and set the little one in a field next to the path. He jumped and crawled back and forth between the clods, and then slipped down a mouse hole that he found.

"Good evening, gentlemen," he called out, "you no longer have me!"

They ran up and poked sticks into the opening, but it was wasted effort. Thumbthick crawled further and further back until it was pitch dark. Full of anger, but with empty purses, the two men made their way home.

When Thumbthick saw that they had gone, he crawled from the underground passageway. "It is dangerous to walk across this field in the dark," he said. "I could easily break my neck and a leg!" Fortunately he came upon an empty snail shell. "Praise God! Here is a safe place to spend the night!" and he crawled inside.

A little later, just as he was about to fall asleep, he heard two men passing by. One said to the other, "How are we going to get that rich priest's gold and silver?"

52

"I could tell you how," interrupted Thumbthick.

"What was that!" cried out the one thief, frightened, "I heard someone talking."

They stopped and listened, and Thumbthick spoke up again, "Take me along, and I'll help you."

"Where are you?"

"Just look here on the ground, and you'll see where the voice is coming from," he answered. The thieves finally found him and picked him up.

"You little rascal, how can you help us?" they said.

"Look," he answered, "I'll crawl between the iron bars into the priest's storeroom and reach out to you everything that you want."

"Well," they said, "let's see what you can do."

They went to the rectory, and Thumbthick crept into the storeroom, then shouted out with all his might, "Do you want everything that's here?"

The frightened thieves said, "Speak softly, and don't wake anyone up."

Thumbthick, pretending that he didn't understand them, yelled out, "What do you want? Do you want everything that's here?"

The cook, who was sleeping in the next room, sat up in bed and listened. The frightened thieves, who had run a little way off, gathered their courage, thinking that the little fellow was teasing them, and came back and whispered to him, "Be serious now, and reach something out to us."

Then Thumbthick again shouted as loudly as he could, "I'll give you everything. Just reach your hands inside." The maid, who was listening carefully, heard this very clearly, jumped out of bed, and staggered in through the door. The thieves took off as though they were running from a fire, while the maid went to light a candle, because she could not see a thing. She came back with a light, but Thumbthick made his way out into the barn without being seen. The maid, after having searched in every corner without finding anything, finally went back to bed, thinking that she had been dreaming with open eyes and ears.

Thumbthick climbed about in the hay and found a good place to sleep. He wanted to rest until morning and then return to his parents, but what happened to him instead? Yes, there is so much suffering and need in the world! As usual, the maid got up at dawn to feed the cattle. First off she went to the barn and gathered up an armful of hay, and precisely that bundle of hay where Thumbthick was lying fast asleep. He was sleeping so soundly, that he was not aware of anything, and he did not wake up until he was in the mouth of the cow that had eaten him with the hay.

"Oh, God," he cried, how did I fall into the fulling mill?"[60] But soon he discovered where he was. He took care to not be crushed by her teeth, but he could not escape sliding down into her stomach. "They forgot the windows," he said. "The sun does not shine here at all. I wish that I had a light."

He did not like these quarters at all. The worst thing was that more and more fresh hay was coming in at the door, and there was less and less space for him. Finally he shouted out with fear and as loudly as he could, "Don't bring me anything

---

[60]A mill where wool was beaten and boiled as a part of the felt-making process.

more to eat! Don't bring me anything more to eat!" The maid was just milking the cow when she heard someone talking without seeing anyone. It was the same voice that she had heard in the night, and it so frightened her, that she fell off her stool and spilled the milk.

She ran with great haste to her master, and said, "Oh God, father, the cow is talking."

The priest answered the maid, "You are crazy!" and then went to the barn to see for himself what was the matter. He had scarcely set his foot inside when Thumbthick shouted anew, "Don't bring me anything more to eat! Don't bring me anything more to eat!" The terrified priest thought that it must be an evil spirit, and ordered that the cow be killed.

So the cow was slaughtered. The stomach with Thumbthick inside was thrown onto the manure pile. Thumbthick attempted to free himself, but it was not easy. Finally he succeeded in making a little room for himself, but just as he was about to stick his little head out, a wolf came by and downed the entire stomach with a single hungry gulp.

Thumbthick did not lose his courage. "Perhaps," he thought, "I can talk to the wolf, and he called to him from inside his paunch, "Wolf, I know where you can get a great feast."

"Where?" said the wolf.

"In thus and such a house. You can get in through the drain hole, and there you will find cakes and bacon, and sausage, as much as you can eat." And he exactly described his father's house. The wolf did not have to be told twice. That night he squeezed his way through the drain hole into the storage room, and ate to his heart's content. When he was full, he wanted to leave, but he had become so fat that he could not get back out the same way. Thumbthick had counted on this, and now he began to make a mighty noise from within the wolf's body. He stormed and shouted as loudly as he could.

"Be quiet!" said the wolf. "You'll wake the people up."

"So what?" answered the little one. "You've eaten your fill, and now I want to have a good time too!" And he began anew to scream with all his strength. This woke up his father and mother. They ran to the storage room and peered in through a crack. When they saw that a wolf was inside, they were horrified. The man fetched an ax and the woman a scythe.

"Stay behind me," said the man, as they stepped into the room. I'll hit him first, but if that doesn't kill him, you cut him to pieces."

Then Thumbthick heard his father's voice and called out, "Father dear, here I am. I'm inside the wolf!"

The father spoke with joy, "Praise God! Our dearest child has found his way back!" He told his wife to put the scythe away, in order not to injure him. Then he struck the wolf a blow to the head, and he fell down dead. They found a knife and scissors, cut open his belly, and pulled out their dear child.

"Oh," said the father, "we were so worried about you!"

"Yes, father, I've seen a lot of the world now, and thank God that once again I can get a breath of fresh air."

"Where all have you been?"

"Oh, father, I was in a mouse hole, in a cow's belly, and in a wolf's paunch, and now I am going to stay here with you."

"And we will never again sell you, not for all the riches in the world."

Then they hugged and kissed their dear Thumbthick, gave him something to eat and drink, and had new clothes made for him, for his old ones had been ruined on his trip.[61]

The Old Man Who Had a Large Family

Denmark

There was once a very old man who had four hundred and twenty-seven sons. When they were grown they went to their father and said that they wanted to get married, and asked him how they should go about it. "Let me attend to the matter," he said, "I understand such things better than you do, and will find a wife for each one. Saddle my old horse, and I will ride forth to woo for you."

But the old man had to ride far before he discovered a man who had four hundred and twenty-seven daughters, all unmarried. At last, however, he found such a man, and stopped at his house and told him that he had come to ask the young women to marry his sons.

At last they came to an understanding, and agreed that the young people should live with the father of the sons, while the other man was to bear the expenses of the wedding and of the young women's outfits. When the business was concluded the old man asked the servant to saddle and lead out his horse.

"Has he been fed?" he asked; "I have a long journey before me, and do not want to stop on the way to feed him."

"Yes," replied the servant, "I think that he has had enough to eat, for I have given him seven bales of hay."

"Has he had anything to drink?"

"No, I did not have time to give him anything."

"Never mind, I shall pass some pond or lake and it will not take long to water him."

The old man rode away and soon came to a lake. The horse walked into it and began to drink, and before long he had drained it because he was very thirsty. On

---

[61]Type 700. Source: *Kinder- und Hausmärchen*, 2nd ed. (Berlin, 1819), no. 37. Thumb-sized characters are found in folktales throughout Europe. Not all, however, are as fortunate as the Grimms' Thumbthick and Perrault's Little Thumb. The "Tom Thumb" characters in English stories, for example, are usually too bold for their size, and end up being killed by a spider or the like.

the bottom there were many fishes left, and a multitude of birds flew down and carried them away. And as the old man sat on his horse and looked up to see where the birds were carrying their booty, something fell into his eye. He tried to get it out, but was not successful. So there was nothing for him to do but to ride home as fast as he could, holding his hand before his eye, which pained him very much.

As soon as the father got home he told his sons that he had been lucky enough to get a bride for each one of them, but that he had been so unfortunate as to have something fall into his eye, which they would have to help him remove. They searched and searched, but could find nothing. At last the eldest son, who was very clever, said, "We will put our boats into your eye and sail around until we find the thing." That they did, and for seven days they sailed about until at last they found the thing that they were looking for. And it turned out to be a large fish bone that a bird had dropped. So they pulled it out, and took away their boats, and the old man was comfortable once more.

Then the men had to find a carpenter who would make them four hundred and twenty-seven bedsteads for the four hundred and twenty-seven couples. And the fish bone was so large that the carpenter was able to make posts for the four hundred and twenty-seven beds.

When they were all ready, the old man one day thought that he would like to lie down and take a nap on one of the beds; so he put on his red night cap, and stretched himself out. When he was nearly asleep, a fox sneaked in, and began to gnaw at one of the bedposts. And it seemed to him that it tasted of birds and fish. That, however, made the old man angry, and he took off his red cap and threw it at the fox, which was so frightened that it jumped up and hid itself in the man's beard.

The old man tried to seize the fox as it slipped into his beard, but could not catch it; and later on it was quite impossible to find the animal. Then he called his sons to help him find the fox. The oldest son now suggested that each son take his scythe and cut off some of the beard. So for seven days the four hundred and twenty-seven sons mowed until they found the fox in its hiding place, where it had installed itself very comfortably and had given birth to seven young ones.

At last everything was arranged in a satisfactory manner, and the four hundred and twenty-seven sons and their father went to the home of the father of the four hundred and twenty-seven young women, and a great wedding was celebrated which lasted four hundred and twenty-seven days.[62]

---

[62]Type 2014. Source: Sven Grundtvig, *Danish Fairy Tales*, translated by J. Grant Cramer (Boston, 1919), no. 8.

Home and Nation

The Tortoise That Refused to Leave Home

The Jataka Tales

Once on a time, when Brahmadatta was reigning in Benares, the Bodhisatta was born in a village as a potter's son. He plied the potter's trade, and had a wife and family to support.

At that time there lay a great natural lake close by the great river of Benares. When there was much water, river and lake were one; but when the water was low, they were apart. Now fish and tortoises know by instinct when the year will be rainy and when there will be a drought. So at the time of our story the fish and tortoises which lived in that lake knew there would be a drought; and when the two were one water, they swam out of the lake into the river. But there was one tortoise that would not go into the river, because, said he, "Here I was born, and here I have grown up, and here is my parents' home. Leave it I cannot!"

Then in the hot season the water all dried up. He dug a hole and buried himself, just in the place where the Bodhisatta was used to come for clay. There the Bodhisatta came to get some clay. With a big spade he dug down, until he cracked the tortoise's shell, turning him out on the ground as though he were a large piece of clay. In his agony the creature thought, "Here I am, dying, all because I was too fond of my home to leave it!" And in the words of these following verses, he made his moan:

> Here was I born, and here I lived; my refuge was the clay;
> And now the clay has played me false in a most grievous way;
> Thee, thee I call, oh Bhaggava; hear what I have to say!
>
> Go where thou canst find happiness, where'er the place may be;
> Forest or village, there the wise both home and birthplace see;
> Go where there's life; nor stay at home for death to master thee.

So he went on and on, talking to the Bodhisatta, until he died. The Bodhisatta picked him up, and collecting all the villagers addressed them thus, "Look at this tortoise. When the other fish and tortoises went into the great river, he was too fond of home to go with them, and buried himself in the place where I get my clay. Then as I was digging for clay, I broke his shell with my big spade, and turned him out on the ground in the belief that he was a large lump of clay. Then he called to mind what he had done, lamented his fate in two verses of poetry, and expired. So you see he came to his end because he was too fond of his home. Take care not to

57

be like this tortoise. Don't say to yourselves, 'I have sight, I have hearing, I have smell, I have taste, I have touch, I have a son, I have a daughter, I have numbers of men and maids for my service, I have precious gold.' Do not cleave to these things with craving and desire. Each being passes through three stages of existence.''[63]

Thus did he exhort the crowd with all a Buddha's skill. The discourse was bruited abroad all over India, and for full seven thousand years it was remembered. All the crowd abode by his exhortation, and gave alms, and did good until at last they went to swell the hosts of heaven.[64]

The Dog That Went Abroad

The Panchatantra

In a certain place there once lived a dog by the name of Tschitrânga, which means "having a spotted body." A lengthy famine set in. Because they had no food, the dogs and other animals began to leave their families. Tschitrânga, whose throat was emaciated with hunger, was driven by fear to another country. There in a certain city he went to a certain house day after day where, due to the carelessness of the housekeeper, many good things to eat were left lying about, and he ate his fill. However, upon leaving the house, other vicious dogs surrounded him on all sides and tore into him on all parts of his body with their teeth. Then he reconsidered his situation, and said, "It is better at home. Even during a famine you can live there in peace, and no one bites you to pieces. I will return to my own city."

Having thus thought it through, set forth to his own city. When he arrived there, all of his relatives asked him, "Tschitrânga, tell us about where you have been. What is the country like? How do the people behave? What do they eat? What do they do?"

He answered, "How can I explain to you the essence of a foreign place? There are good things to eat in great variety, and housekeepers who do not keep watch! There is only one evil in a foreign country:—You will be hated there because of who you are!''[65]

---

[63]Sense, form, and formless existence.

[64]Source: *The Jataka; or, Stories of the Buddha's Former Births*, edited by E. B. Cowell (Cambridge, 1895), book 2, no. 178.

[65]Similar to type 112 (The Town Mouse and the Country Mouse). Source: *Pantschatantra: Fünf Bücher indischer Fabeln, Märchen und Erzählungen*, translated from the Sanskrit into German by Theodor Benfey (Leipzig, 1859), v. 2, book 4, story 11.

The Town Mouse and the Country Mouse

Aesop

Now you must know that a town mouse once upon a time went on a visit to his cousin in the country. He was rough and ready, this cousin, but he loved his town friend and made him heartily welcome. Beans and bacon, cheese and bread, were all he had to offer, but he offered them freely. The town mouse rather turned up his long nose at this country fare, and said, "I cannot understand, cousin, how you can put up with such poor food as this, but of course you cannot expect anything better in the country; come you with me and I will show you how to live. When you have been in town a week you will wonder how you could ever have stood a country life." No sooner said than done: The two mice set off for the town and arrived at the town mouse's residence late at night.

"You will want some refreshment after our long journey," said the polite town mouse, and took his friend into the grand dining room. There they found the remains of a fine feast, and soon the two mice were eating up jellies and cakes and all that was nice. Suddenly they heard growling and barking.

"What is that?" said the country mouse.

"It is only the dogs of the house," answered the other.

"Only," said the country mouse, "I do not like that music at my dinner!" Just at that moment the door flew open; in came two huge mastiffs; and the two mice had to scamper down and run off.

"Good-bye, cousin," said the country mouse.

"What! Going so soon?" said the other.

"Yes," he replied. "Better beans and bacon in peace than cakes and ale in fear."[66]

The Town Mouse and the Field Mouse

Romania

A mouse living in the town one day met a mouse which lived in the field. "Where do you come from?" asked the latter when she saw the town mouse. "I come from yonder town," replied the first mouse. "How is life going there with you?"

---

[66]Type 112. Source: Joseph Jacobs, *The Fables of Aesop* (London, 1894), no. 7.

"Very well, indeed. I am living in the lap of luxury. Whatever I want of sweets or any other good things is to be found in abundance in my master's house. But how are you living?"

"I have nothing to complain of. You just come and see my stores. I have grain and nuts, and all the fruits of the tree and field in my storehouse."

The town mouse did not quite believe the story of her new friend, and, driven by curiosity, went with her to the latter's house. How great was her surprise when she found that the field mouse had spoken the truth; her garner was full of nuts and grain and other stores, and her mouth watered when she saw all the riches which were stored up there.

Then she turned to the field mouse and said, "Oh, yes, you have here a nice snug place and something to live upon, but you should come to my house and see what I have there. Your stock is as nothing compared with the riches which are mine."

The field mouse, who was rather simple by nature and trusted her new friend, went with her into the town to see what better things the other could have. She had never been into the town and did not know what her friend could mean when she boasted of her greater riches. So they went together, and the town mouse took her friend to her master's house. He was a grocer, and there were boxes and sacks full of every good thing the heart of a mouse could desire. When she saw all these riches, the field mouse said she could never have believed it, had she not seen it with her own eyes.

While they were talking together, who should come in but the cat. As soon as the town mouse saw the cat, she slipped quietly behind a box and hid herself. Her friend, who had never yet seen a cat, turned to her and asked her who that gentleman was who had come in so quietly.

"Do you not know who he is? Why, he is our priest, and he has come to see me. You must go and pay your respects to him and kiss his hand. See what a beautiful glossy coat he has on, and how his eyes sparkle, and how demurely he keeps his hands in the sleeves of his coat."

Not suspecting anything, the field mouse did as she was told and went up to the cat. He gave her at once his blessing, and the mouse had no need of another after that. The cat gave her extreme unction there and then. That was just what the town mouse had intended. When she saw how well stored the home of the field mouse was, she made up her mind to trap her and to kill her, so that she might take possession of all that the field mouse had gathered up. She had learned the ways of the townspeople and had acted accordingly.[67]

---

[67]Type 112. Source: M. Gaster, *Rumanian Bird and Beast Stories* (London, 1915), no. 105.

The Dog and the Wolf

Aesop

A gaunt wolf was almost dead with hunger when he happened to meet a house dog who was passing by. "Ah, cousin," said the dog. "Your irregular life will soon be the ruin of you. Why do you not work steadily as I do, and get your food regularly given to you?"

"I would have not objection," said the wolf, "if I could only get a place."

"I will easily arrange that for you," said the dog. "Come with me to my master and you shall share my work."

So the wolf and the dog went towards the town together. On the way there the wolf noticed that the hair on the dog's neck was very much worn away, so he asked him how that had come about.

"Oh, it is nothing," said the dog. "That is where the collar is put on at night to keep me chained up. It chafes a bit, but one soon gets used to it."

"Is that so?" said the wolf. And with that he took leave of his cousin and returned to the woods.

Moral: Better to starve free than to be a fat slave.[68]

The Bat, the Birds, and the Beasts

Aesop

A great conflict was about to come off between the birds and the beasts. When the two armies were collected together the bat hesitated which to join. The birds that passed his perch said, "Come with us"; but he said, "I am a beast." Later on, some beasts who were passing underneath him looked up and said, "Come with us"; but he said, "I am a bird." Luckily at the last moment peace was made, and no battle took place, so the bat came to the birds and wish to join in their celebration, but they all turned against him, and he had to fly away. He then went to the beasts, but had to retreat again, or else they would have torn him to pieces.

Moral: He that is neither one thing nor the other has no friends.[69]

---

[68]Type 201. Source: Joseph Jacobs, *The Fables of Aesop* (London, 1894), no. 28.

[69]Type 222. Source: Joseph Jacobs, *The Fables of Aesop* (London, 1894), no. 24.

The Man Who Became Rich through a Dream

1001 Nights

Once there lived in Baghdad a wealthy man who lost all his means and was thus forced to earn his living by hard labor. One night a man came to him in a dream, saying, "Your fortune is in Cairo; go there and seek it." So he set out for Cairo. He arrived there after dark and took shelter for the night in a mosque. As Allah would have it, a band of thieves entered the mosque in order to break into an adjoining house. The noise awakened the owners, who called for help. The Chief of Police and his men came to their aid. The robbers escaped, but when the police entered the mosque they found the man from Baghdad asleep there. They laid hold of him and beat him with palm rods until he was nearly dead, then threw him into jail.

Three days later the Chief of Police sent for him and asked, "Where do you come from?"

"From Baghdad," he answered.

"And what brought you to Cairo?"

"A man came to me in a dream and told me to come to Cairo to find my fortune," answered the man from Baghdad "But when I came here, the promised fortune proved to be the palm rods you so generously gave to me."

"You fool," said the Chief of Police, laughing until his wisdom teeth showed. "A man has come to me three times in a dream and has described a house in Baghdad where a great sum of money is supposedly buried beneath a fountain in the garden. He told me to go there and take it, but I stayed here. You, however, have foolishly journeyed from place to place on the faith of a dream which was nothing more than a meaningless hallucination." He then gave him some money saying, "This will help you return to your own country."

The man took the money. He realized that the Chief of Police had just described his own house in Baghdad, so he forthwith returned home, where he discovered a great treasure beneath the fountain in his garden. Thus Allah gave him abundant fortune and brought the dream's prediction to fulfillment.[70]

---

[70]Type 1645. Source: *The Book of the Thousand Nights and a Night*, translated by Richard F. Burton (Privately printed, 1885), v. 4, pp. 289-290. Revised.

The Peddler of Swaffham

England

Constant tradition says that there lived in former times in Soffham (Swaffham), *alias* Sopham, in Norfolk, a certain peddler, who dreamed that if he went to London Bridge, and stood there, he should hear very joyful news, which he at first slighted, but afterwards, his dream being doubled and trebled upon him, he resolved to try the issue of it, and accordingly went to London, and stood on the bridge there two or three days, looking about him, but heard nothing that might yield him any comfort. At last it happened that a shopkeeper there, hard by, having noted his fruitless standing, seeing that he neither sold any wares nor asked any alms, went to him and most earnestly begged to know what he wanted there, or what his business was; to which the peddler honestly answered that he had dreamed that if he came to London and stood there upon the bridge he should hear good news; at which the shopkeeper laughed heartily, asking him if he was such a fool as to take a journey on such a silly errand, adding, "I'll tell you, country fellow, last night I dreamed that I was at Sopham, in Norfolk, a place utterly unknown to me where I thought that behind a peddler's house in a certain orchard, and under a great oak tree, if I dug I should find a vast treasure! Now think you," says he, "that I am such a fool to take such a long journey upon me upon the instigation of a silly dream? No, no. I'm wiser. Therefore, good fellow, learn wit from me, and get you home, and mind your business." The peddler observing his words, what he had said he dreamed, and knowing they concerned him, glad of such joyful news, went speedily home, and dug and found a prodigious great treasure, with which he grew exceeding rich; and Soffham (Church) being for the most part fallen down, he set on workmen and rectified it most sumptuously, at his own charges; and to this day there is his statue therein, but in stone, with his pack at his back and his dog at his heels; and his memory is also preserved by the same form or picture in most of the old glass windows, taverns, and alehouses of that town unto this day.[71]

---

[71]Type 1645. Source: Edwin Sidney Hartland, *English Fairy and Other Folk Tales* (London, ca. 1890), pp. 76-77. Hartland's source is the diary of Abraham de la Pryme, Nov. 10, 1699. This story was brought to Europe by crusaders during the middle ages, where it took root and flourished, always with a local setting. Cf. Jacob and Wilhelm Grimm, *Deutsche Sagen* (Berlin, 1816/1818), no. 212.

The Two Travelers and the Farmer

North America

A traveler came upon an old farmer hoeing in his field beside the road. Eager to rest his feet, the wanderer hailed the countryman, who seemed happy enough to straighten his back and talk for a moment.

"What sort of people live in the next town?" asked the stranger.

"What were the people like where you've come from?" replied the farmer, answering the question with another question.

"They were a bad lot. Troublemakers all, and lazy too. The most selfish people in the world, and not a one of them to be trusted. I'm happy to be leaving the scoundrels."

"Is that so?" replied the old farmer. "Well, I'm afraid that you'll find the same sort in the next town."

Disappointed, the traveler trudged on his way, and the farmer returned to his work.

Some time later another stranger, coming from the same direction, hailed the farmer, and they stopped to talk. "What sort of people live in the next town?" he asked.

"What were the people like where you've come from?" replied the farmer once again.

"They were the best people in the world. Hard working, honest, and friendly. I'm sorry to be leaving them."

"Fear not," said the farmer. "You'll find the same sort in the next town."[72]

---

[72]Source: Personal recollection, Idaho, ca. 1950.

Rules for Living

The Greedy Monkey

India

O nce upon a time a monkey noticed some wheat which had fallen into a small hollow in a rock. Thrusting in his hand, he filled it with the grain, but the entrance was so narrow that he was unable to draw it out without relinquishing most of his prize. This, however, he was unwilling to do, greedily desiring to have it all. So the consequence was that he remained without any, and finally went hungry away.[73]

The Dog and the Reflection

Aesop

A dog was carrying home a piece of meat in his mouth to eat it in peace. On his way he had to cross a plank lying across a brook. As he crossed, he looked down and saw his own reflection in the water beneath. Thinking it was another dog with another piece of meat, he made up his mind to have that also. So he made a snap at the reflection in the water, but as he opened his mouth, the piece of meat fell out, dropped into the water, and was never seen again.

> Moral: Beware lest you lose the substance by grasping at the reflection.[74]

---

[73]Source: Charles Swynnerton, *Indian Nights' Entertainment; or, Folk-Tales from the Upper Indus* (London, 1892), no. 4.

[74]Type 34A. Source: Joseph Jacobs, *The Fables of Aesop* (London, 1894), no. 3.

The Fox and the Crow

Aesop

A fox once saw a crow fly off with a piece of cheese in its beak and settle on a branch of a tree. "That's for me, as I am a fox," said Master Renard, and he walked up to the foot of the tree. "Good day, Mistress Crow," he cried. "How well you are looking today. How glossy your feathers, how bright your eye. I feel sure your voice must surpass that of other birds, just as your figure does. Let me hear but one song from you that I may greet you as the Queen of Birds." The crow lifted up her head and began to caw her best, but the moment she opened her mouth the piece of cheese fell to the ground, only to be snapped up by Master Fox. "That will do," said he. "That was all I wanted."

Moral: Do not trust flatterers.[75]

The Fox and the Grapes

Aesop

One hot summer's day a fox was strolling through an orchard when he came to a bunch of grapes just ripening on a vine which had been trained over a lofty branch. "Just the thing to quench my thirst," he said. Drawing back a few paces, he took a run and a jump, and just missed the bunch. Turning around, he jumped again, but with no greater success. Again and again he tried to reach the tempting fruit, but at last had to give it up. He walked away with his nose in the air, saying, "I am sure that they are sour."

Moral: It is easy to despise what you cannot get.[76]

---

[75]Type 57. Source: Joseph Jacobs, *The Fables of Aesop* (London, 1894), no. 8.

[76]Type 59. Source: Joseph Jacobs, *The Fables of Aesop* (London, 1894), no. 31.

The Jackal and the Fleas

India

There was once a jackal so infested with fleas that life was a burden to him. Determined to be rid of them, he sought for a pool of water, and snatching up a small piece of dry wood in his mouth, he began to enter the water with measured steps and slow. Gradually, as he advanced, the astonished fleas rushed up his legs and took refuge on his back. The rising water again drove them in multitudes from his back to his head, and from his head to his nose, whence they escaped on to the piece of wood, which became perfectly black with them. When the sly jackal perceived the situation of his foes, he suddenly bobbed his head into the water, relinquished the wood, and with a chuckle swam back to the shore, leaving the fleas to their fate.[77]

The Fox and the Fleas

Scotland

The fox is much troubled by fleas, and this is the way in which he gets rid of them. He hunts about until he finds a lock of wool, and then he takes it to the river, and holds it in his mouth, and so puts the end of his brush into the water, and down he goes slowly. The fleas run away from the water, and at last they all run over the fox's nose into the wool, and then the fox dips his nose under and lets the wool go off with the stream.[78]

---

[77]Type 63. Source: Charles Swynnerton, *Indian Nights' Entertainment; or, Folk-Tales from the Upper Indus* (London, 1892), no. 66.

[78]Type 63. Source: J. F. Campbell, *Popular Tales of the West Highlands* (London, 1890), v. 1, p. 276. Campbell heard the tale from a namesake, John Campbell, piper, "and many other sources." J. F. Campbell adds the following note: "This is told as a fact. The place where an 'old gray fellow' was seen performing this feat, was mentioned by one of my informants. The fox was seen in the sea near the Caithness hills."

The Lion and the Mouse

Aesop

Once when a lion was asleep a little mouse began running up and down upon him; this soon wakened the lion, who placed his huge paw upon him, and opened his big jaws to swallow him. "Pardon, oh king," cried the little mouse;" forgive me this time, I shall never forget it. Who knows but what I may be able to do you a turn some of these days?" The lion was so tickled at the idea of the mouse being able to help him, that he lifted up his paw and let him go. Some time after the lion was caught in a trap, and the hunters, who desired to carry him alive to the king, tied him to a tree while they went in search of a wagon to carry him on. Just then the little mouse happened to pass by, and seeing the sad plight in which the lion was, went up to him and soon gnawed away the ropes that bound the King of the Beasts.

> Moral: Little friends may prove great friends.[79]

The Story of the Three Little Pigs

England

> Once upon a time when pigs spoke rhyme
> And monkeys chewed tobacco,
> And hens took snuff to make them tough,
> And ducks went quack, quack, quack, O!

There was an old sow with three little pigs, and as she had not enough to keep them, she sent them out to seek their fortune. The first that went off met a man with a bundle of straw, and said to him, "Please, man, give me that straw to build me a house." Which the man did, and the little pig built a house with it.

Presently came along a wolf, and knocked at the door, and said, "Little pig, little pig, let me come in."

To which the pig answered, "No, no, by the hair of my chiny chin chin."

The wolf then answered to that, "Then I'll huff, and I'll puff, and I'll blow your house in." So he huffed, and he puffed, and he blew his house in, and ate up the little pig.

---

[79]Type 75. Source: Joseph Jacobs, *The Fables of Aesop* (London, 1894), no. 11.

The second little pig met a man with a bundle of sticks, and said, "Please, man, give me those sticks to build a house." Which the man did, and the pig built his house.

Then along came the wolf, and said, "Little pig, little pig, let me come in."

"No, no, by the hair of my chiny chin chin."

"Then I'll puff, and I'll huff, and I'll blow your house in." So he huffed, and he puffed, and he puffed, and he huffed, and at last he blew the house down, and he ate up the little pig.

The third little pig met a man with a load of bricks, and said, "Please, man, give me those bricks to build a house with." So the man gave him the bricks, and he built his house with them.

So the wolf came, as he did to the other little pigs, and said, "Little pig, little pig, let me come in."

"No, no, by the hair of my chiny chin chin."

"Then I'll huff, and I'll puff, and I'll blow your house in."

Well, he huffed, and he puffed, and he huffed and he puffed, and he puffed and huffed; but he could *not* get the house down. When he found that he could not, with all his huffing and puffing, blow the house down, he said, "Little pig, I know where there is a nice field of turnips."

"Where?" said the little pig.

"Oh, in Mr. Smith's home field, and if you will be ready tomorrow morning I will call for you, and we will go together and get some for dinner."

"Very well," said the little pig, "I will be ready. What time do you mean to go?"

"Oh, at six o'clock."

Well, the little pig got up at five, and got the turnips before the wolf came (which he did about six) and who said, "Little pig, are you ready?"

The little pig said, "Ready! I have been and come back again, and got a nice potful for dinner."

The wolf felt very angry at this, but thought that he would be up to the little pig somehow or other, so he said, "Little pig, I know where there is a nice apple tree."

"Where?" said the pig.

"Down at Merry Garden," replied the wolf, "and if you will not deceive me I will come for you, at five o'clock tomorrow and get some apples."

Well, the little pig bustled up the next morning at four o'clock, and went off for the apples, hoping to get back before the wolf came; but he had further to go, and had to climb the tree, so that just as he was coming down from it, he saw the wolf coming, which, as you may suppose, frightened him very much.

When the wolf came up he said, "Little pig, what! Are you here before me? Are they nice apples?"

"Yes, very," said the little pig. "I will throw you down one." And he threw it so far, that, while the wolf was gone to pick it up, the little pig jumped down and ran home.

The next day the wolf came again, and said to the little pig, "Little pig, there is a fair at Shanklin this afternoon. Will you go?"

"Oh yes," said the pig, "I will go. What time shall you be ready?"

"At three," said the wolf. So the little pig went off before the time as usual, and got to the fair, and bought a butter churn, which he was going home with, when he saw the wolf coming. Then he could not tell what to do. So he got into the churn to hide, and by so doing turned it around, and it rolled down the hill with the pig in it, which frightened the wolf so much, that he ran home without going to the fair. He went to the pig's house, and told him how frightened he had been by a great round thing which came down the hill past him.

Then the little pig said, "Ha, I frightened you, then. I had been to the fair and bought a butter churn, and when I saw you, I got into it, and rolled down the hill."

Then the wolf was very angry indeed, and declared he *would* eat up the little pig, and that he would get down the chimney after him. When the little pig saw what he was about, he hung on the pot full of water, and made up a blazing fire, and, just as the wolf was coming down, took off the cover, and in fell the wolf; so the little pig put on the cover again in an instant, boiled him up, and ate him for supper, and lived happily ever afterwards.[80]

Androcles and the Lion

Joseph Jacobs

It happened in the old days at Rome that a slave named Androcles escaped from his master and fled into the forest, and he wandered there for a long time until he was weary and well nigh spent with hunger and despair. Just then he heard a lion near him moaning and groaning and at times roaring terribly. Tired as he was Androcles rose up and rushed away, as he thought, from the lion; but as he made his way through the bushes he stumbled over the root of a tree and fell down lamed, and when he tried to get up there he saw the lion coming towards him, limping on three feet and holding his forepaw in front of him. Poor Androcles was in despair; he had not strength to rise and run away, and there was the lion coming upon him. But when the great beast came up to him instead of attacking him it kept on moaning and groaning and looking at Androcles, who saw that the lion was holding out his right paw, which was covered with blood and much swollen. Looking more closely at it Androcles saw a great big thorn pressed into the paw, which was the cause of all the lion's trouble. Plucking up courage he seized hold of the thorn and drew it out of the lion's paw, who roared with pain when the thorn came out, but soon after found such relief from it that he fawned upon Androcles and showed, in every way that he knew, to whom he owed the relief. Instead of

---

[80]Type 124. Source: Joseph Jacobs, *English Fairy Tales* (London, 1898), no. 14. Jacobs' source: James Orchard Halliwell, *Nursery Rhymes and Nursery Tales* (London, ca. 1843).

eating him up he brought him a young deer that he had slain, and Androcles managed to make a meal from it. For some time the lion continued to bring the game he had killed to Androcles, who became quite fond of the huge beast.

But one day a number of soldiers came marching through the forest and found Androcles, and as he could not explain what he was doing they took him prisoner and brought him back to the town from which he had fled. Here his master soon found him and brought him before the authorities, and he was condemned to death because he had fled from his master. Now it used to be the custom to throw murderers and other criminals to the lions in a huge circus, so that while the criminals were punished the public could enjoy the spectacle of a combat between them and the wild beasts. So Androcles was condemned to be thrown to the lions, and on the appointed day he was led forth into the Arena and left there alone with only a spear to protect him from the lion. The Emperor was in the royal box that day and gave the signal for the lion to come out and attack Androcles. But when it came out of its cage and got near Androcles, what do you think it did? Instead of jumping upon him it fawned upon him and stroked him with its paw and made no attempt to do him any harm. It was of course the lion which Androcles had met in the forest. The Emperor, surprised at seeing such a strange behavior in so cruel a beast, summoned Androcles to him and asked him how it happened that this particular lion had lost all its cruelty of disposition. So Androcles told the Emperor all that had happened to him and how the lion was showing its gratitude for his having relieved it of the thorn. Thereupon the Emperor pardoned Androcles and ordered his master to set him free, while the lion was taken back into the forest and let loose to enjoy liberty once more.[81]

Of the Remembrance of Benefits

Gesta Romanorum

There was a knight who devoted much of his time to hunting. It happened one day, as he was pursuing this diversion, that he was met by a lame lion, who showed him his foot. The knight dismounted, and drew from it a sharp thorn; and then applied an unguent to the wound, which speedily healed it. A while after this, the king of the country hunted in the same wood, and caught that lion, and held him captive for many years. Now, the knight, having offended the king, fled from his anger to the very forest in which he had been accustomed to hunt.

---

[81]Type 156. Source: Joseph Jacobs, *European Folk and Fairy Tales* (New York, 1916), no. 13. In 1913 George Bernard Shaw created a delightful play from this tale, delightful—that is—if you are not offended by Shaw's irreverent wit.

There he betook himself to plunder, and spoiled and slew a multitude of travelers. But the king's sufferance was exhausted; he sent out an army, captured, and condemned him to be delivered to a fasting lion. The knight was accordingly thrown into a pit, and remained in terrified expectation of the hour when he should be devoured. But the lion, considering him attentively, and remembering his former friend, fawned upon him; and remained seven days with him destitute of food. When this reached the ears of the king, he was struck with wonder, and directed the knight to be taken from the pit. "Friend," said he, "by what means have you been able to render the lion harmless?"

"As I once rode along the forest, my lord, that lion met me lame. I extracted from his foot a large thorn, and afterward healed the wound, and therefore he has spared me."

"Well," returned the king, "since the lion has spared you, I will for this time ratify your pardon. Study to amend your life."

The knight gave thanks to the king, and ever afterwards conducted himself with all propriety. He lived to a good old age, and ended his days in peace.

> Application: My beloved, the knight is the world; the lame lion is the human race; the thorn, original sin, drawn out by baptism. The pit represents penitence, whence safety is derived.[82]

The King, the Falcon, and the Drinking Cup

Bidpai

In bygone days there lived a king, who was very fond of hunting. The king had a falcon, which he counted among his chief treasures. This falcon the king always fed from his own hand, and always carried on his own wrist when he went on the hunt. One day, when the court was out a hunting, a deer ran across their path and the king started in pursuit. Some of the royal party followed, but none of them could ride as well and as fast as the king. Through some accident the king did not overtake the deer, and became separated from his companions. Hot and thirsty from his long ride, he dismounted to find some water. For a long time he sought in vain, but at last came to the foot of a hill, where a small stream was trickling down over the rocks. The king took a drinking cup from his sash and held it beneath the stream, catching the water drop by drop. As soon as it was full, he

---

[82]Type 156. Source: *Gesta Romanorum*, translated by Charles Swan (London, 1877), no. 104. "The Deeds of the Romans" is a collection of some 283 legends and fables. Created as a collection ca. 1330 in England, it served as a source of stories and plots for many of Europe's greatest writers.

raised the cup to his lips, and was just about to drink when the falcon flew up, hit the cup, and upset it.

"You awkward bird!" exclaimed the king, and began once more patiently to fill the cup from the stream. A second time the king raised it to his lips, and a second time the falcon flew against it, knocking it from the king's hand. The thirsty king could no longer control his rage. He threw the falcon to the ground with such force that he killed it instantly.

Just then one of the attendants rode up, and, hearing that the king was thirsty, drew out his flask to give the king to drink. But the king shook his head.

"I have set my heart," he said, "on drinking from this stream which runs down the mountainside; but it takes a long time to fill a cup drop by drop here at the bottom. Go therefore to the top of the hill, and bring me down a cup of water from the source of this spring."

The attendant did as the king commanded, but returned with his cup empty.

"Your majesty," he cried," you have been perilously near death. At the source of the spring lies a dead dragon, whose poison has polluted the entire stream. Will your majesty not drink of the water in my flask?"

He held out the cup, and as the king drank, the tears rolled down his face.

"Alas, why does the king weep?" asked the attendant, in great alarm.

The king picked up the dead bird. "This falcon, the dearest of all my treasures," he said sadly, "saved my life twice, and I, by my own act of anger, killed it with one cruel blow!"[83]

The Talkative Tortoise

The Jataka Tales

O nce upon a time, when Brahmadatta was reigning in Benares,[84] the future Buddha was born in a minister's family; and when he grew up, he became the king's adviser in things temporal and spiritual.

Now this king was very talkative; while he was speaking, others had no

---

[83]Type 178. Source: *The Tortoise and the Geese and other Fables of Bidpai*, retold by Maude Barrows Dutton (Boston, 1908), pp. 60-63. Bidpai is, according to tradition, the author of the Panchatantra.

[84]Now called Varanasi, Benares is a city in north central India on the Ganges River. One of the world's oldest cities, Varanasi is the most sacred place for Hindus. Buddhists and Muslims also have important religious sites nearby. According to tradition, Buddha began his teaching at Sarnath a short distance from the city.

opportunity for a word. And the future Buddha, wanting to cure this talkativeness of his, was constantly seeking for some means of doing so.

At that time there was living, in a pond in the Himalayan Mountains, a tortoise. Two young wild ducks who came to feed there made friends with him. And one day, when they had become very intimate with him, they said to the tortoise, "Friend tortoise, the place where we live, at the Golden Cave on Mount Beautiful in the Himalayan country, is a delightful spot. Will you come there with us?"

"But how can I get there?"

"We can take you, if you can only hold your tongue, and will say nothing to anybody."

"Oh, that I can do. Take me with you."

"That's right," said they. And making the tortoise bite hold of a stick, they themselves took the two ends in their teeth, and flew up into the air.

Seeing him thus carried by the ducks, some villagers called out, "Two wild ducks are carrying a tortoise along on a stick!"

Whereupon the tortoise wanted to say, "If my friends choose to carry me, what is that to you, you wretched slaves?" So just as the swift flight of the wild ducks had brought him over the king's palace in the city of Benares, he let go of the stick he was biting, and falling in the open courtyard, split in two!

And there arose a universal cry, "A tortoise has fallen in the open courtyard, and has split in two!"

The king, taking the future Buddha, went to the place, surrounded by his courtiers, and looking at the tortoise, he asked the Bodisat, "Teacher, how has it possible that he has fallen here?"

The future Buddha thought to himself, "Long expecting, wishing to admonish the king, I have sought for some means of doing so. This tortoise must have made friends with the wild ducks; and they must have made him bite hold of the stick, and have flown up into the air to take him to the hills. But he, being unable to hold his tongue when he hears anyone else talk, must have wanted to say something, and let go of the stick; and so must have fallen down from the sky, and thus lost his life." And saying, "Truly, oh king, those who are called chatterboxes—people whose words have no end—come to grief like this," he uttered these verses:

> Verily, the tortoise killed himself
> While uttering his voice;
> Though he was holding tight to stick,
> By a word he slew himself.
>
> Behold him then, oh excellent by strength!
> And speak wise words, not out of season.
> You see how, by his talking overmuch,
> The tortoise fell into this wretched plight!

The king saw that he was himself referred to, and said, "Oh teacher, are you speaking of us?"

And the Bodisat spoke openly, and said, "Oh great king, be it you, or be it any other, whoever talks beyond measure meets with some mishap like this."

74

And the king henceforth refrained himself, and became a man of few words.[85]

The Tortoise and the Hare

Aesop

The hare was once boasting of his speed before the other animals. "I have never yet been beaten," said he, "when I put forth my full speed. I challenge anyone here to race with me."

The tortoise said quietly, "I accept your challenge."

"That is a good joke," said the hare. "I could dance around you all the way."

"Keep your boasting until you've beaten," answered the tortoise. "Shall we race?"

So a course was fixed and a start was made. The hare darted almost out of sight at once, but soon stopped and, to show his contempt for the tortoise, lay down to have a nap. The tortoise plodded on and plodded on, and when the hare awoke from his nap, he saw the tortoise nearing the finish line, and he could not catch up in time to save the race.

Moral: Plodding wins the race.[86]

---

[85]Type 225A. Source: *Buddhist Birth-Stories; or, Jataka Tales*, edited by V. Fausbøll and translated by T. W. Rhys Davids (London, 1880), pp. viii-x. This ancient story is found in fable collections throughout India, the Middle East, and Europe. La Fontaine's version from seventeenth century France has the ill-fated tortoise meet his end when he tries to fly to America. Although most versions stress the value of keeping one's mouth shut, two additional teachings also emerge: "Poverty at home is better than death on the road," and, "If God had intended turtles to fly, he would have given them wings."

[86]Type 275A. Source: Joseph Jacobs, *The Fables of Aesop* (London, 1894), no. 68.

The Shepherd Who Called "Wolf!"

Aesop

There was once a young shepherd boy who tended his sheep at the foot of a mountain near a dark forest. It was rather lonely for him all day, so he thought upon a plan by which he could get a little company and some excitement. He rushed down towards the village calling out, "Wolf! Wolf!" and the villagers came out to help him. This pleased the boy so much that a few days afterwards he tried the same trick, and again the villagers came to his aid. But shortly after this a wolf actually did come out from the forest, and began to attack the sheep. The boy cried out, "Wolf! Wolf!" even louder than before. But this time the villagers, who had been fooled twice before, thought the boy was again deceiving them. Nobody stirred to come to his help, and the wolf made a good meal off the boy's flock.

Moral: A liar will not be believed, even when he speaks the truth.[87]

The Frogs Desiring a King

Aesop

The frogs were living as happy as could be in a marshy swamp that just suited them; they went splashing about caring for nobody and nobody troubling with them. But some of them thought that this was not right, that they should have a king and a proper constitution, so they determined to send up a petition to Jove to give them what they wanted. "Mighty Jove," they cried," send unto us a king that will rule over us and keep us in order." Jove laughed at their croaking, and threw down into the swamp a huge log, which came down—splash—into the swamp. The frogs were frightened out of their lives by the commotion made in their midst, and all rushed to the bank to look at the horrible monster; but after a time, seeing that it did not move, one or two of the boldest of them ventured out towards the log, and even dared to touch it; still it did not move. Then the greatest hero of the frogs jumped upon the log and commenced dancing up and down upon it, thereupon all the frogs came and did the same; and for some time the frogs went about their business ever without taking the slightest notice of new King Log lying in their midst. But this did not suit them, so they sent another petition to Jove, and said to him, "We want a real king; one that will really rule over us." Now this

---

[87]Type 1333. Source: Joseph Jacobs, *The Fables of Aesop* (London, 1894), no. 43.

made Jove angry, so he sent among them a big stork that soon set to work gobbling them all up.

Moral: Better no rule than cruel rule.[88]

The Frog and the Farrier

India

A farrier was once engaged in shoeing a fine Arab horse at the door of his smithy. Just then a frog came hopping up, and, thrusting out one of his feet with a consequential air, he cried, "Ho, farrier, shoe me too! Shoe me too!"[89]

The Frog and the Ox

Aesop

Oh father," said a little frog to the big one sitting by the side of a pool, "I have seen such a terrible monster! It was as big as a mountain, with horns on its head, and a long tail, and it had hoofs divided in two."

"Tush, child, tush," said the old frog, "that was only a farmer's ox. It isn't so big either; he may be a little bit taller than I, but I could easily make myself quite as broad; just you see." So he blew himself out, and blew himself out, and blew himself out." Was he as big as that? " asked he.

"Oh, much bigger than that," said the young frog.

Again the old one blew himself out, and asked the young one if the ox was as big as that.

"Bigger, father, bigger," was the reply.

So the frog took a deep breath, and blew and blew and blew, and swelled and swelled and swelled. And then he said, "I'm sure the ox is not as big as — —" But at this moment he burst.

---

[88]Type 277. Source: Joseph Jacobs, *The Fables of Aesop* (London, 1894), no. 13.

[89]Type 277A (variant). Source: Charles Swynnerton, *Indian Nights' Entertainment; or, Folk-Tales from the Upper Indus* (London, 1892), no. 24.

Moral: Self conceit may lead to self destruction.[90]

The Gold-Giving Snake

The Panchatantra

In a certain place there lived a Brahman by the name of Haridatta. He tilled the soil, but his time in the field brought him no harvest. Then one day, as the hottest hours were just over, tormented by the heat, he lay down in the shade of a tree in the middle of his field for a sleep. He saw a frightful snake, decorated with a large hood, crawl from an anthill a little way off, and thought to himself, "This is surely the goddess of the field, and I have not once paid her homage. That is why the field remains barren. I must bring her an offering." After thus thinking it over, he got some milk, poured it into a basin, then went to the anthill, and said, "Oh, protector of this field, for a long time I did not know that you live here. For this reason I have not yet brought you an offering. Please forgive me!"

Having said this, he set forth the milk, and went home. The next day he returned to see what had happened, and he found a dinar in the basin. And thus it continued day by day. He brought the snake milk, and always found a dinar there the next morning.

One day the Brahman asked his son to take the milk to the anthill, and he himself went into the village. The son brought the milk, set it there, and returned home. When he came back the next day and found a dinar, he said to himself, "This anthill must be full of gold dinars. I will kill the snake and take them all at once!" Having decided this, the Brahman's son returned the next day with the milk and a club. As he gave the milk to the snake, he struck her on the head with the club. The snake, as fate willed it, escaped with her life. Filled with rage, she bit the boy with her sharp, poisoned teeth, and the boy fell dead at once. His people built a funeral pyre not far from the field and cremated him.

Two days later his father returned. When he discovered under what circumstances his son had died, he said that justice had prevailed. The next morning, he once again took milk, went to the anthill, and praised the snake with a loud voice. A good while later the snake appeared in the entrance to the anthill, and said, "You come here from greed, letting even your grief for your son pass by. From now on friendship between you and me will no longer be possible. Your son, in his youthful lack of understanding, struck me. I bit him. How can I forget the club's blow? How can you forget the pain and sorrow for your son?" After saying this she gave

---

[90]Type 277A. Source: Joseph Jacobs, *The Fables of Aesop* (London, 1894), no. 22.

78

him a costly pearl for a pearl chain, said, "Do not come back," and disappeared into her cave.

The Brahman took the pearl, cursed his son's lack of understanding, and returned home.[91]

Of Good Advice

Gesta Romanorum

In the reign of the Emperor Fulgentius, a certain knight, named Zedechias, married a very beautiful but imprudent wife. In a certain chamber of their mansion a serpent dwelt. Now, the knight's vehement inclination for tournaments and jousting brought him to extreme poverty. He grieved immoderately, and, like one who was desperate, walked backward and forward, ignorant of what he should do. The serpent, beholding his misery, like the ass of Balaam, was on that occasion miraculously gifted with a voice, and said to the knight, "Why do you lament? Take my advice, and you shall not repent it. Supply me every day with a certain quantity of sweet milk, and I will enrich you."

This promise exhilarated the knight, and he faithfully followed the instructions of his subtle friend. The consequence was that he had a beautiful son, and became exceedingly wealthy. But it happened that his wife one day said to him, "My lord, I am sure that serpent has great riches hidden in the chamber where he dwells. Let us kill him and get possession of the whole."

The advice pleased the knight, and at the request of his wife he took a hammer to destroy the serpent, and a vessel of milk. Allured by the milk, it put its head out of the hole, as it had been accustomed; and the knight lifted the hammer to strike it. The serpent, observing his perfidy, suddenly drew back its head; and the blow fell upon the vessel. No sooner had he done this, than his offspring died, and he lost everything that he formerly possessed.

The wife, taught by their common loss, said to him, "Alas! I have ill counseled you; but go now to the hole of the serpent, and humbly acknowledge your offense. Peradventure you may find grace." The knight complied, and standing before the dwelling place of the serpent, shed many tears, and entreated that he might once more be made rich.

"I see," answered the serpent, "I see now that you are a fool, and will always be a fool. For how can I forget that blow of the hammer which you designed me, for

---

[91]Type 285D. Source: *Pantschatantra: Fünf Bücher indischer Fabeln, Märchen und Erzählungen,* translated from the Sanskrit into German by Theodor Benfey (Leipzig, 1859), v. 2, book 3, story 5.

which reason I slew your son and took away your wealth? There can be no real peace between us."

The knight, full of sorrow, replied thus, "I promise the most unshaken fidelity, and will never meditate the slightest injury, provided I may this once obtain your grace."

"My friend," said the serpent, "it is the nature of my species to be subtle and venomous. Let what I have said suffice. The blow offered at my head is fresh upon my recollection; get you gone before you receive an injury."

The knight departed in great affliction, saying to his wife, "Fool that I was to take your counsel!" But ever afterwards they lived in the greatest indigence.

> Application: My beloved, the king is God; the knight is Adam, who by following his wife's advice lost Paradise. The serpent in the chamber signifies Christ retained in the human heart, by virtue of baptism.[92]

The Miserly Moslem Priest and His Wife

India

In a village situated on the banks of the Indus, the "Abaseine," or Father of Rivers as it is called, there dwelt many years ago, an imam, or mullah, a president of the mosque, who had come to be much respected by the people for the constant and regular manner in which he officiated, and walked closely in the ways of the Prophet. In his time many used to go to mosque who never went before. This imam had his fees of course, for the performance of marriages and other rites of the Muslim faith, some of which he bestowed on the sick and poor. On festival days, besides an increase of fees, he generally received clothes and other articles from the faithful, so that in point of fact he had a rich harvest.

Towards the latter end of his days, however, this imam contracted habits of stinginess, yet he never failed to preach liberality to others, and above all, the giving of alms to the sick and poor.

He would tell the faithful, "You must always give what you can, and if you have no money, give them of the food you prepare for yourselves, and ever remember," he said, "that those who do this the most exactly will obtain the best blessings, and if you give them dishes of a savory nature, so much the greater merit, and so much the better for you."

---

[92]Type 285D. Source: *Gesta Romanorum*, translated by Charles Swan (London, 1877), no. 141.

This imam had but one wife, devoted to his interests in every way, and with the strongest belief in her husband's sanctity and sincerity. She looked up to him as her spiritual guide and teacher.

She had noticed for some time, however, how niggardly he was becoming, and her neighbors had also remarked this to her, "But," they said, "he never ceases to preach to us to give dainty dishes to the poor."

All this distressed the wife, so she made up her mind that she would try one day to hear what the imam actually did preach to the people.

Now, the mosque was situated on the roadside, and there was an open window to that side, and as his wife knew that she could not be admitted to the mosque, she made up her mind to listen at the window.

One day when she got there quite unperceived, she saw the imam with his face toward Mecca, and he was telling the people just as the neighbors had told her, namely, "That whatever you do, give alms to the poor, and nice dishes when you can, for this will bring you a blessing at the last."

When she heard this she said to herself, "If this is so, and I believe it, I make a vow from this day forward to send nice dishes to the poor, for I am not going to be behind others in this duty." Whereupon she at once prepared and cooked daily such dishes as she could, and then sent them to the poor living round about her; and sometimes she would spend a good deal of money in the purchases she made for the cooking of "Pulao" and "Paratha" (sweet pudding and cake).

This she had continued to do for some time, when one day her husband returned from the mosque a little earlier than usual, and she was herself a little late. Coming into the house and seeing the dishes ready and on a tray, he thought that they had been sent as a gift. Opening the covers he exclaimed, "Oh! Mother of Mohammed! we are indeed in luck's way. Who in the name of fortune, can be the blessed of the faithful who has sent us such a savory meal? Why! here is Pulao! and cakes! and I do not know what beside! What a delicious feast!"

"No one, sir," replied the wife, "has sent this, but I have prepared it for the poor!"

"What!" said he, "of our money? And what have you spent, pray?" He became very angry, and she could only wait until he was quiet; then she said, "Did you not preach to the people, and I dare say do so still, that those who give dainty dishes to the poor shall be blessed hereafter? Did you not say that prayer carries us halfway to Allah, fasting to His palace gates; but only almsgiving gets us in? Yes, I have heard you say so myself!" He replied, "You wretched woman, how and when did you hear this? And if you did hear it, my advice was for others, not for ourselves; I never meant that we were to send to others, but that others were to send to us, and you must stop this waste at once; do you hear me?"

"Yes, I hear you, but I cannot stop it now, for I have made a solemn promise and vow that I will continue this to my dying day. You have said, and I always believe what you say, that the best blessings attend those who give dainty dishes to the poor; and you don't want me to be blessed, eh?"

81

The imam then said, "If you go on in this way, and spend my money, I shall be ill." And sure enough, he did not rise the next morning in time to go to the mosque, a duty he had not failed in for years.

His wife went to rouse him, but he would not get up. At last she said, "All the people will be waiting for you."

"I cannot help that," he replied, "but if you will break your wicked vow, I will at once get up and go to the mosque."

"No," she said, "I have already told you I will on no account break my vow, and all your talking will never shake my purpose."

"Well, then," said the imam, "I shall certainly take to my bed and die."

"Then die you must," said she, "but remember that if you do not go to the mosque, they will put in some other man instead of you, and you will be the loser."

This, however, had no effect upon him, and when she went again to see him he once more asked her to break her vow, and she as steadily refused. She then left him for the night, and the next morning when she went to see him he was to all appearances dead, and failing to get any response, she called in her friends and neighbors, who pronounced that he had truly passed away; and then they sent up the usual cries and lamentations in such cases. The day following, according to custom, the body was washed, covered with a shroud, and laid ready on a bier, and shortly after carried to the cemetery under a chorus of mournful voices, saying, "There is no Deity but Allah, and Mohammed is his prophet."

The wife contrived to secret herself in the procession, for she well knew that no woman could go to the graveside, and when the bier was waiting, after the funeral prayers had been said, she came to the front, and asked to have one more look at her husband. Those round about the body were for moving her away, but others cried, "Let her be! Let her be!"

Going near the bier she whispered, "You are just going into the grave; you had better think better of it."

"So I will," he replied softly, "if you will break your vow."

Drawing her lips tightly together, she gave a final "No!" and then called out at the top of her voice, "Friends and neighbors, this is the time for charity; you see my husband is dead; now go to my house, and take away what things you like. I shall not want them any more, and they are of no further use to your old imam.

She had scarcely uttered these words when the imam rose from the bier like a ghost, scaring away many of the sorrowing mourners nearby. "Wait!" he cried out; "release me; I am not dead, but only in a trance. Hear ye! all of you, what this wretched woman says, and mark well her extravagance and waste. When I lived with her she squandered my money, and now, when I was on the point of being buried, she gives away my possessions. She shall not, however, have her way now with what I possess at my death, do what she will with the moneybag while I am alive."

It was some time before the people could be reconciled to the belief that their old imam had come to life again, but when they were, he was taken back amid much wonder and rejoicing. He appeared again at mosque, and lived for some time afterwards, determined to defy his wife as to the disposal of his goods after death, while she gained her wicked will in regard to his property while alive, and continued to send her savory dishes to the poor.

So you see, my friends, it was the woman, after all, who won the day.[93]

Hans Dumb

Jacob and Wilhelm Grimm

Once there was a king who lived happily with his daughter, his only child. Quite suddenly the princess had a baby, but no one knew who the father was. For some time the king was beside himself. Finally he ordered the princess to take the child to the church. A lemon would be placed in his hand, and whoever he should give it to would be the child's father and the princess's husband. This happened, but only fine people were admitted into the church. However, in the town there was a small, crooked, hunchbacked lad who was not very smart and who was therefore known as Hans Dumb. He mingled with the others and slipped into the church without being seen. When the child reached out with the lemon, it was to Hans Dumb!

The princess was horrified, and the king was so taken aback that he had her, the child, and Hans Dumb placed into a cask and set adrift at sea. The cask soon drifted away, and when they were alone at sea the princess cried out bitterly, "You horrid, hunchbacked, impudent rogue, you are the cause of my suffering. Why did you force your way into the church? You have nothing to do with the child."

"Oh yes," said Hans Dumb. "I have a lot to do with it, because one day I wished that you would have a child, and my wishes come true."

"If that is so, then wish us something to eat."

"I can do that too," said Hans Dumb, and he wished for a plate filled with potatoes. The princess would have liked something better, but because she was so hungry she helped him eat the potatoes. After they had eaten their fill, Hans Dumb said, "Now I shall wish us a fine ship!" He had scarcely said this and they were sitting in a splendid ship, with an excess of everything that they might want. The helmsman steered straight for land, and as they were going ashore Hans Dumb said, "Here there shall be a castle!" And there was a splendid castle there, and servants dressed in gold came and led the princess and the child inside, and when they were in the middle of the great hall, Hans Dumb said, "Now I wish to become a young and intelligent prince!" Then his hump disappeared, and he was handsome

---

[93]Source: J. F. A. McNair and Thomas Lambert Barlow, *Oral Tradition from the Indus* (Brighton, 1908), no. 4.

and straight and friendly. He found favor with the princess, and he became her husband, and they lived happily for a long time.

One day the old king got lost while out riding and came to their castle. He was amazed, because he had never seen it before, and he went inside. The princess recognized her father at once, but he did not know who she was, for he thought that she had long since drowned in the ocean. She received him with splendor, but when he wanted to go back home, she secretly placed a golden goblet into his pocket. After he had ridden away she sent some knights after him to stop him and see if he hadn't stolen the golden goblet. They found it in his pocket and brought him back. He swore to the princess that he had not stolen it and did not know how it came to be in his pocket. She said, "You see, one should always be cautious about accusing another person." With this she revealed herself as his daughter. The king was overjoyed, and they lived happily together, and after his death Hans Dumb became king.[94]

---

[94]Type 675. Source: *Kinder- und Hausmärchen*, 1st ed. (Berlin, 1812/1815), v. 1, no. 54. This story was not included in later editions of the Grimms' famous collection.

Children at Risk

Sacrifice

Jephthah and His Daughter

The Book of Judges, Chapter Eleven

Then the Spirit of the LORD came upon Jephthah, and he passed over Gilead, and Manasseh, and passed over Mizpeh of Gilead, and from Mizpeh of Gilead he passed over unto the children of Ammon.

30. And Jephthah vowed a vow unto the LORD, and said, "If thou shalt without fail deliver the children of Ammon into mine hands,

31. Then it shall be, that whatsoever cometh forth of the doors of my house to meet me, when I return in peace from the children of Ammon, shall surely be the LORD'S, and I will offer it up for a burnt offering."

32. So Jephthah passed over unto the children of Ammon to fight against them; and the LORD delivered them unto his hands.

33. And he smote them from Aroer, even until thou come to Minnith, even twenty cities, and unto the plain of the vineyards, with a very great slaughter. Thus the children of Ammon were subdued before the children of Israel.

34. And Jephthah came to Mizpeh unto his house, and, behold, his daughter came out to meet him with timbrels and with dances: and she was his only child; beside her he had neither son nor daughter.

35. And it came to pass, when he saw her, that he rent his clothes, and said, "Alas, my daughter! thou hast brought me very low, and thou art one of them that trouble me: for I have opened my mouth unto the LORD, and I cannot go back."

36. And she said unto him, "My father, if thou hast opened thy mouth unto the LORD, do to me according to that which hath proceeded out of thy mouth; forasmuch as the LORD hath taken vengeance for thee of thine enemies, even of the children of Ammon."

37. And she said unto her father, "Let this thing be done for me: let me alone two months, that I may go up and down upon the mountains, and bewail my virginity, I and my fellows."

38. And he said, "Go." And he sent her away for two months: and she went with her companions, and bewailed her virginity upon the mountains.

39. And it came to pass at the end of two months, that she returned unto her father, who did with her according to his vow which he had vowed: and she knew no man. And it was a custom in Israel,

40. That the daughters of Israel went yearly to lament the daughter of Jephthah the Gileadite four days in a year.

The Children of Hameln

Germany

In the year 1284 a mysterious man appeared in Hameln. He was wearing a coat of many colored, bright cloth, for which reason he was called the Pied Piper. He claimed to be a rat catcher, and he promised that for a certain sum that he would rid the city of all mice and rats. The citizens struck a deal, promising him a certain price. The rat catcher then took a small fife from his pocket and began to blow on it. Rats and mice immediately came from every house and gathered around him. When he thought that he had them all he led them to the River Weser where he pulled up his clothes and walked into the water. The animals all followed him, fell in, and drowned.

Now that the citizens had been freed of their plague, they regretted having promised so much money, and, using all kinds of excuses, they refused to pay him. Finally he went away, bitter and angry. He returned on June 26, between Saint John the Baptist's Day and Saint Paul's Day, early in the morning at seven o'clock (others say it was at noon), now dressed in a hunter's costume, with a dreadful look on his face and wearing a strange red hat. He sounded his fife in the streets, but this time it wasn't rats and mice that came to him, but rather children: a great number of boys and girls from their fourth year on. Among them was the mayor's grown daughter. The swarm followed him, and he led them into a mountain, where he disappeared with them....

Until the middle of the eighteenth century, and probably still today, the street through which the children were led out to the town gate was called the *bunge-lose* (drumless, soundless, quiet) street, because no dancing or music was allowed there. Indeed, when a bridal procession on its way to church crossed this street, the musicians would have to stop playing. The mountain near Hameln where the children disappeared is called Poppenberg. Two stone monuments in the form of crosses have been erected there, one on the left side and one on the right. Some say that the children were led into a cave, and that they came out again in Transylvania.

The citizens of Hameln recorded this event in their town register, and they came to date all their proclamations according to the years and days since the loss of their children.

According to Seyfried the 22nd rather than the 26th of June was entered into the town register.

The following lines were inscribed on the town hall:

> In the year 1284 after the birth of Christ
> From Hameln were led away
> One hundred thirty children, born at this place
> Led away by a piper into a mountain.

And on the new gate was inscribed:

> *Centum ter denos cum magus ab urbe puellos*
> *duxerat ante annos CCLXXII condita porta fuit.*[95]

In the year 1572 the mayor had the story portrayed in the church windows. The accompanying inscription has become largely illegible. In addition, a coin was minted in memory of the event.[96]

Abandonment and Infanticide

King Aistulf

Jacob and Wilhelm Grimm

The following legend is told about King Aistulf, who ruled the Langobards in the middle of the eighth century: It is said that his mother brought five children to the world in one hour's time. The king only wanted to let one child live, and he said, "The child that takes hold of my spear shall live. The other four shall be set out!"[97] One child reached out for the spear. The king named him Aistulf and allowed him to live.[98]

---

[95]This gate was built 272 years after the magician led the 130 children from the city.

[96]Jacob and Wilhelm Grimm, *Deutsche Sagen* (Berlin, 1816/1818), no. 245. Slightly abridged.

[97]The German word *aussetzen*, literally "to set out," carried with it the meaning of abandoning a

The Abandoned Child

Iceland

A young woman who lived on a farm became pregnant. After giving birth to the child she set it out to die of exposure, not an uncommon act in this country before it became punishable by severe penalties. Now one day it happened that the young woman was invited to a celebration. However, she had no good clothes, so she stayed at home in a sour mood. That evening, while milking the ewes in the fold, she complained aloud that for the want of a proper dress she could not go to the celebration. She had scarcely spoken when she heard the following song:

> Mother mine, in the fold
> You need not be so sad.
> You can wear my castoff rags
> To the dance tonight.

The young woman who had let her child die of exposure thought that she recognized its voice. She took such a fright that she lost her mind and remained insane the rest of her life.[99]

The Snow Child

Europe

A seaman lived with his wife in their cottage by the shore. Their's was not an easy life, for his voyages kept him away from home many months at a time. One homecoming following a particularly long and arduous voyage, the seaman was greeted by his wife and an infant child. He was surprised, but not especially pleased, to see the newborn baby, as he had been at sea for nearly a year.

The wife countered the husband's inquiring look with an explanation.

"No, it is not your son," she admitted. "It's a miracle boy, a Snow Child!" She continued, "One winter's day while returning home from church I slipped on the ice

child so he or she would die of exposure.

[98]Source: *Deutsche Sagen* (Berlin, 1816/1818), no. 411.

[99]Source: Retold from Jón Arnason, *Islenzkar Thjódsögur og Æfintyri* (Reykjavik, 1862/1864). Legends, often in the form of ballads, depicting the murder of a child by its unwed mother are very common in Europe.

and fell into a snowbank. Nine months later I gave birth to our Snow Child. Is he not a wonder!"

The husband had to admit that the child was a wonder, for he had no color. His hair and his skin were a bleached white. The seaman seemed to accept the new family member.

Many voyages and seasons later, it was on a hot summer's day, the seaman, announced to his wife that he would be going to market in the next village. "I'll take the Snow Child along for an outing," he said.

The seaman arrived back home that evening, but he was alone.

"Where is our son?" asked the anxious mother.

"Something terrible happened," responded the husband. "We were walking across a broad meadow in the hot sun, and he...," the husband faltered. "And he melted."[100]

Hansel and Gretel

Jacob and Wilhelm Grimm

Next to a great forest there lived a poor woodcutter who had come upon such hard times that he could scarcely provide daily bread for his wife and his two children, Hansel and Gretel. Finally he could no longer even manage this, and he did not know where to turn for help. One evening as he was lying in bed worrying about his problems, his wife said to him, "Listen, man, early tomorrow take the two children, give each of them a piece of bread, then lead them into the middle of the woods where it is thickest, make a fire for them, and leave them there, for we can no longer feed them."

"No, woman," said the man, "I cannot bring myself to abandon my own children to wild animals that would quickly tear them to pieces."

"If you don't do it," said the woman, "all of us will starve together," and she gave him no peace until he said yes.

The two children were still awake from hunger and heard everything that their mother[101] had said to their father. Gretel thought that she was doomed and began to cry pitifully, but Hansel said, "Be quiet, Gretel, and don't worry. I know what to do." With that he got up, pulled on his jacket, opened the lower door, and crept outside. The moon was shining brightly, and the white pebbles were glistening like

---

[100]Type 1362. Retold. This story was very popular among the writers of medieval and renaissance jest books. Folklore versions have been collected in many countries. See, for example, Lutz Röhrich, *Erzählungen des späten Mittelalters* (Bern, 1962), v. 1, pp. 204-298.

[101]In the 1840 edition the Grimms turned the mother into a stepmother.

silver coins. Hansel bent over and filled his jacket with them, as many as would fit, and then went back into the house. "Don't worry, Gretel; sleep well," he said, climbed back into bed himself, and fell asleep.

The next morning their mother woke them both before sunrise, "Get up, you children. We are going into the woods. Here is a piece of bread. Take care and save it until midday." Gretel put the bread under her apron, because Hansel's pockets were full of stones, and they set forth into the woods. After they had walked a little way, Hansel began stopping again and again and looking back toward the house. Their father said, "Hansel, why are you stopping and looking back? Pay attention now and keep up with us."

"Oh, father, I am looking at my white cat that is sitting on the roof and wants to say good-bye to me."

"The mother said, "You fool, that isn't your cat. That's the morning sun shining on the chimney." However, Hansel had not been looking at his cat but instead had been dropping the shiny pebbles from his pocket onto the path.

Hansel and Gretel sat by the fire until midday, and then ate their bread. They sat on until evening, but their mother and father did not return, and no one came to get them. When it became dark, Gretel began to cry, but Hansel said, "Wait a little until the moon comes up." After the moon had come up, he took Gretel by the hand. The pebbles were lying there like newly minted coins. Glistening, they showed them the way. They walked throughout the entire night, and as morning was breaking, they arrived at their father's house. The father was overjoyed when he saw his children once more, for he had not wanted to leave them alone. The mother pretended that she too was happy, but secretly she was angry.

Not long afterward there was once again no bread in the house, and one evening Hansel and Gretel heard their mother say to their father, "The children found their way back once, and I let it be, but once again we have only a half loaf of bread in the house. Tomorrow you must take them even deeper into the woods, so they cannot find their way home; otherwise there will be no help for us." The man was very disheartened, and he thought it would be better to share the last bit with the children, but because he had done it once, he could not say no.

Hansel and Gretel heard their parents' conversation. Hansel got up and wanted to gather pebbles once again, but when he came to the door, he found that his mother had locked it. Still, he comforted Gretel and said, "Just go to sleep, Gretel dear, God will help us."

Early the next morning they received their little pieces of bread, even less than the last time. On the way, Hansel crumbled his piece in his pocket, then often stood still, and threw crumbs onto the ground. "Why are you always stopping and looking around," said his father. "Keep walking straight ahead."

"Oh!, I can see my pigeon sitting on the roof. It wants to say good-bye to me."

"You fool," said his mother, "that isn't your pigeon. That's the morning sun shining on the chimney." But Hansel crumbled all of his bread and dropped the crumbs onto the path.

The mother took them deeper into the woods than they had ever been in their whole lifetime. There they were told to sleep by a large fire, and that their parents would come get them in the evening. At midday Gretel shared her bread with Hansel, because he had scattered all of his along the path. Midday passed, and evening passed, but no one came to get the poor children. Hansel comforted Gretel and said, "Wait, when the moon comes up I will be able to see the crumbs of bread that I scattered, and they will show us the way back home."

The moon came up, but when Hansel looked for the crumbs, they were gone. The thousands of birds in the forest had found them and pecked them up. Hansel thought that he would still be able to find the way home, and he and Gretel set forth, but they soon became totally lost in the great wilderness. They walked through the night and the entire next day, and then, exhausted, they fell asleep. They walked another day, but they could not find their way out of the woods. They were terribly hungry, for they had eaten only a few small berries that they found growing on the ground.

On the third day they walked until midday when they came to a little house built entirely from bread with a roof made of cake and windows of clear sugar. "Let's sit down and eat our fill," said Hansel. "I'll eat from the roof, and Gretel, you eat from the window. That will be nice and sweet for you." Hansel had already eaten a piece from the roof and Gretel had eaten a few round windowpanes, and she had just broken out another one when she heard a gentle voice calling out from inside:

Nibble, nibble, little mouse,
Who is nibbling at my house?

Hansel and Gretel were so frightened that they dropped what they were holding in their hands, and immediately they saw a little woman, as old as the hills, creeping out the door.

She shook her head and said, "Oh, you dear children, where did you come from? Come inside with me, and you will be just fine." She took them by the hand and led them into her house. Then she served them a good meal, pancakes with sugar, apples, and nuts; and made two beds for them. Hansel and Gretel went to bed, thinking it was though they were in heaven.

But the old woman was a wicked witch who was lying in wait there for children. She had built her house of bread in order to lure them to her, and if she captured one, she would kill him, cook him, and eat him; and for her that was a day to celebrate. So she was overjoyed that Hansel and Gretel had found their way to her.

Early the next morning, before they awoke, she got up, went to their beds, and looked at the two of them lying there so peacefully. "They will be a good mouthful," she thought. She grabbed Hansel and put him in a little stall, and when he awoke, he found himself in a cage, locked up like a young dog, and he could walk only a few steps. Then she shook Gretel and cried, "Get up, lazy bones! Fetch water. Go into the kitchen and cook something to eat. Your brother is locked in that stall there. I want to fatten him up, and when he is fat I am going to eat him. For now, you have to feed him. Gretel was frightened and cried, but she had to do what the witch demanded. Now Hansel was given the best things to eat every day, so he would get fat, but Gretel received nothing but crayfish shells. Every day the old woman came and said, "Hansel, stick out your finger, so I can feel if you are fat enough yet." But Hansel always stuck out a little bone, and she kept wondering why he didn't get any fatter.

After four weeks, one evening she said to Gretel, "Hurry up and fetch water. Whether your brother is fat enough now or not, tomorrow I am going to slaughter him and boil him. In the meantime I want to start the dough that we will bake to go with him." With a sad heart Gretel fetched the water in which Hansel was to be boiled. The next morning Gretel had to get up early, make a fire, and hang up the kettle with water. "Watch it until it boils," said the witch. "I am going to make a fire in the oven and put the bread into it." Gretel stood in the kitchen and cried tears of blood and thought that it would have been better if wild animals had devoured them in the forest, for then they would at least have died together and would not now be suffering so, and she herself would not have to be boiling the water that would kill her dear brother; and she prayed, "Dear God, save us poor children."

Then the old woman called, "Gretel, come here right now to the oven." And when Gretel came, she said, "Look inside and see if the bread is nicely brown and done, for my eyes are weak, and I can't see that far. If you can't see that far either, then sit on the board, and I'll push you inside, then you can walk around inside and take a look." But once Gretel was inside the witch wanted to close the door and bake her in the hot oven and eat her as well. That is what the wicked witch was thinking, and that is why she called Gretel. However, God let Gretel know this, so she said, "I don't know how to do that. First show me. You sit on the board, and I will push you inside." So the old woman sat on the board, and since she was light, Gretel pushed her all the way inside, then quickly closed the door and secured it with an iron bar. The old woman in the hot oven began to cry and to wail, but Gretel ran away, and the witch burned up miserably.

Gretel ran to Hansel and unlocked his door. He jumped out, and they kissed each other and were overjoyed. The whole house was filled with precious stones and pearls. They filled their pockets, then ran away and found their way back home. Their father rejoiced when he saw them once more, for he had not had a happy day since they had been gone, and now he was a rich man. However, their mother had died.[102]

---

[102]Type 327A. Source: *Kinder- und Hausmärchen*, 1st ed. (Berlin, 1812/1815), v. 1, no. 15.

Little Thumb

Charles Perrault

Once upon a time there lived a woodcutter and his wife; they had seven children, all boys. The eldest was but ten years old, and the youngest only seven. People were astonished that the woodcutter had had so many children in such a short time, but his wife was very fond of children, and never had less than two at a time

They were very poor, and their seven children inconvenienced them greatly, because not one of them was able to earn his own way. They were especially concerned, because the youngest was very sickly. He scarcely ever spoke a word, which they considered to be a sign of stupidity, although it was in truth a mark of good sense. He was very little, and when born no bigger than one's thumb, for which reason they called him Little Thumb.

The poor child bore the blame of everything that went wrong in the house. Guilty or not, he was always held to be at fault. He was, notwithstanding, more cunning and had a far greater share of wisdom than all his brothers put together. And although he spoke little, he listened well.

There came a very bad year, and the famine was so great that these poor people decided to rid themselves of their children. One evening, when the children were all in bed and the woodcutter was sitting with his wife at the fire, he said to her, with his heart ready to burst with grief, "You see plainly that we are not able to keep our children, and I cannot see them starve to death before my face. I am resolved to lose them in the woods tomorrow, which may very easily be done; for, while they are busy in tying up the bundles of wood, we can leave them, without their noticing."

"Ah!" cried out his wife; "and can you yourself have the heart to take your children out along with you on purpose to abandon them?"

In vain her husband reminded her of their extreme poverty. She would not consent to it. Yes, she was poor, but she was their mother. However, after having considered what a grief it would be for her to see them perish with hunger, she at last consented, and went to bed in tears.

Little Thumb heard every word that had been spoken; for observing, as he lay in his bed, that they were talking very busily, he got up softly, and hid under his father's stool, in order to hear what they were saying without being seen. He went to bed again, but did not sleep a wink all the rest of the night, thinking about what he had to do. He got up early in the morning, and went to the riverside, where he filled his pockets with small white pebbles, and then returned home.

They all went out, but Little Thumb never told his brothers one syllable of what he knew. They went into a very thick forest, where they could not see one another at ten paces distance. The woodcutter began his work, and the children gathered up the sticks into bundles. Their father and mother, seeing them busy at their work, slipped away from them without being seen, and returned home along a byway through the bushes.

93

When the children saw they had been left alone, they began to cry as loudly as they could. Little Thumb let them cry, knowing very well how to get home again, for he had dropped the little white pebbles all along the way. Then he said to them, "Don't be afraid, brothers. Father and mother have left us here, but I will lead you home again. Just follow me."

They did so, and he took them home by the very same way they had come into the forest. They dared not go in, but sat down at the door, listening to what their father and mother were saying.

The woodcutter and his wife had just arrived home, when the lord of the manor sent them ten crowns, which he had owed them a long while, and which they never expected. This gave them new life, for the poor people were almost famished. The woodcutter sent his wife immediately to the butcher's. As it had been a long while since they had eaten, she bought three times as much meat as would be needed for two people.

When they had eaten, the woman said, "Alas! Where are our poor children now? They would make a good feast of what we have left here; but it was you, William, who decided to abandon them. I told you that we would be sorry for it. What are they now doing in the forest? Alas, dear God, the wolves have perhaps already eaten them up. You are very inhuman to have abandoned your children in this way."

The woodcutter at last lost his patience, for she repeated it more than twenty times, that they would be sorry for it, and that she was right for having said so. He threatened to beat her if she did not hold her tongue. It was not that the woodcutter was less upset than his wife, but that she was nagging him. He, like many others, was of the opinion that wives should say the right thing, but that they should not do so too often.

She nearly drowned herself in tears, crying out, "Alas! Where are now my children, my poor children?"

She spoke this so very loud that the children, who were at the gate, began to cry out all together, "Here we are! Here we are!"

She immediately ran to open the door, and said, hugging them, "I am so glad to see you, my dear children; you are very hungry and tired. And my poor Peter, you are horribly dirty; come in and let me clean you." Now, you must know that Peter was her eldest son, whom she loved above all the rest, because he had red hair, as she herself did.

They sat down to supper and ate with a good appetite, which pleased both father and mother. They told them how frightened they had been in the forest, speaking almost always all together. The parents were extremely glad to see their children once more at home, and this joy continued while the ten crowns lasted; but, when the money was all gone, they fell again into their former uneasiness, and decided to abandon them again. This time they resolved to take them much deeper into the forest than before.

Although they tried to talk secretly about it, again they were overheard by Little Thumb, who made plans to get out of this difficulty as well as he had the last time. However, even though he got up very early in the morning to go and pick up some little pebbles, he could not do so, for he found the door securely bolted and locked. Their father gave each of them a piece of bread for their breakfast, and he fancied he might make use of this instead of the pebbles, by throwing it in little bits all along the way; and so he put it into his pocket.

Their father and mother took them into the thickest and most obscure part of the forest, then, slipping away by an obscure path, they left them there. Little Thumb was not concerned, for he thought he could easily find the way again by means of his bread, which he had scattered along the way; but he was very much surprised when he could not find so much as one crumb. The birds had come and had eaten every bit of it up. They were now in great distress, for the farther they went the more lost and bewildered they became.

Night now came on, and there arose a terrible high wind, which made them dreadfully afraid. They fancied they heard on every side of them the howling of wolves coming to eat them up. They scarcely dared to speak or turn their heads. After this, it rained very hard, which drenched them to the skin; their feet slipped at every step they took, and they fell into the mire, getting them muddy all over. Their hands were numb with cold.

Little Thumb climbed to the top of a tree, to see if he could discover anything. Turning his head in every direction, he saw at last a glimmering light, like that of a candle, but a long way from the forest. He came down, but from the ground, he could no longer see it no more, which concerned him greatly. However, after walking for some time with his brothers in the direction where he had seen the light, he perceived it again as he came out of the woods.

They came at last to the house where this candle was, but not without many fearful moments, for every time they walked down into a hollow they lost sight of it. They knocked at the door, and a good woman opened it. She asked them what they wanted.

Little Thumb told her they were poor children who had been lost in the forest, and begged her, for God's sake, to give them lodging.

The woman, seeing that they were good looking children, began to weep, and said to them, "Alas, poor babies, where are you from? Do you know that this house belongs to a cruel ogre who eats up little children?"

"Ah! dear madam," answered Little Thumb (who, as well as his brothers, was trembling all over), "what shall we do? If you refuse to let us sleep here then the wolves of the forest surely will devour us tonight. We would prefer the gentleman to eat us, but perhaps he would take pity upon us, especially if you would beg him to."

The ogre's wife, who believed she could hide them from her husband until morning, let them come in, and had them to warm themselves at a very good fire. There was a whole sheep on the spit, roasting for the ogre's supper.

After they warmed up a little, they heard three or four great raps at the door. This was the ogre, who was come home. Hearing him, she hid them under the bed and opened the door. The ogre immediately asked if supper was ready and the wine drawn, and then sat down at the table. The sheep was still raw and bloody, but he preferred it that way. He sniffed about to the right and left, saying, "I smell fresh meat."

His wife said, "You can smell the calf which I have just now killed and flayed."

"I smell fresh meat, I tell you once more," replied the ogre, looking crossly at his wife, "and there is something here which I do not understand."

As he spoke these words he got up from the table and went directly to the bed. "Ah, hah!" he said. "I see then how you would cheat me, you cursed woman; I don't know why I don't eat you as well. It is fortunate for you that you are tough old carrion. But here is good game, which has luckily arrived just in time to serve to three ogre friends who are coming here to visit in a day or two."

With that he dragged them out from under the bed, one by one. The poor children fell upon their knees, and begged his pardon; but they were dealing with one of the cruelest ogres in the world. Far from having any pity on them, he had already devoured them with his eyes. He told his wife that they would be delicate eating with good savory sauce. He then took a large knife, and, approaching the poor children, sharpened it on a large whetstone which he held in his left hand. He had already taken hold of one of them when his wife said to him, "Why do it now? Is it not tomorrow soon enough?"

"Hold your chatter," said the ogre; "they will be more tender, if I kill them now."

"But you have so much meat already," replied his wife. "You have no need for more. Here are a calf, two sheep, and half a hog."

"That is true," said the ogre. "Feed them so they don't get too thin, and put them to bed."

The good woman was overjoyed at this, and offered them a good supper, but they were so afraid that they could not eat a bit. As for the ogre, he sat down to drink, being highly pleased that now had something special to treat his friends. He drank a dozen glasses more than ordinary, which went to his head and made him sleepy.

The ogre had seven little daughters. These young ogresses all had very fine complexions, because they ate fresh meat like their father; but they had little gray eyes, quite round, hooked noses, and very long sharp teeth, well spaced from each other. As yet they were not overly mischievous, but they showed great promise for it, for they had already bitten little children in order to suck their blood.

They had been put to bed early, all seven in a large bed, and each of them wearing a crown of gold on her head. The ogre's wife gave the seven little boys a bed just as large and in the same room, then she went to bed to her husband.

Little Thumb, who had observed that the ogre's daughters had crowns of gold upon their heads, and was afraid lest the ogre should change his mind about not killing them, got up about midnight, and, taking his brothers' caps and his own, went very softly and put them on the heads of the seven little ogresses, after having taken off their crowns of gold, which he put on his own head and his brothers', that the ogre might take them for his daughters, and his daughters for the little boys whom he wanted to kill.

All of this happened according to his plan for, the ogre awakened about midnight and, regretting that he had put off until morning that which he might have done

96

tonight, he hastily got out of bed and picked up his large knife. "Let us see," he said, "how our little rogues are doing! We'll not make that mistake a second time!"

He then went, groping all the way, into his daughters' room. He came to the bed where the little boys lay. They were all fast asleep except Little Thumb, who was terribly afraid when he felt the ogre feeling about his head, as he had done about his brothers'. Feeling the golden crowns, the ogre said, "That would have been a terrible mistake. Truly, I did drink too much last night."

Then he went to the bed where the girls lay. Finding the boys' caps on them, he said, "Ah, hah, my merry lads, here you are. Let us get to work." So saying, and without further ado, he cut all seven of his daughters' throats. Well pleased with what he had done, he went to bed again to his wife.

As soon as Little Thumb heard the ogre snore, he wakened his brothers and told them to put on their clothes immediately and to follow him. They stole softly down into the garden, and climbed over the wall. They kept running nearly the whole night, trembling all the while, and not knowing which way they were going.

The ogre, when he awoke, said to his wife, "Go upstairs and dress those young rascals who came here last night."

The ogress was very much surprised at this goodness of her husband, not dreaming how he intended that she should dress them, thinking that he had ordered her to go and put their clothes on them, she went up, and was horribly astonished when she saw her seven daughters with their throats cut and lying in their own blood.

She fainted away, for this is the first expedient almost all women find in such cases. The ogre, fearing his wife would be too long in doing what he had ordered, went up himself to help her. He was no less amazed than his wife at this frightful spectacle.

"What have I done?" he cried. "Those wretches shall soon pay for this!" He threw a pitcher of water on his wife's face, and, having brought her to herself, cried, "Bring me my seven-league boots at once, so that I can catch them."

He went out, and ran this way and that over a vast amount of ground. At last he came to the very road where the poor children were, and not more than a hundred paces from their father's house. They saw the ogre coming, who was stepping from mountain to mountain, and crossing over rivers as easily as if they were little streams. Little Thumb hid himself and his brothers in a nearby hollow rock, all the while keeping watch on the ogre.

The ogre was very tired from his long and fruitless journey (for seven-league boots are very tiring to wear), and decided to take a rest. By chance he sat on the rock where the little boys had hid themselves. He was so tired that he fell asleep, and began to snore so frightfully that the poor children were no less afraid of him than when he had held up his large knife and was about to cut their throats. However, Little Thumb was not as frightened as his brothers were, and told them that they immediately should run away towards home while the ogre was asleep so soundly, and that they should not worry about him. They took his advice, and soon reached home. Little Thumb came up to the ogre, pulled off his boots gently and put them on his own feet. The boots were very long and large, but because they were enchanted, they became big or little to fit the person who was wearing them. So they fit his feet and legs as well as if they had been custom made for him. He immediately went to the ogre's house, where he saw his wife crying bitterly for the loss of her murdered daughters.

"Your husband," said Little Thumb, "is in very great danger. He has been captured by a gang of thieves, who have sworn to kill him if he does not give them all his gold and silver. At the very moment they were holding their daggers to his throat he saw me, and begged me to come and tell you the condition he is in. You should give me everything he has of value, without keeping back anything at all, for otherwise they will kill him without mercy. Because his case is so very urgent, he lent me his boots (you see I have them on), that I might make the more haste and to show you that he himself has sent me to you."

The good woman, being sadly frightened, gave him all she had, for although this ogre ate up little children, he was a good husband. Thus Little Thumb got all the ogre's money. He returned with it to his father's house, where he was received with great joy.

There are many people who do not agree with this last detail. They claim that Little Thumb never robbed the ogre at all, that he only made off with the seven-league boots, and that with a good conscience, because the ogre's only use of them was to pursue little children. These folks affirm that they are quite sure of this, because they have often drunk and eaten at the woodcutter's house.

These people claim that after taking off the ogre's boots, Little Thumb went to court, where he learned that there was much concern about the outcome of a certain battle and the condition of a certain army, which was two hundred leagues off. They say that he went to the king, and told him that, if he desired it, he would bring him news from the army before night. The king promised him a great sum of money if he could do so. Little Thumb was as good as his word, and returned that very same night with the news. This first feat brought him great fame, and he could then name his own price. Not only did the king pay him very well for carrying his orders to the army, but the ladies of the court paid him handsomely to bring them information about their lovers. Occasionally wives gave him letters for their husbands, but they paid so poorly, that he did not even bother to keep track of the money he made in this branch of his business.

After serving as a messenger for some time and thus acquiring great wealth, he went home to his father, where he was received with inexpressible joy. He made the whole family very comfortable, bought positions for his father and brothers, all the while handsomely looking after himself as well.

> Moral: It is no affliction to have many children, if they all are good looking, courteous, and strong, but if one is sickly or slow-witted, he will be scorned, ridiculed, and despised. However, it is often the little urchin who brings good fortune to the entire family.[103]

---

[103]Type 327B. Source: Andrew Lang, *The Blue Fairy Book* (London, ca. 1889), pp. 231-241. Lang's source: Charles Perrault, *Histoires ou contes du temps passé, avec des moralités: Contes*

The Twelve Brothers

Jacob and Wilhelm Grimm

Once upon a time there was a king who had twelve children, all boys. He also wanted to have a girl and said to the queen, "If our thirteenth child, which you are soon going to bring to the world, is a girl, then I shall have the twelve others killed, but if it is also a boy, then they may all live together." The queen tried to dissuade him, but the king would not listen to her. "If it happens as I said, then they must die. I would rather strike off their heads myself than to have a girl among them."

This saddened the queen, for she loved her sons greatly and did not know how to save them. Finally she went to the youngest one, whom she loved even more than the others, and revealed to him what the king had decided, saying, "Dear child, go out into the forest with your eleven brothers. Stay there and do not return home. One of you must keep watch from a tree and look toward the tower here. If I bring a little son into the world, then I shall fly a white flag from the top of the tower, but if it is a little daughter, then it shall be a red flag. Then you must save yourselves by fleeing into the world, and may God protect you. I will get up every night and pray for you, in the cold of winter that you may not freeze and that a warm fire may be burning before you, and in the heat of summer that you may rest and sleep in a cool forest."

Thus she blessed her children, and they went forth into the forest. They often looked toward the tower, and one of them always had to sit high in a tall oak tree and keep watch. Soon a flag was raised, but it was not the white one, but rather the red-blood flag that threatened their destruction. When the boys saw it they became angry and cried out, "Are we to lose our lives for the sake of a girl!" Then they swore among themselves to remain in the middle of the forest, and whenever they might happen upon a girl, they would kill her without mercy.

They found a cave in the darkest part of the forest, and there they lived. Every morning eleven of them set forth to hunt, but one of them had to stay at home to cook and keep house. Every girl that the eleven came upon was done away with without mercy. And so it was for many years.

The little sister at home grew up as an only child. One day she discovered twelve men's shirts in the wash. "Whose shirts are these?" asked the princess. "They are much too small for my father." Then the washerwoman told her that she had had twelve brothers who had secretly left home because the king had wanted to have them killed, and no one knew where they now were. The twelve shirts belonged to these twelve brothers. The little sister was amazed that she had never heard anything of her twelve brothers. That afternoon she sat in a meadow bleach-

de ma mère l'Oye (Paris, 1697). Entitled "Le petit Pouçet" in French, this tale is also known in English as "Hop o' My Thumb," or as "Little Tom Thumb." The thumb-sized French hero has little in common with his English namesake.

ing the wash and pondering the words of the washerwoman. Finally she stood up, took the twelve shirts, and walked into the forest where her brothers lived.

The little sister came to the cave where they lived. Eleven were out hunting, and only one of them was at home doing the cooking. When he saw the girl he grabbed her and reached for his sword, saying, "Kneel down! Your red blood will flow this instant!"

"Master, let me live!" she begged. "I will stay here and serve you well. I will cook and keep house." Now this was the youngest brother, and the girl's beauty softened him, and he spared her life. The eleven returned home and were amazed to find a live girl in their cave. He said to them, "Brothers, this girl came to our cave. I was about to strike her down, but she begged so fervently for her life, and agreed to serve us faithfully and to keep house for us, so I spared her." The others agreed that this was to their advantage, and that now all twelve would be able to go out hunting, and they were satisfied. Then she showed them the twelve shirts and said that she was their sister. They rejoiced and were happy that they had not killed her.

The little sister took over the household. While the brothers were out hunting, she gathered wood and herbs, tended the fire, made the clean, white beds, and did everything eagerly and well. One day it happened that when she was finished with her work she went for a walk in the woods. She came to a place where there were twelve tall white lilies, and because she liked them so much, she plucked them all. This had scarcely happened when an old woman appeared before her. "Oh, my daughter," she said. "Why didn't you leave the twelve flowers standing? They are your twelve brothers, who have now been transformed into ravens and are lost forever."

The little sister began to cry. "Oh!" she said. "Is there no way to redeem them?"

"No, there is only one way in the world, and it is so difficult that you will never succeed. You must remain silent for twelve whole years. If you speak a single word, even if all but one hour has passed, then it will all be for nothing, and your brothers will die that instant."

The little sister took a seat high in a tall tree in the forest where she would spin in silence for twelve years and thus redeem her brothers. One day a king was hunting in this forest. His dog stopped at the tree and barked. The king halted, looked up, and was amazed at the princess's beauty. He called to her, asking her if she would become his wife. She remained silent, but nodded a little with her head. The king himself climbed up and lifted her down, set her before him on his horse, and took her home to his castle, where their wedding was celebrated with splendor. The princess never spoke a word, and the king thought that she was a mute.

They would have lived happily together if it had not been for the king's mother, who began to slander her to him, "You have brought home a common beggar girl, and behind your back she is doing the most unspeakable things."[104]

---

[104]The young queen's "unspeakable" acts are specified in less inhibited versions of this episode. They include, in some instances, cannibalizing her own newborn children, and in others, giving birth to animals.

Because the queen could not defend herself, the king was led into believing his mother, and finally he had his wife sentenced to death. A large fire was set in the courtyard where she was to be burned to death. She was already standing in the fire, with the flames jumping at her dress when the last minutes of the twelve years elapsed. There was a rushing sound in the air, and twelve ravens came flying down and landed. When they touched the earth they turned into twelve handsome princes, who scattered the fire about, and pulled out their sister. Then she spoke once again, telling the king everything, how she had had to redeem her twelve brothers, and they all rejoiced that everything turned out so well.

But what should they do with the wicked stepmother? She was thrown into a barrel filled with boiling oil and poisonous snakes, and died a miserable death.[105]

Little Snow-White

Jacob and Wilhelm Grimm

Once upon a time in mid winter, when the snowflakes were falling like feathers from heaven, a beautiful queen sat sewing at her window, which had a frame of black ebony wood. As she sewed, she looked up at the snow and pricked her finger with her needle. Three drops of blood fell into the snow. The red on the white looked so beautiful, that she thought, "If only I had a child as white as snow, as red as blood, and as black as this frame." Soon afterward she had a little daughter that was as white as snow, as red as blood, and as black as ebony wood, and therefore they called her Little Snow-White.

Now the queen[106] was the most beautiful woman in all the land, and very proud of her beauty. She had a mirror, which she stood in front of every morning, and asked:

> Mirror, mirror, on the wall,
> Who in this land is fairest of all?

And the mirror always said:

> You, my queen, are fairest of all.

And then she knew for certain that no one in the world was more beautiful than she.

---

[105]Type 451. Source: *Kinder- und Hausmärchen*, 1st ed. (Berlin, 1812/1815), v. 1, no. 9.

[106]In later editions, the Grimms add the statement that Snow-White's mother died during childbirth, and that her father remarried. Note that in the first edition, presumably the version closest to its oral sources, Snow-White's jealous antagonist is her own mother, not a stepmother.

Now Snow-White grew up, and when she was seven years old, she was so beautiful, that she surpassed even the queen herself. Now when the queen asked her mirror:

> Mirror, mirror, on the wall,
> Who in this land is fairest of all?

The mirror said:

> You, my queen, are fair; it is true.
> But Little Snow-White is still
> A thousand times fairer than you.

When the queen heard the mirror say this, she became pale with envy, and from that hour on, she hated Snow-White. Whenever she looked at her, she thought that Snow-White was to blame that she was no longer the most beautiful woman in the world. This turned her heart around. Her jealousy gave her no peace. Finally she summoned a huntsman and said to him, "Take Snow-White out into the woods to a remote spot, and stab her to death. As proof that she is dead bring her lungs and her liver back to me. I shall cook them with salt and eat them."

The huntsman took Snow-White into the woods. When he took out his hunting knife to stab her, she began to cry, and begged fervently that he might spare her life, promising to run away into the woods and never return. The huntsman took pity on her because she was so beautiful, and he thought, "The wild animals will soon devour her anyway. I'm glad that I don't have to kill her." Just then a young boar came running by. He killed it, cut out its lungs and liver, and took them back to the queen as proof of Snow-White's death. She cooked them with salt and ate them, supposing that she had eaten Snow-White's lungs and liver.

Snow-White was now all alone in the great forest. She was terribly afraid, and began to run. She ran over sharp stones and through thorns the entire day. Finally, just as the sun was about to set, she came to a little house. The house belonged to seven dwarfs. They were working in a mine, and not at home. Snow-White went inside and found everything to be small, but neat and orderly. There was a little table with seven little plates, seven little spoons, seven little knives and forks, seven little mugs, and against the wall there were seven little beds, all freshly made.

Snow-White was hungry and thirsty, so she ate a few vegetables and a little bread from each little plate, and from each little glass she drank a drop of wine. Because she was so tired, she wanted to lie down and go to sleep. She tried each of the seven little beds, one after the other, but none felt right until she came to the seventh one, and she lay down in it and fell asleep.

When night came, the seven dwarfs returned home from the work. They lit their seven little candles, and saw that someone had been in their house.

The first one said, "Who has been sitting in my chair?"

The second one, "Who has been eating from my plate?"

The third one, "Who has been eating my bread?"

The fourth one, "Who has been eating my vegetables?"

102

The fifth one, "Who has been sticking with my fork?"
The sixth one, "Who has been cutting with my knife?"
The seventh one, "Who has been drinking from my mug?"
Then the first one said, "Who stepped on my bed?"
The second one, "And someone has been lying in my bed."
And so forth until the seventh one, and when he looked at his bed, he found Snow-White lying there, fast asleep. The seven dwarfs all came running, and they cried out with amazement. They fetched their seven candles and looked at Snow-White. "My God! My God!" they cried. "She is so beautiful!" They liked her very much. They did not wake her up, but let her lie there in the bed. The seventh dwarf had to sleep with his companions, one hour with each one, and then the night was done.

When Snow-White woke up, they asked her who she was and how she had found her way to their house. She told them how her mother had tried to kill her, how the huntsman had spared her life, how she had run the entire day, finally coming to their house. The dwarfs pitied her and said, "If you will keep house for us, and cook, sew, make beds, wash, and knit, and keep everything clean and orderly, then you can stay here, and you'll have everything that you want. We come home in the evening, and supper must be ready by then, but we spend the days digging for gold in the mine. You will be alone then. Watch out for the queen, and do not let anyone in."

The queen thought that she was again the most beautiful woman in the land, and the next morning she stepped before the mirror and asked:

> Mirror, mirror, on the wall,
> Who in this land is fairest of all?

The mirror answered once again:

> You, my queen, are fair; it is true.
> But Little Snow-White beyond the seven mountains
> Is a thousand times fairer than you.

It startled the queen to hear this, and she knew that she had been deceived, that the huntsman had not killed Snow-White. Because only the seven dwarfs lived in the seven mountains, she knew at once that they must have rescued her. She began to plan immediately how she might kill her, because she would have no peace until the mirror once again said that she was the most beautiful woman in the land. At last she thought of something to do. She disguised herself as an old peddler woman and painted her face, so that no one would recognize her, and went to the dwarf's house. Knocking on the door she called out, "Open up. Open up. I'm the old peddler woman with good wares for sale."

Snow-White peered out the window, "What do you have?"

"Bodice laces, dear child," said the old woman, and held one up. It was braided from yellow, red, and blue silk. "Would you like this one?"

"Oh, yes," said Snow-White, thinking, "I can let the old woman come in. She means well." She unbolted the door and bargained for the bodice laces.

"You are not laced up properly," said the old woman. "Come here, I'll do it better." Snow-White stood before her, and she took hold of the laces and pulled them so tight that Snow-White could not breathe, and she fell down as if she were dead. Then the old woman was satisfied, and she went away.

Nightfall soon came, and the seven dwarfs returned home. They were horrified to find their dear Snow-White lying on the ground as if she were dead. They lifted her up and saw that she was laced up too tightly. They cut the bodice laces in two, and then she could breathe, and she came back to life. "It must have been the queen who tried to kill you," they said. "Take care and do not let anyone in again."

The queen asked her mirror:

> Mirror, mirror, on the wall,
> Who in this land is fairest of all?

The mirror answered once again:

> You, my queen, are fair; it is true.
> But Little Snow-White with the seven dwarfs
> Is a thousand times fairer than you.

She was so horrified that the blood all ran to her heart, because she knew that Snow-White had come back to life. Then for an entire day and a night she planned how she might catch her. She made a poisoned comb, disguised herself differently, and went out again. She knocked on the door, but Snow-White called out, "I am not allowed to let anyone in."

Then she pulled out the comb, and when Snow-White saw how it glistened, and noted that the woman was a complete stranger, she opened the door, and bought the comb from her. "Come, let me comb your hair," said the peddler woman. She had barely stuck the comb into Snow-White's hair, before the girl fell down and was dead. "That will keep you lying there," said the queen. And she went home with a light heart.

The dwarfs came home just in time. They saw what had happened and pulled the poisoned comb from her hair. Snow-White opened her eyes and came back to life. She promised the dwarfs not to let anyone in again.

The queen stepped before her mirror:

> Mirror, mirror, on the wall,
> Who in this land is fairest of all?

The mirror answered:

> You, my queen, are fair; it is true.
> But Little Snow-White with the seven dwarfs
> Is a thousand times fairer than you.

When the queen heard this, she shook and trembled with anger, "Snow-White will die, if it costs me my life!" Then she went into her most secret room—no one else was allowed inside—and she made a poisoned, poisoned apple. From the outside it was red and beautiful, and anyone who saw it would want it. Then she

104

disguised herself as a peasant woman, went to the dwarfs' house and knocked on the door.

Snow-White peeped out and said, "I'm not allowed to let anyone in. The dwarfs have forbidden it most severely."

"If you don't want to, I can't force you," said the peasant woman. "I am selling these apples, and I will give you one to taste."

"No, I can't accept anything. The dwarfs don't want me to."

"If you are afraid, then I will cut the apple in two and eat half of it. Here, you eat the half with the beautiful red cheek!" Now the apple had been so artfully made that only the red half was poisoned. When Snow-White saw that the peasant woman was eating part of the apple, her desire for it grew stronger, so she finally let the woman hand her the other half through the window. She bit into it, but she barely had the bite in her mouth when she fell to the ground dead.

The queen was happy, went home, and asked her mirror:

> Mirror, mirror, on the wall,
> Who in this land is fairest of all?

And it answered:

> You, my queen, are fairest of all.

"Now I'll have some peace," she said, "because once again I'm the most beautiful woman in the land. Snow-White will remain dead this time."

That evening the dwarfs returned home from the mines. Snow-White was lying on the floor, and she was dead. They loosened her laces and looked in her hair for something poisonous, but nothing helped. They could not bring her back to life. They laid her on a bier, and all seven sat next to her and cried and cried for three days. They were going to bury her, but they saw that she remained fresh. She did not look at all like a dead person, and she still had beautiful red cheeks. They had a glass coffin made for her, and laid her inside, so that she could be seen easily. They wrote her name and her ancestry on it in gold letters, and one of them always stayed at home and kept watch over her.

Snow-White lay there in the coffin a long, long time, and she did not decay. She was still as white as snow and as red as blood, and if she had been able to open her eyes, they still would have been as black as ebony wood. She lay there as if she were asleep.

One day a young prince came to the dwarfs' house and wanted shelter for the night. When he came into their parlor and saw Snow-White lying there in a glass coffin, illuminated so beautifully by seven little candles, he could not get enough of her beauty. He read the golden inscription and saw that she was the daughter of a king. He asked the dwarfs to sell him the coffin with the dead Snow-White, but they would not do this for any amount of gold. Then he asked them to give her to him, for he could not live without being able to see her, and he would keep her, and honor her as his most cherished thing on earth. Then the dwarfs took pity on him and gave him the coffin.

The prince had it carried to his castle, and had it placed in a room where he sat by it the whole day, never taking his eyes from it. Whenever he had to go out and was unable to see Snow-White, he became sad. And he could not eat a bite, unless the coffin was standing next to him. Now the servants who always had to carry the coffin to and fro became angry about this. One time one of them opened the coffin, lifted Snow-White upright, and said, "We are plagued the whole day long, just because of such a dead girl," and he hit her in the back with his hand. Then the terrible piece of apple that she had bitten off came out of her throat, and Snow-White came back to life.[107]

She walked up to the prince, who was beside himself with joy to see his beloved Snow-White alive. They sat down together at the table and ate with joy.

Their wedding was set for the next day, and Snow-White's godless mother was invited as well. That morning she stepped before the mirror and said:

> Mirror, mirror, on the wall,
> Who in this land is fairest of all?

The mirror answered:

> You, my queen, are fair; it is true.
> But the young queen
> Is a thousand times fairer than you.

She was horrified to hear this, and so overtaken with fear that she could not say anything. Still, her jealousy drove her to go to the wedding and see the young queen. When she arrived she saw that it was Snow-White. Then they put a pair of iron shoes into the fire until they glowed, and she had to put them on and dance in them. Her feet were terribly burned, and she could not stop until she had danced herself to death.[108]

The Magic Fiddle

India

Once upon a time there lived seven brothers and a sister. The brothers were married, but their wives did not do the cooking for the family. It was done by their sister, who stopped at home to cook. The wives for this reason bore their sister-in-law much ill will, and at length they combined together to oust

---

[107]In later editions the poisoned apple is dislodged when a servant accidentally stumbles while carrying the coffin to the prince's castle.

[108]Type 709. Source: *Kinder- und Hausmärchen*, 1st ed. (Berlin, 1812/1815), v. 1, no. 53.

her from the office of cook and general provider, so that one of themselves might obtain it. They said, "She does not go out to the fields to work, but remains quietly at home, and yet she has not the meals ready at the proper time." They then called upon their bonga, and vowing vows unto him they secured his goodwill and assistance; then they said to the bonga, "At midday, when our sister-in-law goes to bring water, cause it thus to happen, that on seeing her pitcher, the water shall vanish, and again slowly reappear. In this way she will be delayed. Let the water not flow into her pitcher, and you may keep the maiden as your own."

At noon when she went to bring water, it suddenly dried up before her, and she began to weep. Then after a while the water began slowly to rise. When it reached her ankles she tried to fill her pitcher, but it would not go under the water. Being frightened she began to wail and cry to her brother:

> Oh! my brother, the water reaches to my ankles,
> Still, Oh! my brother, the pitcher will not dip.

The water continued to rise until it reached her knee, when she began to wail again:

> Oh! my brother, the water reaches to my knee,
> Still, Oh! my brother, the pitcher will not dip.

The water continued to rise, and when it reached her waist, she cried again:

> Oh! my brother, the water reaches to my waist,
> Still, Oh! my brother, the pitcher will not dip.

The water still rose, and when it reached her neck she kept on crying:

> Oh! my brother, the water reaches to my neck,
> Still, Oh! my brother, the pitcher will not dip.

At length the water became so deep that she felt herself drowning, then she cried aloud:

> Oh! my brother, the water measures a man's height,
> Oh! my brother, the pitcher begins to fill.

The pitcher filled with water, and along with it she sank and was drowned. The bonga then transformed her into a bonga like himself, and carried her off.

After a time she reappeared as a bamboo growing on the embankment of the tank in which she had been drowned. When the bamboo had grown to an immense size, a jogi, who was in the habit of passing that way, seeing it, said to himself, "This will make a splendid fiddle."

So one day he brought an ax to cut it down; but when he was about to begin, the bamboo called out, "Do not cut at the root, cut higher up." When he lifted his ax to cut high up the stem, the bamboo cried out, "Do not cut near the top, cut at the root." When the jogi again prepared himself to cut at the root as requested, the bamboo said, "Do not cut at the root, cut higher up." And when he was about to cut higher up, it again called out to him, "Do not cut high up, cut at the root." The jogi by this time felt sure that a bonga was trying to frighten him, so becoming angry he cut down the bamboo at the root, and taking it away made a fiddle out of it. The instrument had a superior tone and delighted all who heard it. The jogi carried it with him when he went a begging, and through the influence of its sweet music he returned home every evening with a full wallet.

He now and then visited, when on his rounds, the house of the bonga girl's brothers, and the strains of the fiddle affected them greatly. Some of them were moved even to tears, for the fiddle seemed to wail as one in bitter anguish. The elder brother wished to purchase it, and offered to support the jogi for a whole year if he would consent to part with his wonderful instrument. The jogi, however, knew its value, and refused to sell it.

It so happened that the jogi some time after went to the house of a village chief, and after playing a tune or two on his fiddle asked for something to eat. They offered to buy his fiddle and promised a high price for it, but he refused to sell it, as his fiddle brought to him his means of livelihood. When they saw that he was not to be prevailed upon, they gave him food and a plentiful supply of liquor. Of the latter he drank so freely that he presently became intoxicated. While he was in this condition, they took away his fiddle, and substituted their own old one for it. When the jogi recovered, he missed his instrument, and suspecting that it had been stolen asked them to return it to him. They denied having taken it, so he had to depart, leaving his fiddle behind him. The chief's son, being a musician, used to play on the jogi's fiddle, and in his hands the music it gave forth delighted the ears of all who heard it.

When all the household were absent at their labors in the fields, the bonga girl used to come out of the bamboo fiddle, and prepared the family meal. Having eaten her own share, she placed that of the chief's son under his bed, and covering it up to keep off the dust, reentered the fiddle. This happening every day, the other members of the household thought that some girl friend of theirs was in this manner showing her interest in the young man, so they did not trouble themselves to find out how it came about. The young chief, however, was determined to watch, and see which of his girl friends was so attentive to his comfort. He said in his own mind, "I will catch her today, and give her a sound beating; she is causing me to be ashamed before the others." So saying, he hid himself in a corner in a pile of firewood. In a short time the girl came out of the bamboo fiddle, and began to dress her hair. Having completed her toilet, she cooked the meal of rice as usual, and having eaten some herself, she placed the young man's portion under his bed, as before, and was about to enter the fiddle again, when he, running out from his hiding place, caught her in his arms. The bonga girl exclaimed, "Fie! Fie! You may be a dom, or you may be a hadi of some other caste with whom I cannot marry."

He said, "No. But from today, you and I are one." So they began lovingly to hold converse with each other. When the others returned home in the evening, they saw that she was both a human being and a bonga, and they rejoiced exceedingly.

Now in course of time the bonga girl's family became very poor, and her brothers on one occasion came to the chief's house on a visit. The bonga girl recognized them at once, but they did not know who she was. She brought them water on their arrival, and afterwards set cooked rice before them. Then sitting down near them, she began in wailing tones to upbraid them on account of the treatment she had been subjected to by their wives. She related all that had befallen her, and wound up by saying, "You must have known it all, and yet you did not interfere to save me." And that was all the revenge she took.[109]

The Singing Bone

Jacob and Wilhelm Grimm

A wild boar was wreaking havoc throughout the country. No one dared venture into the forest where it ran about. With its tusks it ripped to pieces anyone who was bold enough to pursue it and attempt to kill it. Then the king proclaimed that anyone who could kill the boar would receive his daughter for a wife.

There were three brothers in the kingdom. The oldest was sly and clever; the second was of ordinary intelligence; but the third and youngest was innocent and slow-witted. They wanted to win the princess, so they set forth to seek out the wild boar and kill it.

The two oldest ones went together, while the youngest one went by himself. When he entered the woods an old man approached him. He was holding a black lance in his hand, and said to him, "Take this lance and fearlessly attack the boar with it, and you will kill it." And that is what happened. He struck the boar with the lance, and it fell dead to the earth. Then he lifted it onto his shoulder, and cheerfully set off toward home.

On the way he came to a house where his brothers were making merry and drinking wine. When they saw him with the boar on his back, they called to him, "Come in and have a drink with us. You must be tired." The innocent simpleton, not thinking about any danger, went inside and told them how he had killed the boar with the black lance, and rejoiced in his good fortune. That evening they returned home together. The two oldest ones plotted to kill their brother. They let him walk ahead of them, and when they came to a bridge just outside the city, they attacked him, striking him dead. They buried him beneath the bridge. Then the oldest one took the boar, carried it to the king, claimed that he had killed it, and received the princess for a wife.

Many years passed, but it was not to remain hidden. One day a shepherd was crossing the bridge when he saw a little bone beneath him in the sand. It was so

---

[109]Type 780. Source: Joseph Jacobs, *Indian Fairy Tales* (London, 1892), pp. 40-45. Jacobs' source: A. Campbell, *Santal Folk-Tales* (Pokhuria, 1891).

pure and snow-white that he wanted it to make a mouthpiece from, so he climbed down and picked it up. Afterward he made a mouthpiece from it for his horn, and when he put it to his lips to play, the little bone began to sing by itself:

> Oh, dear shepherd
> You are blowing on my bone.
> My brothers struck me dead,
> And buried me beneath the bridge,
> To get the wild boar
> For the king's daughter.

The shepherd took the horn to the king, and once again it sang the same words. After hearing this, the king had his people dig under the bridge, and they soon uncovered the skeleton. The two wicked brothers confessed their crime and were thrown into the water. The murdered brother's bones were laid to rest in a beautiful grave in the churchyard.[110]

Binnorie

England

Once upon a time there were two king's daughters who lived in a bower near the bonny mill dams of Binnorie. And Sir William came wooing the eldest and won her love, and plighted troth with glove and with ring. But after a time he looked upon the youngest, with her cherry cheeks and golden hair, and his love went out to her until he cared no longer for the eldest one. So she hated her sister for taking away Sir William's love, and day by day her hate grew and grew and she plotted and she planned how to get rid of her.

So one fine morning, fair and clear, she said to her sister, "Let us go and see our father's boats come in at the bonny mill stream of Binnorie." So they went there hand in hand. And when they came to the river's bank the youngest got upon a stone to watch for the beaching of the boats. And her sister, coming behind her, caught her round the waist and dashed her into the rushing mill stream of Binnorie.

"Oh sister, sister, reach me your hand!" she cried, as she floated away, "and you shall have half of all I've got or shall get."

"No, sister, I'll reach you no hand of mine, for I am the heir to all your land. Shame on me if I touch her hand that has come 'twixt me and my own heart's love."

---

[110]Type 780. Source: *Kinder- und Hausmärchen*, 1st ed. (Berlin, 1812/1815), v. 1, no. 28.

"Oh sister, oh sister, then reach me your glove!" she cried, as she floated further away, "and you shall have your William again."

"Sink on," cried the cruel princess, "no hand or glove of mine you'll touch. Sweet William will be all mine when you are sunk beneath the bonny mill stream of Binnorie." And she turned and went home to the king's castle.

And the princess floated down the mill stream, sometimes swimming and some-times sinking, until she came near the mill. Now the miller's daughter was cooking that day, and needed water for her cooking. And as she went to draw it from the stream, she saw something floating towards the mill dam, and she called out, "Father! father! draw your dam. There's something white—a merrymaid or a milk white swan—coming down the stream." So the miller hastened to the dam and stopped the heavy cruel mill wheels. And then they took out the princess and laid her on the bank.

Fair and beautiful she looked as she lay there. In her golden hair were pearls and precious stones; you could not see her waist for her golden girdle, and the golden fringe of her white dress came down over her lily feet. But she was drowned, drowned!

And as she lay there in her beauty a famous harper passed by the mill dam of Binnorie, and saw her sweet pale face. And though he traveled on far away he never forgot that face, and after many days he came back to the bonny mill stream of Binnorie. But then all he could find of her where they had put her to rest were her bones and her golden hair. So he made a harp out of her breast bone and her hair, and traveled on up the hill from the mill dam of Binnorie, until he came to the castle of the king her father.

That night they were all gathered in the castle hall to hear the great harper: king and queen, their daughter and son, Sir William, and all their court. And first the harper sang to his old harp, making them joy and be glad, or sorrow and weep just as he liked. But while he sang he put the harp he had made that day on a stone in the hall. And presently it began to sing by itself, low and clear, and the harper stopped and all were hushed.

And this was what the harp sung:

> Oh yonder sits my father, the king,
> Binnorie, oh Binnorie;
> And yonder sits my mother, the queen;
> By the bony mill dams o' Binnorie.

> And yonder stands my brother Hugh,
> Binnorie, oh Binnorie;
> And by him, my William, false and true;
> By the bonny mill dams o' Binnorie.

Then they all wondered, and the harper told them how he had seen the princess lying drowned on the bank near the bonny mill dams o' Binnorie, and how he had afterwards made this harp out of her hair and breast bone. Just then the harp began singing again, and this was what it sang out loud and clear:

And there sits my sister who drownèd me
By the bonny mill dams o' Binnorie.

And the harp snapped and broke, and never sang more.[111]

The King and His Daughters

India

There was once a king who had several daughters. To the first he said, "How do you love me?"

"I love you as sugar," said she.

To the next he said, "And how do you love me?"

"I love you as honey," said she.

To the third he said, "And how do you love me?"

"I love you as sherbet," said she.

To the last and youngest he said, "And how do you love me?"

"I love you as salt," said she.

On hearing the answer of his youngest daughter the king frowned, and, as she persisted in repeating it, he drove her out into the forest.

There, when wandering sadly along, she heard the tramping of a horse, and she hid herself in a hollow tree. But the fluttering of her dress betrayed her to the rider, who was a prince, and who instantly fell in love with her and married her.

Some time after, the king, her father, who did not know what had become of her, paid her husband a visit. When he sat down to meat, the princess took care that all the dishes presented to him should be made-up sweets, which he either passed by altogether or merely tasted. He was very hungry, and was longing sorely for something which he could eat, when the princess sent him a dish of common spinach, seasoned with salt, such as farmers eat, and the king signified his pleasure by eating it with relish.

Then the princess threw off her veil, and, revealing herself to her father, said, "Oh my father, I love you as salt. My love may be homely, but it is true, genuine and lasting, and I entreat your forgiveness."

Then the king perceived how great a mistake he had made, and there followed a full reconciliation.[112]

---

[111]Type 780. Source: Joseph Jacobs, *English Fairy Tales* (London, 1898), no. 9.

[112]Type 923. Source: Charles Swynnerton, *Indian Nights' Entertainment; or, Folk-Tales from the Upper Indus* (London, 1892), no. 27.

Changelings

Brewery of Eggshells

Wales

In Treneglwys there is a certain shepherd's cot known by the name of Twt y Cymrws because of the strange strife that occurred there. There once lived there a man and his wife, and they had twins whom the woman nursed tenderly. One day she was called away to the house of a neighbor at some distance. She did not much like going and leaving her little ones all alone in a solitary house, especially as she had heard tell of the good folk haunting the neighborhood.

Well, she went and came back as soon as she could, but on her way back she was frightened to see some old elves of the blue petticoat crossing her path though it was midday. She rushed home, but found her two little ones in the cradle and everything seemed as it was before.

But after a time the good people began to suspect that something was wrong, for the twins didn't grow at all.

The man said, "They're not ours."

The woman said, "Then whose should they be?"

And so arose the great strife so that the neighbors named the cottage after it. It made the woman very sad, so one evening she made up her mind to go and see the Wise Man of Llanidloes, for he knew everything and would advise her what to do.

So she went to Llanidloes and told the case to the Wise Man. Now there was soon to be a harvest of rye and oats, so the Wise Man said to her, "When you are getting dinner for the reapers, clear out the shell of a hen's egg and boil some pottage in it, and then take it to the door as if you meant it as a dinner for the reapers. Then listen if the twins say anything. If you hear them speaking of things beyond the understanding of children, go back and take them up and throw them into the waters of Lake Elvyn. But if you don't hear anything remarkable, do them no injury."

So when the day of the reap came the woman did all that the Wise Man ordered, and put the eggshell on the fire and took it off and carried it to the door, and there she stood and listened. Then she heard one of the children say to the other:

> Acorn before oak I knew,
> An egg before a hen,
> But I never heard of an eggshell brew
> A dinner for harvest men.

113

So she went back into the house, seized the children and threw them into the Llyn, and the goblins in their blue trousers came and saved their dwarfs and the mother had her own children back and so the great strife ended.[113]

Changeling Is Beaten with a Switch

Jacob and Wilhelm Grimm

The following true story took place in the year 1580. Near Breslau there lived a distinguished nobleman who had a large crop of hay every summer which his subjects were required to harvest for him. One year there was a new mother among his harvest workers, a woman who barely had had a week to recover from the birth of her child. When she saw that she could not refuse the nobleman's decree, she took her child with her, placed it on a small clump of grass, and left it alone while she helped with the haymaking. After she had worked a good while, she returned to her child to nurse it. She looked at it, screamed aloud, hit her hands together above her head, and cried out in despair, that this was not her child. It sucked the milk from her so greedily and howled in such an inhuman manner that it was nothing like the child she knew.

As is usual in such cases, she kept the child for several days, but it was so ill behaved that the good woman nearly collapsed. She told her story to the nobleman. He said to her, "Woman, if you think that this is not your child, then do this one thing. Take it out to the meadow where you left your previous child and beat it hard with a switch. Then you will witness a miracle."

The woman followed the nobleman's advice. She went out and beat the child with a switch until it screamed loudly. Then the Devil brought back her stolen child, saying, "There, you have it!" And with that he took his own child away.

This story is often told and is known by both the young and the old in and around Breslau.[114]

---

[113]Migratory legend type 5085; folktale type 504. Source: Joseph Jacobs, *Celtic Fairy Tales* (London, 1892), no. 25. Jacobs' source: *Cambrian Quarterly Magazine*, 1830. Changeling tales, generally presented as believed legends, are found from the orient and North Africa to Iceland. They are especially well represented in Germany, Scandinavia, and the British Isles.

[114]Migratory legend type 5085; folktale type 504. Source: *Deutsche Sagen* (Berlin, 1816/1818), no. 88. Other descriptions of changelings in the Grimms' *Deutsche Sagen* are found in nos. 60, 82, 83, 89, 90, 91, 153.

Young Giants

The Young Giant

Jacob and Wilhelm Grimm

A peasant had a son who was only as big as a thumb and did not grow any larger. In several years he did not grow even the width of a hair. One day the peasant wanted to go to the field and plow, and the little one said, "Father, I want to go out with you."

"No," said the father," you have to stay here. There's nothing that you could do to help me, and besides that you might get lost." Then the thumbling began to cry and was not going to give the father any peace until he took him along. So the father put him in his pocket and carried him to the field, where he placed him in a fresh furrow. While he was sitting there a large giant came over the mountain towards them. "Do you see that bogeyman?" said the father, in order to frighten the little one into being good. "He's coming to get you." Now the giant had very long legs, and he reached the furrow in only a few steps, picked up the little thumbling, and walked away with him. The father stood there so frightened that he could not speak a word. He believed that his child was lost, and that he would never see him again as long as he lived.

The giant took the child home and let him suckle at his breast, and the thumbling grew large and strong like a giant. After two years had passed, the old giant took him into the woods in order to test him. He said, "Pull out a switch from over there." The boy was so strong already that a pulled a young tree up by the roots. The giant thought that he could do better and took him back home and suckled him for two more years. When he took him into the woods to test him this time, he pulled up a much larger tree. This was still not good enough for the giant, and he suckled him for yet another two years, took him into the woods, and said, "Now pull out a decent switch for once." This time the boy pulled the thickest oak tree out of the ground. He cracked it and laughed. When the old giant saw this, he said, "That's good enough. You've passed the test." And he took him back to the field where he found him.

The father was plowing again, and the young giant walked up to him and said, "Father, see what has become of me. I am your son."

The peasant was frightened and said, "No, you are not my son. Get away from me."

"Of course I am your son. Just let me plow. I can do it just as well as you can."

"No, you are not my son. You can't plow. Get away from me." He was so afraid of the large man that he let go of the plow and walked to the edge of the field.

115

The boy picked up the handle to plow, but he pushed so hard with his one hand that the plow sank deep into the earth. The peasant could not watch this, and called to him, "If you insist on plowing, then don't push down so hard, or you will ruin the field."

Then the boy hitched himself in front of the plow and said, "Go on home and tell mother that she should cook up a big plate of something to eat. In the meantime, I'll tear around the field." The peasant went home and told his wife to fix something to eat, and she cooked up a large dinner, and the boy plowed the field: two full acres all by himself. Then he hitched himself to the harrow and harrowed the entire thing, pulling two harrows at the same time. When he was finished he went into the woods, pulled up two oak trees, laid them on his shoulders, then put a harrow on each end and a horse on each end as well, and carried the whole thing home like a bundle of straw.

When he walked into the farmyard, his mother did not recognize him and asked, "Who is this terrible large man?"

The peasant said, "This is our son."

She said, "No, this could never be our son. We did not have such a large child. Ours was a little thing. Go away. We don't want you."

The boy said nothing. He pulled his horses into the stall, gave them oats and hay, and put everything in order. When he was finished he went into the house, sat down on the bench, and said, "Mother, I'd like to eat. Will it be ready soon?"

She said, "Yes," and did not dare to contradict him. She brought in two very large plates, more than she and her husband could have eaten in an entire week. He ate it all and asked if they didn't have more. "No," she said. "That's all that we have."

"That was only a taste. I have to have more." Then she went out and filled a large hog cauldron and put it on the fire, and when it was done she brought it in. "That's a nice little bit," he said, and ate the whole thing, but it still wasn't enough. Then he said, "Father, I see that I'll never be full if I stay here with you. If you can get me an iron rod that is so strong I can't break it against my knees, then I'll go away again."

The peasant was happy to hear this. He hitched his two horses to his wagon and drove to the blacksmith and got a rod so large and thick that the two horses could barely pull it. The boy held it against his knees and—crash!—he broke it in two like a bean pole. Then the peasant hitched up four horses and brought back a rod that was so large and thick that the four horses could barely pull it. The son picked up this one as well, cracked it in two against his knee, tossed it aside, and said, "Father, this one is of no use to me. Hitch up more horses and get me a stronger staff." So the father hitched up eight horses and fetched one so large and thick that the eight horses could barely pull it. When the son received this one, he broke a little piece from the top of it and said, "Father, I see that you can't get me a proper staff, so I'll just go away anyhow."

So he went on his way, claiming to be a journeyman blacksmith. He came to a village where a smith lived who was a real cheapskate. He would never give anything to anyone, and always wanted everything for himself. The young giant

116

walked into his smithy and asked him if he could use a journeyman. "Yes," answered the smith, looking at him and thinking what a strong fellow he was, someone who could really earn his keep. "What kind of wages do you want?"

"I don't want any wages at all," said the young giant. "But at the end of every two weeks when the other journeymen receive their pay, just let me hit you twice. And you'll have to be able to take it." The cheapskate was only too happy with this arrangement, for he thought that it would save him a lot of money.

The next morning the new journeyman was to have the first turn at the anvil. The master brought out a glowing rod, and the young giant knocked it into two pieces with his first blow, at the same time driving the anvil so deep into the ground that they could not get it back out again. This made the cheapskate angry, and he said, "I can't use you here. Your blows are too rough. What do you need for pay?"

The young giant said, "Just a little kick, nothing more." He lifted up his foot and gave him a kick that sent him flying over four loads of hay. Then he took the thickest rod from the smithy to use as a walking stick, and went on his way.

Sometime later he came to an estate and asked the foreman if he could use a chief farmhand. "Yes," said the foreman. "You look like a strong fellow who knows how to work. What kind of yearly wage do you want." The young giant replied that the only pay he wanted was to be able to give the foreman three blows, and that he would have to be able to stand them. The foreman was satisfied with this, for he too was a cheapskate.

The next morning the workers were supposed to go to work in the woods. The others were already up, but the young giant was still lying in bed. One of them shouted to him, "Get up now. It's time to go to the woods, and you have to come along too."

He replied, coarsely and sarcastically, "Go on without me. I'll be finished before any of you." The others reported to the foreman that the new chief farmhand was still lying in bed and would not go to the woods with them. The foreman told them to wake him up again and tell him to harness the horses. The young giant answered the same as before, "Go on without me. I'll be finished before any of you." He slept two more hours, then finally got out of bed, got two shovels full of peas from the barn, cooked them, ate them at his leisure, and when he had finished all this, he harnessed the horses and drove them to the woods. Just before the woods, the road passed through a hollow. He drove his wagon through the hollow, but then filled it in with such a pile of trees and branches that no horse would ever be able to get through.

He had just arrived in the woods when he met the others on their way home with their loaded wagons. He said to them, "Drive on. I'll be home before you are." He drove a little further into the woods, ripped two of the largest trees out of the ground, loaded them onto his wagon, and turned around. When he came to the pile of trees and branches, the others were just standing there, unable to get through. He said, "See, if you had stayed with me, you could have gone straight home, and you'd be able to sleep an extra hour." He started to drive through, but his four horses couldn't make it, so he unhitched them, hitched himself to the wagon, and

117

pulled it through as easily as if it had been loaded with feathers. When he was on the other side of the rubble he called out, "See, I got through before you did," and he drove off, leaving them standing there. When he arrived at the farmyard he picked up a tree with one hand, showed it to the foreman, and said, "How is this for a measuring stick?"

Then the foreman said to his wife, "This chief farmhand is all right. Even when he sleeps in, he arrives home before the others.

He worked for the foreman for one year. When the year had passed and the other workers received their wages, he said that it was also time for his payment. The foreman became frightened that he was going to have to receive his blows, and he asked him to spare him. If he would do so, the foreman himself would become chief farmhand, and the young giant could become foreman. "No," replied the young giant. "I do not want to be foreman. I am chief farmhand and will remain chief farmhand. I only want to deliver what was promised me." The foreman offered to give him anything that he asked for, but there was no way out. The chief farmhand insisted on the original agreement.

The foreman did not know what else to do, so he asked for an extension of two weeks, and then called all of his clerks together and asked for their advice. They thought for a long time, and finally concluded that the chief farmhand would have to die. He would be asked to bring a load of large millstones to the edge of the well in the farmyard, then he would be sent down into the well to clean it, and while he was down there, they would throw the millstones onto his head. The foreman was delighted with this plan. Everything was prepared. The largest millstones were brought in. As soon as the chief farmhand was down in the well, they rolled the stones in on top of him. They fell with a great splash. Everyone thought that they had crushed his head, but he called out, "Chase the chickens away from the well. They are scratching in the sand, and throwing little grains into my eyes until I can't see."

The foreman called out, "Shoo! Shoo!" as though he were chasing the chickens away. When the chief farmhand was finished, he climbed out and said, "Look at this nice necklace." He was wearing the millstones around his neck.

The two weeks were now up, and the young giant demanded that he receive his wages. The foreman, beside himself with fear, and with sweat dripping from his face, opened the window for some fresh air. Before he knew what had happened, the young giant kicked him from behind. He flew so far through the air, that no one has seen him since.

Then the young giant turned to the foreman's wife and said that she would have to receive the next blow. "No, I'd never be able to withstand it," she said, and opened a window, because of the sweat dripping from her face. He gave her a kick as well, and she flew even higher than her husband.

"Come to me," he called to her.

"No, you come to me," she called back. "I can't come to you."

And they soared through the air, neither of them able to get to the other one. I do not know if they are still soaring. But as for the young giant, he picked up his iron rod and went on his way.[115]

The Hairy Boy

Switzerland

Once upon a time a king was out hunting when he came upon a hollow tree that his dogs would not pass by. They barked and jumped about and could not be brought to move on. Taking a closer look, the king discovered a beautiful maiden sitting in the hollow trunk. She was entirely naked and looked at him with terror. He threw his coat over her, and whistled to his servants. They came immediately, and he showed them the maiden, saying, "See what a beautiful animal I have captured!" Then he whistled again, and his coach came. He placed the maiden inside, rode home with her to his castle, and married her.

The old queen, the king's mother, still lived in the castle, and she did not like the young queen and did everything to make her life miserable. With time the king had to go off to war, and while he was away his wife gave birth to a son. The old queen cooked up a brew and gave it to the newborn, which caused hair to grow all over his body. Then the wicked old woman wrote to the king, "Your wife has given birth to a hairy animal. We do not know whether it is a dog or a cat." This news greatly angered the king, and he commanded that the newborn be tied to his wife's back, and that they both be driven away.

Thus the young queen and her hairy son were put out of the castle, and she returned to the hollow tree where the king had first seen her. She lived there as before. However, life in the woods was so good for the hairy boy that he grew a foot every day, and soon there was not enough room in the hollow tree. One day he went out and pulled up a bundle of large fir trees. He broke them over his knee and built a comfortable cabin for himself and his mother. Soon afterward he said to his mother, "Now tell me once and for all, who is my father?"

"Alas," answered the mother, "your father is the king, but you will never see him as long as you live."

"But I want to see him right now!" said the hairy boy, and he ripped a fir tree out of the ground, roots and all. He set forth carrying it, and did not rest until he had found the royal castle. The king had just sat down to eat and had a great quantity of

---

[115]Type 650A. Source: *Kinder- und Hausmärchen*, 1st ed. (Berlin, 1812/1815), v. 2, no. 4 (no. 90 in the final edition). I have shortened the tale by one episode, in which the foreman unsuccessfully attempts to do away with the young giant by sending him to a haunted mill.

expensive food before him. The hairy boy acted as if he were right at home, walked up to the king and said to him, "I am here too. I am your son, and I want to eat at your table with you." The king was terrified and wanted to stop him, but the hairy boy continued without hindrance, reaching his hairy hands into the king's plates and dishes. No one dared say a thing, for the king's people were all terrified and stood by helplessly. After the hairy boy had eaten every last morsel from the table, he said to the king, "I am going now, but I will be back tomorrow."

"Wait," thought the king, "I'll see that you do not come back." He quickly summoned five hundred soldiers, and placed them immediately before the castle with the command to shoot at the hairy boy on sight. The next day when the hairy boy returned carrying his fir tree the soldiers all fired at him. But the hairy boy calmly plucked the bullets from his body and threw them, fifty at a time, back at the soldiers, until he had killed them all.

He entered the castle just as the king was again sitting down to eat. The hairy boy said to him, "But father, what are you up to? Your soldiers are all lying dead outside, struck down by their own bullets. I am your son, and I want to eat at your table with you." And once again he reached his hairy hands into the king's plates and dishes, and did not stop eating until every last morsel had disappeared from the table. "I am going now," he said at last, "but I will be back tomorrow, and I am bringing my mother along."

"Stop!" thought the king, "That you will not do!" He immediately called up ten hundred soldiers and positioned them before the castle, half in the courtyard and half surrounding the castle, commanding them by their very lives to not let the hairy boy inside.

The next day the hairy boy returned, leading his mother by her hand. When soldiers shot at him, he placed himself in front of his mother. He again plucked the bullets from his body and threw them back, one hundred at a time, until all the soldiers lay dead on the ground. Then he walked into the castle and approached his father, saying, "But father, what are you up to again? Your soldiers are all dead as doornails, struck down by their own bullets! Go and see for yourself!" Then he took him by the hand and threw him into the courtyard below. He took him by the hand a second time and threw him back inside through the window. He threw him to the floor a third time, and the king was dead.

The old queen hurried in, and the hairy boy threatened to kill her if she did not treat him well, and she had to promise to rid his body of the ugly hair. Once again she cooked up a brew, and it removed the hair from his body and hands. From this hour on he had no more power than ordinary people. But the kingdom was now his, and he ruled with his mother in peace and splendor.[116]

---

[116]Type 650A. Source: Otto Sutermeister, *Kinder- und Hausmärchen aus der Schweiz* (Aarau, 1873), no. 52. Sutermeister's source is an "oral tradition" from the canton Aargau. The opening scene of this tale is reminiscent of type 510B. The motif of the woman unfairly accused of giving birth to a monster (or, alternatively, of cannibalizing her own newborn children) is often included in tales of type 451 and 710.

The Blue Belt

Norway

Once upon a time there was an old beggar woman, who had gone out to beg. She had a little boy with her, and when she had got her bag full, she struck across the hills towards her own home. When they had gone a bit up the hillside they came upon a little blue belt, which lay where two paths met, and the boy asked his mother's permission to pick it up.

"No," she said, "maybe there's witchcraft in it;" and so with threats she forced him to follow her. But when they had gone a bit farther, the boy said he must turn aside a moment out of the road, and meanwhile his mother sat down on a tree stump. But the boy was a long time gone, for as soon as he got so far into the wood that the old woman could not see him, he ran off to where the belt lay, picked it up, tied it round his waist and lo! he felt so strong that he could lift the whole mountain. When he got back, the old woman was very angry, and wanted to know what he had been doing so long. "You don't care how much time you waste, and yet you know the night is drawing on, and we must cross the mountain before it gets dark!" So on they tramped, but when they had got about halfway, the old woman grew tired, and said she must rest under a bush.

"Dear mother," said the boy, may I just go up to the top of this high crag while you rest, and try if I can't see some sign of folk hereabouts?"

Yes, he might do that. When he reached the top he saw a light shining from the north. So he ran down and told his mother.

"We must get on, mother; we are near a house, for I see a bright light shining quite close to us in the north." Then she got up, shouldered her bag, and set off to see. They hadn't gone far, before they came to a steep cliff, right across their path.

"Just as I thought!" said the old woman; "now we can't go a step farther; a pretty bed we shall have here!"

But the boy took the bag under one arm, and his mother under the other, and ran straight up the steep cliff with them."

"Now, don't you see! Don't you see that we are close to a house! Don't you see the bright light?"

The old woman said those were not Christians, but trolls, for she knew her way about that forest far and near, and knew there was not a living soul in it until you were well over the ridge and had come down on the other side. But they went on, and in a little while they came to a large house which was all painted red.

"What's the good of it?" asked the old woman. "We don't dare go inside, for trolls live here."

"Don't say that; we must go in. There must be men where the lights shine so," said the boy. So in he went, and his mother followed him, but he had barely opened the door before she fainted, for there she saw a great stout man at least twenty feet high, sitting on the bench.

"Good evening, grandfather!" said the boy.

"Well, I've sat here three hundred years," said the man on the bench, "and no one has ever come and called me grandfather before." Then the boy sat down by the man's side, and began to talk to him as if they had been old friends.

"But what's come over your mother?" said the man, after they had chatted a while. "I think she fainted; you had better look after her."

So the boy took hold of the old woman and dragged her up the hall along the floor. That brought her to herself, and she kicked and scratched, and flung herself about, and at last sat down on a heap of firewood in the corner; but she was so frightened that she scarcely dared to look one in the face.

After a while, the boy asked if they could spend the night there.

"Yes, to be sure," said the man.

So they went on talking again, but the boy soon got hungry, and wanted to know if they could get food as well as lodging.

"Of course," said the man, "you may have that too." And after he had sat a while longer, he rose up and threw six loads of dry pitch-pine on the fire. This made the old woman still more afraid.

"Oh! now he's going to roast us alive," she said, in the corner where she sat. And when the wood had burned down to glowing embers, the man got up and walked out of his house.

"Heaven bless and help us! You are so brave," said the old woman; "don't you see we have ended up with trolls?"

"Stuff and nonsense!" said the boy; "no harm if we have."

In a little while, the man came back with an ox so fat and big, the boy had never seen its like, and he gave it one blow with his fist under the ear, and it fell down dead on the floor. When that was done, he took it up by all four legs, and laid it on the glowing embers, and turned it and twisted it about until it was roasted brown outside. After that, he went to a cupboard and took out a great silver dish and laid the ox on it; and the dish was so big that none of the ox hung over on any side. This he put on the table, and then he went down into the cellar, and fetched a cask of wine, knocked out one end, and put the cask on the table, together with two knives, which were each six feet long. When this was done, he asked them go and sit down to supper and eat. So they went, the boy first and the old woman after, but she began to whimper and wail, and to wonder how she should ever use such knives. But her son seized one and began to cut slices out of the thigh of the ox, which he placed before his mother. And when they had eaten a bit, he took up the cask with both hands, and lifted it down to the floor; then he told his mother to come and drink, but it was still so high she couldn't reach up to it; so he caught her up, and held her up to the edge of the cask while she drank. As for himself, he clambered up and hung down like a cat inside the cask while he drank. So when he had quenched his thirst, he picked up the cask and put it back on the table, and thanked the man for the good meal, and told his mother to come and thank him too. Afraid though she was, she dared do nothing else but thank the man. Then the boy sat down again next to the man and began to gossip. After they had sat a while, the man said, "Well, I must just go and get a bit of supper too," and so he went to the table and ate up the whole ox—hoofs, and horns, and all—and drained the cask to the last drop, and then went back and sat on the bench.

"As for beds," he said, "I don't know what's to be done. I've only got one bed and a cradle; but we could get on pretty well if you would sleep in the cradle, and then your mother might lie in the bed yonder."

"Thank you kindly, that will do nicely," said the boy; and with that he pulled off his clothes and lay down in the cradle; but to tell you the truth, it was quite as big as a four-poster. As for the old woman, she had to follow the man, who showed her to bed, though she was out of her wits for fear.

"Well," thought the boy to himself, "it will never do to go to sleep yet. I'd best lie awake and listen how things go as the night wears on."

After a while the man began to talk to the old woman, and at last he said, "We two might live here quite happily together could we only be rid of this son of yours."

"But do you know how to take care of him? Is that what you're thinking of?" she asked.

"Nothing easier," he said; at any rate he would try. He would just say that he wished the old woman would stay and keep house for him a day or two. Then he would take the boy with him up the mountain to quarry cornerstones, and roll down a large rock on him. As they spoke, the boy lay still and listened.

The next day the troll—for it was a troll, as clear as day—asked if the old woman would stay and keep house for him a few days. Later that day he took a large iron crowbar and asked the boy if he had a mind to go with him up the mountain and quarry a few cornerstones. With all his heart, he said, and went with him; and so, after they had split a few stones, the troll wanted him to go down below and look for cracks in the rock. While he was doing this, the troll worked away, and wearied himself with his crowbar until he moved a whole crag out of its bed, which came rolling right down on the place where the boy was; but he held it up until he could get to one side, and then let it roll on.

"Oh!" said the boy to the troll, "now I see what you mean to do with me. You want to crush me to death; so just go down yourself and look for cracks and splits in the rock, and I'll stand up above."

The troll did not dare to do otherwise than the boy asked him, and the end of it was that the boy rolled down a large rock, which fell on the troll and broke one of his thighs.

"Well! you are in a sad plight," said the boy, as he strode down, lifted up the rock, and set the man free. After that he had to put him on his back and carry him home; so he ran with him as fast as a horse, and shook him, so that the troll screamed and screeched as if a knife had been run into him. When he got home, they had to put the troll to bed, and there he lay in a sad pickle.

The night wore on, and the troll began to talk to the old woman again, and to wonder however they could be rid of the boy.

"Well," said the old woman, "if you can't hit on a plan to get rid of him, I'm sure I can't."

"Let me see," said the troll; "I've got twelve lions in a garden. If they could only get hold of the boy they'd soon tear him to pieces."

So the old woman said it would be easy enough to get him there. She would pretend to be sick and say she felt so poorly, nothing would do her any good but lion's milk. All that the boy lay and listened to; and when he got up in the morning his mother said she was worse than she looked, and she thought she should never be well again unless she could get some lion's milk.

"Then I'm afraid you'll be sick a long time, mother," said the boy, "for I'm sure I don't know where any is to be got."

"Oh! if that be all," said the troll, "there's no lack of lion's milk, if we only had the man to fetch it," and then he went on to say how his brother had a garden with twelve lions in it, and how the boy might have the key if he had a mind to milk the lions. So the boy took the key and a milking pail and walked off. When he unlocked the gate and entered the garden, there stood all the twelve lions on their hind paws, raging and roaring at him. But the boy laid hold of the biggest, and led him about by the forepaws, and dashed him against sticks and stones, until there wasn't a bit of him left but the two paws. When the rest saw that, they were so afraid that they crept up and lay at his feet like so many curs. After that they followed him about wherever he went, and when he got home they laid down outside the house, with their forepaws on the door sill.

"Now, mother, you'll soon be well," said the boy, when he went in, "for here is the lion's milk."

He had just milked a drop in the pail.

But the troll, as he lay in bed, swore it was all a lie. He was sure the boy was not the man to milk lions.

When the boy heard that, he forced the troll to get out of bed, threw open the door, and all the lions rose up and seized the troll, and at last the boy had to make them leave their hold.

That night the troll began to talk to the old woman again. "I'm sure I can't tell how to put this boy out of the way. He is so awfully strong. Can't you think of some way?"

"No," said the old woman; "if you can't tell, I'm sure I can't."

"Well," said the troll, "I have two brothers in a castle; they are twelve times as strong as I am, and that's why I was turned out and had to put up with this farm. They hold that castle, and nearby there is an apple orchard, and whoever eats those apples sleeps for three days and three nights. If we could only get the boy to go for the fruit, he wouldn't be able to keep from tasting the apples, and as soon as he fell asleep my brothers would tear him to pieces."

The old woman said she would pretend to be sick, and say she could never be herself again unless she tasted those apples, for she had set her heart on them.

All this the boy lay and listened to.

When the morning came the old woman was so ill that she couldn't utter a word but groans and sighs. She was sure she should never be well again, unless she had some of the apples that grew in the orchard near the castle where the man's brothers lived; only she had no one to send for them.

The boy was ready to go that instant, and the eleven lions went with him. He came to the orchard, he climbed the apple tree and ate as many apples as he could. He was barely down again before he fell into a deep sleep; but the lions all lay around him in a ring. On the third day the troll's brothers came, but they did not come in human shape. They came snorting like man-eating steeds, and wondered who it was that dared to be there, and said they would tear him to pieces so small that there would be nothing left of him. But the lions rose up and tore the trolls into small pieces, so that the place looked as if a manure pile had been tossed about. After they had finished the trolls, they lay down again. The boy did not wake up until late in the afternoon, and when he got on his knees, and rubbed the sleep out of his eyes, and saw the hoof marks, he wondered what had been going on. He walked towards the castle, and a girl who had seen all that had happened looked out of a window said, "You may thank your stars that you weren't in that tussle, or you surely would have lost your life."

"What! I lose my life! No fear of that, I think," said the boy.

She begged him to come in and talk with her, for she hadn't seen a Christian soul ever since she came there. But when she opened the door the lions wanted to go in too, and she got so frightened that she began to scream, and so the boy had them lie outside. Then the two talked and talked, and the boy asked how it came that she, who was so lovely, could put up with those ugly trolls. She never wished it, she said; it was quite against her will. They had seized her by force, and she was the King of Arabia's daughter. So they talked on, and at last she asked him what he would do; whether she should go back home, and if he would take her as a wife. Of course he would marry her, and she shouldn't go home.

After that they went around the castle, and at last they came to a great hall, where the trolls' two great swords hung high up on the wall.

"I wonder if you are man enough to wield one of these," said the princess.

"Who? I?" said the boy. "It would be a pretty thing if I couldn't wield one of these."

With that he stacked two or three chairs on top of each other, jumped up, and touched the biggest sword with his finger tips, tossed it up in the air, and caught it again by the hilt; leapt down, and at the same time dealt such a blow with it on the floor that the whole hall shook. After he had thus got down he put the sword under his arm and carried it about with him.

So when they had lived a little while in the castle, the princess thought she ought to go home to her parents and let them know what had become of her; so they loaded a ship, and she set sail from the castle.

After she had gone, and the boy had wandered about a little, he remembered that he had been sent on an errand, and had come to fetch something for his mother's health. He said to himself, "After all, the old woman was not so bad, and she's probably all right by now." Still, he thought he ought to go and just see how she was. So he went and found both the man and his mother quite fresh and healthy.

"What wretches you are to live in this beggarly hut," said the boy. "Come with me up to my castle, and you shall see what a fine fellow I am."

Well! they were both ready to go, and on the way his mother talked to him, and asked how it was he had become so strong.

"If you must know, it came from that blue belt which lay on the mountainside that time when you and I were out begging," said the boy.

"Have you got it still?" asked she.

"Yes," he had. It was tied around his waist.

"May I see it?"

"Yes, you may." And with that he pulled open his waistcoat and shirt to show it to her.

Then she seized it with both hands, tore it off, and twisted it around her fist. "Now," she cried, "what shall I do with such a wretch as you? I'll just give you one blow, and dash your brains out!"

"Far too good a death for such a scamp," said the troll. "No! let's first burn out his eyes, and then turn him adrift in a little boat."

So they burned out his eyes and turned him adrift, in spite of his prayers and tears; but, as the boat drifted, the lions swam after, and at last they laid hold of it and dragged it ashore on an island, and placed the boy under a fir tree. They caught game for him, and they plucked the birds and made him a bed of down; but he was forced to eat his meat raw, and he was blind. At last, one day the biggest lion was chasing a hare which was blind, for it ran straight over stock and stone, and in the end, it ran right up against a fir stump and tumbled head over heels across the field right into a spring; but lo! when it came out of the spring it saw its way quite plain, and thus saved its life.

"So, so!" thought the lion, and dragged the boy to the spring, and dipped his head and ears into it. When he had his sight again, he went down to the shore and made signs to the lions that they should all lie close together like a raft; then he stood on their backs while they swam with him to the mainland. When he had reached the shore he went up into a birch grove and made the lions lie quiet. Then he stole up to the castle, like a thief, to see if he couldn't lay hands on his belt. When he arrived at the door, he peeped through the keyhole, and there he saw his belt hanging over a door in the kitchen. He crept softly across the floor, for there was no one there; but as soon as he got hold of the belt, he began to kick and stomp about as though he were crazy. Just then his mother came rushing out.

"Dear heart, my darling little boy! Do give me the belt again," she said.

"Thank you kindly," he said. "Now you shall have the fate that you gave to me," and he finished the task at once. The old troll heard what was happening and came in. He begged fervently that his life might be spared.

"Well, you may live," said the boy, "but you shall undergo the same punishment that you gave me;" and so he burned out the troll's eyes, and set him adrift at sea in a little boat, but he had no lions to follow him.

Now the boy was all alone, and he went about longing and longing for the princess. Finally he could bear it no longer. He had to look for her, his heart was so bent on having her. So he loaded four ships and set sail for Arabia. For some time they had fair wind and fine weather, but after that they lay wind-bound near a rocky island. The sailors went ashore and strolled about to spend the time, and

126

there they found a huge egg, almost as big as a little house. So they began to knock it about with large stones, but they couldn't crack the shell. Then the boy came up with his sword to see what all the noise was about. When he saw the egg, he thought it a simple matter to crack it. He gave it one blow, and the egg split, and out came a chicken as big as an elephant.

"We have done a bad thing," said the boy; "this can cost us all our lives." He then asked his sailors if they were men enough to sail to Arabia in twenty-four hours, if they had a good wind. Yes, they would be able to do that, they said, so they set sail with a fine breeze, and got to Arabia in twenty-three hours. As soon as they landed, the boy ordered all the sailors to go and bury themselves up to their eyes in a sand hill, so that they could barely see the ships. The boy and the captains climbed a high crag and sat down under a fir tree. In a little while a great bird came flying with an island in its claws, which it let fall down on the fleet, sinking every ship. After it had done that, it flew up to the sand hill and flapped its wings, so that the wind nearly blew off the sailors' heads, and it flew past the fir tree with such force that it turned the boy right around, but he was ready with his sword, and gave the bird one blow and brought it down dead.

After that he went to the town, where everyone was glad, because the king had got his daughter back. However, the king had now hidden her away himself, and promised her hand as a reward to anyone who could find her, even though she was already engaged. Now as the boy went along he met a man who had white bearskins for sale. He bought one of the hides and put it on. One of the captains took an iron chain and lead him about, and so disguised he went into the town and began to play pranks. The news came to the king's ears that there never had been such fun in the town before, for here was a white bear that danced and cut capers just as it was asked. A messenger came to say that the bear must come to the castle at once, for the king wanted to see its tricks. When it got to the castle everyone was afraid, for they had never seen such a beast before. However, the captain said there was no danger unless they laughed at it. They mustn't do that, or else it would tear them to pieces. When the king heard that, he warned all the court not to laugh. But while the fun was going on, in came one of the king's maids, and began to laugh and make fun of the bear. The bear pounced on her and clawed her until there was barely a rag of her left. Then all the court began to cry, and the captain most of all.

"Stuff and nonsense," said the king; "she's only a maid, besides it's more my affair than yours."

When the show was over, it was late at night. "It's no good your going away when it's so late," said the king. "The bear had best sleep here."

"Perhaps it might sleep in the inglenook by the kitchen fire," said the captain.

"No," said the king, "it shall sleep up here, and it shall have pillows and cushions to sleep on." So a whole heap of pillows and cushions was brought, and the captain had a bed in a side room.

At midnight the king came with a lamp in his hand and a big bunch of keys, and led the white bear away. He passed along gallery after gallery, through doors and rooms, upstairs and downstairs, until at last he came to a pier which ran out into the sea. Then the king began to pull and haul at posts and pins, this one up and that

127

one down, until at last a little house floated up to the water's edge. There he kept his daughter, for she was so dear to him that he had hid her, so that no one could find her. He left the white bear outside while he went in and told her how it had danced and played its pranks. She said she was afraid, and did not dare to look at it; but he convinced her that there was no danger, if she only wouldn't laugh. So they brought the bear in, and locked the door, and it danced and played its tricks. Just when the fun was at its height the princess's maid began to laugh. Then the boy pounced on her and tore her to bits, and the princess began to cry and sob.

"Stuff and nonsense," cried the king; "all this fuss about a maid! I'll get you just as good a one again. But now I think the bear had best stay here until morning, for I don't want to lead it along all those galleries and stairs at this time of night."

"Well," said the princess, "if it sleeps here I'm sure I won't."

But just then the bear curled himself up and lay down by the stove. It was determined that the princess should sleep there too, with a light burning. As soon as the king was gone, the white bear begged her to undo his collar. The princess was so frightened that she almost fainted; but she felt about until she found the collar. She had barely undone it before the bear pulled his head off. Then she recognized him, and was so glad that there was no end to her joy. She wanted to tell her father at once that her rescuer had come, but the boy would not hear of it. He would earn her once more, he said. So in the morning, when they heard the king rattling at the posts outside, the boy pulled on the hide, and lay down by the stove.

"Well, has it lain still?" the king asked.

"I should think so," said the princess. "It hasn't so much as turned or stretched itself once."

When they got up to the castle again, the captain took the bear and led it away. Then the boy threw off the hide and went to a tailor and ordered clothes fit for a prince. When they were ready he went to the king, and said he wanted to find the princess.

"You're not the first who has wished the same thing," said the king, "but they have all lost their lives; for if anyone who tries can't find her in twenty-four hours his life is forfeited."

Yes, the boy knew all that. Still he wished to try, and if he couldn't find her, it would be his responsibility. Now in the castle there was a band that played sweet tunes, and there were fair maids to dance with, and so the boy danced away. When twelve hours were gone, the king said, "I pity you with all my heart. You are not very good at seeking; you will surely lose your life."

"Stuff!" said the boy. "While there's life there's hope. So as long as there's breath in the body there's no fear. we have lots of time." And so he went on dancing until there was only one hour left.

Then he said he would begin to search.

"It's no use now," said the king. "Time's up."

"Light your lamp; out with your big bunch of keys," said the boy, "and follow me where I want to go. There is still a whole hour left."

So the boy went the same way which the king had led him the night before, and he asked the king to unlock door after door until they came to the pier which ran out into the sea.

"It's all no use, I tell you," said the king; "time's up, and this will only lead you out into the sea."

"Still five minutes more," said the boy, as he pulled and pushed at the posts and pins, and the house floated up.

"Now the time *is* up," bawled the king. "Come here, headsman, and cut off his head."

"No, no!" said the boy; "stop a bit, there are still three minutes. Out with the key, and let me get into this house."

But the king stood there and fumbled with his keys, to draw out the time. At last he said he didn't have the key.

"Well, if you haven't, I have," said the boy, and he gave the door such a kick that it flew to splinters inwards on the floor.

The princess met him at the door, and told her father this was her rescuer, on whom her heart was set. So she got him, and this was how the beggar boy came to marry the daughter of the King of Arabia.[117]

Sexual and Physical Abuse

The Wicked Stepmother

India

One day a Brahman adjured his wife not to eat anything without him lest she should become a she goat. In reply the Brahman's wife begged him not to eat anything without her, lest he should be changed into a tiger. A long time passed by and neither of them broke their word, until one day the Brahman's wife, while giving food to her children, herself took a little to taste; and her husband was not present. That very moment she was changed into a goat.

When the Brahman came home and saw the she goat running about the house he was intensely grieved, because he knew that it was none other than his own

---

[117]Type 590. Source: Peter Christen Asbjørnsen and Jørgen Moe, *Norske Folkeeventyr* (Christiania [Oslo], 1842-1852), translated by George Webb Dasent (1859). Revised.

beloved wife. He kept the goat tied up in the yard of his house, and tended it very carefully.

In a few years he married again, but this wife was not kind to the children. She at once took a dislike to them, and treated them unkindly and gave them little food. Their mother, the she goat, heard their complainings, and noticed that they were getting thin, and therefore called one of them to her secretly, and bade the child tell the others to strike her horns with a stick whenever they were very hungry, and some food would fall down for them. They did so, and instead of getting weaker and thinner, as their stepmother had expected, they became stronger and stronger. She was surprised to see them getting so fat and strong while she was giving them so little food.

In course of time a one-eyed daughter was born to this wicked woman. She loved the girl with all her heart, and grudged not any expense or attention that she thought the child required. One day, when the girl had grown quite big and could walk and talk well, her mother sent her to play with the other children, and ordered her to notice how and whence they obtained anything to eat. The girl promised to do so, and most rigidly stayed by them the whole day, and saw all that happened.

On hearing that the goat supplied her stepchildren with food the woman got very angry, and determined to kill the beast as soon as possible. She pretended to be very ill, and sending for the hakim, bribed him to prescribe some goat's flesh for her. The Brahman was very anxious about his wife's state, and although he grieved to have to slay the goat (for he was obliged to kill the goat, not having money to purchase another), yet he did not mind if his wife really recovered. But the little children wept when they heard this, and went to their mother, the she goat, in great distress, and told her everything.

"Do not weep, my darlings," she said. "It is much better for me to die than to live such a life as this. Do not weep. I have no fear concerning you. Food will be provided for you, if you will attend to my instructions. Be sure to gather my bones, and bury them all together in some secret place, and whenever you are very hungry go to that place and ask for food. Food will then be given you."

The poor she goat gave this advice only just in time. Scarcely had it finished these words and the children had departed than the butcher came with a knife and slew it. Its body was cut into pieces and cooked, and the stepmother had the meat, but the stepchildren got the bones. They did with them as they had been directed, and thus got food regularly and in abundance.

Some time after the death of the she goat one morning one of the stepdaughters was washing her face in the stream that ran by the house, when her nose ring unfastened and fell into the water. A fish happened to see it and swallowed it, and this fish was caught by a man and sold to the king's cook for his majesty's dinner. Great was the surprise of the cook when, on opening the fish to clean it, he found the nose ring. He took it to the king, who was so interested in it that he issued a proclamation and set it to every town and village in his dominions, that whosoever had missed a nose ring should apply to him. Within a few days the brother of the girl reported to the king that the nose ring belonged to his sister, who had lost it one day while bathing her face in the river. The king ordered the girl to appear before him, and was so fascinated by her pretty face and nice manner that he married her, and provided amply for the support of her family.[118]

Cinderella; or, The Little Glass Slipper

Charles Perrault

Once there was a gentleman who married, for his second wife, the proudest and most haughty woman that was ever seen. She had, by a former husband, two daughters of her own, who were, indeed, exactly like her in all things. He had likewise, by another wife, a young daughter, but of unparalleled goodness and sweetness of temper, which she took from her mother, who was the best creature in the world.

No sooner were the ceremonies of the wedding over but the stepmother began to show herself in her true colors. She could not bear the good qualities of this pretty girl, and the less because they made her own daughters appear the more odious. She employed her in the meanest work of the house. She scoured the dishes, tables, etc., and cleaned madam's chamber, and those of misses, her daughters. She slept in a sorry garret, on a wretched straw bed, while her sisters slept in fine rooms, with floors all inlaid, on beds of the very newest fashion, and where they had looking glasses so large that they could see themselves at their full length from head to foot.

The poor girl bore it all patiently, and dared not tell her father, who would have scolded her; for his wife governed him entirely. When she had done her work, she used to go to the chimney corner, and sit down there in the cinders and ashes, which caused her to be called Cinderwench. Only the younger sister, who was not so rude and uncivil as the older one, called her Cinderella. However, Cinderella, notwithstanding her coarse apparel, was a hundred times more beautiful than her sisters, although they were always dressed very richly.

It happened that the king's son gave a ball, and invited all persons of fashion to it. Our young misses were also invited, for they cut a very grand figure among those of quality. They were mightily delighted at this invitation, and wonderfully busy in selecting the gowns, petticoats, and hair dressing that would best become them. This was a new difficulty for Cinderella; for it was she who ironed her sisters' linen and pleated their ruffles. They talked all day long of nothing but how they should be dressed.

"For my part," said the eldest, "I will wear my red velvet suit with French trimming."

---

[118]Type 511. Source: J. Hinton Knowles, *Folk-Tales of Kashmir* (London, 1893), pp. 127-129.

"And I," said the youngest, "shall have my usual petticoat; but then, to make amends for that, I will put on my gold-flowered cloak, and my diamond stomacher, which is far from being the most ordinary one in the world."

They sent for the best hairdresser they could get to make up their headpieces and adjust their hairdos, and they had their red brushes and patches from Mademoiselle de la Poche.

They also consulted Cinderella in all these matters, for she had excellent ideas, and her advice was always good. Indeed, she even offered her services to fix their hair, which they very willingly accepted. As she was doing this, they said to her, "Cinderella, would you not like to go to the ball?"

"Alas!" said she, "you only jeer me; it is not for such as I am to go to such a place."

"You are quite right," they replied. "It would make the people laugh to see a Cinderwench at a ball."

Anyone but Cinderella would have fixed their hair awry, but she was very good, and dressed them perfectly well. They were so excited that they hadn't eaten a thing for almost two days. Then they broke more than a dozen laces trying to have themselves laced up tightly enough to give them a fine slender shape. They were continually in front of their looking glass. At last the happy day came. They went to court, and Cinderella followed them with her eyes as long as she could. When she lost sight of them, she started to cry.

Her godmother, who saw her all in tears, asked her what was the matter.

"I wish I could. I wish I could." She was not able to speak the rest, being interrupted by her tears and sobbing.

This godmother of hers, who was a fairy, said to her, "You wish that you could go to the ball; is it not so?"

"Yes," cried Cinderella, with a great sigh.

"Well," said her godmother, "be but a good girl, and I will contrive that you shall go." Then she took her into her chamber, and said to her, "Run into the garden, and bring me a pumpkin."

Cinderella went immediately to gather the finest she could get, and brought it to her godmother, not being able to imagine how this pumpkin could help her go to the ball. Her godmother scooped out all the inside of it, leaving nothing but the rind. Having done this, she struck the pumpkin with her wand, and it was instantly turned into a fine coach, gilded all over with gold.

She then went to look into her mousetrap, where she found six mice, all alive, and ordered Cinderella to lift up a little the trapdoor. She gave each mouse, as it went out, a little tap with her wand, and the mouse was that moment turned into a fine horse, which altogether made a very fine set of six horses of a beautiful mouse colored dapple gray.

Being at a loss for a coachman, Cinderella said, "I will go and see if there is not a rat in the rat trap that we can turn into a coachman."

"You are right," replied her godmother, "Go and look."

Cinderella brought the trap to her, and in it there were three huge rats. The fairy chose the one which had the largest beard, touched him with her wand, and turned

132

him into a fat, jolly coachman, who had the smartest whiskers that eyes ever beheld.

After that, she said to her, "Go again into the garden, and you will find six lizards behind the watering pot. Bring them to me."

She had no sooner done so but her godmother turned them into six footmen, who skipped up immediately behind the coach, with their liveries all bedaubed with gold and silver, and clung as close behind each other as if they had done nothing else their whole lives. The fairy then said to Cinderella, "Well, you see here an equipage fit to go to the ball with; are you not pleased with it?"

"Oh, yes," she cried; "but must I go in these nasty rags?"

Her godmother then touched her with her wand, and, at the same instant, her clothes turned into cloth of gold and silver, all beset with jewels. This done, she gave her a pair of glass slippers, the prettiest in the whole world. Being thus decked out, she got up into her coach; but her godmother, above all things, commanded her not to stay past midnight, telling her, at the same time, that if she stayed one moment longer, the coach would be a pumpkin again, her horses mice, her coachman a rat, her footmen lizards, and that her clothes would become just as they were before.

She promised her godmother to leave the ball before midnight; and then drove away, scarcely able to contain herself for joy. The king's son, who was told that a great princess, whom nobody knew, had arrived, ran out to receive her. He gave her his hand as she alighted from the coach, and led her into the hall, among all the company. There was immediately a profound silence. Everyone stopped dancing, and the violins ceased to play, so entranced was everyone with the singular beauties of the unknown newcomer.

Nothing was then heard but a confused noise of, "How beautiful she is! How beautiful she is!"

The king himself, old as he was, could not help watching her, and telling the queen softly that it was a long time since he had seen so beautiful and lovely a creature.

All the ladies were busied in considering her clothes and headdress, hoping to have some made next day after the same pattern, provided they could find such fine materials and as able hands to make them.

The king's son led her to the most honorable seat, and afterwards took her out to dance with him. She danced so very gracefully that they all more and more admired her. A fine meal was served up, but the young prince ate not a morsel, so intently was he busied in gazing on her.

She went and sat down by her sisters, showing them a thousand civilities, giving them part of the oranges and citrons which the prince had presented her with, which very much surprised them, for they did not know her. While Cinderella was thus amusing her sisters, she heard the clock strike eleven and three-quarters, whereupon she immediately made a courtesy to the company and hurried away as fast as she could.

Arriving home, she ran to seek out her godmother, and, after having thanked her, she said she could not but heartily wish she might go to the ball the next day as well, because the king's son had invited her.

As she was eagerly telling her godmother everything that had happened at the ball, her two sisters knocked at the door, which Cinderella ran and opened.

"You stayed such a long time!" she cried, gaping, rubbing her eyes and stretching herself as if she had been sleeping; she had not, however, had any manner of inclination to sleep while they were away from home.

"If you had been at the ball," said one of her sisters, "you would not have been tired with it. The finest princess was there, the most beautiful that mortal eyes have ever seen. She showed us a thousand civilities, and gave us oranges and citrons."

Cinderella seemed very indifferent in the matter. Indeed, she asked them the name of that princess; but they told her they did not know it, and that the king's son was very uneasy on her account and would give all the world to know who she was. At this Cinderella, smiling, replied, "She must, then, be very beautiful indeed; how happy you have been! Could not I see her? Ah, dear Charlotte, do lend me your yellow dress which you wear every day."

"Yes, to be sure!" cried Charlotte; "lend my clothes to such a dirty Cinderwench as you are! I should be such a fool."

Cinderella, indeed, well expected such an answer, and was very glad of the refusal; for she would have been sadly put to it, if her sister had lent her what she asked for jestingly.

The next day the two sisters were at the ball, and so was Cinderella, but dressed even more magnificently than before. The king's son was always by her, and never ceased his compliments and kind speeches to her. All this was so far from being tiresome to her, and, indeed, she quite forgot what her godmother had told her. She thought that it was no later than eleven when she counted the clock striking twelve. She jumped up and fled, as nimble as a deer. The prince followed, but could not overtake her. She left behind one of her glass slippers, which the prince picked up most carefully. She reached home, but quite out of breath, and in her nasty old clothes, having nothing left of all her finery but one of the little slippers, the mate to the one that she had dropped.

The guards at the palace gate were asked if they had not seen a princess go out. They replied that they had seen nobody leave but a young girl, very shabbily dressed, and who had more the air of a poor country wench than a gentlewoman.

When the two sisters returned from the ball Cinderella asked them if they had been well entertained, and if the fine lady had been there.

They told her, yes, but that she hurried away immediately when it struck twelve, and with so much haste that she dropped one of her little glass slippers, the prettiest in the world, which the king's son had picked up; that he had done nothing but look at her all the time at the ball, and that most certainly he was very much in love with the beautiful person who owned the glass slipper.

What they said was very true; for a few days later, the king's son had it proclaimed, by sound of trumpet, that he would marry her whose foot this slipper would just fit. They began to try it on the princesses, then the duchesses and all the court, but in vain; it was brought to the two sisters, who did all they possibly could to force their foot into the slipper, but they did not succeed.

Cinderella, who saw all this, and knew that it was her slipper, said to them, laughing, "Let me see if it will not fit me."

Her sisters burst out laughing, and began to banter with her. The gentleman who was sent to try the slipper looked earnestly at Cinderella, and, finding her very handsome, said that it was only just that she should try as well, and that he had orders to let everyone try.

He had Cinderella sit down, and, putting the slipper to her foot, he found that it went on very easily, fitting her as if it had been made of wax. Her two sisters were greatly astonished, but then even more so, when Cinderella pulled out of her pocket the other slipper, and put it on her other foot. Then in came her godmother and touched her wand to Cinderella's clothes, making them richer and more magnificent than any of those she had worn before.

And now her two sisters found her to be that fine, beautiful lady whom they had seen at the ball. They threw themselves at her feet to beg pardon for all the ill treatment they had made her undergo. Cinderella took them up, and, as she embraced them, said that she forgave them with all her heart, and wanted them always to love her.

She was taken to the young prince, dressed as she was. He thought she was more charming than before, and, a few days after, married her. Cinderella, who was no less good than beautiful, gave her two sisters lodgings in the palace, and that very same day matched them with two great lords of the court.

> Moral: Beauty in a woman is a rare treasure that will always be admired. Graciousness, however, is priceless and of even greater value. This is what Cinderella's godmother gave to her when she taught her to behave like a queen. Young women, in the winning of a heart, graciousness is more important than a beautiful hairdo. It is a true gift of the fairies. Without it nothing is possible; with it, one can do anything.

> Another moral: Without doubt it is a great advantage to have intelligence, courage, good breeding, and common sense. These, and similar talents come only from heaven, and it is good to have them. However, even these may fail to bring you success, without the blessing of a godfather or a godmother.[119]

---

[119]Type 510A. Source: Andrew Lang, *The Blue Fairy Book* (London, ca. 1889), pp. 64-71. Lang's source: Charles Perrault, *Histoires ou contes du temps passé, avec des moralités: Contes de ma mère l'Oye* (Paris, 1697).

Cinderella

Jacob and Wilhelm Grimm

Once upon a time there was a rich man who lived happily for a long time with his wife. Together they had a single daughter. Then the woman became ill, and when she was lying on her deathbed, she called her daughter to her side, and said, "Dear child, I must leave you now, but I will look down on you from heaven. Plant a little tree on my grave, and when you want something, just shake the tree, and you shall get what you want. I will help you in time of need. Just remain pious and good." Then she closed her eyes and died. The child cried, and planted a little tree on her mother's grave. She did not need to carry any water to it, because her tears provided all the water that it needed.

The snow fell over the mother's grave like a white cloth; then after the sun had retired from it a second time, and the little tree had become green a second time, the man took another wife.

The stepmother already had two daughters by her first husband. They were beautiful to look at, but in their hearts they were proud, arrogant, and evil. After the wedding was over, the three moved into the man's house, and times grew very bad for his poor child.

"What is that useless creature doing in the best room?" asked the stepmother. "Away to the kitchen with her! And if she wants to eat, then she must earn it. She can be our maid."

Her stepsisters took her dresses away from her and made her wear an old gray skirt. "That is good enough for you!" they said, making fun of her and leading her into the kitchen. Then the poor child had to do the most difficult work. She had to get up before sunrise, carry water, make the fire, cook, and wash. To add to her misery, her stepsisters ridiculed her and then scattered peas and lentils into the ashes, and she had to spend the whole day sorting them out again. At night when she was tired, there was no bed for her to sleep in, but she had to lie down next to the hearth in the ashes. Because she was always dirty with ashes and dust, they gave her the name *Cinderella*.

The time came when the king announced a ball. It was to last, in all splendor, for three days, and there his son, the prince, would choose a wife for himself. The two proud sisters were invited. "Cinderella," they cried, "Come here. Comb our hair. Brush our shoes, and tighten our laces. We are going to the prince's ball."

Cinderella did the best that she could, but they rewarded her only with curses. When they were ready, they said with scorn, "Cinderella, wouldn't you like to go to the ball?"

"Oh, yes. But how can I go? I don't have a dress."

"No," said the oldest one, "and we would be ashamed if you were to be seen there, and people learned that you are our sister. You belong in the kitchen. Here is a basin of lentils. Sort the good ones from the bad ones, and if there is a single bad one in the lot when we return, you can expect the worst."

With that, they left. Cinderella stood and watched until she could no longer see them. Then she sadly went into the kitchen and spread the lentils out over the hearth. There was a very, very large pile of them. "Oh," she said with a sigh. "I'll have to sit here sorting lentils until midnight, and I can't close my eyes, no matter how much they hurt. If only my mother knew about this!"

She kneeled down in the ashes next to the hearth and was about to begin her work when two white pigeons flew in through the window. They lit on the hearth next to the lentils. Nodding their heads, they said, "Cinderella, do you want us to help you sort the lentils?"

"Yes," she answered:

> The bad ones go into your crop,
> The good ones go into the pot.

And peck, peck, peck, peck, they started at once, eating up the bad ones and leaving the good ones lying. In only a quarter of an hour there was not a single bad lentil among the good ones, and she brushed them all into the pot.

Then the pigeons said to her, "Cinderella, if you would like to see your sisters dancing with the prince, just climb up to the pigeon roost." She followed them and climbed to the top rung of the ladder to the pigeon roost. There she could see into the hall, and she saw her sisters dancing with the prince. Everything glistened by the glow of a thousand lights. After she had seen enough, she climbed back down. With a heavy heart she lay down in the ashes and fell asleep.

The next morning the two sisters came to the kitchen. They were angry when they saw that she had sorted the lentils, for they wanted to scold her. Because they could not, they began telling her about the ball. They said, "Cinderella, it was so grand at the ball. The prince, who is the best looking man in the whole world, escorted us, and he is going to choose one of us to be his wife."

"Yes," said Cinderella, "I saw the glistening lights. It must have been magnificent."

"Now just how did you do that?" asked the oldest one.

"By standing up there on the pigeon roost."

When she heard this, her envy drove her to have the pigeon roost torn down immediately.

Cinderella had to comb their hair and get them ready again. The youngest sister, who had a little sympathy in her heart, said, "Cinderella, when it gets dark you can go and look through the windows from the outside."

"No!" said the oldest one. "That would only make her lazy. Here is a sackful of seeds. Sort the good ones from the bad ones, and do it well. If tomorrow there are any bad ones in the lot, then I will dump the whole sackful into the ashes, and you will have to go without eating until you have picked them all out again."

Cinderella sadly sat down on the hearth and spread out the seeds. The pigeons flew in again, and said, "Cinderella, do you want us to help you sort the seeds?"

"Yes," she answered:

> The bad ones go into your crop,
> The good ones go into the pot.

137

Peck, peck, peck, peck, it went as fast as if twelve hands were at work. When they were finished, the pigeons said, "Cinderella, would you like to go dancing at the ball?"

"Oh, my goodness," she said, "how could I go in these dirty clothes?"

"Just go to the little tree on your mother's grave, shake it, and wish yourself some beautiful clothes. But come back before midnight."

So Cinderella went and shook the little tree, and said:

> Shake yourself, shake yourself, little tree.
> Throw some nice clothing down to me!

She had scarcely spoken these words when a splendid silver dress fell down before her. With it were pearls, silk stockings with silver decorations, silver slippers, and everything else that she needed. Cinderella carried it all home. After she had washed herself and put on the beautiful clothing, she was as beautiful as a rose washed in dew. She went to the front door, and there was a carriage with six black horses all decorated with feathers, and servants dressed in blue and silver. They helped her into the carriage, and away they galloped to the king's castle.

The prince saw the carriage stop before the gate, and thought that a foreign princess was arriving. He himself walked down the steps, helped Cinderella out, and escorted her into the hall. Many thousand lights shone upon her, and she was so beautiful that everyone there was amazed. The sisters stood there, angry that someone was more beautiful than they were, but they had no idea that it was Cinderella, who they thought was lying at home in the ashes. The prince danced with Cinderella and paid her every royal honor. He thought to himself, "I am supposed to choose myself a bride. I will have no one but her."

However long she had suffered in ashes and sorrow, Cinderella was now living in splendor and joy. As midnight approached, before the clock struck twelve, she stood up, bowed, and said that she had to go, in spite of the prince's requests for her to stay. The prince escorted her out. Her carriage stood there waiting for her. And she rode away just as splendidly as she had come.

Back at home, Cinderella returned to the tree on her mother's grave, and said:

> Shake yourself, shake yourself, little tree!
> Take the clothing back from me!

The tree took back the clothes. Cinderella put on her old ash-dress again, went home, dirtied her face, and lay down in the ashes to sleep.

The next morning the two sisters came in looking out of sorts, and without saying a word. Cinderella said, "Did you have a good time yesterday evening?"

"No. A princess was there who danced with the prince almost the whole time, but no one knew who she was nor where she came from."

"Was she the one in the splendid carriage drawn by six black horses?" asked Cinderella.

"How did you know that?"

"I was standing in the front door when she rode by the house."

"In the future do not leave your work," said the oldest one, giving Cinderella an evil look. "What were you doing, standing in the front door?"

Cinderella had to get her sisters ready a third time. Her reward was a basin filled with peas, which she was supposed to sort. "And do not dare to leave your work," shouted the oldest one, as she was leaving.

Cinderella thought, "If only my pigeons will come again," and her heart beat a little faster. The pigeons did come, just as they had the evening before, and said, "Cinderella, would you like us to help you sort the peas."

"Yes," she said:

> The bad ones go into your crop,
> The good ones go into the pot.

Once again the pigeons picked out the bad ones, and soon they were finished. Then they said, "Cinderella, shake the little tree, and it will throw down even more beautiful clothes. Go to the ball, but be careful to come back before midnight." Cinderella went and said:

> Shake yourself, shake yourself, little tree.
> Throw some nice clothing down to me!

Then a dress fell down that was even more magnificent and more splendid than the other one, made entirely of gold and precious stones. With it were stockings decorated with gold, and slippers made of gold. Cinderella put them on, and she glistened like the sun at midday. A carriage with six white horses pulled up at the door. The horses had tall white plumes on their heads, and the servants were dressed in red and gold.

When Cinderella arrived, the prince was waiting for her at the stairway. He escorted her into the hall. If everyone had been astounded at her beauty yesterday, today they were even more astounded. The sisters stood in the corner, pale with envy. If they had known that this was Cinderella, who they thought was at home lying in the ashes, they would have died of jealousy.

The prince wanted to know who the foreign princess was, where she was from, and where she was going. He placed his people in the street to keep watch. To prevent her from running away so fast, he had the stairway covered with pitch. Cinderella danced with the prince again and again. Filled with joy, she did not think about midnight. Suddenly, in the middle of a dance, she heard the clock strike. She suddenly remembered what the pigeons had warned her. Frightened, she rushed to the door and ran down the stairs. Because they were covered with pitch, one of her golden slippers stuck fast, and in her fear she did not think to pick it up. She reached the last step just as the clock struck twelve. The carriage and the horses disappeared, and Cinderella was left standing there in the dark street dressed in her ash-clothes.

The prince had rushed after her. He found the golden slipper on the stairway, pulled it loose, and picked it up. But by the time he arrived below, she had disappeared. The people whom he had ordered to keep watch came and said that they had seen nothing.

Cinderella was glad that it had not been worse. She returned home, lit her simple oil lamp, hung it in the chimney, and lay down in the ashes. Before long the two sisters returned, and called out, "Cinderella, get up and light the way for us."

Cinderella yawned and acted as though she had been asleep. While lighting their way, she heard one of them say, "God knows who the cursed princess is. I wish that she were lying beneath the earth! The prince danced only with her, and after she left, he did not want to stay any longer, and the whole party came to an end."

"It was as though they suddenly blew out all the lights," said the other one. Cinderella knew exactly who the foreign princess was, but she did not say a word.

Now the prince decided that since nothing else had succeeded, he would let the slipper help him find his bride. He had it proclaimed that he would marry the person whose foot fit the golden slipper. But it was too small for everyone. Indeed, some could not have gotten their foot inside, if it had been twice as large. Finally it came time for the two sisters to try on the slipper. They were happy, for they had small, beautiful feet, and each one believed that she could not fail. "If only the prince would come here sooner!" they thought.

"Listen," said the mother secretly. "Take this knife, and if the slipper is too tight, just cut off part of your foot. It will hurt a little, but what harm is that? The pain will soon pass, and then one of you will be queen." Then the oldest one went to her bedroom and tried on the slipper. The front of her foot went in, but her heel was too large, so she took the knife and cut part of it off, so she could force her foot into the slipper. Then she went out to the prince, and when he saw that she was wearing the slipper, he said that she was to be his bride. He escorted her to his carriage and was going to drive away with her. When he arrived at the gate, the two pigeons were perched above, and they called out:

> Rook di goo, rook di goo!
> There's blood in the shoe.
> The shoe is too tight,
> This bride is not right!

The prince bent over and looked at the slipper. Blood was streaming from it. He saw that he had been deceived, and he took the false bride back.

The mother then said to her second daughter, "Take the slipper, and if it is too short for you, then cut off your toes." So she took the slipper into her bedroom, and because her foot was too long, she bit her teeth together, and cut off a large part of her toes, then quickly pulled on the slipper. When she stepped out wearing it, the prince thought that she was the right one, and wanted to ride away with her. But when they came to the gate, the pigeons again called out:

> Rook di goo, rook di goo!
> There's blood in the shoe.
> The shoe is too tight,
> This bride is not right!

The prince looked down and saw that her white stockings were stained red, and that blood and had come up high on them. The prince took her back to her mother and said, "She is not the right bride either. Is there not another daughter here in this house?"

"No," said the mother. "There is only a dirty cinder girl here. She is sitting down there in the ashes. The slipper would never fit her." She did not want to call her, but the prince insisted. So they called Cinderella, and when she heard that the prince was there, she quickly washed her hands and face. She stepped into the best room and bowed. The prince handed her the golden slipper, and said, "Try it on. If it fits you, you shall be my wife." She pulled the heavy shoe from her left foot, then put her foot into the slipper, pushing ever so slightly. It fit as if it had been poured over her foot. As she straightened herself up, she looked into the prince's face, and he recognized her as the beautiful princess. He cried out, "This is the right bride." The stepmother and the two proud sisters turned pale with horror.[120] The prince escorted Cinderella away. He helped her into his carriage, and as they rode through the gate, the pigeons called out:

> Rook di goo, rook di goo!
> No blood's in the shoe.
> The shoe's not too tight,
> This bride is right![121]

Conkiajgharuna, the Little Rag-Girl

Georgia

There was and there was not, there was a miserable peasant. He had a wife and a little daughter. So poor was this peasant that his daughter was called Conkiajgharuna (Little Rag-Girl).

Some time passed, and his wife died. He was unhappy before, but now a greater misfortune had befallen him. He grieved and grieved, and at last he said to himself, "I will go and take another wife; she will mind the house, and tend my orphan child." So he arose and took a second wife, but this wife brought with her a daughter of her own. When this woman came into her husband's house and saw his child, she was angry in heart.

She treated Little Rag-Girl badly. She petted her own daughter, but scolded her stepdaughter, and tried to get rid of her. Every day she gave her a piece of badly cooked bread, and sent her out to watch the cow, saying, "Here is a loaf; eat of it,

---

[120]In the edition of 1819 (and all subsequent editions) the stepsisters' punishment is more severe: The pigeons attack them and peck out their eyes, leaving them blind for life.

[121]Type 510A. Source: *Kinder- und Hausmärchen*, 1st ed. (Berlin, 1812/1815), v. 1, no. 21.

give to every wayfarer, and bring the loaf home whole." The girl went, and felt very miserable.

Once she was sitting sadly in the field, and began to weep bitterly. The cow listened, and then opened its mouth, and said, "Why are you weeping? What troubles you?" The girl told her sad tale. The cow said, "In one of my horns is honey, and in the other is butter, which you can take if you want to, so why be unhappy?" The girl took the butter and the honey, and in a short time she grew plump. When the stepmother noticed this she did not know what to do for rage. She rose, and after that every day she gave her a basket of wool with her; this wool was to be spun and brought home in the evening finished. The stepmother wished to tire the girl out with toil, so that she should grow thin and ugly.

Once when Little Rag-Girl was tending the cow, it ran away onto a roof.[122] She pursued it, and wished to drive it back to the road, but she dropped her spindle on the roof. Looking inside she saw an old woman seated, and said to her, "Good mother, will you give me my spindle?"

The old dame replied, "I am not able, my child, come and take it yourself." The old woman was a *devi*.

The girl went in and was lifting up her spindle, when the old dame called out, "Daughter, daughter, come and look at my head a moment. I am almost eaten up."

The girl came and looked at her head. She was filled with horror; all the worms in the earth seemed to be crawling there. The little girl stroked her head and removed some, and then said, "You have a clean head. Why should I look at it?"

This conduct pleased the old woman very much, and she said, "When you leave here, go along such and such a road, and in a certain place you will see three springs—one white, one black, and one yellow. Pass by the white and black, and put your head in the yellow and rinse it with your hands."

The girl did this. She went on her way, and came to the three springs. She passed by the white and black, and bathed her head with her hands in the yellow fountain. When she looked up she saw that her hair was quite golden, and her hands, too, shone like gold. In the evening, when she went home, her stepmother was filled with fury. After this she sent her own daughter with the cow. Perhaps the same good fortune would visit her!

So Little Rag-Girl stayed at home while her stepsister drove out the cow. Once more the cow ran onto the roof. The girl pursued it, and her spindle fell down. She looked in, and seeing the *devi* woman, called out, "Dog of an old woman! Here! Come and give me my spindle!"

The old woman replied, "I am not able, child, come and take it yourself." When the girl came near, the old woman said, "Come, child, and look at my head."

The girl came and looked at her head, and cried out, "Ugh! What a horrid head you have! You are a disgusting old woman!"

---

[122]In some parts of the Caucasus the houses of the peasantry are built in the ground, and it is quite possible to walk onto a roof unwittingly. [Note by Wardrop]

The old woman said, "I thank you, my child; when you go on your way you will see a yellow, a white, and a black spring. Pass by the yellow and the white springs, and rinse your head with your hands in the black one."

The girl did this. She passed by the yellow and white springs, and bathed her head in the black one. When she looked at herself she was black as an African, and on her head there was a horn. She cut it off again and again, but it grew larger and larger.

She went home and complained to her mother, who was almost frenzied, but there was no help for it. Her mother said to herself, "This is all the cow's fault, so it shall be killed."

This cow knew the future. When it learned that it was to be killed, it went to Little Rag-Girl and said, "When I am dead, gather my bones together and bury them in the earth. When you are in trouble come to my grave, and cry aloud, 'Bring my steed and my royal robes!'" Little Rag-Girl did exactly as the cow had told her. When it was dead she took its bones and buried them in the earth.

After this, some time passed. One holiday the stepmother took her daughter, and they went to church. She placed a trough in front of Little Rag-Girl, spread a large measure of millet in the courtyard, and said, "Before we come home from church fill this trough with tears, and gather up this millet, so that not one grain is left." Then they went to church.

Little Rag-Girl sat down and began to weep. While she was crying a neighbor came in a said, "Why are you in tears? What is the matter?" The little girl told her tale. The woman brought all the brood hens and chicken, and they picked up every grain of millet, then she put a lump of salt in the trough and poured water over it. "There, child," said she, "there are your tears! Now go and enjoy yourself."

Little Rag-Girl then thought of the cow. She went to its grave and called out, "Bring me my steed and my royal robes!" There appeared at once a horse and beautiful clothes. Little Rag-Girl put on the garments, mounted the horse, and went to the church.

There all the folk began to stare at her. They were amazed at her grandeur. Her stepsister whispered to her mother when she saw her, "This girl is very much like our Little Rag-Girl!"

Her mother smiled scornfully and said, "Who would give that sun darkener such robes?"

Little Rag-Girl left the church before anyone else; she changed her clothes in time to appear before her stepmother in rags. On the way home, as she was leaping over a stream, in her haste she let her slipper fall in.

A long time passed. Once when the king's horses were drinking water in this stream, they saw the shining slipper and were so afraid that they would drink no more water. The king was told that there was something shining in the stream, and that the horses were afraid.

The king commanded his divers to find out what it was. They found the golden slipper, and presented it to the king. When he saw it, he commanded his viziers, saying, "Go and seek the owner of this slipper, for I will wed none but her." His viziers sought the maiden, but they could find no one whom the slipper would fit.

Little Rag-Girl's mother heard this, adorned her daughter, and placed her on a throne. Then she went and told the king that she had a daughter whose foot he might look at. It was exactly the model for the shoe. She put Little Rag-Girl in a corner, with a big basket over her. When the king came into the house he sat down on the basket, in order to try on the slipper.

Little Rag-Girl took a needle and pricked the king from under the basket. He jumped up, stinging with pain, and asked the stepmother what she had under the basket. The stepmother replied, "It is only a turkey I have there."

The king sat down on the basket again, and Little Rag-Girl again stuck the needle into him. The king jumped up, and cried out, "Lift the basket. I will see underneath!"

The stepmother pleaded with him, saying, "Do not blame me, your majesty, it is only a turkey, and it will run away."

But the king would not listen to her pleas. He lifted the basket up, and Little Rag-Girl came forth, and said, "This slipper is mine, and fits me well." She sat down, and the king found that it was indeed a perfect fit. Little Rag-Girl became the king's wife, and her shameless stepmother was left with a dry throat.[123]

Pepelyouga

Serbia

On a high pasture land, near an immense precipice, some maidens were occupied in spinning and attending to their grazing cattle, when an old strange looking man with a white beard reaching down to his girdle approached, and said, "Oh fair maidens, beware of the abyss, for if one of you should drop her spindle down the cliff, her mother would be turned into a cow that very moment!"

So saying the aged man disappeared, and the girls, bewildered by his words, and discussing the strange incident, approached near to the ravine which had suddenly become interesting to them. They peered curiously over the edge, as though expecting to see some unaccustomed sight, when suddenly the most beautiful of the maidens let her spindle drop from her hand, and before she could recover it, it was bounding from rock to rock into the depths beneath. When she returned home that evening she found her worst fears realized, for her mother stood before the door transformed into a cow.

---

[123]Types 480 "Frau Holle" and 510A "Cinderella." Source: Marjory Wardrop, *Georgian Folk Tales* (London, 1894), pp. 63-67. Wardrop's heroine and the story itself are both named "Conkiajgharuna," which means "the little girl in rags."

A short time later her father married again. His new wife was a widow, and brought a daughter of her own into her new home. This girl was not particularly well favored, and her mother immediately began to hate her stepdaughter because of the latter's good looks. She forbade her henceforth to wash her face, to comb her hair or to change her clothes, and in every way she could think of she sought to make her miserable.

One morning she gave her a bag filled with hemp, saying, "If you do not spin this and make a fine top of it by tonight, you need not return home, for I intend to kill you."

The poor girl, deeply dejected, walked behind the cattle, industriously spinning as she went, but by noon when the cattle lay down in the shade to rest, she observed that she had made but little progress and she began to weep bitterly.

Now, her mother was driven daily to pasture with the other cows, and seeing her daughter's tears she drew near and asked why she wept, whereupon the maiden told her all. Then the cow comforted her daughter, saying, "My darling child, be consoled! Let me take the hemp into my mouth and chew it; through my ear a thread will come out. You must take the end of this and wind it into a top." So this was done; the hemp was soon spun, and when the girl gave it to her stepmother that evening, she was greatly surprised.

Next morning the woman roughly ordered the maiden to spin a still larger bag of hemp, and as the girl, thanks to her mother, spun and wound it all, her stepmother, on the following day, gave her twice the quantity to spin. Nevertheless, the girl brought home at night even that unusually large quantity well spun, and her stepmother concluded that the poor girl was not spinning alone, but that other maidens, her friends, were giving her help. Therefore she, next morning, sent her own daughter to spy upon the poor girl and to report what she saw. The girl soon noticed that the cow helped the poor orphan by chewing the hemp, while she drew the thread and wound it on a top, and she ran back home and informed her mother of what she had seen. Upon this, the stepmother insisted that her husband should order that particular cow to be slaughtered. Her husband at first hesitated, but as his wife urged him more and more, he finally decided to do as she wished.

On learning what had been decided, the stepdaughter wept more than ever, and when her mother asked what was the matter, she told her tearfully all that had been arranged. Thereupon the cow said to her daughter, "Wipe away your tears, and do not cry any more. When they slaughter me, you must take great care not to eat any of the meat, but after the repast, carefully collect my bones and inter them behind the house under a certain stone; then, should you ever be in need of help, come to my grave and there you will find it."

The cow was killed, and when the meat was served the poor girl declined to eat of it, pretending that she had no appetite; after the meal she gathered with great care all the bones and buried them on the spot indicated by her mother.

Now, the name of the maiden was Marra, but, as she had to do the roughest work of the house, such as carrying water, washing, and sweeping, she was called by her stepmother and stepsister Pepelyouga (Cinderella).

145

One Sunday, when the stepmother and her daughter had dressed themselves for church, the woman spread about the house the contents of a basktetful of millet, and said, "Listen, Pepelyouga; if you do not gather up all this millet and have dinner ready by the time we return from church, I will kill you!"

When they had gone, the poor girl began to weep, reflecting, "As to the dinner I can easily prepare it, but how can I possibly gather up all this millet?" But that very moment she recalled the words of the cow, that, if she ever should be struck by misfortune, she need but walk to the grave behind the house, when she would find instant help there. Immediately she ran out, and, when she approached the grave, lo! a chest was lying on the grave wide open, and inside were beautiful dresses and everything necessary for a lady's toilet. Two doves were sitting on the lid of the chest, and as the girl drew near, they said to her, "Marra, take from the chest the dress you like the best, clothe yourself, and go to church. As to the millet and other work, we ourselves will attend to that and see that everything is in good order!"

Marra needed no second invitation; she took the first silk dress she touched, made her toilet, and went to church, where her entrance created quite a sensation. Everybody, men and women, greatly admired her beauty and her costly attire, but they were puzzled as to who she was, and where she came from. A prince happened to be in the church on that day, and he, too, admired the beautiful maiden.

Just before the service ended, the girl stole from the church, went hurriedly home, took off her beautiful clothes and placed them back in the chest, which instantly shut and became invisible. She then rushed to the kitchen, where she discovered that the dinner was quite ready, and that the millet was gathered into the basket. Soon the stepmother came back with her daughter, and they were astounded to find the millet gathered up, dinner prepared, and everything else in order. A desire to learn the secret now began to torment the stepmother mightily.

Next Sunday everything happened as before, except that the girl found in the chest a silver dress, and that the prince felt a greater admiration for her, so much so that he was unable, even for a moment to take his eyes from her. On the third Sunday, the mother and daughter again prepared to go to church, and, having scattered the millet as before, she repeated her previous threats. As soon as they disappeared, the girl ran straight to her mother's grave, where she found, as on the previous occasions, the open chest and the same two doves. This time she found a dress made of gold lace, and she hastily clad herself in it and went to church, where she was admired by all, even more than before. As for the czar's son, he had come with the intention not to let her this time out of his sight, but to follow and see where she went. Accordingly, as the service drew near to its close, and the maiden withdrew quietly as before, the enamored prince followed after her. Marra hurried along, for she had none too much time, and, as she went, one of her golden slippers came off, and she was too agitated to stop and pick it up. The prince, however, who had lost sight of the maiden, saw the slipper and put it in his pocket. Reaching home, Marra took off her golden dress, laid it in the chest, and rushed back to the house.

The prince now resolved to go from house to house throughout his father's realm in search of the owner of the slipper, inviting all the fair maidens to try on the golden slipper. But, alas! his efforts seemed to be doomed to failure; for some girls the slipper was too long, for others too short, for others, again, too narrow. There was no one whom it would fit.

Wandering from door to door, the sad prince at length came to the house of Marra's father. The stepmother was expecting him, and she had hidden her stepdaughter under a large trough in the courtyard. When the prince asked whether she had any daughters, the stepmother answered that she had but one, and she presented the girl to him. The prince requested the girl to try on the slipper, but, squeeze as she would, there was not room in it even for her toes! Thereupon the prince asked whether it was true that there were no other girls in the house, and the stepmother replied that indeed it was quite true.

That very moment a cock flew onto the trough and crowed out lustily, "*Kook-oo-ryeh-koooo!* Here she is under this very trough!"

The stepmother, enraged, exclaimed, "Sh! Go away! May an eagle seize you and fly off with you!" The curiosity of the prince was aroused. He approached the trough, lifted it up, and, to his great surprise, there was the maiden whom he had seen three times in church, clad in the very same golden dress she had last worn, and having only one golden slipper.

When the prince recognized the maiden he was overcome with joy. Quickly he tried the slipper on her dainty foot. It not only fit her admirably, but it exactly matched the one she already wore on her left foot. He lifted her up tenderly and escorted her to his palace. Later he won her love, and they were happily married.[124]

The Baba Yaga

Aleksandr Afanasyev

Once upon a time there was an old couple. The husband lost his wife and married again. But he had a daughter by the first marriage, a young girl, and she found no favor in the eyes of her evil stepmother, who used to beat her, and consider how she could get her killed outright. One day the father went away somewhere or other, so the stepmother said to the girl, "Go to your aunt, my sister, and ask her for a needle and thread to make you a shift."

Now that aunt was a Baba Yaga. Well, the girl was no fool, so she went to a real aunt of hers first, and says she, "Good morning, auntie!"

"Good morning, my dear! What have you come for?"

---

[124]Type 510A. Source: Woislav M. Petrovitch, *Hero Tales and Legends of the Serbians* (London, 1917), pp. 224-230.

"Mother has sent me to her sister, to ask for a needle and thread to make me a shift."

Then her aunt instructed her what to do. "There is a birch tree there, niece, which would hit you in the eye—you must tie a ribbon round it; there are doors which would creak and bang—you must pour oil on their hinges; there are dogs which would tear you in pieces—you must throw them these rolls; there is a cat which would scratch your eyes out—you must give it a piece of bacon."

So the girl went away, and walked and walked, till she came to the place. There stood a hut, and in it sat weaving the Baba Yaga, the bony-shanks.

"Good morning, auntie," says the girl.

"Good morning, my dear," replies the Baba Yaga.

" Mother has sent me to ask you for a needle and thread to make me a shift."

"Very well; sit down and weave a little in the meantime."

So the girl sat down behind the loom, and the Baba Yaga went outside, and said to her servant maid, "Go and heat the bath, and get my niece washed; and mind you look sharp after her. I want to breakfast off her."

Well, the girl sat there in such a fright that she was as much dead as alive. Presently she spoke imploringly to the servant maid, saying, "Kinswoman dear, do please wet the firewood instead of making it burn; and fetch the water for the bath in a sieve." And she made her a present of a handkerchief.

The Baba Yaga waited awhile; then she came to the window and asked, "Are you weaving, niece? Are you weaving, my dear?"

"Oh yes, dear aunt, I'm weaving."

So the Baba Yaga went away again, and the girl gave the cat a piece of bacon, and asked, "Is there no way of escaping from here?"

"Here's a comb for you and a towel," said the cat; "take them, and be off. The Baba Yaga will pursue you, but you must lay your ear on the ground, and when you hear that she is close at hand, first of all, throw down the towel. It will become a wide, wide river. And if the Baba Yaga gets across the river, and tries to catch you, then you must lay your ear on the ground again, and when you hear that she is close at hand, throw down the comb. It will become a dense, dense forest; through that she won't be able to force her way anyhow."

The girl took the towel and the comb and fled. The dogs would have rent her, but she threw them the rolls, and they let her go by; the doors would have begun to bang, but she poured oil on their hinges, and they let her pass through; the birch tree would have poked her eyes out, but she tied the ribbon around it, and it let her pass on. And the cat sat down to the loom, and worked away; muddled everything about, if it didn't do much weaving.

Up came the Baba Yaga to the window, and asked, "Are you weaving, niece? Are you weaving, my dear?"

"I'm weaving, dear aunt, I'm weaving," gruffly replied the cat.

The Baba Yaga rushed into the hut, saw that the girl was gone, and took to beating the cat, and abusing it for not having scratched the girl's eyes out. "Long as I've served you," said the cat, "you've never given me so much as a bone; but she gave me bacon." Then the Baba Yaga pounced upon the dogs, on the doors,

148

on the birch tree, and on the servant maid, and set to work to abuse them all, and to knock them about.

Then the dogs said to her, "Long as we've served you, you've never so much as pitched us a burnt crust; but she gave us rolls to eat."

And the doors said, "Long as we've served you, you've never poured even a drop of water on our hinges; but she poured oil on us."

The birch tree said, "Long as I've served you, you've never tied a single thread around me; but she fastened a ribbon around me."

And the servant maid said, "Long as I've served you, you've never given me so much as a rag; but she gave me a handkerchief."

The Baba Yaga, bony of limb, quickly jumped into her mortar, sent it flying along with the pestle, sweeping away the while all traces of its flight with a broom, and set off in pursuit of the girl. Then the girl put her ear to the ground, and when she heard that the Baba Yaga was chasing her, and was now close at hand, she flung down the towel. And it became a wide, such a wide river! Up came the Baba Yaga to the river, and gnashed her teeth with spite; then she went home for her oxen, and drove them to the river. The oxen drank up every drop of the river, and then the Baba Yaga began the pursuit anew. But the girl put her ear to the ground again, and when she heard that the Baba Yaga was near, she flung down the comb, and instantly a forest sprang up, such an awfully thick one! The Baba Yaga began gnawing away at it, but however hard she worked, she couldn't gnaw her way through it, so she had to go back again.

But by this time the girl's father had returned home, and he asked, "Where's my daughter?"

"She's gone to her aunt's," replied her stepmother.

Soon afterwards the girl herself came running home.

" Where have you been?" asked her father.

"Ah, father!" she said, "mother sent me to aunt's to ask for a needle and thread to make me a shift. But aunt's a Baba Yaga, and she wanted to eat me!"

"And how did you get away, daughter?"

"Why like this," said the girl, and explained the whole matter. As soon as her father had heard all about it, he became wroth with his wife, and shot her. But he and his daughter lived on and flourished, and everything went well with them.[125]

---

[125]Type 313H*. Source: W. R. S. Ralston, *Russian Folk-Tales* (London, 1873), pp. 139-142. Ralston's source: Aleksandr Afanasyev.

Kora and His Sister

India

There were once seven brothers and they had one sister who was the youngest of the family. The six eldest brothers were married but no wife had been found for the youngest; for three years inquiries were made to try and find a suitable bride for him, but all in vain. At last the young man, whose name was Kora, told his parents and brothers not to trouble any more, as he would find a wife for himself; he intended to bring a flowering plant from the forest and plant it by the stand on which the watering pots were kept, and then he would marry any maiden who picked one of the flowers and put it in her hair.

His father and mother approved of this proposal, so the next day he brought some sort of flowering plant and planted it by the water pot stand. He charged all his family to be most careful that no one of his own relations picked the flower and also to warn any of the village girls who wanted to pick it, that if she did so and put it in her hair, she would thereby become his wife; but if, knowing this, anyone wished to do so, they were not to prevent her.

The neighbors soon got to hear what the plant meant and used often to come and look at it, and Kora watched it growing, until after a time it produced a bud and then a beautiful and sweet-scented flower. All the village girls came to see the beautiful flower; and one day Kora's sister when she went to the water stand to get some water to drink, caught hold of it and longed to pick it, it looked so pretty. Her mother saw what she was doing and scolded her for touching the forbidden flower, but the girl begged to see what it would look like in her hair; there could be no harm done if she pulled the whole plant up by its roots and put it in her hair and then replanted it; no one would know what had happened. In spite of her mother's remonstrances she insisted on doing this and having seen how the flower looked in her hair carefully replanted it.

Soon afterwards Kora came home and went to see his flower; he knew at once that someone had worn it and called to his mother and asked who it was. She protested that she knew nothing about the matter, but Kora said that he could tell by the smell that it had been worn and then he showed that there was also a hair sticking to the flower. Then his mother admitted that in spite of all she could say, his sister had worn the flower and planted it again in the ground.

When she saw that she was found out, the girl began to cry, but her father said that it was clearly fated that she and Kora should marry and this was the reason why they had been unable to find any other bride; so they must now arrange for the wedding. Accordingly rice was got ready and all the usual preparations made for a marriage. The unfortunate girl saw that flight was her only means of escape from such a fate, so one day she ran away; all she took with her was a pet parrot.

For many days she traveled on and one day she stopped by a pool to bathe and as she rubbed her limbs she collected the scurf that she rubbed off her skin and put it on the ground in one place; then she went on with her bathing; but at the place where she had put the scurf of her skin, a palm tree sprang up and grew so rapidly, that, by the time she came out of the water, it had become a large tree.

The girl was struck by this strange sight and at once thought that the tree would afford her a safe refuge; so she climbed up it with her parrot in her hand and when safely seated among the leaves she begged the palm tree to grow so tall that no one would be able to find her, and the tree grew until it reached an unusual height. So the girl stayed in the tree top and the parrot used to go every day and bring her food. Meanwhile her parents and brothers searched high and low for her for two or three days, for the wedding day was close at hand, but their search was of course in vain; and they concluded that the girl must have drowned herself in some river.

Time passed and one day at noon a Mahuli girl, who was taking her basket ware to market, stopped to rest in the shade of the palm tree. And as she sat there, Kora's sister called to her from the top of the tree and asked her to give her a small winnowing fan in exchange for a bracelet. The Mahuli girl told her to throw the bracelet down first. Kora's sister made no objection to this, and when she had got the bracelet, the Mahuli girl threw up a winnowing fan which soared right up to where Kora's sister was sitting. Before the Mahuli girl went on her way, Kora's sister made her promise never to let anyone see the bracelet when she went about selling her baskets as otherwise it would be stolen from her; and secondly, on no account to let it be known that there was anyone in the palm tree, on pain of death. The Mahuli girl kept her promise and whenever she went out selling baskets she used to keep her bracelet covered with her cloth.

One day it chanced that she went to the house where Kora lived to sell her wares and they asked her why it was that she kept her arm covered; she told them that she had a sore on it; they wanted to see how big the sore was, but she refused to show it, saying that if she showed it she would die. They laughed at such a ridiculous story and at last forced her to show her arm, which of course was quite well; but they at once recognized the bracelet and asked where she had got it from. The Mahuli girl refused to tell them and said that if she did, she would die. "What a foolish girl you are," they objected, "first you say you will die if you show us your arm and then if you tell us where you got this bracelet from; it belonged to our daughter whom we have lost, and so you must tell us! Come, we will give you a basket full of rice if you tell us." The Mahuli girl could not resist this offer, and when the basket of rice was produced, she told them where the palm tree was, in which Kora's sister was hiding. In all haste the father and mother went to the tree and found that it was much too high for them to climb. So they begged their daughter to come down and promised not to marry her to her brother; but she would not come down. Then they sang:

> You have made a palm tree from the scraping of your skin
> And have climbed up into it, daughter!
> Come daughter, come down.

But she only answered:

Father and mother, why do you cry?
I must spend my life here.
Do you return home.

So they went home in despair.
Then her sister-in-law came in their turn and sang:

Palm tree, palm tree, give us back our sister.
The brother and sister have got to be married.

But she would not answer them, nor come down from the tree, so they had to go home without her.

Then all her other relations came and besought her to come down, but she would not listen to them. So they went away and invoked a storm to come to their aid. And a storm arose, and cold rain fell till the girl in the palm tree was soaked and shivering, and the wind blew and swayed the palm tree so that its top kept touching the ground. At last she could bear the cold and wet no more, and, seizing an opportunity when the tree touched the ground, she slipped off. Her relations had made all the villagers promise on no account to let her into their houses; so when she went into the village and called out at house after house no one answered her or opened to her. Then she went to her own home and there also they refused to open to her.

But Kora had lit a big fire in the cow house and sat by it warming himself, knowing that the girl would have to come to him; and as she could find no shelter elsewhere she had to go to his fire, and then she sat and warmed herself and thought, "I fled for fear of this man and now I have come back to him; this is the end, I can no longer stay in this world; the people will not even let me into their houses. I have no wish to see them again."

So she sat and thought, and when she was warmed, she lay down by the side of Kora; and he wore tied to his waist a nail cutter; she unfastened this and cut her throat with it as she lay. Her death struggles aroused Kora, and he got up and saw the ground covered with her blood and he saw that she had killed herself with his nail cutter; then he took counsel with himself and also cut his throat in the same way. In the morning the two corpses were found lying side by side, and it was seen that their blood refused to mingle but had flowed in opposite directions.

So they took the bodies away to burn them and laid them on one pyre; and when the fire was lit, it was seen that the smoke from the two bodies rose separately into the air. Then all who saw it said, "We wished to marry brother and sister but Chando would not approve of it; see how their blood would not mingle though spilt on the same floor, and how the smoke from the pyre rises in two separate columns; it is plain that the marriage of brother and sister is wrong." From that time such marriages have been discontinued.[126]

---

[126]Type 510B (variant). Source: Cecil Henry Bompas, *Folklore of the Santal Parganas* (London, 1909), no. 50.

The She-Bear

Giambattista Basile

Now it is said that once upon a time there lived a king of Roccaspra, who had a wife who for beauty, grace, and comeliness exceeded all other women. Truly she was the mother of beauty, but this beautiful being, at the full time of her life, fell from the steed of health, and broke the threads of life. But before the candle of life was finally put out, she called her husband, and said, "I know well, that you have loved me with excessive love, therefore show me a proof of your love and give me a promise that you will never marry, unless you meet one beautiful as I have been; and if you will not so promise, I will leave you a curse, and I will hate you even in the other world." The king, who loved her above all things, hearing this her last will, began to weep and lament, and for a while could not find a word to say; but after his grief subsided, he replied, "If I ever think of taking a wife, may the gout seize me, and may I become as gaunt as an asparagus; oh my love, forget it. Do not believe in dreams, nor that I can ever put my affection upon another woman. You will take with you all my joy and desire." And while he was thus speaking, the poor lady, who was at her last, turned up her eyes and stretched her feet.

When the king saw that her soul had taken flight, his eyes became fountains of tears, and he cried with loud cries, buffeted his face, and wept, and wailed, so that all the courtiers ran to his side. He continually called upon the name of that good soul and cursed his fate, which had deprived him of her, and tore his hair, and pulled out his beard, and accused the stars of having sent to him this great misfortune. But he did as others do. A bump on the elbow and the loss of a wife cause much pain, but it does not last. The one pain disappears at one's side, and the other into the grave.

Night had not yet come forth to look about the heavens for the bats, when he began to make count on his fingers, saying "My wife is dead, and I am a widower, and sad hearted without hope of any kind but my only daughter, since she left me. Therefore it will be necessary to find another wife that will bear me a son. But where can I find one? Where can I meet a woman endowed with my wife's beauty, when all other females seem witches in my sight? There is the rub! Where shall I find another like unto her? Where am I to seek her with a bell, if nature formed Nardella (may her soul rest in glory), and then broke the mold? Alas! in what labyrinth am I! What a mistake was the promise I made her! But what? I have not seen the wolf yet, but I am running away already. Let us seek, let us see, and let us understand. Is it possible, that there is no other donkey in the stable except for Nardella? Is it possible that the world will be lost for me? Will there be such a plague that all women will be destroyed and their seed lost?"

And thus saying, he commanded the public crier to proclaim that all the beautiful women in the world should come and undergo the comparison of beauty, that he would take to wife the best looking of all, and make her the queen of his realm. This news spread in all parts of the world, and not one of the women in the whole universe failed to come and try this venture. Not even flayed hags stayed behind, they came by the dozen, because, when the point of beauty is touched, there is none who will yield, there is no sea monster who will give herself up as hideous; each and everyone boasts of uncommon beauty. If a donkey speaks the truth, the mirror is blamed for not reflecting the form as it is naturally; it is the fault of the quicksilver at the back. And now the land was full of women, and the king ordered that they should all stand in file, and he began to walk up and down, like a sultan when he enters his harem, to choose the best Genoa stone to sharpen his damascene blade. He came and went, up and down, like a monkey who is never still, looking and staring at this one and that one. One had a crooked brow, another a long nose, one a large mouth, and another thick lips. This one was too tall and gaunt, that other was short and badly formed, this one was too much dressed, another was too slightly robed. He disliked the Spanish woman because of the hue of her skin; the Neapolitan was not to his taste because of the way in which she walked; the German seemed to him too cold and frozen; the French woman too light of brains; the Venetian a spinning wheel full of flax. At last, for one reason or another, he sent them all about their business with one hand in front and another behind.

Seeing so many beautiful heads of celery turned to hard roots and having resolved to marry nevertheless, he turned to his own daughter, saying, "What am I seeking about these Marys of Ravenna, if my daughter Preziosa is made from the same mold as her mother? I have this beautiful face at home, and yet I should go to the end of the world seeking it?" Thus he explained to his daughter his desire, and was severely reproved and censured by her, as Heaven knows. The king was angry at her rejection, and said to her, "Be quiet and hold your tongue. Make up your mind to tie the matrimonial knot with me this very evening; otherwise when I finish with you there will be nothing left but your ears."

Preziosa, hearing this threat, retired to her room, and wept and lamented her evil fate. And while she lay there in this plight, an old woman, who used to bring her cosmetics, came to her, and finding her in such a plight, looking like one more ready for the other world than for this one, inquired the cause of her distress. When the old woman learned what had happened, she said, "Be of good cheer, my daughter, and despair not, for every evil has a remedy. Death alone has no cure. Now listen to me: When your father comes to you this evening—donkey that he is, wanting to act the stallion—put this piece of wood into your mouth, and you will at once become a she-bear. Then you can make your escape, for he will be afraid of you and let you go. Go straight to the forest, for it was written in the book of fate, the day that you were born, that there you should meet your fortune. When you want to turn back into a woman as you are and will ever be, take the bit of wood out of your mouth, and you will return to your pristine form." Preziosa embraced and thanked the old woman, told the servants to give her an apron full of flour and some slices of ham, and sent her away. When the sun began to change her quarters like a bankrupt strumpet, the king sent for his minister, and had him issue invitations to all the lords and grandees to come to the marriage feast. They all crowded in. After spending five or six hours in high revelry and unrestrained eating, the king made his way to the bed chamber, and called to the bride to come and fulfill his desire. But she put the bit of wood into her mouth, and instantly took the shape of a fierce she-bear, and stood thus before him. He, frightened at the sudden change, rolled himself up in the bedding, and did not put forth a finger or an eye until morning.

Meanwhile Preziosa made her way toward the forest, where the shadows met concocting together how they could annoy the sun. There she lay in good fellowship and at one with the other animals. When the day dawned, it happened by chance that the son of the King of Acquacorrente should come to that forest. He sighted the she-bear and was greatly frightened, but the beast came forward, and wagging her tail, walked around him, and put her head under his hand for him to caress her. He took heart at this strange sight, smoothed its head as he would have done to a dog, and said to it, "Lie down, down, quiet, quiet, there there, good beast." Seeing that the beast was very tame, he took her home with him, commanding his servants to put her in the garden by the side of the royal palace, and there to attend to and feed her well, and treat her as they would his own person, and to take her to a particular spot so that he might see her from the windows of his palace whenever he had a mind to.

Now it so happened that one day all his people were away on some errand, and the prince being left alone, thought about the bear, and looked out of the window to see her. However, at that very moment Preziosa, believing she was utterly alone, had taken the bit of wood from her mouth, and stood combing her golden hair. The prince was amazed at this woman of great beauty, and he descended the stairs and ran to the garden. But Preziosa, perceiving the ambush, at once put the bit of wood into her mouth, and became a she-bear once more. The prince looked about, but could not see what he had sighted from above, and not finding what he came to seek, remained very disappointed, and was melancholy and sad hearted, and in a few days became grievously ill. He kept repeating, "Oh my bear, oh my bear." His mother, hearing this continual cry, imagined that perhaps the bear had bit him or done him some evil, and therefore ordered the servants to kill her. But all the servants loved the beast because it was so very tame, even the stones in the roadway could not help liking her, so they had compassion and could not think of killing her. Therefore they led her to the forest, and returning to the queen, told her that she was dead. When this deed came to the prince's ears, he acted as a madman, and leaving his bed, ill as he was, was about to make mincemeat of the servants. They told him the truth of the affair. He mounted his steed and searched backward and forward until at length he came to a cave and found the bear.

He carried her home with him and put her in a chamber, saying, "Oh you beautiful morsel fit for kings, why do you hide your passing beauty in a bear's hide? Oh light of love, why are you closed in such a hairy lantern? Why have you acted this way toward me, is it so that you may see me die a slow death? I am dying of despair, charmed by your beautiful form, and you can see the witness of my words in my failing health and sickening form. I am become skin and bone, and the fever burns my very marrow, and consumes me with heart-sore pain. Therefore lift the veil from that stinking hide, and let me behold once more your grace and beauty; lift up the leaves from this basket's mouth, and let me take a view of the splendid fruit

155

within; lift the tapestry, and allow my eyes to feast upon the luxury of your charms. Who has enclosed in a dreary prison such a glorious work? Who has enclosed in a leather casket such a priceless treasure? Let me behold your passing grace, and take in payment all my desires. Oh my love, only this bear's grease can cure the nervous disease of which I suffer." But perceiving that his words had no effect, and that all was time lost, he took to his bed, and his illness increased daily, until the doctors feared for his life. The queen, his mother, who had no other love in the world, sat at his bedside, and said to him, "Oh my son, where does your heartsickness come from? What is the cause of all this sadness? You are young, you are rich, you are beloved, you are great. What do you want, my son? Speak, for only a shameful beggar carries an empty pocket. If you desire to take a wife, choose, and I will command; take, and I will pay. Can you not see that your sickness is my sickness and that your pulse beats in unison with my heart? If you burn with fever in your blood, I burn with fever on the brain. I have no other support for my old age but you. Therefore, my son, be cheerful, and cheer my heart, and do not darken this realm, and raze to the ground this house, and bereave your mother."

The prince, hearing these words, said, "Nothing can cheer me, if I may not see the bear; therefore, if you desire to see me in good health again, let her stay in this room, and I do not wish that any other serve me, and make my bed, and cook my meals, if it be not herself, and if what I desire be done, I am sure that I shall be well in a few days." To the queen it seemed folly for her son to ask that a bear should act as cook and housemaid. She believed that the prince must be delirious; nevertheless, to please his fancy, she went for the bear, and when the beast came to the prince's bedside she lifted her paw and felt the invalid's pulse. The queen smiled at the sight, thinking that by and by the bear would scratch the prince's nose. But the prince spoke to the bear, and said, "Oh mischievous mine, will you not cook for me, and feed me, and serve me?" And the bear nodded yes with her head, showing that she would accept the charge. Then the queen sent for some chickens, and had a fire lit in the fireplace in the same chamber, and had a kettle with boiling water put on the fire. The bear took hold of a chicken, scalded it, dexterously plucked off its feathers, cleaned it, put half of it on the spit, and stewed the other half. When it was ready, the prince, who could not before eat even sugar, ate it all and licked his fingers. When he had ended his meal, the bear brought him some drink, and handed it so gracefully that the queen kissed her on the head. After this the prince arose, and went to the salon to receive the doctors, and to be directed by their judgment. The bear at once made the bed, ran to the garden and gathered a handful of roses and orange blossoms, which she scattered upon the bed. She fulfilled her various duties so well that the queen said to herself, "This bear is worth a treasure, and my son is quite right in being fond of the beast."

When the prince returned to his chambers, and saw how well the bear had fulfilled her duties, it was like adding fuel to the fire. If he had been consumed himself in a slow fire before, he was now burning with intense heat. He said to the queen "Oh my lady mother, if I cannot give a kiss to this bear, I shall give up the ghost." The queen, seeing her son nearly fainting, said to the bear, "Kiss him, kiss him, oh my beautiful bear, do not leave my poor son to die in despair." Then the bear obediently neared the prince, who took her cheeks between his fingers, could not stop kissing her on the lips.

While thus engaged, I do not know how it happened, the bit of wood fell from Preziosa's mouth, and she remained in the prince's embrace, the most beautiful and ravishing being in the world. He strained her to his bosom with tightly clasped arms, and said, "You are caught at last, and you shall not escape so easily without a reason." Preziosa, reddening with the lovely tint of modesty and of shame, the most beautiful of natural beauties, answered, "I am in your hands. I surrender my honor to your loyalty. Do with me what you will." The queen asked who this charming woman was, and what had caused her to live such a wild life. She related to them all her misfortunes, and the queen praised her as a good and honored child, and said to her son that she was well satisfied that he should marry the princess. The prince, who wanted nothing else, at once announced his betrothal to her. Kneeling before the queen, they both received her blessing, and with great feasting the marriage took place. Thus Preziosa demonstrated the truth of the proverb:

Those who do good may expect good in return.[127]

All-Kinds-of-Fur

Jacob and Wilhelm Grimm

Once upon a time there was a king whose wife was the most beautiful woman in the world, with hair of pure gold. Together they had a daughter, and she was as beautiful as her mother, and she had the same golden hair. The queen became ill, and when she felt that she was about to die, she called the king to her side and asked him not to marry anyone following her death, unless she was just as beautiful as she, and unless her hair was just as golden as hers. The king made this promise, and she died.

For a long time the king was so grieved that he did not think about a second wife, but finally his councilors advised him to marry again. He sent messengers to all the princesses, but none was as beautiful as the deceased queen, and such golden hair could not be found anywhere in the world.

Then one day the king's glance fell on his daughter, and he saw that she looked just like her mother, and that she had the same golden hair. He thought to himself, "You will never find anyone in the world this beautiful. You will have to marry your daughter." And in that instant he felt such a strong love for her, that he im-

---

[127]Type 510B. Source: *The Pentameron of Giambattista Basile*, translated by Richard F. Burton (Privately printed, 1893), day 2, tale 6. Revised. Basile's *Il Pentamerone* was first published in five installments between 1634 and 1636.

mediately announced his decision to his councilors. They tried to dissuade him, but to no avail.[128]

The princess was horrified at his godless intentions, but because she was clever, she told the king that he should first get her three dresses: one as golden as the sun, one as white as the moon, one that glistened like the stars. Further, he was to get her a coat made from a thousand kinds of fur. Every animal in the kingdom would have to give up a piece of its skin for it.

The king was so fervent in his desires, that he had his huntsmen capture animals from across the entire kingdom. They were skinned, and a coat was made from their pelts. Thus, it did not take long before he brought the princess everything that she had asked for.

The princess said that she would marry him the next day. That night she sought out the presents that she had received from her fiancé: a golden ring, a little golden spinning wheel, and a little golden yarn reel.[129] She put the three dresses into a nutshell, blackened her hands and face with soot, put on the coat of all kinds of fur, and left. She walked the entire night until she came to a great forest. She would be safe there. Because she was tired, she sat down in a hollow tree and fell asleep.

She was still asleep the next day when the king, her fiancé, came to this forest to hunt. His dogs ran up to the tree and sniffed at it. The king sent his huntsmen to see what kind of animal was in the tree. They came back and said that it was a strange animal, the likes of which they had never seen before. It had every kind of fur on its skin, and it was lying there asleep. The king ordered them to capture it and to tie it onto the back of his carriage. As the huntsmen were doing this, they saw that it was a girl. They tied her onto the back of the carriage and rode home with her.

"All-Kinds-of-Fur," they said, "you are good for the kitchen. You can carry water and wood, and clean out the ashes." Then they gave her a little stall beneath

---

[128]Incest, one of our strongest taboos, has, until our own era, largely escaped exposure and discussion on the printed page. Publishers of folktales dealing with incest have gotten around the taboo in various ways. One of the most disingenuous solutions was used in the following passage from a nineteenth-century English "translation" of the Grimms' "All-Kinds-of-Fur":

Now, the King had a daughter, who was just as beautiful as her dead mother, and had just such golden hair. One day when she had grown up, her father looked at her, and saw that she was exactly like her mother, so he said to his councilors, "I will marry my daughter to one of you, and she shall be queen, for she is exactly like her dead mother, and when I die her husband shall be king." But when the Princess heard of her father's decision, she was not at all pleased, and said to him, "Before I do your bidding, I must have three dresses; one as golden as the sun, one as silver as the moon, and one as shining as the stars. Besides these, I want a cloak made of a thousand different kinds of skin; every animal in your kingdom must give a bit of his skin to it." But she thought to herself, "This will be quite impossible, and I shall not have to marry someone I do not care for." —Andrew Lang, *The Green Fairy Book* (London, ca. 1892), p. 276.

[129]Other versions of the story (including later Grimm editions) make it abundantly clear that the fiancé mentioned here is a different king, not her own father.

the steps, where the light of day never shone, and said, "This is where you can live and sleep."

So she had to help the cook in the kitchen. She plucked chickens, tended the fire, gathered vegetables, and did all the dirty work. Because she did very well at all this, the cook was good to her, and in the evening he often invited her in and gave her something to eat from the leftovers. Before the king went to bed, she had to go upstairs and pull off his boots. When she had pulled them off, he always threw them at her head.[130] Poor All-Kinds-of-Fur lived like this for a long time. Oh, you beautiful maiden, what will become of you?

Once there was a ball at the castle, and All-Kinds-of-Fur thought that she might see her fiancé once again, so she went to the cook and asked him if he would allow her to go upstairs a little and look in at the splendor from the doorway. "Go ahead," said the cook, "but do not stay longer than a half hour. You still have to clean out the ashes tonight."

Then All-Kinds-of-Fur took her little oil lamp and went to her stall where she washed off the soot. Her beauty came forth just like blossoms in the springtime. She took off the fur coat, opened up the nut and took out the dress that glistened like the sun. She put it on and went upstairs. Everyone made room for her, and thought that a noble princess had entered the hall. The king immediately invited her to dance, and as he danced with her, he thought how closely this unknown princess resembled his own fiancée. The longer he looked at her, the stronger the resemblance. He was almost certain that this was his fiancée, and at the end of the dance, he was going to ask her. However, when they finished dancing, she bowed, and before the king knew what was happening, she disappeared.

He asked the watchmen, but none of them had seen the princess leave the castle. She had run quickly to her stall, taken off the dress, blackened her hands and face, and put on the fur coat once again. Then she went to the kitchen to clean out the ashes, but the cook said, "Leave them until morning. I want to go upstairs and have a look at the dance. You make some soup for the king, but don't let any hairs fall into it, or there will be nothing more to eat for you."

All-Kinds-of-Fur made some bread soup for the king, then she put the golden ring in it that he had given her. When the ball was over, the king had his bread soup brought to him. It tasted better than any he had ever eaten. When he was finished, he found the ring on the bottom of the bowl. Looking at it carefully, he saw that it was his engagement ring. Astonished, he could not understand how it had gotten there. He summoned the cook, who then became very angry with All-Kinds-of-Fur. "You must have let a hair fall into the soup," he said. "If you did, there will be blows for you."

However, when the cook went upstairs, the king asked him who had made the soup, because it had been better than usual. The king had to confess that it had

---

[130]Beginning with the edition of 1819, the Grimms omitted this episode, apparently wanting to de-emphasize the abusive nature of the relationship between the two lovers. However, most versions of the tale describe how the "hero" belittles, and possibly beats the woman he will later marry.

been All-Kinds-of-Fur. Then the king had her sent up to him. "Who are you?" he asked upon her arrival. "What are you doing in my castle, and where did you get the ring that was lying in the soup?"

She answered, "I am only a poor child whose father and mother are dead. I have nothing, and I am good for nothing more than having boots thrown at my head. And I know nothing about the ring." With that she ran away.

Soon there was another ball. All-Kinds-of-Fur again asked the cook to allow her to go upstairs. The cook gave his permission, but only for a half hour, because by then she would have to be back in the kitchen to make the king's bread soup. All-Kinds-of-Fur went to her stall, washed herself clean, and took out the moon-dress. It was purer and brighter than newly fallen snow. When she arrived upstairs the dance had just begun. The king extended his hand to her, and danced with her, and no longer doubted that this was his fiancée, for no one else in the world had such golden hair. However, the princess immediately slipped out when the dance ended, and the king, in spite of his great effort, could not find her. Further, he had not spoken a single word with her.

She was All-Kinds-of-Fur once again, with blackened hands and face. She took her place in the kitchen and made bread soup for the king, while the cook went upstairs to have a look. When the soup was ready, she put the golden spinning wheel in it. The king ate the soup, and thought that it was even better this time. When he found the golden spinning wheel, he was even more astonished, because it had been a present from him to his fiancée some time ago. The cook was summoned again, and then All-Kinds-of-Fur, but once again she answered by saying that she knew nothing about it, and that she was there only to have boots thrown at her head.

For the third time, the king held a ball. He hoped that his fiancée would come again, and he would not let her escape this time. All-Kinds-of-Fur again asked the cook to allow her to go upstairs, but he scolded her, saying, "You are a witch. You are always putting things in the soup. And you can cook better than I can." But because she begged so, and promised to behave herself, he gave her permission to go upstairs for a half hour.

She put on the dress of stars. It glistened like stars in the night. She went upstairs and danced with the king, and he thought that he had never seen her more beautiful. While dancing, he slipped a ring onto her finger. He had ordered that it should be a very long dance. He could not bring himself to speak to her, nor could he keep her from escaping. As soon as the dance ended, she jumped into the crowd and disappeared before he could turn around.

She ran to her stall. Because she had been gone more than a half hour, she quickly took off her dress, and in her rush she failed to blacken herself entirely. One finger remained white. When she returned to the kitchen, the cook had already left. She quickly made some bread soup and put the golden yarn reel into it.

The king found it, just as he had found the ring and the golden spinning wheel, and now he knew for sure that his fiancée was nearby, for no one else could have had these presents. All-Kinds-of-Fur was summoned. Once again she tried to make an excuse and then run away, but as she ran by, the king noticed a white finger on her hand, and he held her fast. He found the ring that he had slipped onto her finger, and then he ripped off her fur coat. Her golden hair flowed out, and he saw that it was his dearly beloved fiancée. The cook received a generous reward. Then they got married and lived happily until they died.[131]

Fair Maria Wood

Italy

There was once a husband and wife who had but one child, a daughter. Now it happened that the wife fell ill and was at the point of death. Before dying she called her husband, and said to him, weeping, "I am dying; you are still young; if you ever wish to marry again, be mindful to choose a wife whom my wedding ring fits; and if you cannot find a lady whom it fits well, do not marry."

Her husband promised that he would do so. When she was dead he took off her wedding ring and kept it until he desired to marry again. Then he sought for someone to please him. He went from one to another, but the ring fitted no one. He tried so many but in vain. One day he thought of calling his daughter, and trying the ring on her to see whether it fitted her. The daughter said, "It is useless, dear father; you cannot marry me, because you are my father."

He did not heed her, put the ring on her finger, and saw that it fitted her well, and wanted to marry his daughter *nolens volens*. She did not oppose him, but consented. The day of the wedding, he asked her what she wanted. She said that she wished four silk dresses, the most beautiful that could be seen. He, who was a gentleman, gratified her wish and took her the four dresses, one handsomer than the other, and all the handsomest that had ever been seen.

"Now, what else do you want?" said he.

"I want another dress, made of wood, so that I can conceal myself in it." And at once he had this wooden dress made. She was well pleased. She waited until one day her husband was out of sight, put on the wooden dress, and under it the four silk dresses, and went away to a certain river not far off, and threw herself in it. Instead of sinking and drowning, she floated, for the wooden dress kept her up.

The water carried her a long way, when she saw on the bank a gentleman, and began to cry, "Who wants the fair Maria Wood?"

That gentleman who saw her on the water, and whom she addressed, called her and she came to the bank and saluted him.

"How is it that you are thus dressed in wood, and come floating on the water without drowning?"

---

[131]Type 510B. Source: *Kinder- und Hausmärchen*, 1st ed. (Berlin, 1812/1815), v. 1, no. 65.

She told him that she was a poor girl who had only that dress of wood, and that she wanted to go out to service.

"What can you do?"

"I can do all that is needed in a house, and if you would only take me for a servant you would be satisfied."

He took her to his house, where his mother was, and told her all that had happened, saying, "If you, dear mother, will take her as a servant, we can try her." In short, she took her and was pleased with this woman dressed in wood.

It happened that there were balls at that place which the best ladies and gentlemen attended. The gentleman who had the servant dressed in wood prepared to go to the ball, and after he had departed, the servant said to his mother, "Do me this kindness, mistress: let me go to the ball too, for I have never seen any dancing."

"What, you wish to go to the ball so badly dressed that they would drive you away as soon as they saw you!" The servant was silent and when the mistress was in bed, dressed herself in one of her silk dresses and became the most beautiful woman that was ever seen. She went to the ball, and it seemed as if the sun had entered the room; all were dazzled. She sat down near her master, who asked her to dance, and would dance with no one but her. She pleased him so much that he fell in love with her. He asked her who she was and where she came from. She replied that she came from a distance, but told him nothing more.

At a certain hour, without anyone perceiving it, she went out and disappeared. She returned home and put on her wooden dress again. In the morning the master returned from the ball, and said to his mother, "Oh! if you had only seen what a beautiful lady there was at the ball! She appeared like the sun, she was so beautiful and well dressed. She sat down near me, and would not dance with anyone but me."

His mother then said, "Did you not ask her who she was and where she came from?"

"She would only tell me that she came from a distance; but I thought I should die; I wish to go again this evening." The servant heard all this dialogue, but kept silent, pretending that the matter did not concern her.

In the evening he prepared himself again for the ball, and the servant said to him, "Master, yesterday evening I asked your mamma to let me, too, go to the ball, for I have never seen dancing, but she would not; will you have the kindness to let me go this evening?"

"Be still, you ugly creature, the ball is no place for you!"

"Do me this favor," she said, weeping, "I will stand out of doors, or under a bench, or in a corner so no one shall see me; but let me go!"

He grew angry then, and took a stick and began to beat the poor servant. She wept and remained silent.

After he had gone, she waited until his mother was in bed, and put on a dress finer than the first, and so rich as to astonish, and away to the ball! When she arrived all began to gaze at her, for they had never seen anything more beautiful. All the handsomest young men surrounded her and asked her to dance; but she would have nothing to do with anyone but her master. He again asked her who she was, and she said she would tell him later.

They danced and danced, and all at once she disappeared. Her master ran here and there, asked one and another, but no one could tell him where she had gone. He returned home and told his mother all that had passed. She said to him, "Do you know what you must do? Take this diamond ring, and when she dances with you give it to her; and if she takes it, it is a sign that she loves you." She gave him the ring. The servant listened, saw everything, and was silent.

In the evening the master prepared for the ball and the servant again asked him to take her, and again he beat her. He went to the ball, and after midnight, as before, the beautiful lady returned more beautiful than before, and as usual would dance only with her master. At the right moment he took out the diamond ring, and asked her if she would accept it. She took it and thanked him, and he was happy and satisfied. Afterward he asked her again who she was and where from. She said that she was of that country,

> That when they speak of going to a ball
> They are beaten on the head

and said no more. At the usual hour she stopped dancing and departed. He ran after her, but she went like the wind, and reached home without his finding out where she went. But he ran so in all directions, and was in such suffering, that when he reached home he was obliged to go to bed more dead than alive. Then he fell ill and grew worse every day, so that all said he would die. He did nothing but ask his mother and everyone if they knew anything of that lady, and that he would die if he did not see her. The servant heard everything; and one day, when he was very ill, what did she think of? She waited until her mistress's eye was turned, and dropped the diamond ring in the broth her master was to eat. No one saw her, and his mother took him the broth. He began to eat it, when he felt something hard, saw something shine, and took it out. You can imagine how he looked at it and recognized the diamond ring! They thought he would go mad. He asked his mother if that was the ring and she swore that it was, and all happy, she said that now he would see her again.

Meanwhile the servant went to her room, took off her wooden dress, and put on one all of silk, so that she appeared a beauty, and went to the room of the sick man. His mother saw her and began to cry, "Here she is; here she is!" She went in and saluted him, smiling, and he was so beside himself that he became well at once. He asked her to tell him her story: who she was, where she came from, how she came, and how she knew that he was ill.

She replied, "I am the woman dressed in wood who was your servant. It is not true that I was a poor girl, but I had that dress to conceal myself in, for underneath it I was the same that I am now. I am a lady; and although you treated me so badly when I asked to go to the ball, I saw that you loved me, and now I have come to save you from death." You can believe that they stayed to hear her story. They were married and have always been happy and still are.[132]

The Story of Catskin

England

There once was a gentleman grand,
Who lived at his country seat;
He wanted an heir to his land,
For he'd nothing but daughters yet.

His lady's again in the way,
So she said to her husband with joy,
"I hope some or other fine day,
To present you, my dear, with a boy."

The gentleman answered gruff,
"If't should turn out a maid or a mouse,
For of both we have more than enough,
She shan't stay to live in my house."

The lady, at this declaration,
Almost fainted away with pain;
But what was her sad consternation,
When a sweet little girl came again.

She sent her away to be nurs'd,
Without seeing her gruff papa;
And when she was old enough,
To a school she was packed away.

Fifteen summers are fled,
Now she left good Mrs. Jervis;
To see home she was forbid,
She determined to go and seek service.

---

[132]Type 510B. Source: Thomas Frederick Crane, *Italian Popular Tales* (Boston and New York, 1885), no. 10.

164

Her dresses so grand and so gay,
She carefully rolled in a knob;
Which she hid in a forest away,
And put on a catskin robe.

She knock'd at a castle gate,
And pray'd for charity;
They sent her some meat on a plate,
And kept her a scullion to be.

My lady look'd long in her face,
And prais'd her great beauty;
I'm sorry I've no better place,
And you must our scullion be.

So Catskin was under the cook,
A very sad life she led,
For often a ladle she took,
And broke poor Catskin's head.

There is now a grand ball to be,
When ladies their beauties show;
"Mrs. Cook," said Catskin, "dear me,
How much I should like to go!"

"You go with your catskin robe,
You dirty impudent slut!
Among the fine ladies and lords,
A very fine figure you'd cut."

A basin of water she took,
And dash'd in poor Catskin's face;
But briskly her ears she shook,
And went in her hiding place.

She washed every stain from her skin,
In some crystal waterfall;
Then put on a beautiful dress,
And hasted away to the ball.

When she entered, the ladies were mute,
Overcome by her figure and face;
But the lord, her young master, at once
Fell in love with her beauty and grace;

He pray'd her his partner to be,
She said, "Yes!" with a sweet smiling glance;
All night with no other lady
But Catskin, our young lord would dance.

"Pray tell me, fair maid, where you live?"
For now was the sad parting time;
But she no other answer would give,
Than this distich of mystical Rhyme,—

Kind sir, if the truth I must tell,
At the sign of the Basin of Water I dwell.

Then she flew from the ballroom, and put
On her catskin robe again;
And slipt in unseen by the cook,
Who little thought where she had been.

The young lord, the very next day,
To his mother his passion betrayed;
He declared he never would rest,
Till he'd found out this beautiful maid.

There's another grand ball to be,
Where ladies their beauties show;
"Mrs. Cook," said Catskin, "dear me,
How much I should like to go!"

"You go with your catskin robe,
You dirty impudent slut!
Among the fine ladies and lords,
A very fine figure you'd cut."

In a rage the ladle she took,
And broke poor Catkin's head;
But off she went shaking her ears,
And swift to her forest she fled.

She washed every blood stain off
In some crystal waterfall;
Put on a more beautiful dress,
And hasted away to the ball.

My lord, at the ballroom door,
Was waiting with pleasure and pain;
He longed to see nothing so much
As the beautiful Catskin again.

When he asked her to dance, she again
Said "Yes!" with her first smiling glance;
And again, all the night, my young Lord
With none but fair Catskin did dance.

"Pray tell me," said he, "where you live?"
For now 'twas the parting time;
But she no other answer would give,
Than this distich of mystical rhyme,—

Kind sir, if the truth I must tell,
At the sign of the Broken Ladle I dwell.

Then she flew from the ball, and put on
Her catskin robe again;
And slipt in unseen by the cook,
Who little thought where she had been.

My lord did again, the next day,
Declare to his mother his mind,
That he never more happy should be,
Unless he his charmer should find.

Now another grand ball is to be,
Where ladies their beauties show;
"Mrs. Cook", said Catskin, "dear me,
How much I should like to go!"

"You go with your catskin robe,
You impudent, dirty slut!
Among the find ladies and lords,
A very fine figure you'd cut."

In a fury she took the skimmer,
And broke poor Catskin's head;
But heart-whole and lively as ever,
Away to her forest she fled.

She washed the stains of blood
In some crystal waterfall;
Then put on her most beautiful dress,
And hasted away to the ball.

My lord, at the ballroom door,
Was waiting with pleasure and pain;
He longed to see nothing so much
As the beautiful Catskin again.

When he asked her to dance, she again
Said "Yes!" with her first smiling glance;
And all the night long, my young Lord
With none but fair Catskin would dance.

"Pray tell me, fair maid, where you live?"
For now was the parting time;
But she no other answer would give,
Than this distich of mystical rhyme,—

Kind sir, if the truth I must tell,
At the sign of the Broken Skimmer I dwell.

Then she flew from the hall, and threw on
Her catskin cloak again;
And slipt in unseen by the cook,
Who little thought where she had been.

But not by my lord unseen,
For this time he followed too fast;
And, hid in the forest green,
Saw the strange things that past.

Next day he took to his bed,
And sent for the doctor to come;
And begg'd him no other than Catskin,
Might come into his room.

He told him how dearly he lov'd her,
Not to have her his heart would break;
Then the doctor kindly promised
To the proud old lady to speak.

There's a struggle of pride and love,
For she fear'd her son would die;
But pride at the last did yield,
And love had the mastery.

Then my lord got quickly well,
When he was his charmer to wed;
And Catskin, before a twelvemonth,
Of a young lord was brought to bed.

To a wayfaring woman and child,
Lady Catskin one day sent an alms;
The nurse did the errand, and carried
The sweet little lord in her arms.

The child gave the alms to the child,
This was seen by the old lady mother;
"Only see," said that wicked old woman,
"How the beggars' brats take to each other!"

This throw went to Catskin's heart,
She flung herself down on her knees,
And pray'd her young master and lord
To seek out her parents would please.

They sent out in my lord's own coach;
They traveled, but naught befell
Till they reach'd the town hard by
Where Catskin's father did dwell.

They put up at the head inn,
Where Catskin was left alone;
But my lord went to try if her father
His natural child would own.

When folks are away, in short time
What great alterations appear;
For the cold touch of death had all chill'd
The hearts of her sisters dear.

Her father repented too late,
And the loss of his youngest bemoan'd;
In his old and childless state,
He his pride and cruelty own'd.

The old gentleman sat by the fire,
And hardly looked up at my lord;
He had no hope of comfort
A stranger could afford.

But my lord drew a chair close by,
And said, in a feeling tone,
"Have you not, sir, a daughter, I pray,
You never would see or own?"

The old man alarm'd, cried aloud,
"A hardened sinner am I!
I would give all my worldly goods,
To see her before I die."

Then my lord brought his wife and child
To their home and parent's face,
Who fell down and thanks returned
To God, for his mercy and grace.

The bells, ringing up in the tower,
Are sending a sound to the heart;
There's a charm in the old church bells,
Which nothing in life can impart.[133]

The Girl without Hands

Jacob and Wilhelm Grimm

A miller, who was so poor that he had nothing more than his mill and a large apple tree which stood behind it, went into the forest to gather wood. There he was approached by an old man, who said, "Why do you torment yourself so? I will make you rich if you will sign over to me that which is standing behind your mill. I will come and claim it in three years." The miller thought, "That is my apple tree," agreed, and signed it over to the man. When he came home, his wife said to him, "Miller, where did all the wealth come from that suddenly has filled every chest and cupboard in our house?"

"I received it from an old man in the forest by signing over to him that which is standing behind the mill."

"Man!" said the woman, terrified. "This is going to be very bad. The old man was the devil, and he had our daughter in mind, who was just then standing behind the mill sweeping the yard."

Now the miller's daughter was very beautiful and pious. Three years later when the devil came, early in the morning, and wanted to take her, she had drawn a circle around herself with chalk and had washed herself clean. Therefore the devil could not approach her, and angrily he said to the miller, "Keep wash water away from her, so she cannot wash herself any more, and I can have power over her." The miller was frightened and did what he was told. The next day the devil returned, but she had wept into her hands and washed herself with her tears, and was entirely clean. Because the devil still could not approach her, he was very angry, and ordered the miller, "Chop off her hands, so I can get to her."

The miller was horrified and answered, "How could I chop off my dear child's hands? No, I will not do it."

"Then do you know what? I will take you, if you don't do it!"

That frightened the miller terribly, and driven by fear he promised to do what the devil had ordered. He went to his daughter and said, "My child, the devil will take

---

[133]Type 510B. Source: James Orchard Halliwell, *The Nursery Rhymes of England* (London, 1853), pp. 22-31.

me if I don't chop off both your hands, and I have promised him that I will do it. I beg for your forgiveness."

"Father," she said, "do with me what you will," stretched forth her hands, and let him chop them off. The devil came a third time, but she had wept so long onto her stumps, that she was still entirely clean, and the devil had lost all power over her.

The miller, because he had become so wealthy through her, promised to take the best care of her for the rest of her life, but she did not want to remain there. "I must leave here," she said. "Compassionate people will give me enough to keep me alive." She had the chopped-off hands tied to her back, and she set forth with the rising sun, walking the entire day until evening, when she came to the king's garden. There was a gap in the garden hedge. She went inside, found a fruit tree, shook it with her body until the apples fell to the ground, bent over and picked them up with her teeth, and ate them. Thus she lived for two days, but on the third day the garden watchmen saw her, captured her, and threw her into prison.

The next morning she was brought before the king and sentenced to be banished from the land, but the prince said, "Wait, wouldn't it be better to let her tend the chickens in the courtyard?" So she stayed there for a time and tended the chickens. The prince saw her often and grew very fond of her.

Meanwhile the time came when he was to get married. Messengers were sent everywhere in the world to find him a beautiful bride. "You needn't look so far and wide," he said. "I know where one is very nearby."

The old king pondered this back and forth, but he could not think of a single maiden in his kingdom who was both beautiful and rich, "You surely don't want to marry the one who tends the chickens in the courtyard?" But his son declared that he would marry no one else, so finally the king had to agree. Soon afterward he died, and the prince succeeded him as king and lived happily for a time with his wife.

Once the king had to go away to war, and during his absence his wife gave birth to a beautiful child. She sent a messenger with a letter telling her husband the joyful news. On the way the messenger stopped to rest by a brook and fell asleep. The devil, who was still trying to harm her, came to him and exchanged the letter with one that stated that the queen had given birth to a changeling. The king was very saddened to read this, but he wrote that the queen and the child should be well cared for until his return. The messenger started back with this letter. When he stopped to rest at the same spot and fell asleep, the devil again appeared, this time exchanging the king's letter with one that ordered the queen and the child to be driven from the kingdom. This had to be done, however much the people all wept with sorrow.

"I did not come here to become queen," she said. "I have no luck, and I demand none. Just tie my child and my hands onto my back, and I will set forth into the world." That evening she came to a place in a thick forest where a good old man was sitting by a spring. "Be so kindhearted as to hold my child to my breast until I have nursed him," she said.

The man did that, after which he said to her, "Go to that thick tree over there and wrap your maimed arms around it three times!" And when she had done this, her hands grew back on. Then he showed her a house. "You can live there," he said, "but do not go outside, and do not open the door for anyone unless he asks three times to come in, for God's sake."

Meanwhile the king returned home and discovered how he had been deceived. Accompanied by a single servant he set forth, and after a long journey he finally happened, one night, into the same forest where the queen was living, but he did not know that she was so close to him. "There is a little light from a house back there," said his servant. "We can rest there."

"No," said the king. "I do not want to rest so long, but rather to continue searching for my wife. I cannot rest until I find her." But the servant begged so much and complained so about his weariness that out of compassion, the king gave in. When they came to the house, the moon was shining, and they saw the queen standing by the window. "That must be our queen; she looks just like her," said the servant, "but I see now that she is not the one, for this one has hands." The servant asked her for shelter, but she refused, because he had not asked "for God's sake." He was about to go on and seek another place for their night's lodging when the king himself came up and said, "Let me in, for God's sake!"

"I cannot let you in until you have asked me three time, for God's sake," she replied. And after the king had asked two more times, she opened the door. His little son ran to him and led him in to his mother. The king recognized her immediately as his beloved wife. The next morning they all journeyed together back to their kingdom, and as soon as they had left the house, it disappeared behind them.[134]

---

[134]Type 706. Source: *Kinder- und Hausmärchen*, 1st ed. (Berlin, 1812/1815), v. 1, no. 31.

Coming of Age

Girls Become Women

Rapunzel

Jacob and Wilhelm Grimm

Once upon a time there was a man and a woman who had long wished for a child but had never received one. Finally, however, the woman came to be with child. Through the rear window of these people's house they could see into a fairy's garden that was filled with flowers and herbs of all kinds. No one dared enter this garden.

One day the woman was standing at this window, and she saw the most beautiful rapunzel[135] in a bed. She longed for some, but not knowing how to get any, she became miserably ill. Her husband was frightened, and asked her why she was doing so poorly. "Oh, if I do not get some rapunzel from the garden behind our house, I shall surely die," she said.

The man, who loved her dearly, decided to get her some, whatever the cost. One night he climbed over the high wall, hastily dug up a handful of rapunzel, and took it to his wife. She immediately made a salad from it, which she devoured greedily. It tasted so good to her that by the next day her desire for more had grown threefold. The man saw that there would be no peace for him, so once again he climbed into the garden. To his horror, the fairy was standing there. She scolded him fiercely for daring to enter and steal from her garden. He excused himself as best he could with his wife's pregnancy, and how it would be dangerous to deny her anything. Finally the fairy spoke, "I will accept your excuse and even let you take as much rapunzel as you want, if you will give me the child that your wife is now carrying.

In his fear the man agreed to everything. When the woman gave birth, the fairy appeared, named the little girl Rapunzel, and took her away.

---

[135]The German word "Rapunzel" is defined variously as "field salad," "corn salad" or "lamb's lettuce."

This Rupunzel became the most beautiful child under the sun, but when she was twelve years old, the fairy locked her in a high tower that had neither a door nor a stairway, but only a tiny little window at the very top. When the fairy wanted to enter she stood below and called out:

Rapunzel, Rapunzel!
Let down your hair.

Rapunzel had splendid hair, as fine as spun gold. When the fairy called out, she untied it, wound it around a window hook, let it fall twenty yards to the ground, and the fairy climbed up it.

One day a young prince came through the forest where the tower stood. He saw the beautiful Rapunzel standing at her window, heard her sing with her sweet voice, and fell in love with her. Because there was no door in the tower and no ladder was tall enough to reach her, he fell into despair. He came to the forest every day, until once he saw the fairy, who said:

Rapunzel, Rapunzel!
Let down your hair.

Then he knew which ladder would get him into the tower. He remembered the words that he would have to speak, and the next day, as soon as it was dark, he went to the tower and called upward:

Rapunzel, Rapunzel!
Let down your hair.

She let her hair fall. He tied himself to it and was pulled up.

At first Rapunzel was frightened, but soon she came to like the young king so well that she arranged for him to come every day and be pulled up. Thus they lived in joy and pleasure for a long time, and the fairy did not discover what was happening until one day Rapunzel said to her, "Frau Gotel, tell me why it is that my clothes are all too tight. They no longer fit me."

"You godless child" said the fairy. "What am I hearing from you?" And she immediately saw how she had been deceived and was terribly angry. She took Rapunzel's beautiful hair, wrapped it a few times around her left hand, grabbed a pair of scissors with her right hand, and snip snip, cut it off. Then she sent Rapunzel into a wilderness where she suffered greatly and where, after a time, she gave birth to twins, a boy and a girl.

On the evening of the same day that she sent Rapunzel away, the fairy tied the hair to the hook at the top of the tower, and when the prince called out:

Rapunzel, Rapunzel!
Let down your hair!

she let down the hair. The prince was startled to find the fairy instead of his beloved Rapunzel. "Do you know what, evil one?" cried the angry fairy. "You have lost Rapunzel forever!"

174

The prince, in his despair, threw himself from the tower. He escaped with his life, but he lost his eyesight in the fall. Sorrowfully he wandered about in the forest weeping and, eating nothing but grass and roots. Some years later he happened into the wilderness where Rapunzel lived miserably with her children. She thought that his voice was familiar. She recognized him instantly and threw her arms around his neck. Two of her tears fell into his eyes, and they became clear once again, and he could see as well as before.[136]

The False Grandmother

France

Once upon a time a girl was walking through the woods with a basket of goodies for her grandmother, when she met a wolf.

"Good day," said the wolf. "Where are you going so early in the morning?"

Now the girl did not know that the wolf was a wicked animal, so she told him that she was going to visit her grandmother, who lived on the other side of the woods. She continued merrily on her way. The wicked wolf ran on ahead and arrived at the grandmother's house before the girl. He crept inside, leaped on the poor grandmother, and ate her up, saving only a pitcher of blood and a piece of flesh. He then climbed into the grandmother's bed, and waited for the girl. The girl soon arrived, and knocked at the door.

"Just let yourself in," said the wolf, disguising his voice. "You must be hungry from your long walk through the woods. Do eat some of the meat that's on the kitchen table.

And the girl ate from her grandmother's flesh.

"You must be thirsty from your long walk through the woods. Do drink from the pitcher that's on the kitchen table.

And the girl drank from her grandmother's blood.

"You must be tired from your long walk through the woods. Do come to bed with me.

And the girl climbed into bed with the wolf.

She soon saw that it was not her grandmother in the bed with her, and she became frightened. Not knowing how else to escape, she said, "I have to go to the privy."

"You can just do it in the bed," answered the wicked wolf.

"I don't have to go little. I have to go big," said the girl.

---

[136]Type 310. Source: *Kinder- und Hausmärchen*, 1st ed. (Berlin, 1812/1815), v. 1, no. 12.

"All right," said the wolf, "but hurry right back as soon as you are done.

The girl ran out of the house, and she ran past the privy, and she ran through the woods, and she did not stop until she was safely back at home.[137]

Little Red Riding Hood

Charles Perrault

Once upon a time there lived in a certain village a little country girl, the prettiest creature who was ever seen. Her mother was excessively fond of her; and her grandmother doted on her still more. This good woman had a little red riding hood made for her. It suited the girl so extremely well that everybody called her Little Red Riding Hood.

One day her mother, having made some cakes, said to her, "Go, my dear, and see how your grandmother is doing, for I hear she has been very ill. Take her a cake, and this little pot of butter."

Little Red Riding Hood set out immediately to go to her grandmother, who lived in another village.

As she was going through the wood, she met with a wolf, who had a very great mind to eat her up, but he dared not, because of some woodcutters working nearby in the forest. He asked her where she was going. The poor child, who did not know that it was dangerous to stay and talk to a wolf, said to him, "I am going to see my grandmother and carry her a cake and a little pot of butter from my mother."

"Does she live far off?" said the wolf

"Oh I say," answered Little Red Riding Hood; "it is beyond that mill you see there, at the first house in the village."

"Well," said the wolf, "and I'll go and see her too. I'll go this way and go you that, and we shall see who will be there first."

The wolf ran as fast as he could, taking the shortest path, and the little girl took a roundabout way, entertaining herself by gathering nuts, running after butterflies, and gathering bouquets of little flowers. It was not long before the wolf arrived at the old woman's house. He knocked at the door: tap, tap.

"Who's there?"

"Your grandchild, Little Red Riding Hood," replied the wolf, counterfeiting her voice; "who has brought you a cake and a little pot of butter sent you by mother."

The good grandmother, who was in bed, because she was somewhat ill, cried out, "Pull the bobbin, and the latch will go up."

---

[137]Type 333. Retold from A. Millien, *Mélusine*, v. 3 (1886-1887), col. 428-429.

The wolf pulled the bobbin, and the door opened, and then he immediately fell upon the good woman and ate her up in a moment, for it been more than three days since he had eaten. He then shut the door and got into the grandmother's bed, expecting Little Red Riding Hood, who came some time afterwards and knocked at the door: tap, tap.

"Who's there?"

Little Red Riding Hood, hearing the big voice of the wolf, was at first afraid; but believing her grandmother had a cold and was hoarse, answered, "It is your grandchild Little Red Riding Hood, who has brought you a cake and a little pot of butter mother sends you."

The wolf cried out to her, softening his voice as much as he could, "Pull the bobbin, and the latch will go up."

Little Red Riding Hood pulled the bobbin, and the door opened.

The wolf, seeing her come in, said to her, hiding himself under the bedclothes, "Put the cake and the little pot of butter upon the stool, and come get into bed with me."

Little Red Riding Hood took off her clothes and got into bed. She was greatly amazed to see how her grandmother looked in her nightclothes, and said to her, "Grandmother, what big arms you have!"

"All the better to hug you with, my dear."

"Grandmother, what big legs you have!"

"All the better to run with, my child."

"Grandmother, what big ears you have!"

"All the better to hear with, my child."

"Grandmother, what big eyes you have!"

"All the better to see with, my child."

"Grandmother, what big teeth you have got!"

"All the better to eat you up with."

And, saying these words, this wicked wolf fell upon Little Red Riding Hood, and ate her all up.

> Moral: Children, especially attractive, well bred young ladies, should never talk to strangers, for if they should do so, they may well provide dinner for a wolf. I say "wolf," but there are various kinds of wolves. There are also those who are charming, quiet, polite, unassuming, complacent, and sweet, who pursue young women at home and in the streets. And unfortunately, it is these gentle wolves who are the most dangerous ones of all.[138]

---

[138]Type 333. Source: Andrew Lang, *The Blue Fairy Book* (London, ca. 1889), pp. 51-53. Lang's source: Charles Perrault, *Histoires ou contes du temps passé, avec des moralités: Contes de ma mère l'Oye* (Paris, 1697).

Little Red Cap

Jacob and Wilhelm Grimm

Once upon a time there was a sweet little girl. Everyone who saw her liked her, but most of all her grandmother, who did not know what to give the child next. Once she gave her a little cap made of red velvet. Because it suited her so well, and she wanted to wear it all the time, she came to be known as Little Red Cap.

One day her mother said to her, "Come Little Red Cap. Here is a piece of cake and a bottle of wine. Take them to your grandmother. She is sick and weak, and they will do her well. Mind your manners and give her my greetings. Behave yourself on the way, and do not leave the path, or you might fall down and break the glass, and then there will be nothing for your sick grandmother."

Little Red Cap promised to obey her mother. The grandmother lived out in the woods, a half hour from the village. When Little Red Cap entered the woods a wolf came up to her. She did not know what a wicked animal he was, and was not afraid of him.

"Good day to you, Little Red Cap."

"Thank you, wolf."

"Where are you going so early, Little Red Cap?"

"To grandmother's."

"And what are you carrying under your apron?"

"Grandmother is sick and weak, and I am taking her some cake and wine. We baked yesterday, and they should give her strength."

"Little Red Cap, just where does your grandmother live?"

"A good quarter hour from here in the woods, under the three large oak trees. There's a hedge of hazel bushes there. You must know the house," said Little Red Cap.

The wolf thought to himself, "Now there is a tasty bite for me. Just how are you going to catch her?" Then he said, "Listen, Little Red Cap, haven't you seen the beautiful flowers that are blossoming in the woods? Why don't you go and take a look? And you're not listening to the birds singing. You are walking along as though you were on your way to school in the village. It is very beautiful in the woods."

Little Red Cap opened her eyes and saw the sunlight breaking through the trees and how the ground was covered with beautiful flowers. She thought, "If a take a bouquet to grandmother, she will be very pleased. Anyway, it is still early, and I'll be home on time." And she ran off into the woods looking for flowers. Each time she picked one she thought that she could see an even more beautiful one a little way off, and she ran after it, going further and further into the woods. But the wolf ran straight to the grandmother's house and knocked on the door.

"Who's there?"

"Little Red Cap. I'm bringing you some cake and wine. Open the door for me."

"Just press the latch," called out the grandmother. "I'm too weak to get up."

The wolf pressed the latch, and the door opened. He stepped inside, went straight to the grandmother's bed, and ate her up. Then he took her clothes, put them on, and put her cap on his head. He got into her bed and pulled the curtains shut.

Little Red Cap had run after flowers, and did not continue on her way to grandmother's until she had gathered all that she could carry. When she arrived, she found, to her surprise, that the door was open. She walked into the parlor, and everything looked so strange that she thought, "Oh, my God, why am I so afraid? I usually like it at grandmother's." Then she went to the bed and pulled back the curtains. Grandmother was lying there with her cap pulled down over her face and looking very strange.

"Oh, grandmother, what big ears you have!"

"All the better to hear you with."

"Oh, grandmother, what big eyes you have!"

"All the better to see you with."

"Oh, grandmother, what big hands you have!"

"All the better to grab you with!"

"Oh, grandmother, what a horribly big mouth you have!"

"All the better to eat you with!" And with that he jumped out of bed, jumped on top of poor Little Red Cap, and ate her up. As soon as the wolf had finished this tasty bite, he climbed back into bed, fell asleep, and began to snore very loudly.

A huntsman was just passing by. He thought it strange that the old woman was snoring so loudly, so he decided to take a look. He stepped inside, and in the bed there lay the wolf that he had been hunting for such a long time. "He has eaten the grandmother, but perhaps she still can be saved. I won't shoot him," thought the huntsman. So he took a pair of scissors and cut open his belly.

He had cut only a few strokes when he saw the red cap shining through. He cut a little more, and the girl jumped out and cried, "I was so frightened! It was so dark inside the wolf's body!" And then the grandmother came out alive as well. Then Little Red Cap fetched some large heavy stones. They filled the wolf's body with them, and when he woke up and tried to run away, the stones were so heavy that he fell down dead.

The three of them were happy. The huntsman took the wolf's pelt. Grandmother ate the cake and drank the wine that Little Red Cap had brought. And Little Red Cap said to herself, "As long as I live, I will never leave the path and run off into the woods by myself if mother tells me not to."

They also tell how Little Red Cap was taking some baked things to her grandmother another time, when another wolf spoke to her and wanted her to leave the path. But Little Red Cap took care and went straight to grandmother's. She told her that she had seen the wolf, and that he had wished her a good day, but had stared at her in a wicked manner. "If we hadn't been on a public street, he would have eaten me up," she said.

"Come," said the grandmother. "Let's lock the door, so he can't get in." Soon afterward the wolf knocked on the door and called out, "Open up, grandmother. It's Little Red Cap, and I'm bringing you some baked things."

They remained silent, and did not open the door. The wicked one walked around the house several times, and finally jumped onto the roof. He wanted to wait until Little Red Cap went home that evening, then follow her and eat her up in the darkness. But the grandmother saw what he was up to. There was a large stone trough in front of the house. "Fetch a bucket, Little Red Cap," she said. "Yesterday I cooked some sausage. Carry the water that I boiled them with to the trough." Little Red Cap carried water until the large, large trough was clear full. The smell of sausage arose into the wolf's nose. He sniffed and looked down, stretching his neck so long that he began to slide. He slid off the roof, fell into the trough, and drowned. And Little Red Cap returned home happily and safely.[139]

Sun, Moon, and Talia

Giambattista Basile

There once lived a great lord, who was blessed with the birth of a daughter, whom he named Talia. He sent for the wise men and astrologers in his lands, to predict her future. They met, counseled together, and cast her horoscope, and at length they came to the conclusion that she would incur great danger from a splinter of flax. Her father therefore forbade that any flax, hemp, or any other material of that sort be brought into his house, so that she should escape the predestined danger.

One day, when Talia had grown into a young and beautiful lady, she was looking out of a window, when she beheld passing that way an old woman, who was spinning. Talia, never having seen a distaff or a spindle, was pleased to see the twirling spindle, and she was so curious as to what thing it was, that she asked the old woman to come to her. Taking the distaff from her hand, she began to stretch the flax. Unfortunately, Talia ran a splinter of flax under her nail, and she fell dead upon the ground. When the old woman saw this, she became frightened and ran down the stairs, and is running still.

As soon as the wretched father heard of the disaster which had taken place, he had them, after having paid for this tub of sour wine with casks of tears, lay her out in one of his country mansions. There they seated her on a velvet throne under a canopy of brocade. Wanting to forget all and to drive from his memory his great

---

[139]Type 333. Source: *Kinder- und Hausmärchen*, 1st ed. (Berlin, 1812/1815), v. 1, no. 26.

misfortune, he closed the doors and abandoned forever the house where he had suffered this great loss.

After a time, it happened by chance that a king was out hunting and passed that way. One of his falcons escaped from his hand and flew into the house by way of one of the windows. It did not come when called, so the king had one of his party knock at the door, believing the palace to be inhabited. Although he knocked for a length of time, nobody answered, so the king had them bring a vintner's ladder, for he himself would climb up and search the house, to discover what was inside. Thus he climbed up and entered, and looked in all the rooms, and nooks, and corners, and was amazed to find no living person there. At last he came to the salon, and when the king beheld Talia, who seemed to be enchanted, he believed that she was asleep, and he called her, but she remained unconscious. Crying aloud, he beheld her charms and felt his blood course hotly through his veins. He lifted her in his arms, and carried her to a bed, where he gathered the first fruits of love. Leaving her on the bed, he returned to his own kingdom, where, in the pressing business of his realm, he for a time thought no more about this incident.

Now after nine months Talia delivered two beautiful children, one a boy and the other a girl. In them could be seen two rare jewels, and they were attended by two fairies, who came to that palace, and put them at their mother's breasts. Once, however, they sought the nipple, and not finding it, began to suck on Talia's fingers, and they sucked so much that the splinter of flax came out. Talia awoke as if from a long sleep, and seeing beside her two priceless gems, she held them to her breast, and gave them the nipple to suck, and the babies were dearer to her than her own life. Finding herself alone in that palace with two children by her side, she did not know what had happened to her; but she did notice that the table was set, and food and drink were brought in to her, although she did not see any attendants.

In the meanwhile the king remembered Talia, and saying that he wanted to go hunting, he returned to the palace, and found her awake, and with two cupids of beauty. He was overjoyed, and he told Talia who he was, and how he had seen her, and what had taken place. When she heard this, their friendship was knitted with tighter bonds, and he remained with her for a few days. After that time he bade her farewell, and promised to return soon, and take her with him to his kingdom. And he went to his realm, but he could not find any rest, and at all hours he had in his mouth the names of Talia, and of Sun and Moon (those were the two children's names), and when he took his rest, he called either one or other of them.

Now the king's wife began to suspect that something was wrong from the delay of her husband while hunting, and hearing him name continually Talia, Sun, and Moon, she became hot with another kind of heat than the sun's. Sending for the secretary, she said to him, "Listen to me, my son, you are living between two rocks, between the post and the door, between the poker and the grate. If you will tell me with whom the king your master, and my husband, is in love, I will give you treasures untold; and if you hide the truth from me, you will never be found again, dead or alive." The man was terribly frightened. Greed and fear blinded his eyes to all honor and to all sense of justice, and he related to her all things, calling bread bread, and wine wine.

The queen, hearing how matters stood, sent the secretary to Talia, in the name of the king, asking her to send the children, for he wished to see them. Talia, with great joy, did as she was commanded. Then the queen, with a heart of Medea, told the cook to kill them, and to make them into several tasteful dishes for her wretched husband. But the cook was tender hearted and, seeing these two beautiful golden apples, felt pity and compassion for them, and he carried them home to his wife, and had her hide them. In their place he prepared two lambs into a hundred different dishes. When the king came, the queen, with great pleasure, had the food served. The king ate with delight, saying, "By the life of Lanfusa, how tasteful this is"; or, "By the soul of my ancestors, this is good." Each time she replied, "Eat, eat, you are eating of your own." For two or three times the king paid no attention to this repetition, but at last seeing that the music continued, he answered, "I know perfectly well that I am eating of my own, because you have brought nothing into this house"; and growing angry, he got up and went to a villa at some distance from his palace, to solace his soul and alleviate his anger.

In the meanwhile the queen, not being satisfied of the evil already done, sent for the secretary and told him to go to the palace and to bring Talia back, saying that the king longed for her presence and was expecting her. Talia departed as soon as she heard these words, believing that she was following the commands of her lord, for she greatly longed to see her light and joy, knowing not what was preparing for her. She was met by the queen, whose face glowed from the fierce fire burning inside her, and looked like the face of Nero. She addressed her thus, "Welcome, Madam Busybody! You are a fine piece of goods, you ill weed, who are enjoying my husband. So you are the lump of filth, the cruel bitch, that has caused my head to spin? Change your ways, for you are welcome in purgatory, where I will compensate you for all the damage you have done to me." Talia, hearing these words, began to excuse herself, saying that it was not her fault, because the king her husband had taken possession of her territory when she was drowned in sleep; but the queen would not listen to her excuses, and had a large fire lit in the courtyard of the palace, and commanded that Talia should be cast into it.

The lady, perceiving that matters had taken a bad turn, knelt before the queen, and begged her to allow her at least to take off the garments she wore. The queen, not for pity of the unhappy lady, but to gain also those robes, which were embroidered with gold and pearls, told her to undress, saying, "You can take off your clothes. I agree." Talia began to take them off, and with every item that she removed she uttered a loud scream. Having taken off her robe, her skirt, the bodice, and her shift, she was on the point of removing her last garment, when she uttered a last scream louder than the rest. They dragged her towards the pile, to reduce her to lye ashes which would be used to wash Charon's breeches.

The king suddenly appeared, and finding this spectacle, demanded to know what was happening. He asked for his children, and his wife—reproaching him for his treachery—told him that she had had them slaughtered and served to him as meat. When the wretched king heard this, he gave himself up to despair, saying, "Alas! Then I, myself, am the wolf of my own sweet lambs. Alas! And why did these my veins know not the fountains of their own blood? You renegade bitch, what evil deed is this which you have done? Begone, you shall get your desert as the stumps, and I will not send such a tyrant-faced one to the Coliseum to do her penance!"

So saying, he commanded that the queen should be cast into the fire which she had prepared for Talia, and the secretary with her, because he had been the handle for this bitter play, and weaver of this wicked plot. He was going to do the same with the cook, whom he believed to be the slaughterer of his children, when the man cast himself at his feet, saying, "In truth, my lord, for such a deed, there should be nothing else than a pile of living fire, and no other help than a spear from behind, and no other entertainment than twisting and turning within the blazing fire, and I should seek no other honor than to have my ashes, the ashes of a cook, mixed up with the queen's. But this is not the reward that I expect for having saved the children, in spite of the gall of that bitch, who wanted to kill them and to return to your body that which was of your own body."

Hearing these words, the king was beside himself. He thought he was dreaming, and he could not believe what his own ears had heard. Therefore, turning to the cook, he said, "If it is true that you have saved my children, be sure that I will take you away from turning the spit, and I will put you in the kitchen of this breast, to turn and twist as you like all my desires, giving you such a reward as shall enable you to call yourself a happy man in this world." While the king spoke these words, the cook's wife, seeing her husband's need, brought forth the two children, Sun and Moon, before their father. And he never tired at playing the game of three with his wife and children, making a mill wheel of kisses, now with one and then with the other. He gave a generous reward to the cook, he made him a chamberlain. He married Talia to wife; and she enjoyed a long life with her husband and her children, thus experiencing the truth of the proverb:

> Those whom fortune favors
> Find good luck even in their sleep.[140]

---

[140]Type 410. Source: *The Pentameron of Giambattista Basile*, translated by Richard F. Burton (Privately printed, 1893), day 5, tale 5.

Little Briar-Rose

Jacob and Wilhelm Grimm

A king and queen had no children, although they wanted one very much. Then one day while the queen was sitting in her bath, a crab[141] crept out of the water onto the ground and said, "Your wish will soon be fulfilled, and you will bring a daughter into the world." And that is what happened.

The king was so happy about the birth of the princess that he held a great celebration. He also invited the fairies who lived in his kingdom, but because he had only twelve golden plates, one had to be left out, for there were thirteen of them.

The fairies came to the celebration, and as it was ending they presented the child with gifts. The one promised her virtue, the second one gave beauty, and so on, each one offering something desirable and magnificent. The eleventh fairy had just presented her gift when the thirteenth fairy walked in. She was very angry that she had not been invited and cried out, "Because you did not invite me, I tell you that in her fifteenth year, your daughter will prick herself with a spindle and fall over dead."

The parents were horrified, but the twelfth fairy, who had not yet offered her wish, said, "It shall not be her death. She will only fall into a hundred-year sleep." The king, hoping to rescue his dear child, issued an order that all spindles in the entire kingdom should be destroyed.

The princess grew and became a miracle of beauty. One day, when she had just reached her fifteenth year, the king and queen went away, leaving her all alone in the castle. She walked from room to room, following her heart's desire. Finally she came to an old tower. A narrow stairway led up to it. Being curious, she climbed up until she came to a small door. There was a small yellow key in the door. She turned it, and the door sprang open. She found herself in a small room where an old woman sat spinning flax. She was attracted to the old woman, and joked with her, and said that she too would like to try her hand at spinning. She picked up the spindle, but no sooner did she touch it, than she pricked herself with it and then fell down into a deep sleep.

At that same moment the king and his attendants returned, and everyone began to fall asleep: the horses in the stalls, the pigeons on the roof, the dogs in the courtyard, the flies on the walls. Even the fire on the hearth flickered, stopped moving, and fell asleep. The roast stopped sizzling. The cook let go of the kitchen boy, whose hair he was about to pull. The maid dropped the chicken that she was plucking. They all slept. And a thorn hedge grew up around the entire castle, growing higher and higher, until nothing at all could be seen of it.

Princes, who had heard about the beautiful Briar-Rose, came and tried to free her, but they could not penetrate the hedge. It was as if the thorns were firmly at-

---

[141]In some versions (including later Grimm editions) this harbinger of pregnancy is a frog.

tached to hands. The princes became stuck in them, and they died miserably. And thus it continued for many long years.

Then one day a prince was traveling through the land. An old man told him about the belief that there was a castle behind the thorn hedge, with a wonderfully beautiful princess asleep inside with all of her attendants. His grandfather had told him that many princes had tried to penetrate the hedge, but that they had gotten stuck in the thorns and had been pricked to death.

"I'm not afraid of that," said the prince. "I shall penetrate the hedge and free the beautiful Briar-Rose." He went forth, but when he came to the thorn hedge, it turned into flowers. They separated, and he walked through, but after he passed, they turned back into thorns. He went into the castle. Horses and colorful hunting dogs were asleep in the courtyard. Pigeons, with their little heads stuck under they wings, were sitting on the roof. As he walked inside, the flies on the wall, the fire in the kitchen, the cook and the maid were all asleep. He walked further. All the attendants were asleep; and still further, the king and the queen. It was so quiet that he could hear his own breath. Finally he came to the old tower where Briar-Rose was lying asleep. The prince was so amazed at her beauty that he bent over and kissed her. At that moment she awoke, and with her the king and the queen, and all the attendants, and the horses and the dogs, and the pigeons on the roof, and the flies on the walls. The fire stood up and flickered, and then finished cooking the food. The roast sizzled away. The cook boxed the kitchen boy's ears. And the maid finished plucking the chicken. Then the prince and Briar-Rose got married, and they lived long and happily until they died.[142]

Rumpelstiltskin

Jacob and Wilhelm Grimm

Once upon a time there was a miller who was poor, but who had a beautiful daughter. Now it happened that he got into a conversation with the king and said to him, "I have a daughter who knows the art of turning straw into gold." So the king immediately sent for the miller's daughter and ordered her to turn a whole room full of straw into gold in one night. And if she could not do it, she would have to die. She was locked in the room, and she sat there and cried, because for her life she did not know how the straw would turn into gold.

Then suddenly a little man appeared before her, and said, "What will you give me, if I turn this all into gold?" She took off her necklace and gave it to the little man, and he did what he had promised. The next morning the king found the room

---

[142]Type 410. Source: *Kinder- und Hausmärchen*, 1st ed. (Berlin, 1812/1815), v. 1, no. 50.

filled with gold, and his heart became even more greedy. He put the miller's daughter into an even larger room filled with straw, and told her to turn it into gold. The little man came again. She gave him a ring from her hand, and he turned it all into gold.

The third night the king had her locked in a third room, which was larger than the first two, and entirely filled with straw. "If you succeed this time, I'll make you my wife," he said.

Then the little man came and said, "I'll do it again, but you must promise me the first child that you have with the king." In her distress she made the promise, and when the king saw that this straw too had been turned into gold, he took the miller's daughter as his wife.

Soon thereafter the queen delivered a child. Then the little man appeared before her and demanded the child that had been promised him. The queen begged him to let her keep the child, offering him great riches in its place. Finally he said, "I'll be back to get the child in three days. But if by then you know my name, you can keep the child!"

For two days the queen pondered what the little man's name might be, but she could not think of anything, and became very sad. On the third day the king came home from a hunt and told her how, two days earlier, while hunting deep in a dark forest, he had come upon a little house. A comical little man was there, jumping about as if on one leg, and crying out:

> Today I'll bake; tomorrow I'll brew.
> Then I'll fetch the queen's new child.
> It is good that no one knows
> Rumpelstiltskin is my name.

The queen was overjoyed to hear this.

Then the dangerous little man arrived and asked, "Your majesty, what is my name?"

"Is your name Conrad?"

"No."

"Is your name Heinrich?"

"No."

"Then could your name be Rumpelstiltskin?"

"The devil told you that!" shouted the little man. He ran away angrily, and never came back.[143]

---

[143]Type 500. Source: *Kinder- und Hausmärchen*, 1st ed. (Berlin, 1812/1815), v. 1, no. 55. The Grimms dressed this tale up considerably in succeeding editions. The most notable change is the introduction of the spinning wheel as a device for turning straw into gold. Further, in later editions the queen discovers the dwarf's name through a messenger whom she herself sends forth to collect strange names, not through her husband's chance meeting with the little man.

Habitrot

Scotland

In the old days, when spinning was the constant employment of women, the spinning wheel had its presiding genius or fairy. Her Border name was Habitrot, and Mr. Wilkie tells the following legend about her:

A Selkirkshire matron had one fair daughter, who loved play better than work, wandering in the meadows and lanes better than the spinning wheel and distaff. The mother was heartily vexed at this taste, for in those days no lassie had any chance of a good husband unless she was an industrious spinster. So she cajoled, threatened, even beat her daughter, but all to no purpose; the girl remained what her mother called her, "an idle cuttie."

At last, one spring morning, the gudewife gave her seven heads of lint, saying she would take no excuse; they must be returned in three days spun into yarn. The girl saw her mother was in earnest, so she plied her distaff as well as she could; but her little hands were all untaught, and by the evening of the second day a very small part of her task was accomplished. She cried herself to sleep that night, and in the morning, throwing aside her work in despair, she strolled out into the fields, all sparkling with dew. At last she reached a flowery knoll, at whose foot ran a little burn, shaded with woodbine and wild roses; and there she sat down, burying her face in her hands. When she looked up, she was surprised to see by the margin of the stream an old woman, quite unknown to her, "drawing out the thread" as she basked in the sun. There was nothing very remarkable in her appearance, except the length and thickness of her lips, only she was seated on a self-bored stone. The girl rose, went to the good dame, and gave her a friendly greeting, but could not help inquiring what made her so "long lippit."

"Spinning thread, ma hinnie," said the old woman, pleased with her friendliness, and by no means resenting, the personal remark. It must be noticed that spinners used constantly to wet their fingers with their lips, as they drew the thread from the rock or distaff.

"Ah!" said the girl, "I should be spinning too, but it's a' to no purpose I sall ne'er do my task," on which the old woman proposed to do it for her. Overjoyed, the maiden ran to fetch her lint, and placed it in her new friend's hand, asking her name, and where she should call for the yarn in the evening; but she received no reply; the old woman's form passed away from her among the trees and bushes, and disappeared. The girl, much bewildered, wandered about a little, sat down to rest, and finally fell asleep by the little knoll.

When she awoke she was surprised to find that it was evening. The glories of the western sky were passing into twilight gray. Causleen, the evening star, was beaming with silvery light, soon to be lost in the moon's increasing splendor. While watching these changes, the maiden was startled by the sound of an uncouth voice, which seemed to issue from below a self-bored stone, close beside her. She laid her ear to the stone, and distinctly heard these words, "Little kens the wee lassie on yon brae-head that ma name's Habitrot." Then, looking down the hole,

187

she saw her friend, the old dame, walking backwards and forwards in a deep cavern among a group of spinsters all seated on colludie stones (a kind of white pebble found in rivers), and busy with distaff and spindle. An unsightly company they were, with lips more or less disfigured by their employment, as were old Habitrot's. The same peculiarity extended to another of the sisterhood, who sat in a distant corner reeling the yarn; and she was marked, in addition, by gray eyes, which seemed starting from her head, and a long hooked nose.

As she reeled, she counted thus, "Ae cribbie, twa cribbie, haith cribbie thou's ane; ae cribbie, twa cribbie, haith cribbie thou's twa," and so on. After this manner she continued till she had counted a cut, hank, slip (a cribbie being once round the reel, or a measure of about three feet, the reel being about eighteen inches long).

While the girl was still watching, she heard Habitrot address this singular being by the name of Scantlie Mab, and tell her to bundle up the yarn, for it was time the young lassie should give it to her mother. Delighted to hear this, our listener got up and turned homewards, nor was she long kept in suspense. Habitrot soon overtook her, and placed the yarn in her hands. "Oh, what can I do for ye in return?" exclaimed she, in delight.

"Naething, naething," replied the dame; "but dinna tell yer mither whae spun the yarn."

Scarcely crediting her good fortune, our heroine went home, where she found her mother had been busy making sausters, or black puddings, and hanging them up in the lum to dry, and then, tired out, had retired to rest. Finding herself very hungry after her long day on the knoll, the girl took down pudding after pudding, fried and ate them, and at last went to bed too. The mother was up first the next morning, and when she came into the kitchen and found her sausters all gone, and the seven hanks of yarn lying beautifully smooth and bright upon the table, her mingled feelings of vexation and delight were too much for her. She ran out of the house wildly, crying out:

> Ma daughter's spun se'en, se'en, se'en,
> Ma daughter's eaten se'en, se'en, se'en,
> And all before daylight!

A laird, who chanced to be riding by, heard the exclamation, but could not understand it; so he rode up and asked the gudewife what was the matter, on which she broke out again:

> Ma daughter's spun se'en, se'en, se'en,
> Ma daughter's eaten se'en, se'en, se'en

before daylight; and if ye dinna believe me, why come in and see it." The laird's curiosity was aroused; he alighted and went into the cottage, where he saw the yarn, and admired it so much, he begged to see the spinner.

The mother dragged in the blushing girl. Her rustic grace soon won his heart, and he avowed he was lonely without a wife, and had long been in search of one who was a good spinner. So their troth was plighted, and the wedding took place soon afterwards, the bride stifling her apprehensions that she should not prove so deft at her spinning wheel as her lover expected. And once more old Habitrot came to her aid. Whether the good dame, herself so notable, was as indulgent to all idle damsels does not appear; certainly she did not fail this little pet of hers. "Bring your bonny bridegroom to my cell," said she to the young bride soon after her marriage; "he shall see what comes o' spinning, and never will he tie you to the spinning wheel."

Accordingly the bride led her husband the next day to the flowery knoll, and bade him look through the self-bored stone. Great was his surprise to behold Habitrot dancing and jumping over her rock[144] singing all the time this ditty to her sisterhood, while they kept time with their spindles:

> We who live in dreary den
> Are both rank and foul to see,
> Hidden frae the glorious sun
> That teems the fair earth's canopy;
> Ever must our evenings lone
> Be spent on the colludie stone.
>
> Cheerless is the evening gray
> When Causleen hath died away,
> But ever bright and ever fair
> Are they who breathe this evening air;
> And lean upon the self-bored stone
> Unseen by all but me alone.

The song ended, Scantlie Mab asked Habitrot what she meant by her last line, "Unseen by all but me alone."

"There is ane," replied Habitrot, "whom I bid to come here at this hour, and he has heard my song through the self-bored stone." So saying, she rose, opened another door, which was concealed by the roots of an old tree, and invited the bridal pair to come in and see her family.

The laird was astonished at the weird-looking company, as he well might be, and inquired of one after another the cause of the strange distortion of their lips. In a different tone of voice, and with a different twist of the mouth, each answered that it was occasioned by spinning. At least they tried to say so, but one grunted out, "Nakasind," and another "Owkasaänd," while a third murmured "O-a-a-send." All, however, conveyed the fact to the bridegroom's understanding; while Habitrot slyly hinted that if his wife were allowed to spin, her pretty lips would grow out of shape too, and her pretty face get an ugsome look. So before he left the cave he protested his little wife should never touch a spinning wheel, and he kept his word. She used to wander in the meadows by his side, or ride behind him over the hills, and all the flax grown on his land was sent to old Habitrot to be converted into yarn.[145]

---

[144]Spinning wheel. [Footnote in original]

[145]Type 501 (the three old spinning women), with a hint of type 500 (guessing the helper's name). Source: George Douglas, *Scottish Fairy and Folk Tales* (London, 1901), pp. 109-114.

The Three Spinning Women

Jacob and Wilhelm Grimm

In former times there lived a king who liked nothing better in all the world than having flax spun. The queen and his daughters had to spend the entire day spinning, and he was very angry if he could not hear the spinning wheels humming. One day he had to go abroad, and before taking leave, he gave the queen a great chest filled with flax, and said, "This must all be spun by the time I return."

The princesses were very concerned and started to cry, "If we are to spin all this, we'll have to sit here the whole day, and won't be able to get up at all."

The queen said, "Fear not, I will help you." Now in this country there were three terribly ugly old maids. The first one had such a large lower lip that it hung down over her chin. The second one had a forefinger on her right hand that was so broad and thick that one could have made three normal fingers from it. The third one had a broad flat foot, as wide as half a kitchen table. The queen sent for the three, and on the day that the king was to return, she had them all sit in her parlor. She gave them her spinning wheels, and had them spin. She told each one how she was to answer the king's questions.

When the king arrived, he was pleased to hear the humming of the wheels from afar, and prepared to praise his daughters. He entered the parlor, and when he saw the disgusting old maids sitting there, he was at first repulsed, but then he approached the first one and asked her where she had gotten the terribly large lower lip.

"From licking! From licking!"

Then he asked the second one where she had gotten the thick finger.

"From twisting the thread! From twisting the thread, and wrapping it around!" she said, at the same time letting the thread run around her finger a few times.

Finally he asked the third one where she had gotten the thick foot.

"From peddling! From peddling!"

When the king heard this he ordered the queen and the princesses to never again touch a spinning wheel, and thus they were delivered from their misery.[146]

---

[146]Type 501. Source: *Kinder- und Hausmärchen*, 1st ed. (Berlin, 1812/1815), v. 1, no. 14. Tales of the three deformed spinning women are very common in Europe, although they usually invoke magic to help the heroine achieve a superhuman spinning task. In later editions the Grimms replaced the simple, non-magical tale given above with a more involved, supernatural tale more in keeping with European folklore tradition.

The Princess and the Pea

Hans Christian Andersen

Once there was a prince, who traveled all over the world in search of a princess who might become his bride. He found plenty of princesses, but there was something wrong with each one. He wanted a *real* princess, so, disappointed, he came back home alone.

One stormy evening there was a knock at the city gate. The old king went out and discovered a princess standing there in the rain. She was a sorry sight with her wet hair and drenched clothing, but still, she claimed that she was a real princess.

"We shall see!" thought the old queen as she made a bed for the stranger. She placed a pea at the bottom of the bed; then she laid twenty mattresses on top of the pea, and then twenty featherbeds on top of the mattresses. That was where the princess was to sleep.

The next morning they asked her how she had slept. "Terribly bad!" said the princess. "I could hardly close my eyes the whole night! Goodness knows what was in the bed! I was lying on something so hard that I'm black and blue all over!"

They could now see that she was a real princess, for she had felt the pea through twenty mattresses and twenty featherbeds. Only a real princess could be so sensitive.

The prince married her, for now he knew that he had found a real princess. And the pea was put in the art gallery where it can still be seen, unless someone has taken it.

Now that was a real story![147]

Tatterhood

Norway

Once upon a time there was a king and a queen who had no children, and that made the queen very sad. She seldom had a happy hour. She was always crying and complaining, and saying how dull and lonesome it was in the palace. "If we had children there would be life enough," she said. Wherever she went in all her realm she found God's blessing in children, even in the poorest hut. And wherever she went she heard women scolding their children, and saying how they had done this and that wrong. The queen heard all this, and thought it would be so nice to do as other women did. At last the king and queen took into their

---

[147]Type 704. Retold from "Prinsessen på ærten" (1835).

191

palace an adopted girl to raise, that they might always have her with them, to love her if she did well, and scold her if she did wrong, like their own child.

One day the little girl whom they had taken as their own, ran down into the palace yard, and was playing with a golden apple. Just then an old beggar woman came by, who had a little girl with her, and it wasn't long before the little girl and the beggar's child were great friends, and began to play together, and to toss the golden apple about between them. When the queen saw this, as she sat at a window in the palace, she tapped on the pane for her foster daughter to come up. She went at once, but the beggar girl went up too; and as they went into the queen's apartment, each held the other by the hand. Then the queen began to scold the little lady, and to say, "You ought to be above running about and playing with a tattered beggar's brat." And she started to drive the girl down the stairs.

"If the queen only knew my mother's power, she'd not drive me out," said the little girl; and when the queen asked what she meant more plainly, she told her how her mother could get her children if she chose. The queen wouldn't believe it, but the girl insisted, and said that every word of it was true, and asked the queen only to try and make her mother do it. So the queen sent the girl down to fetch up her mother.

"Do you know what your daughter says?" asked the queen of the old woman, as soon as ever she came into the room.

No, the beggar woman knew nothing about it.

"Well, she says you can get me children if you will," answered the queen.

"Queens shouldn't listen to beggar girls' silly stories," said the old woman, and walked out of the room.

Then the queen got angry, and wanted again to drive out the little girl; but she declared it was true every word that she had said.

"Let the queen only give my mother something to drink," said the girl; "when she gets tipsy she'll soon find out a way to help you."

The queen was ready to try this; so the beggar woman was fetched up again, and treated with as much wine and mead as she wanted; and so it was not long before her tongue began to wag. Then the queen came out again with the same question she had asked before.

"Perhaps I know one way to help you," said the beggar woman. "Your majesty must make them bring in two pails of water some evening before you go to bed. Wash yourself in each of them, and afterwards throw the water under your bed. When you look under your bed the next morning, two flowers will have sprung up, a beautiful one and an ugly one. Eat the beautiful one but leave the ugly alone. Be careful not to forget this last bit of advice." That was what the beggar woman said.

Yes, the queen did what the beggar woman advised her to do; she had the water brought up in two pails, washed herself in them, and emptied them under the bed; and when she looked under the bed the next morning, there stood two flowers; one was ugly and foul, and had black leaves; but the other was so bright, and fair, and lovely, she had never seen anything like it, so she ate it up at once. But the pretty flower tasted so sweet, that she couldn't help herself. She ate the other one too, for, she thought, "I'm sure that it can't hurt or help me much either way."

Well, sure enough, after a while the queen was brought to bed. First of all, she had a girl who had a wooden spoon in her hand, and rode upon a goat. She was disgusting and ugly, and the very moment she came into the world she bawled out "Mamma."

"If I'm your mamma," said the queen, "God give me grace to mend my ways."

"Oh, don't be sorry," said the girl on the goat, "for one will soon come after me who is better looking."

After a while, the queen had another girl, who was so beautiful and sweet that no one had ever set eyes on such a lovely child. You may be sure that the queen was very well pleased. The elder twin they called "Tatterhood," because she was always so ugly and ragged, and because she had a hood which hung about her ears in tatters. The queen could hardly bear to look at her. The nurses tried to shut her up in a room by herself, but it did no good. She always had to be where the younger twin was, and no one could ever keep them apart.

One Christmas eve, when they were half grown up, there arose a frightful noise and clatter in the hallway outside the queen's apartment. Tatterhood asked what it was that was making such a noise outside.

"Oh," said the queen, "it isn't worth asking about."

But Tatterhood wouldn't give in until she found out all about it; and so the queen told her it was a pack of trolls and witches who had come there to celebrate Christmas. So Tatterhood said that she would just go out and drive them away. In spite of all they could say, and however much they begged and asked her to leave the trolls alone, she just had to go out and drive the witches off. She begged the queen to be careful and keep all the doors shut tight, so that not one of them would open the least bit.

Having said this, off she went with her wooden spoon, and began to hunt out and drive away the hags. All the while there was such a commotion out in the gallery that the like of it had never before been heard. The whole palace creaked and groaned as if every joint and beam were going to be torn out of its place. Now I can't say exactly what happened; but somehow or other one door did open a little bit, and her twin sister just peeped out to see how things were going with Tatterhood, and put her head a tiny bit through the opening. But, pop! up came an old witch, and whipped off her head, and stuck a calf's head on her shoulders instead; and so the princess ran back into the room on all fours, and began to "moo" like a calf. When Tatterhood came back and saw her sister, she scolded them all, and was very angry because they hadn't kept better watch, and asked them what they thought of their carelessness now that her sister had been turned into a calf.

"But I'll see if I can't set her free," she said.

Then she asked the king for a ship with a full set of sails and good load of stores, but she would not have a captain or any sailors. No; she would sail away with her sister all alone. There was no holding her back, and at last they let her have her own way.

Tatterhood sailed off, and steered her ship right up to the land where the witches lived. When she came to the landing place, she told her sister to stay quite still on board the ship; but she herself rode on her goat up to the witches' castle. When she

193

got there, one of the windows in the gallery was open, and there she saw her sister's head hung up on the window frame; so she jumped her goat through the window into the gallery, snapped up the head, and set off with it. The witches came after her to try to get the head back. They flocked around her as thick as a swarm of bees or a nest of ants. The goat snorted and puffed, and butted with his horns, and Tatterhood beat and banged them about with her wooden spoon; and so the pack of witches had to give up. So Tatterhood got back to her ship, took the calf's head off her sister, and put her own on again, and then she became a girl as she had been before. After that she sailed a long, long way, to a strange king's realm.

Now the king of this land was a widower, and had an only son. When he saw the strange sail, he sent messengers down to the beach to find out where it came from, and who owned it; but when the king's men came down there, the only person they saw on board was Tatterhood, and there she was, riding around and around the deck on her goat at full speed, until her strands of hair streamed in the wind. The men from the palace were all amazed at this sight, and asked if more people were not on board. Yes, there were; she had a sister with her, said Tatterhood. They wanted to see too, but Tatterhood said no.

"No one shall see her, unless the king comes himself," she said; and so she began to gallop about on her goat until the deck thundered again.

When the servants got back to the palace, and told what they had seen and heard down at the ship, the king wanted to set out at once to see the girl that rode on the goat. When he arrived there, Tatterhood brought out her sister, and she was so beautiful and gentle that the king immediately fell head over heels in love with her. He brought them both back with him to the palace, and wanted to have the sister for his queen; but Tatterhood said "No," the king couldn't have her in any way, unless the king's son would take Tatterhood. That, as you may guess, the prince did not want to do at all, because Tatterhood was such an ugly hussy. However, at last the king and all the others in the palace talked him into it, and he gave in, promising to take her for his queen; but it went sore against his grain, and he was a very sad man.

Now they began making preparations for the wedding, both with brewing and baking; and when all was ready, they went to church. The prince thought it the worst church service he had ever been to in all his life. The king left first with his bride, and she was so lovely and so grand, all the people stopped to look at her along the road, and they stared at her until she was out of sight. After them came the prince on horseback by the side of Tatterhood, who trotted along on her goat with her wooden spoon in her fist. To look at him, he was not going to a wedding, but to a burial, and his own at that. He seemed so sad, and did not speak a word.

"Why don't you talk?" asked Tatterhood, when they had ridden a bit.

"Why, what should I talk about?" answered the prince.

"Well, you might at least ask me why I ride upon this ugly goat," said Tatterhood.

"Why do you ride on that ugly goat?" asked the prince.

"Is it an ugly goat? Why, it's the most beautiful horse that a bride ever rode," answered Tatterhood; and in an instant the goat became a horse, the finest that the prince had ever seen.

They rode on a bit further, but the prince was just as sad as before, and couldn't say a word. So Tatterhood asked him again why he didn't talk, and when the prince answered, he didn't know what to talk about, she said, "Well, you can ask me why I ride with this ugly spoon in my fist."

"Why do you ride with that ugly spoon?" asked the prince.

"Is it an ugly spoon? Why, it's the loveliest silver fan that a bride ever carried," said Tatterhood; and in an instant it became a silver fan, so bright that it glistened.

They rode a little way further, but the prince was still just as sad, and did not say a word. In a little while Tatterhood asked him again why he didn't talk, and told him to ask why she wore the ugly gray hood on her head.

"Why do you wear that ugly gray hood on your head?" asked the prince.

"Is it an ugly hood? Why, it's the brightest golden crown that a bride ever wore," answered Tatterhood, and it became a crown at once.

Now they rode a long way further, and the prince was so sad, that he sat without making a sound or uttering a word, just as before. So his bride asked him again why he didn't talk, and told him to ask now why her face was so ugly and gray?

"Yes," asked the prince, "why is your face so ugly and gray?"

"Am I ugly? You think my sister beautiful, but I am ten times more beautiful," said the bride, and when the prince looked at her, she was so beautiful, he thought that she was the most beautiful woman in the world. After that it was no wonder that the prince found his tongue, and no longer rode along with his head hanging down.

So they drank the bridal cup both deep and long, and, after that, both prince and king set out with their brides to the princesses' palace, and there they had another bridal feast, and drank once more, both deep and long. There was no end to the celebration. Now run quickly to the king's palace, and there will still be a drop of the bridal ale left for you.[148]

---

[148]Type 711. Source: Peter Christen Asbjørnsen and Jørgen Moe, *Norske Folkeeventyr* (Christiania [Oslo], 1842-1852), translated by George Webb Dasent (1859). Revised.

The Shoes That Were Danced to Pieces

Jacob and Wilhelm Grimm

Once upon a time there was a king who had twelve daughters, each one more beautiful than the others. Their beds were all together in one room, and when they went to bed, their doors were all locked and barred, but the next morning their shoes were always danced to pieces, and no one knew where they had been or how it had happened. Then the king proclaimed that whoever could discover where they went dancing each night could chose one of them for his wife and become king after his death. However, anyone who attempted this, but failed to make the discovery after three days and nights, would forfeit his life.

A prince soon presented himself. He was well received, and escorted to the anteroom to the twelve daughters' bedroom. He was given a bed there, and told to watch where they went and danced. So they would not be able to do anything in secret, or go out to some other place, the door to their room was left open. But the prince fell asleep, and when he awoke the next morning, the twelve had been dancing, for their shoes all had holes in their soles. The same thing happened the second and the third evening, and his head was chopped off. Many others came to try this risky venture, but they too all lost their lives.

Now it happened that a poor soldier, who because of his wounds could no longer serve in the army, was making his way to the city where the king lived. He met an old woman who asked him where he was going. "I'm not sure myself," he said. "But I would like to become king and discover where the princesses are dancing their shoes to pieces."

"Oh," said the old woman, "that isn't so difficult. Just do not drink the wine that one of them will bring you in the evening." Then she gave him a cloak and said, "Put this on, and you will be invisible, and you can follow the twelve."

Having receiving this good advice, the soldier became serious, took heart, went to the king, and announced himself as a suitor. He, like the others, was well received, and was given royal clothes to wear. That evening at bedtime he was escorted to the anteroom. Just as he was going to bed, the oldest princess brought him a goblet of wine, but he secretly poured it out. He lay down, and after a little while began to snore as if he were in the deepest sleep. The twelve princesses heard him and laughed. The oldest one said, "He could have spared his life as well!"

Then they got up, opened their wardrobes, chests, and closets, took out their best clothes, and made themselves beautiful in front of their mirrors, all the time jumping about in anticipation of the dance. However, the youngest one said, "I'm not sure. You are all very happy, but I'm afraid that something bad is going to happen!"

"You snow goose," said the oldest one. "You are always afraid! Have you forgotten how many princes have been here for nothing. I wouldn't even have had to give this soldier a sleeping potion. He would never have woken up."

196

When they were ready, they first approached the soldier, but he did not move at all, and as soon as they thought it was safe, the oldest one went to her bed and knocked on it. It immediately sank beneath the floor, revealing a trapdoor. The soldier saw how they all climbed down, one after the other, the oldest one leading the way. He jumped up, put on the cloak, and followed immediately after the youngest one. Halfway down the stairs he stepped on her dress. Frightened, she called out, "It's not right! Something is holding my dress."

"Don't be so simple," said the oldest one. "You just caught yourself on a hook."

They continued until they came to a magnificent walkway between rows of trees. Their leaves were all made of silver, and they shone and glistened. The soldier broke off a twig in order to prove where he had been, and a loud cracking sound came from the tree. The youngest one called out again, "It's not right. Didn't you hear that sound? That has never happened before."

The oldest one said, "That is just a joyful salute that they are firing because soon we will have disenchanted our princes." Then they came to a walkway where the tress were all made of gold, and finally to a third one, where they were made of clear diamonds. He broke a twig from each of these. The cracking sound frightened the youngest one each time, but the oldest one insisted that it was only the sounds of joyful salutes. They continued on until they came to a large body of water. Twelve boats were there, and in each boat there was a handsome prince waiting for them. Each prince took a princess into his boat. The soldier sat next to the youngest princess, and her prince said, "I am as strong as ever, but the boat seems to be much heavier. I am rowing as hard as I can."

"It must be the warm weather," said the youngest princess. It's too hot for me as well."

On the other side of the water there was a beautiful, brightly illuminated castle. Joyful music, kettle drums, and trumpets sounded forth. They rowed over and went inside. Each prince danced with his princess. The invisible soldier danced along as well, and when a princess held up a goblet of wine, he drank it empty as she lifted it to her mouth. This always frightened the youngest one, but the oldest one silenced her every time. They danced there until three o'clock the next morning when their shoes were danced to pieces and they had to stop. The princes rowed them back across the water. This time the soldier took a seat next to the oldest princess in the lead boat. They took leave from their princes on the bank and promised to come back the next night.

When they were on the steps the soldier ran ahead and got into bed. When the twelve tired princesses came in slowly, he was again snoring loudly. "He will be no risk to us," they said. Then they took off their beautiful clothes and put them away, placed their worn out shoes under their beds, and went to bed.

The next morning the soldier said nothing, for he wanted to see the amazing thing once again. He went along the second and third nights, and everything happened as before. Each time they danced until their shoes were in pieces. The third time he also took along a goblet as a piece of evidence.

The hour came when he was to give his answer, and he brought the three twigs and the goblet before the king. The twelve princesses stood behind the door and listened to what he had to say. The king asked, "Where did my daughters dance their shoes to pieces?"

He answered, "in an underground castle with twelve princes." Then he told the whole story and brought forth the pieces of evidence. When they saw that they had been betrayed, and that their denials did no good, they admitted everything. Then the king asked him which one he wanted for a wife. He answered, "I myself am no longer young, so give me the oldest one." Their wedding was held the same day, and the kingdom was promised to him following the king's death. But the princes had as many days added to their curse as they had spent nights dancing with the twelve princesses.[149]

Boys Become Men

Iron Hans

Jacob and Wilhelm Grimm

Far away and long ago a king lived next to a great and dangerous forest. Huntsmen, herdsmen, and woodcutters who ventured into its thickets often failed to return. Legend said that they all had fallen prey to a wild man who lived at the bottom of a lake in the darkest part of the woods.

The king, wanting to secure his realm, broke through the thickets with a troop of soldiers. They found the lake and drained it, discovering at its muddy bottom a small strange wild creature with matted red hair. Although it looked more like a beast than a man, they named it Iron Hans, then bound it with chains and brought it back to the castle where it was kept on display in a cage in the courtyard.

One day the king's son was playing with a golden ball, when he threw it too far, and it fell into the wild man's cage. "I will return your ball," said Iron Hans, "if you will set me free. You will find the key to my cage beneath your mother's pillow." The boy's desire for the golden ball was even greater than his fear of his father's wrath, so he found the key and unlocked the cage. The wild man said, "If you need me, call!" then disappeared into the forest.

---

[149]Type 306. Source: *Kinder- und Hausmärchen*, 1st ed. (Berlin, 1812/1815), v. 2, no. 47 (no. 133 in the final edition).

The father, upon discovering that his wild man had escaped, became so furious that the boy had to run away to save his life. He made his way to the next kingdom, where he took work as a gardener's helper at the royal castle. He had to labor hard and long in the hot sun, but there was one reward: Every evening the princess strolled among the flowers, and sometimes—he thought—she smiled at him as she passed.

Now this kingdom was being invaded by a foreign army, and the gardener boy volunteered to fight for his new king. "Indeed," they scoffed. "A fine soldier you would make!" But he continued to beg, and finally, in order to silence him, they gave him a shovel for a sword and a bucket for a shield, then mounted him on a three-legged horse, and sent him to the battlefield.

Entering the forest, he called for Iron Hans, who responded by bringing him a powerful, majestic horse, a glorious suit of armor, and a set of weapons worthy of any knight. Thus outfitted, he entered the battle and fought so valiantly that the foe soon retreated. Carrying the enemy's flag, he returned to the castle and presented it to the king. The princess, seated nearby, gave the mysterious knight a golden apple before he rode away.

The time soon came for the princess to marry, and she announced that she would have no less a man than the valiant knight who had saved the kingdom. A great search for the golden apple was begun, for this was the token by which the hero would be known. To everyone's surprise, the gardener boy produced the apple and claimed the princess. Preparations were made at once for the wedding. The day arrived, and one of the guests was a mysterious, elegant knight outfitted in red. He was Iron Hans, the wild man, who—as he explained—had been placed under a spell, a spell that was broken when the young prince unlocked the cage, proved himself as a warrior, and found a bride. Everyone rejoiced, and they all lived happily ever after.[150]

The Wild Man and the Prince

Serbia

It happened once upon a time, many years ago, that a certain king went into his forest to hunt, when instead of the usual game he caught a wild man. This wild man the king had taken to his castle, and locked up, for safety, in a dungeon.

---

[150]Type 502. Retold from *Kinder- Hausmärchen*, 6th ed. (1850), no. 136. This story, often with the phrase "Wild Man" as part of the title, is told throughout the Indo-European language and folklore area.

This done, he put out a proclamation that whosoever should dare to set the wild man free should be put to death.

As luck would have it, the dungeon where the creature was confined was just below the sleeping room of the king's youngest son. Now the wild man cried and groaned incessantly to be set free, and these unceasing lamentations at length so moved the young prince that one night he went down and opened the dungeon door, and let out the prisoner.

Next morning the king and all the courtiers and servants were exceedingly astonished to hear no longer the usual sounds of wailing from the dungeon, and the king, suspecting something amiss, went down himself to see what had become of his captive. When he found the den empty he flew into a great passion, and demanded fiercely who had presumed to disobey his commands and let out the wild man. All the courtiers were so terrified at the sight of the king's angry countenance, that not one of them dared speak, not even to assert their innocence. However, the young prince, the king's son, went forward at last and confessed that the pitiful crying of the poor creature had so disturbed him day and night, that at length he himself had opened the door. When the king heard this, it was his turn to be sorry, for he found himself compelled to put his own son to death or give his own proclamation the lie.

However, some of his old counselors, seeing how greatly the king was perplexed and troubled, came and assured his majesty that the proclamation would in reality be carried out if the prince, instead of being put to death, was simply banished from the kingdom forever.

The king was very glad to find this way of getting out of the dilemma, and so ordered his son to leave the country, and never come back to it. At the same time he gave him many letters of recommendation to the king of a very distant kingdom, and directed one of the court servants to go with the young prince to wait upon him. Then the unhappy young prince and his servant started on their long journey.

After traveling some time, the young prince became very thirsty, and, seeing a well not far off, went up to it to drink. However, there happened to be no bucket at the well, nor anything in which to draw water, though the well was pretty full. Seeing this, the young prince said to his servant, "Hold me fast by the heels, and let me down into the pit that I may drink." So saying, he bent over the well, and the servant let him down as he was directed.

When the prince had quenched his thirst, and wished to be pulled back, the servant refused, saying, "Now I can let you fall into the pit in a moment, and I shall do so unless you consent at once to change clothes and places with me. I will be the prince henceforth, and you shall be my servant."

The king's son, seeing that he had foolishly placed himself in the power of the servant, promised readily everything his servant asked, and begged only to be drawn up.

But the faithless servant, without noticing his master's prayers, said roughly, "You must make a solemn oath that you will not speak a word to any one about the change we are going to make."

Of course, since the prince could not help himself, he took the oath at once, and then the servant drew him up, and they changed clothes. Then the wicked servant dressed himself in his master's fine clothes, mounted his master's horse, and rode forward on the journey, whilst the unfortunate prince, disguised in her servant's dress, walked beside him.

In this way they went on until they came to the court of the king to which the exiled son had been recommended by his father.

Faithful to his promise, the unfortunate prince saw his false servant received at the court with great honors as the son of a great king, whilst he himself all unnoticed, stood in the waiting room with the servants, and was treated by them with all familiarity as their equal.

After having some time enjoyed to his heart's content the hospitalities the king lavished upon him, the false servant began to be afraid that his master's patience might be wearied out soon under all the indignities to which he was exposed, and that one day he might be tempted to forget his oath and proclaim himself in his true character. Filled with these misgivings, the wicked man thought over all possible ways by which he could do away with his betrayed master without any danger to himself.

One day, he thought he had found out a way to do this, and took the first opportunity to carry out his cruel plan.

Now you must know that the king at whose court this unhappy prince and the false servant were staying, kept in his gardens a great number of wild beasts fastened up in large cages. One morning, as the seeming prince was walking in these gardens with the king, he said suddenly, "Your majesty has a large number of very fine wild beasts, and I admire them very much. I think, however, it is a pity that you keep them always fastened up, and spend so much money over their food. Why not send them under a keeper to find their own food in the forest? I dare say your majesty would be very glad if I recommended a man to you who could take them out in the morning and bring them back safely at night?"

The king asked, "Do you really think, prince, that you can find me such a man?"

"Of course, I can," replied the cruel man unhesitatingly. "Such a man is now in your majesty's court. I mean my own servant. Only call him and threaten that you will have his head cut off if he does not do it, and compel him to accept the task. I dare say he will try to excuse himself, and say the thing is impossible, but only threaten him with the loss of his head whether he refuses or fails. For my part, I am quite willing your majesty should have him put to death, if he disobeys."

When the king heard this, he summoned the disguised prince before him, and said, "I hear that you can do wonders, that you are able to drive wild beasts out like cattle to find their own food in the forest, and bring them back safely at night into their cages. Therefore, I order you this morning to drive all my bears into the forest, and to bring them back again in the evening. If you don't do this, your head will pay for it; so beware!"

The unlucky prince answered, "I am not able to do this thing, so your majesty had better cut off my head at once."

But the king would not listen to him, only saying, "We will wait until evening; then I shall surely have your head cut off unless you bring back all my bears safely to their cages."

Now nothing was left for the poor prince to do but open the cage doors and try his luck in driving the bears to the forest. The moment he opened the doors all the bears rushed out wildly, and disappeared quickly among the trees.

The prince followed them sadly into the forest, and sat down on a fallen tree to think over his hard fortunes. As he sat thus, he began to weep bitterly, for he saw no better prospect before him than to lose his head at night.

As he sat thus crying, a creature in form like a man, but covered all over with thick hair, came out of a neighboring thicket, and asked him what he was crying for. Then the prince told him all that had happened to him, and that as all the bears had run away he expected to be beheaded at night when he returned without them. Hearing this, the wild man gave him a little bell, and said kindly, "Don't be afraid! Only take care of this bell, and when you wish the bears to return, just ring it gently, and they will all come back and follow you quietly into their cages." And having said this he went away.

When the sun began to go down, the prince rang the little bell gently, and, to his great joy, all the bears came dancing awkwardly around him, and let him lead them back to the gardens, following him like a flock of sheep, whilst he, pleased with his success, took out a flute and played little airs as he walked before them. In this way he was able to fasten them up again in their dens without the least trouble.

Everyone at the court was astonished at this, and the false servant more than all the others, though he concealed his surprise, and said to the king, "Your majesty sees now that I told you the truth. I am quite sure the man can manage the wolves just as well as the bears, if you only threaten him as before."

Thereupon, the next morning the king called the poor prince, and ordered him to lead out the wolves to find their food in the forest and to bring them back to their cages at night. "Unless you do this," said his majesty as before, "you will lose your head."

The prince pleaded vainly the impossibility of his doing such a thing; but the king would not hear him, only saying, "You may as well try, for whether you refuse or fail, you will certainly lose your head."

So the prince was obliged to open the cages of the wolves, and the moment he did this the wild animals sprang past him into the thickets just as the bears had done, and he, following them slowly, went and sat down to bewail his ill luck.

Whilst he sat thus weeping, the wild man came out of the wood and asked him, just as he had done the day before, what he was crying for. The prince told him, whereupon the creature gave him another little bell, and said, "When you want the wolves to come back, just ring this bell, and they will all come and follow you." Having said this he went back into the wood, and left the prince alone.

Just before it grew dark, the prince rang his bell, and to his great joy all the wolves came rushing up to him from all quarters of the forest, and followed him quietly back to their cages.

Seeing this, the false servant advised the king to send out the birds also, and to threaten the disguised prince with the loss of his head if he failed to bring them also back in the evening.

Accordingly the next morning the king ordered the prince to let out all the wild doves, and to bring them all safely to their different cages before night set in.

The instant the poor young man opened the cage doors the wild doves rose like a cloud into the air, and vanished over the tops of the trees. So the prince went into the forest and sat down again on the fallen tree. As he sat there, thinking how hopeless a task he had now before him he could not help crying aloud and bewailing all his past misfortunes and present miserable fate.

Hardly had he begun to lament, however, before the same wild man came from the bushes near him and asked what fresh trouble had befallen him. Then the prince told him. Thereupon the wild man gave him a third bell, saying, "When you wish the wild doves to return to their cages you have only to ring this little bell." And so it indeed happened, for the moment the prince began ringing softly, all the doves came flying about him, and he walked back to the palace gardens and shut them up in their different cages without the least trouble.

Now, happily for the prince, the king had just at this time much more important business on his hands than finding his wild beasts and birds in food without paying for it. No less a matter, in fact, began to occupy him than finding a suitable husband for his daughter. For this purpose he sent out a proclamation that he would hold races during three days, and would reward the victor of each day with a golden apple. Whosoever should succeed in winning all three apples should have the young princess for his wife. Now this princess was far more beautiful than any other princess in the world, and an exceedingly great number of knights prepared to try and win her. This, the poor prince, in his servant's dress, watched with great dismay; for he had fallen deeply in love with the fair daughter of the king. So he puzzled himself day and night with plans how he, too, could try his luck in the great race.

At last he determined to go into the forest and ask the wild man to help him. When the wild man heard the prince calling, he came out of the thicket, and listened to all he had to say about the matter. Seeing how much the prince was interested in the young princess, who was to be the prize of the victor, the wild man brought out some handsome clothes and a fine horse, and gave them to the prince, saying, "When you start in the race, do not urge your horse too much, but at the end, when you are getting near the goal, spur him, and then you will be sure to win. Don't forget, however, to bring me the golden apple as soon as you receive it."

All came to pass just as the wild man had said. The prince won the apples the two first days; but as he disappeared as soon as he received them from the king, no one in the court recognized him in his fine attire, and all wondered greatly who the stranger knight might be. As for the king, he was more perplexed and curious than all the rest, and determined not to let the stranger escape so easily the third day. So he ordered a deep, wide ditch to be dug at the end of the race course, and a high wall built beyond it, thinking thus to stop the victor and find out who he was.

The prince, hearing of the king's orders, and guessing the reason of them, went once again into the forest to ask help from his wild friend. The wild man, thereupon, brought out to him a still more beautiful racer, and a suit of splendid clothes; and, thus prepared, the prince took his place as before among the knights who were going to try for the prize. He won the gold apple this third time also; but, to the surprise of the king and the whole court, who hoped now to find out who he was, he made his horse spring lightly over the ditch, and the great wall, and vanished again in the forest.

The king tried every way to find out who had won the three golden apples, but all in vain. At last, one day, the princess, walking in the gardens of the palace, met the prince disguised in his servant's dress, and saw the shining of the three apples which he carried in his bosom. Thereupon she ran at once to her father, and told him what she had seen, and the king, wondering very much, called the servant before him.

Now the prince thought it time to put an end to all his troubles, and therefore told the king frankly all his misfortunes. He related how he had offended the king, his father, and been exiled for life; how his false servant had betrayed him; and how the wild man he had set free had come to help him out of the fearful snares the wicked servant had spread for him.

After hearing all this, the king very gladly gave him the princess for wife, and ordered the false servant to be put to death immediately.

As for the prince, he lived with his beautiful princess very happily for many years after this, and when the king, his father-in-law, died, he left to them both the kingdom.[151]

The Blood Brothers

Europe

Once upon a time a fisherman caught a fish that said to him, "If you will set me free, I will grant you any wish." Now more than anything else, the fisherman wanted to have a child with his wife, so he made this wish, and turned the fish loose.

Before swimming away, the fish said, "Cast your net again, and give your next catch to your wife to eat."

The fisherman did as he was told. His next cast netted him one little fish, which he took home with him. His wife ate the flesh. His dog ate the insides. And his

---

[151]Type 502. Source: Csedomille Mijatovies, *Serbian Folk-Lore* (London, 1874), pp. 189-199. Original title of story: "One Good Turn Deserves Another."

horse ate the bones. Some time later his wife gave birth to twin boys; the dog had a litter of two pups; and the horse foaled with two colts.

The twin boys gave their parents much pleasure, but with time the older brother became restless, and wanted to seek his fortune abroad. He left a bottle of clear white wine with his younger twin, saying, "All will be well with me as long as the wine is white. But if it ever turns red, I will be in need of your help." With that he took leave of his brother and of his parents, mounted the older twin horse, and, accompanied by the older twin dog, set forth into the world.

After a long journey he came to a kingdom that was being ravished by a terrible dragon. The king had promised his daughter's hand in marriage to whatever man succeeded in killing the dragon. The twin tracked the dragon to its lair, then engaged him in battle. The fight was long and hard, but the brave twin finally prevailed, and the dragon lay dead at his feat. As proof that he had killed the beast, he cut out its tongue, then set out for the castle to claim the princess as his reward.

Now the king had a steward who happened to come upon the dead dragon soon after the twin left. He decided to claim the kill for himself, cut off the dragon's head, and took a shortcut to the castle.

The king was delighted to see the dragon's head, and he arranged for the wedding between the steward and the princess to take place immediately. The twin arrived just as the festivities were starting. Seeing that another man was unfairly claiming his prize, he said, "It is a strange dragon that has no tongue."

"Of course the dragon has a tongue," said the steward, opening the dragon's mouth. But the tongue was not there.

"The dragon had a tongue when I killed it," answered the twin, "and here it is." With this he produced the dragon's tongue. The king now saw that the steward had lied, and had him cast into a dark dungeon. The festivities continued, but this time with the twin as hero and bridegroom.

The twin and the princess lived happily for some time, but after a while he became restless again. He announced that he wanted to go hunting in a nearby forest, named the Forest of No Return. His young wife asked him not to go, but his spirit of adventure prevailed.

Soon after entering the Forest of No Return, the twin met an old woman, who, unknown to him, was a wicked witch. "Good day, young sir," she said. He began to return the greeting, but had scarcely opened his mouth when she cast a spell on him, turning him to stone.

Meanwhile, back at the fisherman's cottage, the younger twin examined the bottle of wine every day. Its clear white color let him know that his older brother was well. One day, however, the wine turned blood red, and the younger brother knew that his twin was in need. He took leave of his parents, mounted the younger twin horse, and, accompanied by the younger twin dog, set forth into the world to find his older brother.

After a long journey he came to the kingdom where his twin brother had killed the dragon. Everyone thought that he was their new prince, and he was escorted to the castle with honor.

"I thought that you would never come back from the Forest of No Return," said the princess tenderly. However, to her dismay and surprise, instead of returning her love, that night he laid his sword between them in their bed.

Early the next morning the younger twin set forth for the Forest of No Return. Soon after entering this forest, he met the old witch. "Good day, young sir," she said.

Sensing her evil design, he said not a word, but leaped on her and pinned her to the ground. Holding his sword to her neck, he shouted, "lead me to my brother, or die at once!" The witch, fearing for her life, led the young twin to his petrified brother. She anointed the stone with salve, and he returned to life.

Overjoyed, the two brothers made they way back toward the castle. On their way, each one told the other of his adventures. When it was the younger brother's turn to speak, he told of how the white wine had turned to blood red, how he had found his way to the castle, how he had slept with the princess — —. He was not able finish his sentence. The older twin, hearing that his brother had slept with his wife, drew his sword and cut off his head.

When the older twin arrived at the castle, he was received by his wife with love. "At last you are yourself!" she said. "Not like the last time you were here, when you put a sword between us in bed."

The older twin now knew that he had unjustly killed his brother. He rushed back to the place where his body lay. Fortunately, he still had some of the witch's salve, and with it he anointed the dead man's wounds, placed the head back on the body, and brought his brother back to life. Together they returned to the castle, where they lived happily ever after.[152]

Jack and the Beanstalk

England

Once upon a time there was a poor widow who lived in a little cottage with her only son Jack. Jack was a giddy, thoughtless boy, but very kind hearted and affectionate. There had been a hard winter, and after it the poor woman had suffered from fever and ague. Jack did no work as yet, and by degrees they grew dreadfully poor. The widow saw that there was no means of keeping Jack and herself from starvation but by selling her cow; so one morning she said to her son, "I am too weak to go myself, Jack, so you must take the cow to market for me, and sell her."

---

[152]Type 303. Retold from various sources. This story is told throughout the Indo-European language and folklore area.

Jack liked going to market to sell the cow very much; but as he was on the way, he met a butcher who had some beautiful beans in his hand. Jack stopped to look at them, and the butcher told the boy that they were of great value, and persuaded the silly lad to sell the cow for these beans.

When he brought them home to his mother instead of the money she expected for her nice cow, she was very vexed and shed many tears, scolding Jack for his folly. He was very sorry, and mother and son went to bed very sadly that night; their last hope seemed gone.

At daybreak Jack rose and went out into the garden. "At least," he thought, "I will sow the wonderful beans. Mother says that they are just common scarlet runners, and nothing else; but I may as well sow them." So he took a piece of stick, and made some holes in the ground, and put in the beans.

That day they had very little dinner, and went sadly to bed, knowing that for the next day there would be none, and Jack, unable to sleep from grief and vexation, got up at day-dawn and went out into the garden.

What was his amazement to find that the beans had grown up in the night, and climbed up and up until they covered the high cliff that sheltered the cottage, and disappeared above it! The stalks had twined and twisted themselves together until they formed quite a ladder.

"It would be easy to climb it," thought Jack. And, having thought of the experiment, he at once resolved to carry it out, for Jack was a good climber. However, after his late mistake about the cow, he thought he had better consult his mother first.

So Jack called his mother, and they both gazed in silent wonder at the Beanstalk, which was not only of great height, but was thick enough to bear Jack's weight. "I wonder where it ends," said Jack to his mother. "I think I will climb up and see."

His mother wished him not to venture up this strange ladder, but Jack coaxed her to give her consent to the attempt, for he was certain there must be something wonderful in the beanstalk; so at last she yielded to his wishes.

Jack instantly began to climb, and went up and up on the ladder-like beanstalk until everything he had left behind him—the cottage, the village, and even the tall church tower—looked quite little, and still he could not see the top of the beanstalk.

Jack felt a little tired, and thought for a moment that he would go back again; but he was a very persevering boy, and he knew that the way to succeed in anything is not to give up. So after resting for a moment he went on. After climbing higher and higher, until he grew afraid to look down for fear he should be giddy, Jack at last reached the top of the beanstalk, and found himself in a beautiful country, finely wooded, with beautiful meadows covered with sheep. A crystal stream ran through the pastures; not far from the place where he had got off the beanstalk stood a fine, strong castle.

Jack wondered very much that he had never heard of or seen this castle before; but when he reflected on the subject, he saw that it was as much separated from the village by the perpendicular rock on which it stood as if it were in another land.

While Jack was standing looking at the castle, a very strange looking woman came out of the wood, and advanced towards him. She wore a pointed cap of quilted red satin turned up with ermine. Her hair streamed loose over her shoulders, and she walked with a staff. Jack took off his cap and made her a bow.

"If you please, ma'am," said he, "is this your house?"

"No," said the old lady. "Listen, and I will tell you the story of that castle:"

Once upon a time there was a noble knight, who lived in this castle, which is on the borders of fairyland. He had a fair and beloved wife and several lovely children; and as his neighbors, the little people, were very friendly towards him, they bestowed on him many excellent and precious gifts.

Rumor whispered of these treasures; and a monstrous giant, who lived at no great distance, and who was a very wicked being, resolved to obtain possession of them.

So he bribed a false servant to let him inside the castle, when the knight was in bed and asleep, and he killed him as he lay. Then he went to the part of the castle which was the nursery, and also killed all the poor little ones he found there.

Happily for her, the lady was not to be found. She had gone with her infant son, who was only two or three months old, to visit her old nurse, who lived in the valley; and she had been detained all night there by a storm.

The next morning, as soon as it was light, one of the servants at the castle, who had managed to escape, came to tell the poor lady of the sad fate of her husband and her pretty babes. She could scarcely believe him at first, and was eager at once to go back and share the fate of her dear ones; but the old nurse, with many tears, besought her to remember that she had still a child, and that it was her duty to preserve her life for the sake of the poor innocent.

The lady yielded to this reasoning, and consented to remain at her nurse's house as the best place of concealment; for the servant told her that the giant had vowed, if he could find her, he would kill both her and her baby. Years rolled on. The old nurse died, leaving her cottage and the few articles of furniture it contained to her poor lady, who dwelt in it, working as a peasant for her daily bread. Her spinning wheel and the milk of a cow, which she had purchased with the little money she had with her, sufficed for the scanty subsistence of herself and her little son. There was a nice little garden attached to the cottage, in which they cultivated peas, beans, and cabbages, and the lady was not ashamed to go out at harvest time, and glean in the fields to supply her little son's wants.

Jack, that poor lady is your mother. This castle was once your father's, and must again be yours.

Jack uttered a cry of surprise. "My mother! Oh, madam, what ought I to do? My poor father! My dear mother!"

"Your duty requires you to win it back for your mother. But the task is a very difficult one, and full of peril, Jack. Have you courage to undertake it?"

"I fear nothing when I am doing right," said Jack.

"Then," said the lady in the red cap, "you are one of those who slay giants. You must get into the castle, and if possible possess yourself of a hen that lays golden eggs, and a harp that talks. Remember, all the giant possesses is really yours." As she ceased speaking, the lady of the red hat suddenly disappeared, and of course Jack knew she was a fairy.

Jack determined at once to attempt the adventure; so he advanced, and blew the horn which hung at the castle portal. The door was opened in a minute or two by a frightful giantess, with one great eye in the middle of her forehead. As soon as Jack saw her he turned to run away, but she caught him, and dragged him into the castle.

"Ho, ho!" she laughed terribly. "You didn't expect to see *me* here, that is clear! No, I shan't let you go again. I am weary of my life. I am so overworked, and I don't see why I should not have a page as well as other ladies. And you shall be my boy. You shall clean the knives, and black the boots, and make the fires, and help me generally when the giant is out. When he is at home I must hide you, for he has eaten up all my pages hitherto, and you would be a dainty morsel, my little lad." While she spoke she dragged Jack right into the castle. The poor boy was very much frightened, as I am sure you and I would have been in his place. But he remembered that fear disgraces a man; so he struggled to be brave and make the best of things.

"I am quite ready to help you, and do all I can to serve you, madam," he said, "only I beg you will be good enough to hide me from your husband, for I should not like to be eaten at all."

"That's a good boy," said the giantess, nodding her head; "it is lucky for you that you did not scream out when you saw me, as the other boys who have been here did, for if you had done so my husband would have awakened and have eaten you, as he did them, for breakfast. Come here, child; go into my wardrobe. He never ventures to open *that*. You will be safe there."

And she opened a huge wardrobe which stood in the great hall, and shut him into it. But the keyhole was so large that it admitted plenty of air, and he could see everything that took place through it. By and by he heard a heavy tramp on the stairs, like the lumbering along of a great cannon, and then a voice like thunder cried out. "There," she said; "that is all that is left of the knight's money. When you have spent it you must go and take another baron's castle."

"That he shan't, if I can help it," thought Jack.

The giant, when his wife was gone, took out heaps and heaps of golden pieces, and counted them, and put them in piles, until he was tired of the amusement. Then he swept them all back into their bags, and leaning back in his chair fell fast asleep, snoring so loud that no other sound was audible.

Jack stole softly out of the wardrobe, and taking up the bags of money (which were his very own, because the giant had stolen them from his father), he ran off, and with great difficulty descending the beanstalk, laid the bags of gold on his mother's table. She had just returned from town, and was crying at not finding Jack.

"There, mother, I have brought you the gold that my father lost."

209

"Oh, Jack! You are a very good boy, but I wish you would not risk your precious life in the giant's castle. Tell me how you came to go there again." And Jack told her all about it.

Jack's mother was very glad to get the money, but she did not like him to run any risk for her. But after a time Jack made up his mind to go again to the giant's castle.

So he climbed the beanstalk once more, and blew the horn at the giant's gate. The giantess soon opened the door; she was very stupid, and did not know him again, but she stopped a minute before she took him in. She feared another robbery; but Jack's fresh face looked so innocent that she could not resist him, and so she bade him come in, and again hid him away in the wardrobe.

By and by the giant came home, and as soon as he had crossed the threshold he roared out:

> "Fee-fi-fo-fum,
> I smell the blood of an Englishman.
> Be he alive, or be he dead,
> I'll grind his bones to make my bread."[153]

"You stupid old giant," said his wife, "you only smell a nice sheep, which I have grilled for your dinner."

And the giant sat down, and his wife brought up a whole sheep for his dinner. When he had eaten it all up, he said, "Now bring me my harp, and I will have a little music while you take your walk."

The giantess obeyed, and returned with a beautiful harp. The framework was all sparkling with diamonds and rubies, and the strings were all of gold.

"This is one of the nicest things I took from the knight," said the giant. "I am very fond of music, and my harp is a faithful servant."

So he drew the harp towards him, and said, "Play!" And the harp played a very soft, sad air.

"Play something merrier!" said the giant. And the harp played a merry tune.

"Now play me a lullaby," roared the giant, and the harp played a sweet lullaby, to the sound of which its master fell asleep.

Then Jack stole softly out of the wardrobe, and went into the huge kitchen to see if the giantess had gone out; he found no one there, so he went to the door and opened it softly, for he thought he could not do so with the harp in his hand.

Then he entered the giant's room and seized the harp and ran away with it; but as he jumped over the threshold the harp called out, "Master! Master!" And the giant

---

[153]I have taken the liberty to change Andrew Lang's verse to the form that I remember from my mother's telling of this story. Lang uses the following verse, which is—I presume—the version that he learned from his mother:

> "Fe, fa, fi-fo-fum,
> I smell the breath of an Englishman.
> Let him be alive or let him be dead,
> I'll grind his bones to make my bread."

woke up. With a tremendous roar he sprang from his seat, and in two strides had reached the door.

But Jack was very nimble. He fled like lightning with the harp, talking to it as he went (for he saw it was a fairy), and telling it he was the son of its old master, the knight.

Still the giant came on so fast that he was quite close to poor Jack, and had stretched out his great hand to catch him. But, luckily, just at the moment he stepped upon a loose stone, stumbled, and fell flat on the ground, where he lay at his full length.

This accident gave Jack time to get on the beanstalk and hasten down it; but just as he reached their own garden he beheld the giant descending after him.

"Mother! mother!" cried Jack, "make haste and give me the ax." His mother ran to him with a hatchet in her hand, and Jack with one tremendous blow cut through all the stems except one.

"Now, mother, stand out of the way!" said he. Jack's mother shrank back, and it was well she did so, for just as the giant took hold of the last branch of the beanstalk, Jack cut the stem quite through and darted from the spot.

Down came the giant with a terrible crash, and as he fell on his head, he broke his neck, and lay dead at the feet of the woman he had so much injured.

Before Jack and his mother had recovered from their alarm and agitation, a beautiful lady stood before them. "Jack," said she, "you have acted like a brave knight's son, and deserve to have your inheritance restored to you. Dig a grave and bury the giant, and then go and kill the giantess."

"But," said Jack, "I could not kill anyone unless I were fighting with him; and I could not draw my sword upon a woman. Moreover, the giantess was very kind to me."

The fairy smiled on Jack. "I am very much pleased with your generous feeling," she said. "Nevertheless, return to the castle, and act as you will find needful."

Jack asked the fairy if she would show him the way to the castle, as the beanstalk was now down. She told him that she would drive him there in her chariot, which was drawn by two peacocks. Jack thanked her, and sat down in the chariot with her. The fairy drove him a long distance round, until they reached a village which lay at the bottom of the hill. Here they found a number of miserable-looking men assembled. The fairy stopped her carriage and addressed them:

"My friends," said she, "the cruel giant who oppressed you and ate up all your flocks and herds is dead, and this young gentleman was the means of your being delivered from him, and is the son of your kind old master, the knight."

The men gave a loud cheer at these words, and pressed forward to say that they would serve Jack as faithfully as they had served his father. The fairy bade them follow her to the castle, and they marched thither in a body, and Jack blew the horn and demanded admittance.

The old giantess saw them coming from the turret loop hole. She was very much frightened, for she guessed that something had happened to her husband; and as she came downstairs very fast she caught her foot in her dress, and fell from the top to the bottom and broke her neck.

When the people outside found that the door was not opened to them, they took crowbars and forced the portal. Nobody was to be seen, but on leaving the hall they found the body of the giantess at the foot of the stairs.

Thus Jack took possession of the castle. The fairy went and brought his mother to him, with the hen and the harp. He had the giantess buried, and endeavored as much as lay in his power to do right to those whom the giant had robbed. Before her departure for fairyland, the fairy explained to Jack that she had sent the butcher to meet him with the beans, in order to try what sort of lad he was.

"If you had looked at the gigantic beanstalk and only stupidly wondered about it," she said, "I should have left you where misfortune had placed you, only restoring her cow to your mother. But you showed an inquiring mind, and great courage and enterprise, therefore you deserve to rise; and when you mounted the beanstalk you climbed the Ladder of Fortune."

She then took her leave of Jack and his mother.[154]

The Master Cat; or, Puss in Boots

Charles Perrault

There was a miller whose only inheritance to his three sons was his mill, his donkey, and his cat. The division was soon made. They hired neither a clerk nor an attorney, for they would have eaten up all the poor patrimony. The eldest took the mill, the second the donkey, and the youngest nothing but the cat.

The poor young fellow was quite comfortless for having received so little. "My brothers," said he, "may make a handsome living by joining their shares together; but, for my part, after I have eaten up my cat, and made myself a muff from his skin, I must then die of hunger."

The cat, who heard all this, but pretended otherwise, said to him with a grave and serious air, "Do not be so concerned, my good master. If you will but give me a bag, and have a pair of boots made for me, that I may scamper through the dirt and the brambles, then you shall see that you are not so poorly off with me as you imagine."

The cat's master did not build very much upon what he said. However, he had often seen him play a great many cunning tricks to catch rats and mice, such as hanging by his heels, or hiding himself in the meal, and pretending to be dead; so he did take some hope that he might give him some help in his miserable condition.

After receiving what he had asked for, the cat gallantly pulled on the boots and slung the bag about his neck. Holding its drawstrings in his forepaws, he went to a

[154]Type 328. Source: Andrew Lang, *The Red Fairy Book* (London, 1890), pp. 133-145.

place where there was a great abundance of rabbits. He put some bran and greens into his bag, then stretched himself out as if he were dead. He thus waited for some young rabbits, not yet acquainted with the deceits of the world, to come and look into his bag.

He had scarcely lain down before he had what he wanted. A rash and foolish young rabbit jumped into his bag, and the master cat, immediately closed the strings, then took and killed him without pity. Proud of his prey, he went with it to the palace, and asked to speak with his majesty. He was shown upstairs into the king's apartment, and, making a low bow, said to him, "Sir, I have brought you a rabbit from my noble lord, the Master of Carabas" (for that was the title which the cat was pleased to give his master)."

"Tell your master," said the king, "that I thank him, and that I am very pleased with his gift."

Another time he went and hid himself in a grain field. He again held his bag open, and when a brace of partridges ran into it, he drew the strings, and caught them both. He presented these to the king, as he had done before with the rabbit. The king, in like manner, received the partridges with great pleasure, and gave him a tip. The cat continued, from time to time for two or three months, to take game to his majesty from his master.

One day, when he knew for certain that the king would be taking a drive along the riverside, with his daughter, the most beautiful princess in the world, he said to his master, "If you will follow my advice your fortune is made. All you must do is to go and bathe yourself in the river, at the place I show you, then leave the rest to me."

The Marquis of Carabas did what the cat advised him to, without knowing why. While he was bathing, the king passed by, and the cat began to cry out, "Help! Help! My Lord Marquis of Carabas is going to be drowned."

At this noise the king put his head out of the coach window, and, finding it was the cat who had so often brought him such good game, he commanded his guards to run immediately to the assistance of his lordship the Marquis of Carabas. While they were drawing the poor Marquis out of the river, the cat came up to the coach and told the king that, while his master was bathing, some rogues had come by and stolen his clothes, even though he had cried out, "Thieves! Thieves!" several times, as loud as he could. In truth, the cunning cat had hidden the clothes under a large stone.

The king immediately commanded the officers of his wardrobe to run and fetch one of his best suits for the Lord Marquis of Carabas.

The king received him very courteously. And, because the king's fine clothes gave him a striking appearance (for he was very handsome and well proportioned), the king's daughter took a secret inclination to him. The Marquis of Carabas had only to cast two or three respectful and somewhat tender glances at her but she fell head over heels in love with him. The king asked him to enter the coach and join them on their drive.

The cat, quite overjoyed to see how his project was succeeding, ran on ahead. Meeting some countrymen, who were mowing a meadow, he said to them, "My good fellows, if you do not tell the king that the meadow you are mowing belongs to my Lord Marquis of Carabas, you shall be chopped up like mincemeat."

The king did not fail to ask the mowers whose meadow it was that they were mowing.

"It belongs to my Lord Marquis of Carabas," they answered altogether, for the cat's threats had frightened them.

"You see, sir," said the Marquis, "this is a meadow which never fails to yield a plentiful harvest every year."

The master cat, still running on ahead, met with some reapers, and said to them:

"My good fellows, if you do not tell the king that all this grain belongs to the Marquis of Carabas, you shall be chopped up like mincemeat."

The king, who passed by a moment later, asked them whose grain it was that they were reaping.

"It belongs to my Lord Marquis of Carabas," replied the reapers, which pleased both the king and the marquis. The king congratulated him for his fine harvest. The master cat, continued to run ahead, and said the same words to all he met. The king was astonished at the vast estates of the Lord Marquis of Carabas.

The master cat came at last to a stately castle, the lord of which was an ogre, the richest that had ever been known. All the lands which the king had just passed by belonged to this castle. The cat, who had taken care to inform himself who this ogre was and what he could do, asked to speak with him, saying he could not pass so near his castle without having the honor of paying his respects to him.

The ogre received him as civilly as an ogre could do, and invited him to sit down. "I have heard," said the cat, "that you are able to change yourself into any kind of creature that you have a mind to. You can, for example, transform yourself into a lion, an elephant, or the like."

"That is true," answered the ogre very briskly; "and to convince you, I shall now become a lion."

The cat was so terrified at the sight of a lion so near him that he leaped onto the roof, which caused him even more difficulty, because his boots were of no use at all to him in walking on the tiles. However, the ogre resumed his natural form, and the cat came down, saying that he had been very frightened indeed.

"I have further been told," said the cat, " that you can also transform yourself into the smallest of animals, for example, a rat or a mouse. But I can scarcely believe that. I must admit to you that I think that that would be quite impossible."

"Impossible!" cried the ogre; "you shall see!"

He immediately changed himself into a mouse, and began to run about the floor. As soon as the cat saw this, he fell upon him and ate him up.

Meanwhile the king, who saw this fine castle of the ogre's, as he passed, decided to go inside. The cat, who heard the noise of his majesty's coach running over the drawbridge, ran out, and said to the king, "Your majesty is welcome to this castle of my Lord Marquis of Carabas."

"What! my Lord Marquis," cried the king, "and does this castle also belong to you? There can be nothing finer than this court and all the stately buildings which surround it; let us go inside, if you don't mind."

214

The marquis gave his hand to the princess, and followed the king, who went first. They passed into a spacious hall, where they found a magnificent feast, which the ogre had prepared for his friends, who were coming to visit him that very day, but dared not to enter, knowing the king was there. His majesty was perfectly charmed with the good qualities of my Lord Marquis of Carabas, as was his daughter, who had fallen violently in love with him, and, seeing the vast estate he possessed, said to him, after having drunk five or six glasses, "It will be your own fault, my Lord Marquis, if you do not become my son-in-law."

The marquis, making several low bows, accepted the honor which his majesty conferred upon him, and forthwith, that very same day, married the princess.

The cat became a great lord, and never again ran after mice, except for entertainment.

> Moral: There is great advantage in receiving a large inheritance, but diligence and ingenuity are worth more than wealth acquired from others.
>
> Another moral: If a miller's son can win the heart of a princess in so short a time, causing her to gaze at him with lovelorn eyes, it must be due to his clothes, his appearance, and his youth. These things do play a role in matters of the heart.[155]

The Flying Ship

Ukraine

Once upon a time there lived an old couple who had three sons; the two elder were clever, but the third was stupid. The mother was very fond of the clever sons and gave them good clothes; but the simpleton was always poorly dressed. He had only one everyday shirt.

One day the czar proclaimed that he would give his daughter in marriage to whoever should build a ship that could fly. The two elder brothers determined to try their luck, and asked the parents for their blessing. The mother outfitted them for their journey, giving each one white bread, meat, bacon, and a bottle of brandy.

The simpleton wanted to go with them, but the mother ridiculed him, "What would become of a dolt like you?" she said, "You would be eaten up by the wolves!"

---

[155]Type 545B. Source: Andrew Lang, *The Blue Fairy Book* (London, ca. 1889), pp. 141-147. Lang's source: Charles Perrault, *Histoires ou contes du temps passé, avec des moralités: Contes de ma mère l'Oye* (Paris, 1697).

But the simpleton kept repeating, "Let me go! Let me go! Let me go!"

Seeing that she could not dissuade him, she gave him a loaf of black bread and a bottle of water and slammed the door behind him.

The simpleton wandered and wandered until he met an old man. They greeted one another, and the old man asked him where he was going.

"The czar has promised his daughter to whoever can build a flying ship," he said.

"Can you build such a ship?"

"No."

"Then why in the world are you going?"

"Only God knows."

"In that case," said the old man, "Sit down with me and rest a while. Let's have something to eat. What do you have in your bag?"

"Nothing to be proud of."

"That doesn't matter. We will be happy with whatever God provides."

The simpleton untied his bag, and could not believe his eyes. Instead of coarse black bread there were white rolls and all sorts of good things to go with them. He offered to share it all with the old man, who said, "God takes pleasure in simpletons. Your mother doesn't love you, but you will find your way. Now let's have a drink of vodka." And the simpleton's bottle contained, not water, but vodka.

After they had eaten, the old man said, "Go into that wood, and stop in front of the first tree. Cross yourself three times. Drive your ax into the tree; then lie down with your face to the ground and wait there until you are awakened. Then you will see the ship before you, and you can climb aboard and fly wherever you want to, but you must take everyone along with you whom you meet underway."

The Simpleton thanked the old man, took leave of him, and entered the wood. He stopped in front of the first tree, and did just as he had been told, driving his ax into the tree and then falling asleep with his face to the ground. When he awoke he saw completed ship before him. He climbed aboard, and the ship flew through the air.

He flew on and on, and when the simpleton looked down, he saw a man beneath him who was kneeling with his ear to the ground.

"Hello, kinsman," he shouted. "What are you doing down there?"

"I'm listening to what is happening in the next world," he replied.

"Come with me in my ship," said the simpleton.

The man got in beside him. They flew on and on until they passed over a man who was hopping on one leg, with his other leg tied up behind his ear.

"Hello, kinsman," he called out. "Why are you hopping along on one leg?"

"I can't help it," replied the man. "I walk so fast that if I did not tie up one leg, I would leap to the end of the earth in a single bound."

"Come with us on my ship," answered the simpleton. The man joined them, and they flew on. Suddenly beneath them they saw a man aiming a gun into the distance.

"Hello, kinsman," the simpleton called out. "What are you aiming at? There are no birds in sight.?

"I can hit beast or bird at a hundred miles' distance," replied the man.

"Come into the ship with us," answered the simpleton. The man got in, and the ship flew on. After a while the simpleton saw a man with a sack of bread on his back.

"Hello, kinsman," he shouted. "Where are you going?"

"To fetch some bread for my noon meal."

"But you already have a sackful on your back."

"That's nothing," answered the man. "I would finish that in one mouthful."

"Then come along with us in my ship."

The glutton joined them, and they flew on and on until they came to a man who was walking along the shore of a great lake.

"Hello, kinsman," shouted the simpleton. "What are you looking for?"

"I'm thirsty, and can't find any water," replied the man.

"There's a whole lake in front of you. Why don't you drink from it?"

"That's nothing," he answered. "I'd drink the whole thing in one gulp."

"Well, come with us in the ship."

He climbed aboard, and they flew on until they came to a man carrying a bundle of wood through the forest.

"Hello, kinsman," shouted the simpleton. "Why are you carrying that wood through the forest?"

"This is not ordinary wood," answered the man. "If you throw it upon the ground, it will be changed into an army of soldiers."

"Come into the ship with us, then."

He climbed aboard, and they flew on until they came to a man carrying a bundle of straw.

"Hello, kinsman," shouted the simpleton. "Where are you taking that straw?"

"To the village," he answered, "for this is not ordinary straw. If you strew it about it will cause winter to come immediately, even in the hottest summer."

The simpleton asked him to join them. He was the last one, and they soon reached the czar's palace.

The czar was just eating dinner, but he at once dispatched a servant to find out who had flown up in this strange ship. The servant saw that there were only common peasants aboard the ship, and reported this to the czar. Not wanting to marry his daughter to a peasant, he said to himself, "I'll get rid of them by giving them some impossible tasks to perform." Then the czar sent a servant to the simpleton with the order to bring him back some Water of Life before he had finished his dinner.

The Simpleton's sharp-eared companion heard the czar's words even while he was giving the instructions to his servant. "What shall I do?" said the simpleton. "It would take me quite a year, and perhaps an entire lifetime, to find what the czar wants."

"Never fear!" said his fleet-footed comrade. The swift runner then untied his foot, and in no time he was at the world's end drawing Water of Life from the well.

"There's still time enough," said the runner to himself. "I'll just rest a little while in the shade of this mill before returning." He lay down, closed his eyes, and fell sound asleep.

When he did not return, the ship's crew grew anxious. The man with the keen hearing put an ear to the ground, then said, "He's lying on the ground, snoring hard."

The marksman aimed his gun in the direction of the mill and pulled the trigger. The shot awakened the runner, who was back with the water in an instant.

The czar now presented a new demand. The simpleton and his companions were to eat up twelve roasted oxen and twelve sacks of bread at a single sitting. But this was nothing for the glutton, who devoured everything, and still wanted more.

Next, the czar ordered the ship's crew to drink forty casks of wine, each containing forty gallons. But this was nothing for the thirsty companion, who drank all forty casks on the spot, and still wanted more.

Then the czar sent an order that the simpleton was to have a bath in the palace bathroom. Now the bathroom was built of iron, and the czar gave orders to heat it until the walls glowed red, and thus to suffocate the simpleton. Fortunately, the companion with the straw entered the bathroom with the simpleton. He scattered his straw about, and the bathroom became so cold that the water froze solid. When the servants opened the door the next morning they found the simpleton wrapped in towels and sitting on the stove singing cheerfully to himself.

When the czar heard this strange tale, he cried out, "Tell the rascal to raise me an army, now at this instant!"

As before, the sharp-eared companion overheard the czar's command and repeated it to the simpleton.

"How should I, a common peasant, raise an army?" he said. "Now I am done for!"

"Have you forgotten me?" asked the man with the sticks, just as the czar's servant arrived with the message from the palace.

"Good!" remarked the simpleton. "I will raise an army for the czar. But if, after that, the czar refuses to accept me as his son-in-law, I will wage war against him, and carry the princess off by force.

During the night the simpleton and his comrade went together into a big field, not forgetting to take the bundle of wood with them, which the man spread out in all directions—and in a moment a mighty army stood on the spot: cavalry, infantry, and grenadiers.

In the morning when the czar awoke, it was his turn to be frightened. He immediately delivered costly robes and clothing to the simpleton, and invited him to come to the palace and marry his daughter. The simpleton put on the costly robes, and he suddenly looked so grand that it was impossible to describe him. He appeared before the czar and married the princess. He received a large dowry, and from now on he was clever and intelligent. The czar and the czaress accepted him, and the princess loved him beyond all measure.[156]

[156]Type 513B. Retold from Andrew Lang, *The Yellow Fairy Book* (London, 1894), pp. 198-205.

218

The Rabbit Herd

Europe

Once upon a time there was a king who had a daughter that would not laugh. His jugglers, clowns, and jesters performed their utmost for her, but she could not, or would not, even break a smile. Finally the king proclaimed that whatever man—rich or poor, young or old, strong or frail—could break his daughter's spell should take her to wife, and receive half the kingdom as well. Men and boys came from every direction to try their luck but no one was successful, until....

The news finally reached a remote corner of the kingdom where a poor peasant lived with his three sons. The youngest—we'll call him Hans (although some say that his name was Jack, or Ivan, or Juan)—decided that he too would try his luck at winning the hand of the princess. He was a droll sort—some called him silly, others just plain stupid—whose capers often brought the villagers to laughter. Yes, he would give it a try. And he set forth, pursued by the jeers of his older and wiser brothers, on the path that led to the king's palace.

At midday he was looking for a shady spot where he could rest and eat the crust of bread he had brought, when suddenly he came upon an old man by the side of the road.

"Would you share your bread with a weary traveler?" asked the stranger.

"Half a dry crust is quite as good as a whole one," replied Hans, and broke off a piece for the old man.

"Bless you, my son," responded the stranger. "I cannot reward you with gold, but this whistle will lead you to that, and more." So saying, he offered Hans a tiny silver flute.

Hans put the flute to his lips, and it began to play, first a marching tune, then a cheerful air, and then a pensive hymn. Before he knew it, Hans had arrived at the palace, and the guards, charmed by his tuneful music, let him pass. His heart leapt for joy, and the flute broke into a lusty jig. The princess, hearing the tune, opened her window and looked out. She nodded her head to the beat, then gave a cautious grin, and then an open smile. She chuckled softly to herself, then broke into a happy laugh.

The king, hearing her joyful laughter, was beside himself with glee, until—that is—until he saw the lad who was playing the flute. Hans, you see, did have the look of a peasant and of a simpleton, and the king, in spite of his promise, was hoping for a finer man.

"That is all well and good," said the king to Hans, "but before you can receive the princess, there is yet another task that you must fulfill." He then had one hundred wild rabbits set loose in a nearby forest. "Keep these animals together in a herd," said the king, and in three days the princess and half the kingdom shall be yours. But if you lose a single rabbit, you shall forfeit everything.

Lang's source: Aleksandr Afanasyev.

Even as they spoke the rabbits ran to the four winds, but Hans did not despair. He blew a few notes into the silver flute, and as if by magic, the hundred rabbits assembled at his feet. Reassured, he made himself comfortable in the shade of a large tree, and waited for the three days to pass.

The king, seeing how easily Hans kept the herd together was filled with worry and anger. No other solution presented itself, so finally he sent his daughter into the woods, telling her to do whatever was necessary to get a rabbit away from the peasant herdsman.

The princess presented herself to Hans, and asked him ever so politely if she might not purchase one of his rabbits. His answer made her blush. "You don't mean that I would have to...," she said, and didn't know whether to pout or to smile.

No, he would accept no other offer, said Hans. "Take it, or leave it."

And so she took it.

The princess left the woods carrying a rabbit in her basket. But well before she arrived home, Hans put the magic flute to his lips, and in an instant the rabbit jumped from her basket and raced back to the herd.

The next day the king, ever more desperate, sent his own wife into the woods with instructions to bring home a rabbit, whatever the cost. When Hans named his price, the queen, like the princess before her, first pouted, then smiled, and then gave in. But she too lost her rabbit when Hans called it back with his magic flute.

On the third day the king himself went into the woods to bargain for a rabbit. Hans, as before, was willing to trade, but this time the price—no, I cannot bring myself to say more than that it involved a mare that was grazing in a nearby clearing. Red with shame, the king took his rabbit and started off for home, but again the flute called the rabbit back into the herd.

The three days had passed, and the rabbit herd was still intact, but now the king found yet another task that Hans would have to fulfill before he could claim the princess and half the kingdom. "A trifle," explained the king. "Just sing three bags full."

"I can manage that," said Hans. "Bring me three empty bags, and I'll sing them full to the top, but only in the presence of the finest lords and ladies of the kingdom.

The king, believing that at last he would be rid of the peasant lad, assembled the lords and ladies in a great hall, then brought in Hans and three empty bags. Hans picked up a bag and started to sing:

> Our princess went into the woods;
> She thought she'd try her luck,
>
> ...

"Stop!" called out the princess. That bag is full!" Hans obligingly stopped singing, tied a string around the mouth of the bag, picked up the next one, and started a new song:

> Our queen she went into the woods;
> She thought she'd try her luck,
>
> . . .

"Stop!" shouted the queen. That bag is full!" Hans stopped, tied this bag shut, picked up the last one, and commenced singing:

> Our king he went into the woods;
> He thought He'd try his luck,
>
> . . .

"Stop!" bellowed the king. The last bag is full!" With that, the king proclaimed that Hans had won the princess's hand in marriage and half the kingdom.

The wedding was celebrated that same day. All the lords and ladies attended the great feast that followed. I too was invited, but I lost my way in the woods and arrived only as the last toast was being drunk.[157]

The Swineherd Who Married a Princess

Europe

Once upon a time in a distant kingdom there was a simple peasant lad who herded swine in a forest next to the king's castle. One of his pigs was smarter than all the rest, and the swineherd taught him how to stand on his hind legs and dance. A swineherd does get lonely, as you must know, alone in the woods with only his animals for company, and he must have been very pleased with himself that he had taught a pig to dance.

One warm summer's day the princess was out walking in the shady woods, and she came upon the swineherd, just as his pig had finished dancing a jig. "Oh, please make him dance once again," asked the princess, ever so courteously, for she had never before seen a pig dance.

"Only if you will lift your skirts to your knees," answered the swineherd.

The princess could see no harm in this, so she lifted her skirts to her knees, and sure enough, the swineherd's pig danced a merry jig.

"That was too short," said the princess. "Can't he dance some more?"

"Only if you lift your skirts to your waist," said the swineherd.

The princess hesitated, but again she could see no harm in his request, so she lifted her skirts to her waist, and the pig danced another merry jig. She still had not

---

[157]Type 570. Retold. This tale, recorded with varying degrees of raciness, is found throughout Europe and the Americas.

had enough and asked, again ever so politely, if the pig couldn't dance just one more time. It was such a cheerful thing to see!

"Only if you lift your skirts to your neck," said the swineherd.

"To my neck?" she asked.

"To your neck!" he replied. Now not even a princess can see a dancing pig every day, so she lifted her skirts to her neck, and the swineherd's pig danced his very best.

Some time later the king decided that it was time for the princess to marry, and because she was the most beautiful maiden in all the land, suitors came from near and far. The king could not choose from the many princes and noblemen who came courting his daughter. Finally he decreed that to win the princess's hand in marriage a suitor would have to describe her secret birthmark. You see, from the day the princess was born she had had a birthmark on her belly, a dainty little spot from which grew three fine golden hairs.

The swineherd soon learned of the proclamation, and went to the castle at once, because, of course, he had seen the mark with the three golden hairs on the day that the princess lifted her skirts in order to make his pig dance.

Now a king's word is a king's word, and even though he did not relish giving his daughter to a simple swineherd, he had to do as he had promised. After all, the swineherd was able to describe the birthmark ever so correctly, down to the last golden hair.

But the story is not yet done, for one of the princes who had come to court the princess offered the princess's lady-in-waiting a bag of gold if she would just describe to him her mistress's birthmark. The faithless servant took the gold and told the unworthy prince what he wanted to know.

When the deceitful prince presented himself to the king and described the princess's birthmark ever so accurately, the king, at first, did not know what to do. But then he struck upon a plan. "Let the princess decide herself!" he proclaimed. She and the two suitors shall spend the night together in the princess's bed. At sunrise I will look in on them, and the one she is facing shall be her husband.

When the swineherd learned of the king's decree, he made plans for the night. First he put a large clump of chocolate (some say that it was marzipan) into his pocket. Then he secretly dropped an herb into the false prince's evening soup, an herb that would summon nature's call quickly and surely.

That night the swineherd, the deceitful prince, and the beautiful princess all lay down in her large bed; the king locked the door behind them; and they closed their eyes. Then suddenly the false prince jumped up with a start and ran to the door, but it was locked.

"I have to also!" said the swineherd, jumping out of bed.

"What can we do? We're locked in!" cried the prince.

"We'll have to do it on the floor." said the swineherd. Then each man deposited something on the floor: the swineherd his clump of chocolate, and the prince ——, well, some things are better left unsaid.

"Now we are in trouble!" said the swineherd. "When the king discovers what we've done, he'll have us killed!"

"What can we do?" asked the terrified prince.

"We've no choice," answered the swineherd. "We'll have to eat it."

Thus the swineherd ate his clump of chocolate, and the false prince ate —— ——, well, again, some things are better left unsaid.

They returned to the sleeping princess's bed, one on one side of her and one on the other. With time the princess turned toward the prince and breathed in deeply, but then she gasped and quickly turned the other way. At sunrise the king looked in on them and found the princess contentedly asleep with her face nearly touching that of the swineherd.

And that is how a simple swineherd came to marry a princess.[158]

The Blue Light

Jacob and Wilhelm Grimm

Walking through the woods, but going nowhere in particular, a soldier, dismissed from service because of his wounds, bemoaned his fate. He came to a hut with an ancient woman peering out through the doorway.

"There's a good reward for you," she said, "if you'll help me get back the lamp that I've dropped down my well."

"Why not?" said he. I'd just as soon drown in an old witch's well as perish from cold and hunger in the woods." So he let her lower him into the well. At the bottom, instead of water, he found a great chamber, stacked high with chests and bags. Atop one the chests he saw the lamp desired by the old woman, took hold of it, and signaled to be pulled up.

As soon as his head and shoulders emerged from the well, the old woman demanded the lamp.

"Not until you've pulled me the rest of the way out!" he replied.

"Then may you rot in hell!" she shouted. "I'll get the lamp another way!" And with that she released the well rope, and the soldier fell back into the underground cavern.

"At least I won't be in the dark," he thought, then taking a flint and steel from his pocket, he started to ignite the lamp.

But to his surprise, instead of flame and light, a spirit emerged from the lamp, saying, "What do you wish, master?"

---

[158]Type 850. Retold from various Scandinavian and German sources. H. C. Andersen included a bowdlerized version of this story in his famous fairy tale collection, explaining in a footnote that "the version I heard, as a child, would be quite unprintable." Yes, cousin Hans, that would certainly have been true in 1842, but the past 150 years have brought many changes in style and taste, admittedly not all for the better. I'll take a chance.

"I wish a house in the royal city," he replied, "and take me there at once." No sooner said, than done. The soldier found himself in a comfortable house not far from the king's palace. Recognizing the power of lamp, the soldier fell to musing. "Now he will pay," he said to himself, thinking of the king, who had unfairly dismissed him from service, turning him out into the world to starve.

With flint and steel he again set a spark to the lamp's wick, and again, instead of flame and light, a spirit emerged, saying, "What do you wish, master."

"Bring me the king's daughter," replied the soldier, "and make her do anything that I ask."

"That is a very dangerous thing," warned the spirit, "but your wish is my command." In an instant he returned with the princess, who had to clean the soldier's house, and do everything that he asked.

The next morning the princess told her father of a strange dream. It seemed that she had been spirited out of her bed the night before, then whisked away to a soldier's house, where she had to do all manner of housework.

"It was probably only a dream," said the king, "but if it happens again, mark the soldier's door with a piece of chalk, and he will pay for his housecleaning with his head."

And the very next it did indeed happen again. Following her father's advice, she marked the soldier's door with chalk. However, the spirit of the lamp saw what she had done, and so he marked every door in the city with chalk. Thus, when the guards were sent out the next day to bring in the man whose door was marked with chalk, they did not know where to begin.

The third night came, and the soldier spirited the princess to his house once again. This time she secretly hid one of her shoes beneath his bed. The next morning she told the king what had happened, and he sent the guards to find the hidden shoe. They found the shoe beneath the soldier's bed, and dragged him off to prison before he could summon the spirit of the lamp.

The soldier, sentenced to die the next day, sat in his cell. Fortunately it had a small window that looked out onto the street. He called to a passing boy, and offered him a reward if he would bring him the lamp and the flint and steel that he would find at thus and such a house. The boy hurried off, returning a short time later with the desired objects.

The next day the soldier was dragged to the execution spot, where the king and all his guards, judges and noblemen were assembled to witness his end. "Do you have a final wish?" they asked.

"Yes," said he. "May I just light my pipe one last time from this old lamp, and take a puff or two." So saying, he took flint and steel and the lamp from his pocket and struck a spark. The spirit came forth, and the soldier turned him loose on the king, the guards, the judges, the nobleman, and the executioner. You never saw such a drubbing. Left and right, up and down, around and about, there was no escape from the spirit's blows. Finally, to save his life, the king surrendered his kingdom to the soldier. Then the soldier married the princess, and if they have not died yet, they are still alive.[159]

[159]Type 562. Retold from *Kinder- und Hausmärchen*, 1st ed. (Berlin, 1812/1815), v. 2, no. 30 (no. 116 in the final edition). H. C. Andersen's "Fyrtøjet" ("The Tinderbox") is a familiar version of the same tale.

Courtship and Marriage

Animal Brides

The Frog's Skin

Georgia

There were once three brothers who wished to marry. They said, "Let us each shoot an arrow, and each shall take his wife from the place where the arrow falls." They shot their arrows; those of the two elder brothers fell on noblemen's houses, while the youngest brother's arrow fell in a lake. The two elder brothers led home their noble wives, and the youngest went to the shore of the lake. He saw a frog creep out of the lake and sit down upon a stone. He took it up and carried it back to the house. All the brothers came home with what fate had given them; the elder brothers with the noble maidens, and the youngest with a frog.

The brothers went out to work. The wives prepared the dinner and attended to all their household duties. The frog sat by the fire croaking, and its eyes glittered. Thus they lived together a long time in love and harmony.

At last the sisters-in-law wearied of the sight of the frog. When they swept the house, they threw out the frog with the dust. If the youngest brother found it, he took it up in his hand; if not, the frog would leap back to its place by the fire and begin to croak. The noble sisters did not like this, and said to their husbands, "Drive this frog out, and get a real wife for your brother." Every day the brothers bothered the youngest.

He replied, saying, "This frog is certainly my fate. I am worthy of no better. I must be faithful to it." His sisters-in-law persisted in telling their husbands that the brother and his frog must be sent away, and at last they agreed.

The young brother was now left quite desolate. There was no one to make his food, no one to stand watching at the door. For a short time a neighboring woman came to wait upon him, but she had not time, so he was left alone. The man became very melancholy.

Once when he was thinking sadly of his loneliness, he went to work. When he had finished his day's labor, he went home. He looked into his house and was

226

struck with amazement. The sideboard was well replenished; in one place was spread a cloth, and on the cloth were many different kinds of tempting dishes. He looked and saw the frog in its place croaking. He said to himself that his sisters-in-law must have done this for him, and went to his work again. He was out all day working, and when he came home he always found everything prepared for him.

Once he said to himself, "I will see for once who is this unseen benefactor, who comes to do good to me and look after me." That day he stayed at home; he seated himself on the roof of the house and watched. In a short time the frog leaped out of the fireplace, jumped over to the doors, and all around the room. Seeing no one there, it went back and took off the frog's skin, put it near the fire, and came forth a beautiful maiden, fair as the sun; so lovely was she that the man could not imagine anything prettier. In the twinkling of an eye she had tidied everything, prepared the food, and cooked it. When everything was ready, she went to the fire, put on the skin again, and began to croak. When the man saw this he was very much astonished; he rejoiced exceedingly that God had granted him such happiness. He descended from the roof, went in, caressed his frog tenderly, and then sat down to his tasty supper.

The next day the man hid himself in the place where he had been the day before. The frog, having satisfied itself that nobody was there, stripped off its skin and began its good work. This time the man stole silently into the house, seized the frog's skin in his hand and threw it into the fire. When the maiden saw this she entreated him, she wept, and she said, "Do not burn it, or you shall surely be destroyed," but the man had burned it in a moment. "Now, if your happiness be turned to misery, it is not my fault," said the sorrow-stricken woman.

In a very short time the whole countryside knew that the man who had a frog now possessed in its place a lovely woman, who had come to him from heaven.

The lord of the country heard of this, and wished to take her from him. He called the beautiful woman's husband to him and said, "Sow a barnful of wheat in a day, or give me your wife." When he had spoken thus, the man was obliged to consent, and he went home melancholy.

When he went in he told his wife what had taken place. She reproached him, saying, "I told you what would happen if you did burn the skin, and you did not heed me; but I will not blame you. Be not sad; go in the morning to the edge of the lake from which I came, and call out, 'Mother and Father! I pray you, lend me your swift bullocks.' Lead them away with you, and the bullocks will in one day plow the fields and sow the grain." The husband did this.

He went to the edge of the lake and called out, "Mother and Father! I entreat you, lend me your swift bullocks today." There came forth from the lake such a team of oxen as was never seen on sea or land.

The youth drove the bullocks away, came to his lord's field, and plowed and sowed them in one day.

His lord was very much surprised. He did not know if there was anything impossible to this man, whose wife he wanted. He called him a second time, and said, "Go and gather up the wheat you have sown, that not a grain may be wanting, and that the barn may be full. If you do not do this, your wife is mine."

"This is impossible," said the man to himself. He went home to his wife, who again reproached him, and then said, "Go to the lake's edge and ask for the jackdaws."

The husband went to the edge of the lake and called out, "Mother and Father! I beg you to lend me your jackdaws today." From the lake came forth flocks of jackdaws; they flew to the plowed ground, each gathered up a seed and put it into the barn.

The lord came and cried out, "There is one seed short; I know each one, and one is missing." At that moment a jackdaw's caw was heard; it came with the missing seed, but owing to a lame foot it was a little late.

The lord was very angry that even the impossible was possible to this man, and could not think what to give him to do.

He puzzled his brain until he thought of the following plan. He called the man and said to him, "My mother, who died in this village, took with her a ring. If you go to the other world and bring that ring back to me, it is well; if not, I shall take away your wife."

The man said to himself, "This is quite impossible." He went home and complained to his wife. She reproached him, and then said, "Go to the lake and ask for the ram."

The husband went to the lake and called out, "Mother and Father! Give me your ram today, I pray you." From the lake there came forth a ram with twisted horns; from its mouth issued a flame of fire. It said to the man, "Mount on my back!"

The man sat down, and, quick as lightning, the ram descended towards the lower regions. It went on and shot like an arrow through the earth.

They traveled on, and saw in one place a man and woman sitting on a bullock's skin, which was not big enough for them, and they were like to fall off. The man called out to them, "What can be the meaning of this, that this bullock skin is not big enough for two people?"

They said, "We have seen many pass by like you, but none has returned. When you come back we shall answer your question."

They went on their way and saw a man and woman sitting on an ax handle, and they were not afraid of falling. The man called out to them, "Are you not afraid of falling from the handle of an ax?"

They said to him, "We have seen many pass by like you, but none has returned. When you come back we shall answer your question."

They went on their way again, until they came to a place where they saw a priest feeding cattle. This priest had such a long beard that it spread over the ground, and the cattle, instead of eating grass, fed on the priest's beard, and he could not prevent it. The man called out, "Priest, what is the meaning of this? Why is your beard pasture for these cattle?"

The priest replied, "I have seen many pass by like you, but none has returned. When you come back I shall answer your question."

They journeyed on again until they came to a place where they saw nothing but boiling pitch, and a flame came forth from it—and this was hell. The ram said, "Sit firmly on my back, for we must pass through this fire." The man held fast. The ram gave a leap, and they escaped through the fire unhurt.

There they saw a melancholy woman seated on a golden throne. She said; "What is it, my child? What troubles you? What has brought you here?" He told her everything that had happened to him. She said, "I must punish this very wicked child of mine, and you must take him a casket from me." She gave him a casket, and said, "Whatever you do, do not open this casket yourself. Take it with you, give it to your lord, and run quickly away from him."

The man took the casket and went away. He came to the place where the priest was feeding the cattle. The priest said, "I promised you an answer. Hearken unto my words: In life I loved nothing but myself; I cared for nothing else. My flocks I fed on other pastures than my own, and the neighboring cattle died of starvation. Now I am paying the penalty."

Then he went on to the place where the man and woman were sitting on the handle of the ax. They said, "We promised you an answer. Hearken unto our words: We loved each other too well on earth, and it is the same with us here."

Then he came to the two seated on the bullock skin, which was not big enough for them. They said, "We promised you an answer. Hearken unto our words: We despised each other in life, and we equally despise each other here."

At last the man came up on earth, descended from the ram, and went to his lord. He gave him the casket and quickly ran away. The lord opened the casket, and there came forth fire, which swallowed him up. Our brother was thus victorious over his enemy, and no one took his wife from him. They lived lovingly together, and blessed God as their deliverer.[160]

The Swan Maidens

Joseph Jacobs

There was once a hunter who used often to spend the whole night stalking the deer or setting traps for game. Now it happened one night that he was watching in a clump of bushes near the lake for some wild ducks that he wished to trap. Suddenly he heard, high up in the air, a whirring of wings and thought the ducks were coming; and he strung his bow and got ready his arrows. But instead of ducks there appeared seven maidens all clad in robes made of feathers, and they alighted on the banks of the lake, and taking off their robes plunged into the waters and bathed and sported in the lake. They were all beautiful, but of them all the youngest and smallest pleased most the hunter's eye, and he

---

[160]Type 402. Source: Marjory Wardrop, *Georgian Folk Tales* (London, 1894), pp. 15-21.

crept forward from the bushes and seized her dress of plumage and took it back with him into the bushes.

After the swan maidens had bathed and sported to their heart's delight, they came back to the bank wishing to put on their feather robes again; and the six eldest found theirs, but the youngest could not find hers. They searched and they searched until at last the dawn began to appear, and the six sisters called out to her, "We must away; 'tis the dawn; you meet your fate whatever it be." And with that they donned their robes and flew away, and away, and away.

When the hunter saw them fly away he came forward with the feather robe in his hand; and the swan maiden begged and begged that he would give her back her robe. He gave her his cloak but would not give her her robe, feeling that she would fly away. And he made her promise to marry him, and took her home, and hid her feather robe where she could not find it. So they were married and lived happily together and had two fine children, a boy and a girl, who grew up strong and beautiful; and their mother loved them with all her heart.

One day her little daughter was playing at hide-and-seek with her brother, and she went behind the wainscoting to hide herself, and found there a robe all made of feathers, and took it to her mother. As soon as she saw it she put it on and said to her daughter, "Tell father that if he wishes to see me again he must find me in the Land East o' the Sun and West o' the Moon;" and with that she flew away.

When the hunter came home next morning his little daughter told him what had happened and what her mother said. So he set out to find his wife in the Land East o' the Sun and West o' the Moon. And he wandered for many days until he came across an old man who had fallen on the ground, and he lifted him up and helped him to a seat and tended him until he felt better.

Then the old man asked him what he was doing and where he was going. And he told him all about the swan maidens and his wife, and he asked the old man if he had heard of the Land East o' the Sun and West o' the Moon.

And the old man said, "No, but I can ask."

Then he uttered a shrill whistle and soon all the plain in front of them was filled with all of the beasts of the world, for the old man was no less than the King of the Beasts.

And he called out to them, "Who is there here that knows where the Land is East o' the Sun and West o' the Moon?" But none of the beasts knew.

Then the old man said to the hunter, "You must go seek my brother who is the King of the Birds," and told him how to find his brother.

And after a time he found the King of the Birds, and told him what he wanted. So the King of the Birds whistled loud and shrill, and soon the sky was darkened with all the birds of the air, who came around him. Then he asked, "Which of you knows where the Land East o' the Sun and West o' the Moon?"

And none answered, and the King of the Birds said, "Then you must consult my brother the King of the Fishes," and he told him how to find him.

And the hunter went on, and he went on, and he went on, until he came to the King of the Fishes, and he told him what he wanted. And the King of the Fishes went to the shore of the sea and summoned all the fishes of the sea. And when they came around him he called out, "Which of you knows where is the Land East o' the Sun and West o' the Moon?"

And none of them answered, until at last a dolphin that had come late called out, "I have heard that at the top of the Crystal Mountain lies the Land East o' the Sun and West o' the Moon; but how to get there I know not save that it is near the Wild Forest."

So the hunter thanked the King of the Fishes and went to the Wild Forest. And as he got near there he found two men quarreling, and as he came near they came towards him and asked him to settle their dispute.

"Now what is it?" said the hunter.

"Our father has just died and he has left but two things, this cap which, whenever you wear it, nobody can see you, and these shoes, which will carry you through the air to whatever place you will. Now I being the elder claim the right of choice, which of these two I shall have; and he declares that, as the younger, he has the right to the shoes. Which do you think is right?"

So the hunter thought and thought, and at last he said, "It is difficult to decide, but the best thing I can think of is for you to race from here to that tree yonder, and whoever gets back to me first I will hand him either the shoes or the cap, whichever he wishes."

So he took the shoes in one hand and the cap in the other, and waited until they had started off running towards the tree. And as soon as they had started running towards the tree he put on the shoes of swiftness and placed the invisible cap on his head and wished himself in the Land East o' the Sun and West o' the Moon. And he flew, and he flew, and he flew, over seven Bends, and seven Glens, and seven Mountain Moors, until at last he came to the Crystal Mountain. And on the top of that, as the dolphin had said, there was the Land East o' the Sun and West o' the Moon.

Now when he got there he took off his invisible cap and shoes of swiftness and asked who ruled over the Land; and he was told that there was a king who had seven daughters who dressed in swans' feathers and flew wherever they wished.

Then the hunter knew that he had come to the Land of his wife. And he went boldly to the king and said, "Hail, oh king, I have come to seek my wife."

And the king said, "Who is she?"

And the hunter said, "Your youngest daughter." Then he told him how he had won her.

Then the king said, "If you can tell her from her sisters then I know that what you say is true." And he summoned his seven daughters to him, and there they all were, dressed in their robes of feathers and looking each like all the rest.

So the hunter said, "If I may take each of them by the hand I will surely know my wife"; for when she had dwelt with him she had sewn the little shifts and dresses of her children, and the forefinger of her right hand had the marks of the needle.

And when he had taken the hand of each of the swan maidens he soon found which was his wife and claimed her for his own. Then the king gave them great gifts and sent them by a sure way down the Crystal Mountain.

231

And after a while they reached home, and lived happily together ever afterwards.[161]

The Mermaid Wife

Shetland Islands

A story is told of an inhabitant of Unst[162], who, in walking on the sandy margin of a voe,[163] saw a number of mermen and mermaids dancing by moonlight, and several sealskins strewed beside them on the ground. At his approach they immediately fled to secure their garbs, and, taking upon themselves the form of seals, plunged immediately into the sea. But as the Shetlander perceived that one skin lay close to his feet, he snatched it up, bore it swiftly away, and placed it in concealment.

On returning to the shore he met the fairest damsel that was ever gazed upon by mortal eyes, lamenting the robbery, by which she had become an exile from her submarine friends, and a tenant of the upper world. Vainly she implored the restitution of her property; the man had drunk deeply of love, and was inexorable; but he offered her protection beneath his roof as his betrothed spouse. The merlady, perceiving that she must become an inhabitant of the earth, found that she could not do better than accept of the offer.

This strange attachment subsisted for many years, and the couple had several children. The Shetlander's love for his merwife was unbounded, but his affection was coldly returned. The lady would often steal alone to the desert strand, and, on a signal being given, a large seal would make his appearance, with whom she would hold, in an unknown tongue, an anxious conference.

Years had thus glided away, when it happened that one of the children, in the course of his play, found concealed beneath a stack of corn a seal's skin; and, delighted with the prize, he ran with it to his mother. Her eyes glistened with rapture—she gazed upon it as her own—as the means by which she could pass through the ocean that led to her native home. She burst forth into an ecstasy of joy, which was only moderated when she beheld her children, whom she was now about to leave; and, after hastily embracing them, she fled with all speed towards the seaside. The husband immediately returned, learned the discovery that had

---

[161]Type 400. Source: Joseph Jacobs, *European Folk and Fairy Tales* (New York, 1916), no. 12.

[162]The northernmost of the Shetland Islands.

[163]A deep inlet, or creek. [Note by Douglas]

232

taken place, ran to overtake his wife, but only arrived in time to see her transformation of shape completed—to see her, in the form of a seal, bound from the ledge of a rock into the sea. The large animal of the same kind with whom she had held a secret converse soon appeared, and evidently congratulated her, in the most tender manner, on her escape. But before she dived to unknown depths, she cast a parting glance at the wretched Shetlander, whose despairing looks excited in her breast a few transient feelings of commiseration.

"Farewell!" said she to him "and may all good attend you. I loved you very well when I resided upon earth, but I always loved my first husband much better."[164]

Animal Bridegrooms

The Frog King; or, Iron Heinrich

Jacob and Wilhelm Grimm

Once upon a time there was a princess who went out into a forest and sat next to a cool well. She took great pleasure in throwing a golden ball into the air and catching it, but once it went too high. She held out her hand with her fingers curved to catch it, but it fell to the ground and rolled and rolled right into the water.

Horrified, the princess followed it with her eyes, but the well was so deep that she could not see its bottom. Then she began to cry bitterly, "I'd give anything, if only I could get my ball back: my clothes, my precious stones, my pearls, anything in the world." At this a frog stuck his head out of the water and said, "Princess, why are you crying so bitterly?"

"Oh," she said, "you ugly frog, how can you help me? My golden ball has fallen into the well."

The frog said, "I do not want your pearls, your precious stones, and your clothes, but if you'll accept me as a companion and let me sit next to you and eat from your plate and sleep in your bed, and if you'll love and cherish me, then I'll bring your ball back to you."

---

[164]Migratory legend type 4080, similar to folktale type 400*. Source: George Douglas, *Scottish Fairy and Folk Tales* (London, 1901), pp. 153-155. Douglas's source: W. W. Gibbings, *Folk-Lore and Legends, Scotland* (London, 1889).

The princess thought, "What is this stupid frog trying to say? After all, he does have to stay here in the water. But still, maybe he can get my ball. I'll go ahead and say yes," and she said aloud, "Yes, for all I care. Just bring me back my golden ball, and I'll promise everything."

The frog stuck his head under the water and dove to the bottom. He returned a short time later with the golden ball in his mouth and threw it onto the land. When the princess saw her ball once again, she rushed toward it, picked it up, and was so happy to have it in her hand again, that she could think of nothing else than to run home with it. The frog called after her, "Wait, princess, take me with you like you promised," but she paid no attention to him.

The next day the princess was sitting at her table when she heard something coming up the marble steps: plip, plop. Then there came a knock at the door, and a voice called out, "Princess, youngest, open the door for me!" She ran and opened the door. It was the frog, whom she had put completely out of her mind. Frightened, she slammed the door shut and returned to the table.

The king saw that her heart was pounding and asked, "Why are you afraid?"

"There is a disgusting frog out there," she said, "who got my golden ball out of the water. I promised him that he could be my companion, but I didn't think that he could leave his water, but now he is just outside the door and wants to come in." Just then there came a second knock at the door, and a voice called out:

> Youngest daughter of the king,
> Open up the door for me,
> Don't you know what yesterday,
> You said to me down by the well?
> Youngest daughter of the king,
> Open up the door for me,

The king said, "What you have promised, you must keep. Go and let the frog in." She obeyed, and the frog hopped in, then followed her up to her chair.

After she had sat down again, he called out, "Lift me up onto your chair and let me sit next to you." The princess did not want to, but the king commanded her to do it. When the frog was seated next to her he said, "Now push your golden plate closer. I want to eat from it." She had to do this as well. When he had eaten all he wanted, he said, "Now I am tired and want to sleep. Take me to your room, make your bed, so that we can lie in it together."

The princess was horrified when she heard that. She was afraid of the cold frog and did not dare to even touch him, and yet he was supposed to lie next to her in her bed; she began to cry and didn't want to at all. Then the king became angry and commanded her to do what she had promised. There was no helping it; she had to do what her father wanted, but in her heart she was bitterly angry. She picked up the frog with two fingers, carried him to her room, and climbed into bed, but instead of laying him next to herself, she threw him bang! against the wall. "Now you will leave me in peace, you disgusting frog!" But when the frog came down onto the bed, he was a handsome young prince, and he was her dear companion,

234

and she held him in esteem as she had promised, and they fell asleep together with pleasure.

The next morning the prince's faithful Heinrich arrived in a splendid carriage drawn by eight horses, decorated with feathers and glistening with gold. He had been so saddened by the prince's transformation that he had had to place three iron bands around his heart to keep it from bursting in sorrow. The prince climbed into the carriage with the princess. His faithful servant stood at the rear to drive them to his kingdom. After they had gone a short distance, the prince heard a loud crack from behind. He turned around and said:

> "Heinrich, the carriage is breaking apart."
> "No, my lord, the carriage it's not,
> But one of the bands surrounding my heart,
> That suffered such great pain,
> When you were sitting in the well,
> When you were a frog."

Once again, and then once again the prince heard a cracking sound and thought that the carriage was breaking apart, but it was the bands springing from faithful Heinrich's heart because his master was now redeemed and happy.[165]

The Frog Prince

Jacob and Wilhelm Grimm

Once upon a time there was a king who had three daughters. In his courtyard there was a well with wonderful clear water. One hot summer day the oldest daughter went down and drew herself a glassful, but when she held it to the sun, she saw that it was cloudy. This seemed strange to her, and she was about to pour it back when a frog appeared in the water, stuck his head into the air, then jumped out onto the well's edge, saying:

> If you will be my sweetheart dear,
> Then I will give you water clear.

"Ugh! Who wants to be the sweetheart of an ugly frog!" exclaimed the princess and ran away. She told her sisters about the amazing frog down at the well who was making the water cloudy. The second one was curious, so she too went down and drew herself a glassful, but it was so cloudy that she could not drink it. Once again the frog appeared at the well's edge and said:

---

[165]Type 440. Source: *Kinder- und Hausmärchen*, 1st ed. (Berlin, 1812/1815), v. 1, no. 1.

If you will be my sweetheart dear,
Then I will give you water clear.

"Not I!" said the princess, and ran away. Finally the third sister came and drew a glassful, but it was no better than before. The frog also said to her:

If you will be my sweetheart dear,
Then I will give you water clear.

"Why not! I'll be your sweetheart. Just give me some clean water," she said, while thinking, "There's no harm in this. You can promise him anything, for a stupid frog can never be your sweetheart."

The frog sprang back into the water, and when she drew another glassful it was so clear that the sun glistened in it with joy. She drank all she wanted and then took some up to her sisters, saying, "Why were you so stupid as to be afraid of a frog?"

The princess did not think anything more about it until that evening after she had gone to bed. Before she fell asleep she heard something scratching at the door and a voice singing:

Open up! Open up!
Youngest daughter of the king.
Remember that you promised me
While I was sitting in the well,
That you would be my sweetheart dear,
If I would give you water clear.

"Ugh! That's my boyfriend the frog," said the princess. "I promised, so I will have to open the door for him." She got up, opened the door a crack, and went back to bed. The frog hopped after her, then hopped onto her bed where he lay at her feet until the night was over and the morning dawned. Then he jumped down and disappeared out the door.

The next evening, when the princess once more had just gone to bed, he scratched and sang again at the door. The princess let him in, and he again lay at her feet until daylight came. He came again on the third evening, as on the two previous ones. "This is the last time that I'll let you in," said the princess. "It will not happen again in the future." Then the frog jumped under her pillow, and the princess fell asleep. She awoke in the morning, thinking that the frog would hop away once again, but now a beautiful young prince was standing before her. He told her that he had been an enchanted frog and that she had broken the spell by promising to be his sweetheart. Then they both went to the king who gave them his blessing, and they were married. The two other sisters were angry with themselves that they had not taken the frog for their sweetheart.[166]

---

[166]Type 440. Source: *Kinder- und Hausmärchen*, 1st ed. (Berlin, 1812/1815), v. 2, no. 13. Because of its close similarity with "The Frog King," this tale was omitted from all future editions of the Grimms' collection. Curiously, the first English translator of the Grimms' tales, Edgar Taylor, combined the two versions. He called the story "The Frog Prince," giving it the beginning of the Grimms' "The Frog King" and the conclusion of the Grimms' "The Frog Prince."

Hans-My-Hedgehog

Jacob and Wilhelm Grimm

Once there was a rich peasant who, with his wife, had no children. Often when he met with other peasants in the city they would mock him and ask him why he had no children. One day he became angry, and when he returned home, he said, "I will have a child, even if it is a hedgehog."

Then his wife had a baby, and the top half was a hedgehog and the bottom half a boy. When she saw the baby, she was horrified and said, "Now see what you have wished upon us!"

The man said, "It cannot be helped. The boy must be baptized, but we cannot ask anyone to be his godfather."

The woman said, "And the only name that we can give him is Hans-My-Hedgehog."

When he was baptized, the pastor said, "Because of his quills he cannot be given an ordinary bed." So they put some straw behind the stove and laid him in it. And he could not drink from his mother, for he would have stuck her with his quills. He lay there behind the stove for eight years, and his father grew tired of him, and thought, "if only he would die." But he did not die, but just lay there.

Now it happened that there was a fair in the city, and the peasant wanted to go. He asked his wife what he should bring her. "Some meat, some bread rolls, and things for the household," she said. Then he asked the servant girl, and she wanted a pair of slippers and some fancy stockings.

Finally, he also said, "Hans-My-Hedgehog, what would you like?"

"Father," he said, "bring me some bagpipes."

When the peasant returned home he gave his wife what he had brought for her. Then he gave the servant girl the slippers and fancy stockings. And finally he went behind the stove and gave Hans-My-Hedgehog the bagpipes. When Hans-My-Hedgehog had them, he said, "Father, go to the blacksmith's and have my cock-rooster shod, then I will ride away and never again come back." The father was happy to get rid of him, so he had his rooster shod, and when it was done, Hans-My-Hedgehog climbed on it and rode away. He took pigs and donkeys with him, to tend in the forest.

In the forest the rooster flew into a tall tree with him. There he sat and watched over the donkeys and the pigs. He sat there for years, until finally the herd had grown large. His father knew nothing about him. While sitting in the tree, he played his bagpipes and made beautiful music. One day a king came by. He was lost and heard the music. He was amazed to hear it, and sent a servant to look around and see where it was coming from. He looked here and there but only saw a little animal sitting high in a tree. There was a rooster up there with a hedgehog sitting on it making the music. The king said to the servant that he should ask him why he was sitting there, and if he knew the way back to his kingdom. Then Hans-My-Hedgehog climbed down from the tree and told him that he would show him the way if the king would promise in writing to give him the first thing that greeted him at the royal court upon his arrival home.

The king thought, "You can do that easily enough. Hans-My-Hedgehog cannot understand writing, and you can put down what you want to." Then the king took pen and ink and wrote something, and after he had written it, Hans-My-Hedgehog showed him the way, and he arrived safely at home. His daughter saw him coming from afar, and was so overjoyed that she ran to meet him and kiss him. He thought about Hans-My-Hedgehog and told her what had happened, that he was supposed to have promised the first thing that greeted him to a strange animal that rode a rooster and made beautiful music. But instead he had written that this would not happen, for Hans-My-Hedgehog could not read. The princess was happy about this, and said that it was a good thing, for she would not have gone with him in any event.

Hans-My-Hedgehog tended the donkeys and pigs, was of good cheer, and sat in the tree blowing into his bagpipes. Now it happened that another king came this way with his servants and messengers. He too got lost and did not know the way back home because the forest was so large. He too heard the beautiful music from afar, and asked one of his messengers to go and see what it was and where it was coming from. The messenger ran to the tree where he saw Hans-My-Hedgehog astride the cock-rooster. The messenger asked him what he was doing. "I am tending my donkeys and pigs. What is it that you want?" replied Hans-My-Hedgehog.

The messenger said that they were lost and could not find their way back to their kingdom, and asked him if he could not show them the way. Then Hans-My-Hedgehog climbed down from the tree with his rooster and told the old king that he would show him the way if he would give him the thing that he first met at home before the royal castle. The king said "yes" and signed a promise to Hans-My-Hedgehog. When that was done, Hans-My-Hedgehog, riding his rooster, led them safely back to their kingdom. When the king arrived at his court there was great joy. Now he had an only daughter who was very beautiful. She came out to him, threw her arms around his neck and kissed him, and was ever so happy that her old father had returned. She asked him where he had been during his long absence, and he told her how he had lost his way and almost not made it home again, but that halfway through a great forest he had come upon a half hedgehog, half human astride a rooster sitting in a tall tree and making beautiful music who had shown him the way, but whom he had promised whatever first met him at the royal court, and it was she herself, and he was terribly sorry. But she promised that she would go with him when he came, for the love of her old father.

Hans-My-Hedgehog tended his pigs, and the pigs had pigs, and so forth, until there were so many that the whole forest was full. Then Hans-My-Hedgehog let his father know that they should empty out all the stalls in the village, because he was coming with such a large herd of pigs that everyone who wanted to would be able to take part in the slaughter. It saddened the father to hear this, for he thought that Hans-My-Hedgehog had long since died. But Hans-My-Hedgehog mounted his cock-rooster, drove the pigs ahead of himself into the village, and had them butchered. What a slaughter! What a commotion! They could hear the noise two hours away! Afterward Hans-My-Hedgehog said, "Father, have my cock-rooster shod a second time at the blacksmith's. Then I will ride away and not come back again as long as I live." So the father had the cock-rooster shod, and was happy that Hans-My-Hedgehog was not coming back.

Hans-My-Hedgehog rode into the first kingdom. The king had ordered that if anyone should approach who was carrying bagpipes and riding on a rooster, that he should be shot at, struck down, and stabbed to prevent him from entering the castle. Thus when Hans-My-Hedgehog rode up, they attacked him with bayonets, but he spurred his rooster on, flew over the gate and up to the king's window. Landing there, he shouted, "Give me what you promised, or it will cost you and your daughter your lives!" Then the king told the princess to go out to him, in order to save his life and her own as well. She put on a white dress, and her father gave her a carriage with six horses, magnificent servants, money, and property. She climbed aboard and Hans-My-Hedgehog took his place beside her with his rooster and bagpipes. They said farewell and drove off. The king thought that he would never see them again. However, it did not go as he thought it would, for when they had traveled a short distance from the city, Hans-My-Hedgehog tore off her clothes and stuck her with his quills until she was bloody all over. "This is the reward for your deceit. Go away. I do not want you." With that he sent her back home, and she was cursed as long as she lived.

Hans-My-Hedgehog, astride his cock-rooster and carrying his bagpipes, rode on to the second kingdom where he had also helped the king find his way. This one, in contrast, had ordered that if anyone looking like Hans-My-Hedgehog should arrive, he should be brought to the royal castle with honors and with a military escort. When the princess saw him she was horrified, because he looked so strange, but she thought that nothing could be done about it, because she had promised her father to go with him. She welcomed Hans-My-Hedgehog, brought him to the royal table, and sat next to him while they ate and drank.

That evening when it was time to go to bed, she was afraid of his quills, but he told her to have no fear, for he would not hurt her. He told the old king to have four men keep watch by their bedroom door. They should make a large fire. He said that he would take off his hedgehog skin after going into the bedroom, and before getting into bed. The men should immediately pick it up and throw it into the fire, and then stay there until it was completely consumed. When the clock struck eleven, he went into the bedroom, took off the hedgehog skin, and laid it down by the bed. The men rushed in, grabbed it, and threw it into the fire, and as soon as the fire consumed it, he was redeemed, and he lay there in bed entirely in the shape of a human. But he was as black as coal, as though he had been charred. The king sent for his physician, who washed him with good salves and balms. Then he became white and was a handsome young gentleman. When the princess saw what had happened, she was overjoyed, and they got up and ate and drank and celebrated their wedding, and Hans-My-Hedgehog inherited the old king's kingdom.

Some years later he traveled with his wife to his father, and said that he was his son. But the father said that he did not have a son. He had had one, but he had been born with quills like a hedgehog and had gone off into the world. Then he said that he was the one, and the old father rejoiced and returned with him to his kingdom.[167]

The Little Donkey

Jacob and Wilhelm Grimm

Once there lived a king and a queen who were rich and had everything that they could wish for, but no children. She complained day and night about this, and said, "I am like a field that nothing will grow in." Finally God fulfilled her desires, but when the child came to the world it did not look like a human child, but like a young donkey. When the mother saw it she wept and wailed. She would sooner have no child at all than a donkey, and she said that they should throw it into the water and let the fish eat it. But the king said, "No, God has given him to us. He shall be my son and heir, and following my death he shall sit on the royal throne and wear the royal crown."

Thus they raised the little donkey. He got bigger, and his ears grew up straight and tall. He was a very cheerful sort, jumped about, and played. He was especially fond of music, so he went to a famous minstrel and said, "Teach me to play the lute as well as you do."

"Oh, my little master," answered the minstrel, "that will be difficult for you, because you don't have quite the right fingers; they are too large. And I am afraid that the strings would not hold up." But no excuse would do. The little donkey insisted on learning to play the lute. He kept at it and practiced hard, and in the end he learned to play just as well as his teacher.

One day while taking a walk he happened to look into a well and saw his donkey shape in the mirror-like water. This made him so sad that he set forth into the world, taking only a single loyal companion with him. They went hither and yon, finally coming to a kingdom where an old king ruled. He had only one daughter, but she was very beautiful. The little donkey said, "This is where we will stay." He knocked at the gate and called out, "There is a guest out here. Open up and let him in." But they did not open the gate, so he took his lute and began to play it most beautifully with his feet.

That opened the gatekeeper's eyes, and he ran to the king, saying, "A little donkey is sitting outside the gate playing the lute like a master."

"Then let the musician in," said the king.

---

[167]Type 441. Source: *Kinder- und Hausmärchen*, 1st ed. (Berlin, 1812/1815), v. 2, no. 22 (no. 108 in the final edition).

When the little donkey entered, they all began to laugh at the lute player. They sent him below to sit and eat with the servants, but he refused, saying, "I am not an ordinary stall donkey, I am a noble one.

"If that is the case, then you can sit with the soldiers," they said.

"No," he replied, "I want to sit next to the king."

The king laughed and said with good humor, "So be it. If you insist, then just come here to me." Then he asked, "Little donkey, how do you like my daughter?"

The donkey turned his head toward her, looked her over, nodded, and then said, "Beyond all measure, she is the most beautiful girl I have ever seen."

"Then you should sit next to her," said the king.

"It is all right with me," said the little donkey, then took a seat at her side and ate, behaving himself like a real gentleman.

After the noble animal had stayed at the king's court for a good while, he thought to himself, "What is the use? I have to go home." He sadly bowed his head, went to the king, and asked for his leave.

But the king, who liked him a great deal, said, "Little donkey, what is the matter with you. You look as sour as a vinegar jug. I will give you whatever you ask for. Do you want gold?"

"No."

"Do you want precious things and jewelry?"

"No."

"Do you want half of my kingdom?"

"Oh, no."

Then the king said, "If I only knew what would make you happy. Would you like to have my beautiful daughter as your wife?"

"Oh, yes," said the little donkey, and was suddenly happy and content, for that was exactly what he had wanted. So they had a large and splendid wedding. That evening when the bride and the bridegroom were led into their bedroom, the king wanted to know if the little donkey would behave himself like a gentleman, so he had a servant hide himself there. When the couple was inside, the bridegroom bolted the door shut, looked around, and thinking that they were all alone, he pulled off his donkey skin and stood there as a handsome, young man of royalty. He said, "Now you see who I am, and that I have been worthy of you." The bride was delighted, kissed him, and loved him with all of her heart. The next morning he jumped up, put his animal skin on again, and no one would have thought what he was like beneath it.

The old king soon came by. "Aha," he said. "The little donkey is awake already!" Then he said to his daughter, "Are you sad that you do not have an ordinary human for a husband?"

"Not at all, father dear. I love him just as much as if he were the handsomest man, and I want to keep him as long as I live."

This surprised the king, but then the servant who had hid himself came and revealed everything to him. The king said, "That cannot be true!"

"Then you keep watch tonight, and you will see it with your own eyes. And do you know what, your majesty, if you take the skin away from him and throw it into the fire, then he will have to show himself in his real form."

"Your advice is good," said the king, and that evening while they slept, he crept into their room, and when he came to their bed, by the light of the moon he saw a handsome young man lying there. The skin was lying on the floor. He took it away, had an enormous fire built outside, and had the skin thrown into it. He himself stayed there until it had burned entirely to ashes. He stayed awake and kept watch the entire night, because he wanted to see what the robbed man would do. When the young man awoke at the first light of morning, he got up and wanted to put on the donkey skin, but he could not find it.

Terrified, he spoke with sadness and fear, "I will have to run away."

He left the room, and the king, who was standing there, said, "My son, where are you going in such a hurry? Just what do you have in mind? Stay here. You are such a handsome man. Don't leave me. I'll give you half my kingdom for now, and after my death you shall receive the other half."

"I wish a good conclusion for this good beginning," said the young man. "I shall stay here with you." Then the old man gave him half his kingdom. He died a year later, and then he had the whole kingdom, and after the death of his father, another one as well. And he was wealthy and happy.[168]

Cupid and Psyche

Apuleius

A certain king and queen had three daughters. The charms of the two elder were more than common, but the beauty of the youngest was so wonderful that the poverty of language is unable to express its due praise. The fame of her beauty was so great that strangers from neighboring countries came in crowds to enjoy the sight, and looked on her with amazement, paying her that homage which is due only to Venus herself. In fact Venus found her altars deserted, while men turned their devotion to this young virgin. As she passed along, the people sang her praises, and strewed her way with chaplets and flowers.

This homage to the exaltation of a mortal gave great offense to the real Venus. Shaking her ambrosial locks with indignation, she exclaimed, "Am I then to be eclipsed in my honors by a mortal girl? In vain then did that royal shepherd, whose judgment was approved by Jove himself, give me the palm of beauty over my illus-

---

[168]Type 430. Source: *Kinder- und Hausmärchen*, 1st ed. (Berlin, 1812/1815), v. 2, no. 58 (no. 144 in the final edition).

trious rivals, Pallas and Juno. But she shall not so quietly usurp my honors. I will give her cause to repent of so unlawful a beauty."

Thereupon she calls her winged son Cupid, mischievous enough in his own nature, and rouses and provokes him yet more by her complaints. She points out Psyche to him and says, "My dear son, punish that contumacious beauty; give your mother a revenge as sweet as her injuries are great; infuse into the bosom of that haughty girl a passion for some low, mean, unworthy being, so that she may reap a mortification as great as her present exultation and triumph."

Cupid prepared to obey the commands of his mother. There are two fountains in Venus's garden, one of sweet waters, the other of bitter. Cupid filled two amber vases, one from each fountain, and suspending them from the top of his quiver, hastened to the chamber of Psyche, whom he found asleep. He shed a few drops from the bitter fountain over her lips, though the sight of her almost moved him to pity; then touched her side with the point of his arrow. At the touch she awoke, and opened eyes upon Cupid (himself invisible), which so startled him that in his confusion he wounded himself with his own arrow. Heedless of his wound, his whole thought now was to repair the mischief he had done, and he poured the balmy drops of joy over all her silken ringlets.

Psyche, henceforth frowned upon by Venus, derived no benefit from all her charms. True, all eyes were cast eagerly upon her, and every mouth spoke her praises; but neither king, royal youth, nor plebeian presented himself to demand her in marriage. Her two elder sisters of moderate charms had now long been married to two royal princes; but Psyche, in her lonely apartment, deplored her solitude, sick of that beauty which, while it procured abundance of flattery, had failed to awaken love.

Her parents, afraid that they had unwittingly incurred the anger of the gods, consulted the oracle of Apollo, and received this answer, "The virgin is destined for the bride of no mortal lover. Her future husband awaits her on the top of the mountain. He is a monster whom neither gods nor men can resist."

This dreadful decree of the oracle filled all the people with dismay, and her parents abandoned themselves to grief. But Psyche said, "Why, my dear parents, do you now lament me? You should rather have grieved when the people showered upon me undeserved honors, and with one voice called me a Venus. I now perceive that I am a victim to that name. I submit. Lead me to that rock to which my unhappy fate has destined me." Accordingly, all things being prepared, the royal maid took her place in the procession, which more resembled a funeral than a nuptial pomp, and with her parents, amid the lamentations of the people, ascended the mountain, on the summit of which they left her alone, and with sorrowful hearts returned home.

While Psyche stood on the ridge of the mountain, panting with fear and with eyes full of tears, the gentle Zephyr raised her from the earth and bore her with an easy motion into a flowery dale. By degrees her mind became composed, and she laid herself down on the grassy bank to sleep. When she awoke refreshed with sleep, she looked round and beheld near a pleasant grove of tall and stately trees. She entered it, and in the midst discovered a fountain, sending forth clear and crystal waters, and fast by, a magnificent palace whose august front impressed the spectator that it was not the work of mortal hands, but the happy retreat of some god. Drawn by admiration and wonder, she approached the building and ventured to enter. Every object she met filled her with pleasure and amazement. Golden pillars supported the vaulted roof, and the walls were enriched with carvings and paintings representing beasts of the chase and rural scenes, adapted to delight the eye of the beholder. Proceeding onward, she perceived that besides the apartments of state there were others filled with all manner of treasures, and beautiful and precious productions of nature and art.

While her eyes were thus occupied, a voice addressed her, though she saw no one, uttering these words, "Sovereign lady, all that you see is yours. We whose voices you hear are your servants and shall obey all your commands with our utmost care and diligence. Retire, therefore, to your chamber and repose on your bed of down, and when you see fit repair to the bath. Supper awaits you in the adjoining alcove when it pleases you to take your seat there."

Psyche gave ear to the admonitions of her vocal attendants, and after repose and the refreshment of the bath, seated herself in the alcove, where a table immediately presented itself, without any visible aid from waiters or servants, and covered with the greatest delicacies of food and the most nectareous wines. Her ears too were feasted with music from invisible performers; of whom one sang, another played on the lute, and all closed in the wonderful harmony of a full chorus.

She had not yet seen her destined husband. He came only in the hours of darkness and fled before the dawn of morning, but his accents were full of love, and inspired a like passion in her. She often begged him to stay and let her behold him, but he would not consent. On the contrary he charged her to make no attempt to see him, for it was his pleasure, for the best of reasons, to keep concealed. "Why should you wish to behold me?" he said. "Have you any doubt of my love? Have you any wish ungratified? If you saw me, perhaps you would fear me, perhaps adore me, but all I ask of you is to love me. I would rather you would love me as an equal than adore me as a god."

This reasoning somewhat quieted Psyche for a time, and while the novelty lasted she felt quite happy. But at length the thought of her parents, left in ignorance of her fate, and of her sisters, precluded from sharing with her the delights of her situation, preyed on her mind and made her begin to feel her palace as but a splendid prison. When her husband came one night, she told him her distress, and at last drew from him an unwilling consent that her sisters should be brought to see her.

So, calling Zephyr, she acquainted him with her husband's commands, and he, promptly obedient, soon brought them across the mountain down to their sister's valley. They embraced her and she returned their caresses. "Come," said Psyche, "enter with me my house and refresh yourselves with whatever your sister has to offer." Then taking their hands she led them into her golden palace, and committed them to the care of her numerous train of attendant voices, to refresh them in her baths and at her table, and to show them all her treasures. The view of these celestial delights caused envy to enter their bosoms, at seeing their young sister possessed of such state and splendor, so much exceeding their own.

They asked her numberless questions, among others what sort of a person her husband was. Psyche replied that he was a beautiful youth, who generally spent the daytime in hunting upon the mountains. The sisters, not satisfied with this reply, soon made her confess that she had never seen him. Then they proceeded to fill her bosom with dark suspicions. "Call to mind," they said, "the Pythian oracle that declared you destined to marry a direful and tremendous monster. The inhabitants of this valley say that your husband is a terrible and monstrous serpent, who nourishes you for a while with dainties that he may by and by devour you. Take our advice. Provide yourself with a lamp and a sharp knife; put them in concealment that your husband may not discover them, and when he is sound asleep, slip out of bed, bring forth your lamp, and see for yourself whether what they say is true or not. If it is, hesitate not to cut off the monster's head, and thereby recover your liberty."

Psyche resisted these persuasions as well as she could, but they did not fail to have their effect on her mind, and when her sisters were gone, their words and her own curiosity were too strong for her to resist. So she prepared her lamp and a sharp knife, and hid them out of sight of her husband. When he had fallen into his first sleep, she silently rose and uncovering her lamp beheld not a hideous monster, but the most beautiful and charming of the gods, with his golden ringlets wandering over his snowy neck and crimson cheek, with two dewy wings on his shoulders, whiter than snow, and with shining feathers like the tender blossoms of spring. As she leaned the lamp over to have a better view of his face, a drop of burning oil fell on the shoulder of the god. Startled, he opened his eyes and fixed them upon her. Then, without saying a word, he spread his white wings and flew out of the window. Psyche, in vain endeavoring to follow him, fell from the window to the ground. Cupid, beholding her as she lay in the dust, stopped his flight for an instant and said, "Oh foolish Psyche, is it thus you repay my love? After I disobeyed my mother's commands and made you my wife, will you think me a monster and cut off my head? But go; return to your sisters, whose advice you seem to think preferable to mine. I inflict no other punishment on you than to leave you for ever. Love cannot dwell with suspicion." So saying, he fled away, leaving poor Psyche prostrate on the ground, filling the place with mournful lamentations.

When she had recovered some degree of composure she looked around her, but the palace and gardens had vanished, and she found herself in the open field not far from the city where her sisters dwelt. She repaired thither and told them the whole story of her misfortunes, at which, pretending to grieve, those spiteful creatures inwardly rejoiced. "For now," said they, "he will perhaps choose one of us." With this idea, without saying a word of her intentions, each of them rose early the next morning and ascended the mountain, and having reached the top, called upon Zephyr to receive her and bear her to his lord; then leaping up, and not being sustained by Zephyr, fell down the precipice and was dashed to pieces.

Psyche meanwhile wandered day and night, without food or repose, in search of her husband. Casting her eyes on a lofty mountain having on its brow a magnificent temple, she sighed and said to herself, "Perhaps my love, my lord, inhabits there," and directed her steps thither.

She had no sooner entered than she saw heaps of corn, some in loose ears and some in sheaves, with mingled ears of barley. Scattered about, lay sickles and rakes, and all the instruments of harvest, without order, as if thrown carelessly out of the weary reapers' hands in the sultry hours of the day.

This unseemly confusion the pious Psyche put an end to, by separating and sorting everything to its proper place and kind, believing that she ought to neglect none of the gods, but endeavor by her piety to engage them all in her behalf. The holy Ceres, whose temple it was, finding her so religiously employed, thus spoke to her, "Oh Psyche, truly worthy of our pity, though I cannot shield you from the frowns of Venus, yet I can teach you how best to allay her displeasure. Go, then, and voluntarily surrender yourself to your lady and sovereign, and try by modesty and submission to win her forgiveness, and perhaps her favor will restore you the husband you have lost."

Psyche obeyed the commands of Ceres and took her way to the temple of Venus, endeavoring to fortify her mind and ruminating on what she should say and how best propitiate the angry goddess, feeling that the issue was doubtful and perhaps fatal.

Venus received her with angry countenance. "Most undutiful and faithless of servants," said she, "do you at last remember that you really have a mistress? Or have you rather come to see your sick husband, yet laid up of the wound given him by his loving wife? You are so ill favored and disagreeable that the only way you can merit your lover must be by dint of industry and diligence. I will make trial of your housewifery." Then she ordered Psyche to be led to the storehouse of her temple, where was laid up a great quantity of wheat, barley, millet, vetches, beans, and lentils prepared for food for her pigeons, and said, "Take and separate all these grains, putting all of the same kind in a parcel by themselves, and see that you get it done before evening." Then Venus departed and left her to her task.

But Psyche, in a perfect consternation at the enormous work, sat stupid and silent, without moving a finger to the inextricable heap.

While she sat despairing, Cupid stirred up the little ant, a native of the fields, to take compassion on her. The leader of the anthill, followed by whole hosts of his six-legged subjects, approached the heap, and with the utmost diligence taking grain by grain, they separated the pile, sorting each kind to its parcel; and when it was all done, they vanished out of sight in a moment.

Venus at the approach of twilight returned from the banquet of the gods, breathing odors and crowned with roses. Seeing the task done, she exclaimed, "This is no work of yours, wicked one, but his, whom to your own and his misfortune you have enticed." So saying, she threw her a piece of black bread for her supper and went away.

Next morning Venus ordered Psyche to be called and said to her, "Behold yonder grove which stretches along the margin of the water. There you will find sheep feeding without a shepherd, with golden-shining fleeces on their backs. Go, fetch me a sample of that precious wool gathered from every one of their fleeces."

Psyche obediently went to the riverside, prepared to do her best to execute the command. But the river god inspired the reeds with harmonious murmurs, which

246

seemed to say, "Oh maiden, severely tried, tempt not the dangerous flood, nor venture among the formidable rams on the other side, for as long as they are under the influence of the rising sun, they burn with a cruel rage to destroy mortals with their sharp horns or rude teeth. But when the noontide sun has driven the cattle to the shade, and the serene spirit of the flood has lulled them to rest, you may then cross in safety, and you will find the woolly gold sticking to the bushes and the trunks of the trees."

Thus the compassionate river god gave Psyche instructions how to accomplish her task, and by observing his directions she soon returned to Venus with her arms full of the golden fleece; but she received not the approbation of her implacable mistress, who said, "I know very well it is by none of your own doings that you have succeeded in this task, and I am not satisfied yet that you have any capacity to make yourself useful. But I have another task for you. Here, take this box and go your way to the infernal shades, and give this box to Proserpine and say, 'My mistress Venus desires you to send her a little of your beauty, for in tending her sick son she has lost some of her own.' Be not too long on your errand, for I must paint myself with it to appear at the circle of the gods and goddesses this evening."

Psyche was now satisfied that her destruction was at hand, being obliged to go with her own feet directly down to Erebus. Wherefore, to make no delay of what was not to be avoided, she goes to the top of a high tower to precipitate herself headlong, thus to descend the shortest way to the shades below. But a voice from the tower said to her, "Why, poor unlucky girl, do you design to put an end to your days in so dreadful a manner? And what cowardice makes you sink under this last danger who have been so miraculously supported in all your former?" Then the voice told her how by a certain cave she might reach the realms of Pluto, and how to avoid all the dangers of the road, to pass by Cerberus, the three-headed dog, and prevail on Charon, the ferryman, to take her across the black river and bring her back again. But the voice added, "When Proserpine has given you the box filled with her beauty, of all things this is chiefly to be observed by you, that you never once open or look into the box nor allow your curiosity to pry into the treasure of the beauty of the goddesses."

Psyche, encouraged by this advice, obeyed it in all things, and taking heed to her ways traveled safely to the kingdom of Pluto. She was admitted to the palace of Proserpine, and without accepting the delicate seat or delicious banquet that was offered her, but contented with coarse bread for her food, she delivered her message from Venus. Presently the box was returned to her, shut and filled with the precious commodity. Then she returned the way she came, and glad was she to come out once more into the light of day.

But having got so far successfully through her dangerous task a longing desire seized her to examine the contents of the box. "What," said she, "shall I, the carrier of this divine beauty, not take the least bit to put on my cheeks to appear to more advantage in the eyes of my beloved husband!" So she carefully opened the box, but found nothing there of any beauty at all, but an infernal and truly Stygian sleep, which being thus set free from its prison, took possession of her, and she fell down in the midst of the road, a sleepy corpse without sense or motion.

247

But Cupid, being now recovered from his wound, and not able longer to bear the absence of his beloved Psyche, slipping through the smallest crack of the window of his chamber which happened to be left open, flew to the spot where Psyche lay, and gathering up the sleep from her body closed it again in the box, and waked Psyche with a light touch of one of his arrows. "Again," said he, "have you almost perished by the same curiosity. But now perform exactly the task imposed on you by my mother, and I will take care of the rest."

Then Cupid, as swift as lightning penetrating the heights of heaven, presented himself before Jupiter with his supplication. Jupiter lent a favoring ear, and pleaded the cause of the lovers so earnestly with Venus that he won her consent. On this he sent Mercury to bring Psyche up to the heavenly assembly, and when she arrived, handing her a cup of ambrosia, he said, "Drink this, Psyche, and be immortal; nor shall Cupid ever break away from the knot in which he is tied, but these nuptials shall be perpetual."

Thus Psyche became at last united to Cupid, and in due time they had a daughter born to them whose name was Pleasure.[169]

East of the Sun and West of the Moon

Norway

Once upon a time there was a poor peasant who had so many children that he did not have enough of either food or clothing to give them. Pretty children they all were, but the prettiest was the youngest daughter, who was so lovely there was no end to her loveliness.

One day—it was on a Thursday evening late in the fall—the weather was wild and rough outside, and it was cruelly dark. The rain was falling and the wind blowing, until the walls of the cottage shook. They were all sitting around the fire busy with this thing and that. Then all at once something gave three taps on the window. The father went out to see what was the matter. Outside, what should he see but a great big white bear.

"Good evening to you," said the white bear.

"The same to you," said the man.

"Will you give me your youngest daughter? If you will, I'll make you as rich as you are now poor," said the bear.

Well, the man would not be at all sorry to be so rich; but still he thought he must have a bit of a talk with his daughter first; so he went in and told them how there

---

[169]Type 425A. Source: Thomas Bulfinch, *The Age of Fable; or, Stories of Gods and Heroes* (1855). Bulfinch's source is *The Golden Ass* by the Roman writer Apuleius (second century).

was a great white bear waiting outside, who had given his word to make them so rich if he could only have the youngest daughter.

The girl said "No!" outright. Nothing could get her to say anything else; so the man went out and settled it with the white bear, that he should come again the next Thursday evening and get an answer. Meantime he talked to his daughter, and kept on telling her of all the riches they would get, and how well off she herself would be. At last she agreed to it, so she washed and mended her rags, and made herself as smart as she could. Soon she was ready for the trip, for she didn't have much to take along.

The next Thursday evening came the white bear to fetch her. She got on his back with her bundle, and off they went. After they had gone a good way, the white bear said, "Are you afraid?"

No, she wasn't.

"Just hold tight to my shaggy coat, and there's nothing to be afraid of," said the bear.

She rode a long, long way, until they came to a large steep cliff. The white bear knocked on it. A door opened, and they came into a castle, where there were many rooms all lit up; rooms gleaming with silver and gold. Further, there was a table set there, and it was all as grand as grand could be. Then the white bear gave her a silver bell; and when she wanted anything, she only had to ring it, and she would get it at once.

Well, after she had eaten, and it became evening, she felt sleepy from her journey, and thought she would like to go to bed, so she rang the bell. She had barely rung it before she found herself in a room, where there was a bed made as fair and white as anyone would wish to sleep in, with silken pillows and curtains, and gold fringe. All that was in the room was gold or silver. After she had gone to bed, and put out the light, a man came and laid himself alongside her. It was the white bear, who cast off his pelt at night; but she never saw him, for he always came after she had put out the light. Before the day dawned he was up and off again. Things went on happily for a while, but at last she became quiet and sad. She was alone all day long, and she became very homesick to see her father and mother and brothers and sisters. So one day, when the white bear asked what was wrong with her, she said it was so lonely there, and how she longed to go home to see her father and mother and brothers and sisters, and that was why she was so sad, because she couldn't get to them.

"Well," said the bear, "that can happen all right, but you must promise me, not to talk alone with your mother, but only when the others are around to hear. She will want to take you by the hand and lead you into a room to talk alone with her. But you must not do that, or else you'll bring bad luck on both of us."

So one Sunday the white bear came and said they could now set off to see her father and mother. Off they went, she sitting on his back; and they went far and long. At last they came to a grand house. Her bothers and sisters were outside running about and playing. Everything was so pretty, it was a joy to see.

"This is where your father and mother live now," said the white bear. "Now don't forget what I told you, else you'll make us both unhappy."

No, heaven forbid, she'd not forget. When they reached the house, the white bear turned around and left her.

She went in to see her father and mother, and there was such joy, that there was no end to it. None of them could thank her enough for all she had done for them. They now had everything they could wish for, as good as good could be. Then they wanted to know how *she* was.

Well, she said, it was very good to live where she did; she had all she wished. I don't know what else she said, but I don't think she told any of them the whole story. That afternoon, after they had eaten dinner, everything happened as the white bear had said it would. Her mother wanted to talk with her alone in her bedroom; but she remembered what the white bear had said, and wouldn't go with her.

"What we have to talk about we can talk about any time," she said, and put her mother off. But somehow or other, her mother got to her at last, and she had to tell her the whole story. She told her, how every night, after she had gone to bed, a man came and lay down beside her as soon as she had put out the light, and how she never saw him, because he was always up and away before the morning dawned; and how she was terribly sad, for she wanted so much to see him, and how she was by herself all day long, and how dreary, and lonesome it was.

"Oh dear," said her mother; "it may well be a troll you are sleeping with! But now I'll give you some good advice how to see him. I'll give you a candle stub, which you can carry home in your bosom; just light it while he is asleep, but be careful not to drop any tallow on him."

Yes, she took the candle, and hid it in her bosom, and that evening the white bear came and took her away.

But when they had gone a piece, the white bear asked if all hadn't happened as he had said.

She couldn't deny that it had.

"Take care," said he, "if you have listened to your mother's advice, you will bring bad luck on us both, and it will be finished with the two of us."

No, by no means!

So when she reached home, and had gone to bed, it was the same as before. A man came and lay down beside her; but in the middle of the night, when she heard that he was fast asleep, she got up and lit the candle. She let the light shine on him, and saw that he was the most handsome prince one ever set eyes on. She fell so deeply in love with him, that she thought she couldn't live if she didn't give him a kiss at once. And so she did, but as she kissed him she let three drops of hot tallow drip onto his shirt, and he woke up.

"What have you done?" he cried; "now you have made us both unlucky, for had you held out only this one year, I would have been free! I have a stepmother who has bewitched me, so that I am a white bear by day, and a man by night. But now all ties are broken between us. Now I must leave you for her. She lives in a castle east of the sun and west of the moon, and there, too, is a princess, one with a nose three yards long, and now I will have to marry her."

She cried and grieved, but there was no help for it; he had to go.

Then she asked if she could go with him.

No, she could not.

"Tell me the way, then" she said, "so I can look for you; surely I may do that."

Yes, she could do that, but there was no way leading to the place. It lay east of the sun and west of the moon, and she'd never find her way there."

The next morning, when she woke up, both the prince and the castle were gone, and she was lying on a little green patch, in the midst of the thick, dark forest, and by her side lay the same bundle of rags she had brought with her from her old home.

When she had rubbed the sleep out of her eyes, and cried until she was tired, she set out on her way, and walked many, many days, until she came to a high cliff. An old woman sat under it, and played with a golden apple which she tossed about. The girl asked her if she knew the way to the prince, who lived with his stepmother in the castle east of the sun and west of the moon, and who was to marry the princess with a nose three yards long.

"How did you come to know about him?" asked the old woman. "Maybe you are the girl who should have had him?"

Yes, she was.

"So, so; it's you, is it?" said the old woman. "Well, all I know about him is, that he lives in the castle east of the sun and west of the moon, and that you'll get there too late or never; but still you may borrow my horse, and you can ride him to my next neighbor. Maybe she'll be able to tell you; and when you get there just give the horse a switch under the left ear, and beg him to be off home. And you can take this golden apple along with you."

So she got on the horse, and rode a long long time, until she came to another cliff, under which sat another old woman, with a golden carding comb. The girl asked her if she knew the way to the castle that lay east of the sun and west of the moon, and she answered, like the first old woman, that she knew nothing about it, except that it was east of the sun and west of the moon.

"And you'll get there too late or never; but you can borrow my horse to my next neighbor; maybe she'll tell you all about it; and when you get there, just switch the horse under the left ear, and beg him to be off for home."

This old woman gave her the golden carding comb; she might find some use for it, she said. So the girl got up on the horse, and again rode a long long way. At last she came to another great cliff, under which sat another old woman, spinning with a golden spinning wheel. She asked her, as well, if she knew the way to the prince, and where the castle was that lay east of the sun and west of the moon. But it was the same thing over again.

"Perhaps you are the one who should have had the prince?" said the old woman.

Yes, that she was.

But she didn't know the way any better than the other two. She knew it was east of the sun and west of the moon, but that was all.

"And you'll get there too late or never; but I'll lend you my horse, and then I think you'd best ride to the east wind and ask him; maybe he knows his way around those parts, and can blow you there. When you get to him, just give the horse a switch under the left ear, and he'll trot home by himself."

251

She too gave her her golden spinning wheel. "Maybe you'll find a use for it," said the old woman.

She rode many weary days, before she got to the east wind's house, but at last she did reach it, and she asked the east wind if he could tell her the way to the prince who lived east of the sun and west of the moon. Yes, the east wind had often heard tell of it, the prince and the castle, but he didn't know the way there, for he had never blown so far.

"But, if you want, I'll go with you to my brother the west wind. Maybe he knows, for he's much stronger. If you will just get on my back I'll carry you there."

Yes, she got on his back, and off they went in a rush.

When they arrived at the west wind's house, the east wind said the girl he had brought was the one who was supposed to have had the prince who lived in the castle east of the sun and west of the moon. She had set out to find him, and he had brought her here, and would be glad to know if the west wind knew how to get to the castle.

"No," said the west wind, "I've never blown so far; but if you want, I'll go with you to our brother the south wind, for he's much stronger than either of us, and he has flown far and wide. Maybe he'll tell you. Get on my back, and I'll carry you to him."

Yes, she got on his back, and so they traveled to the south wind, and I think it didn't take long at all.

When they got there, the west wind asked him if he could tell her the way to the castle that lay east of the sun and west of the moon, for she was the one who was supposed to have had the prince who lived there.

"Is that so?" said the south wind. Is she the one? Well, I have visited a lot of places in my time, but I have not yet blown there. If you want, I'll take you to my brother the north wind; he is the oldest and strongest of us all, and if he doesn't know where it is, you'll never find anyone in the world to tell you. Get on my back, and I'll carry you there."

Yes, she got on his back, and away he left his house at a good clip. They were not long underway. When they reached the north wind's house he was so wild and cross, that he blew cold gusts at them from a long way off. "Blast you both, what do you want?" he roared at them from afar, so that it struck them with an icy shiver.

"Well," said the south wind, "you don't need to bluster so, for here I am, your brother, the south wind, and here is the girl who was supposed to have had the prince who lives in the castle that lies east of the sun and west of the moon, and now she wants to ask you if you ever were there, and can show her the way, for she wants so much to find him again."

"Yes, I know where it is," said the north wind; "a single time I blew an aspen leaf there, but afterward I was so tired that I couldn't blow a puff for many days. But if you really wish to go there, and aren't afraid to come along with me, I'll take you on my back and see if I can blow you there."

Yes, with all her heart; she wanted to and had to get there if it were at all possible; and she wouldn't be afraid, however madly he went.

"Very well, then," said the north wind, "but you must sleep here tonight, for we must have the whole day before us, if we're to get there at all.

Early next morning the north wind woke her, and puffed himself up, and blew himself out, and made himself so stout and big. that he was gruesome to look at. Off they went high up through the air, as if they would not stop until they reached the end of the world.

Here on earth there was a terrible storm; acres of forest and many houses were blown down, and when it swept over the sea, ships wrecked by the hundred.

They tore on and on—no one can believe how far they went—and all the while they still went over the sea, and the north wind got more and more weary, and so out of breath he could barely bring out a puff, and his wings drooped and drooped, until at last he sunk so low that the tops of the waves splashed over his heels.

"Are you afraid?" said the north wind.

No, she wasn't.

They weren't very far from land by now, and the north wind had enough strength left that he managed to throw her up on the shore under the windows of the castle which lay east of the sun and west of the moon. But then he was so weak and worn out, that he had to stay there and rest many days before he could go home again.

The next morning the girl sat down under the castle window, and began to play with the golden apple. The first person she saw was the long-nosed princess who was to have the prince.

"What do you want for your golden apple, you girl?" said the long-nosed one, as she opened the window.

"It's not for sale, for gold or money," said the girl.

"If it's not for sale for gold or money, what is it that you will sell it for? You may name your own price," said the princess.

"Well, you can have it, if I may get to the prince, who lives here, and be with him tonight," said the girl whom the north wind had brought.

Yes, that could be done. So the princess took the golden apple; but when the girl came up to the prince's bedroom that night, he was fast asleep. She called him and shook him, and cried and grieved, but she could not wake him up. The next morning. as soon as day broke, the princess with the long nose came and drove her out.

That day she sat down under the castle windows and began to card with her golden carding comb, and the same thing happened. The princess asked what she wanted for it. She said it wasn't for sale for gold or money, but if she could have permission to go to the prince and be with him that night, the princess could have it. But when she went to his room she found him fast asleep again, and however much she called, and shook, and cried, and prayed, she couldn't get life into him. As soon as the first gray peep of day came, the princess with the long nose came, and chased her out again.

That day the girl sat down outside under the castle window and began to spin with her golden spinning wheel, and the princess with the long nose wanted to have it as well. She opened the window and asked what she wanted for it. The girl said, as she had said twice before, that it wasn't for sale for gold or money, but if she could go to the prince who was there, and be alone with him that night she could have it.

Yes, she would be welcome to do that. But now you must know that there were some Christians who had been taken there, and while they were sitting in their room, which was next to the prince's, they had heard how a woman had been in there, crying, praying, and calling to him for two nights in a row, and they told this to the prince.

That evening, when the princess came with a sleeping potion, the prince pretended to drink it, but threw it over his shoulder, for he could guess it was a sleeping potion. So, when the girl came in, she found the prince wide awake, and then she told him the whole story of how she had come there.

"Ah," said the prince, "you've come in the very nick of time, for tomorrow is to be our wedding day. But now I won't have the long-nose, and you are the only woman in the world who can set me free. I'll say that I want to see what my wife is fit for, and beg her to wash the shirt which has the three spots of tallow on it. She'll agree, for she doesn't know that you are the one who put them there. Only Christians, and not such a pack of trolls, can wash them out again. I'll say that I will marry only the woman who can wash them out, and ask you to try it."

So there was great joy and love between them all the night. But next day, when the wedding was planned, the prince said, "First of all, I'd like to see what my bride is fit for."

"Yes!" said the stepmother, with all her heart.

"Well," said the prince, "I've got a fine shirt which I'd like for my wedding shirt, but somehow or other it got three spots of tallow on it, which I must have washed out. I have sworn to marry only the woman who is able to do that. If she can't, then she's not worth having."

Well, that was no big thing they said, so they agreed, and the one with the long nose began to wash away as hard as she could, but the more she rubbed and scrubbed, the bigger the spots grew.

"Ah!" said the old troll woman, her mother, "you can't wash. Let me try."

But she had hardly touched the shirt, before it got far worse than before, and with all her rubbing, and wringing, and scrubbing, the spots grew bigger and blacker, and the shirt got ever darker and uglier.

Then all the other trolls began to wash, but the longer it lasted, the blacker and uglier the shirt grew, until at last it was as black all over as if it been up the chimney.

"Ah!" said the prince, "none of you is worth a straw; you can't wash. Why there, outside, sits a beggar girl, I'll bet she knows how to wash better than the whole lot of you. Come in, girl!" he shouted.

She came in.

"Can you wash this shirt clean, girl, you?" he said.

"I don't know," she said, "but I think I can."

And almost before she had taken it and dipped it into the water, it was as white as driven snow, and whiter still.

"Yes, you are the girl for me," said the prince.

At that the old troll woman flew into such a rage, she exploded on the spot, and the princess with the long nose after her, and the whole pack of trolls after her—at least I've never heard a word about them since.

As for the prince and princess, they set free all the poor Christians who had been captured and shut up there; and they took with them all the silver and gold, and flew away as far as they could from the castle that lay east of the sun and west of the moon.[170]

The Clinking Clanking Lowesleaf

Germany

Once upon a time there was a king who had three daughters. The youngest was his pride and joy. One day he wanted to go to the fair to buy something, and he asked his three daughters what he should bring home for them. The first one asked for a golden spinning wheel. The second one a golden yarn reel, and the third one a clinking clanking lowesleaf. The king promised to bring these things and rode away. At the fair he bought the golden spinning wheel and the golden yarn reel, but no one had a clinking clanking lowesleaf for sale. He looked everywhere, but could not find one. This saddened him, because the youngest daughter was the joy of his life, and he wanted to please her ever so much.

As he sorrowfully made his way homeward, he came to a great, great forest and to a large birch tree. Under the birch tree there lay a large black poodle dog. Because the king looked so sad, the dog asked him what was the matter. "Oh," answered the king, "I was supposed to bring a clinking clanking lowesleaf to my youngest daughter, whom I love above anything else, but I cannot find one anywhere, and that is why I am so sad."

"I can help you," said the poodle. "The clinking clanking lowesleaf grows in this tree. If a year and a day from now you will give me that which first greets you upon your arrival home today, then you can have it."

At first the king did not want to agree, but he thought about it long and hard, then said to himself, "What could it be but our dog? Go ahead and make the promise." And he made the promise.

The poodle wagged his tail, climbed up into the birch, broke off the leaf with his frizzy-haired paw, and gave it to the king, saying, "You had better keep your word,

---

[170]Type 425A. Source: Peter Christen Asbjørnsen and Jørgen Moe, *Norske Folkeeventyr* (Christiania [Oslo], 1842-1852), translated by George Webb Dasent (1859). Revised.

255

or you will wish that you had!" The king repeated his promise, took the leaf, and rode on joyfully.

As he approached home, his youngest daughter jumped out with joy to greet him. The king was horrified. His heart was so filled with grief that he pushed her aside. She started to cry, thinking, "What does this mean, that father is pushing me away?" and she went inside and complained to her mother. Soon the king came in. He gave the oldest girl the golden spinning wheel, the middle one the golden yarn reel, and the youngest one the clinking clanking lowesleaf, and he was quiet and sad. Then the queen asked him what was wrong with him, and why he had pushed the youngest daughter away; but he said nothing.

He grieved the entire year. He lamented and mourned and became thin and pale, so concerned was he. Whenever the queen asked him what was wrong, he only shook his head or walked away. Finally, when the year was nearly at its end, he could not longer keep still, and he told her about his misfortune, and thought that his wife would die of shock. She too was horrified, but she soon took hold of herself and said, "You men don't think of anything! After all, don't we have the goose herder's daughter? Let's dress her up and give her to the poodle. A stupid poodle will never know the difference."

The day arrived, and they dressed up the goose girl in their youngest daughter's clothes until she looked just perfect. They had scarcely finished when they heard a bark outside, and a scratching sound at the gate. They looked out, and sure enough, it was the large black poodle dog. They wondered who had taught him to count. After all, a year has more than three hundred days, and even a human can lose count, to say nothing of a dog! But he had not lost count. He had come to take away the princess.

The king and queen greeted him in a friendly manner, then led him outside to the goose girl. He wagged his tail and pawed at her, then he lay down on his belly and said,

> Sit upon my tail,
> And I'll take you away!

She sat down on him, and he took off across the heath. Soon they came to a great, great forest. When they came to the large birch tree, the poodle stopped to rest a while, for it was a hot day, and it was cool and shady here. Around and about there were many daisies[171] poking up their white heads from the beautiful grass, and the girl thought about her parents, and sighed, "Oh, if only my father were here. He could graze the geese so nicely here in this beautiful, lush meadow."

The poodle stood up, shook himself, and said, "Just what kind of a girl are you?"

"I am a goose girl, and my father tends geese," she answered. She would have liked to say what the queen had told her to say, but it was impossible for anyone to tell a lie under this tree. She could not, and she could not.

---

[171]The German word for "daisy" is *Gänseblümchen* or *Gänseblume* (goose-flower).

He jumped up abruptly, looked at her threateningly, and said, "You are not the right one. I have no use for you:"

> Sit upon my tail,
> And I'll take you away!

They were not far from the king's house, when the queen saw them and realized which way the wind was blowing. Therefore she took the broom binder's daughter, dressed her up in even more beautiful clothes. When the poodle arrived and made nasty threats, she brought the broom girl out to him, saying, "This is the right girl!"

"We shall see," responded the poodle dog. The queen became very uneasy, and the king's throat tightened, but the poodle wagged his tail and scratched, then lay down on his belly, saying,

> Sit upon my tail,
> And I'll take you away!

The broom girl sat down on him, and he took off across the heath. Soon they too came to the great forest and to the large birch tree. As they sat there resting, the girl thought about her parents, and sighed, "Oh, if only my father were here. He could make brooms so easily, for here there are masses of thin twigs!"

The poodle stood up, shook himself, and said, "Just what kind of a girl are you?"

She wanted to lie, for the queen had ordered her to, and she was a very strict mistress, but she could not, because she was under this tree, and she answered, "I am a broom girl, and my father makes brooms."

He jumped up as though he were mad, looked at her threateningly, and said, "You are not the right one. I have no use for you:"

> Sit upon my tail,
> And I'll take you away!

They approached the king's house, and the king and queen, who had been steadily looking out the window, began to moan and cry, especially the king, for the youngest daughter was the apple of his eye. The court officials cried and sobbed as well, and there was nothing but mourning everywhere. But it was to no avail. The poodle arrived and said, "This time give me the right girl, or you will wish that you had!" He spoke with such a frightful voice and made such angry gestures, that everyone's heart stood still, and their skin shuddered. Then they led out the youngest daughter, dressed in white, and as pale as snow. It was as though the moon had just come out from behind dark clouds. The poodle knew that she was the right one, and said with a caressing voice,

> Sit upon my tail,
> And I'll take you away!

He ran much more gently this time, and did not stop in the great forest under the birch tree, but hurried deeper and deeper into the woods until they finally reached a small house, where he quietly lay the princess, who had fallen asleep, onto a soft bed. She slumbered on and dreamed about her parents, and about the strange ride, and she laughed and cried in her sleep. The poodle lay down in his hut and kept watch over the little house and the princess.

When she awoke the next morning and found herself soul alone, she cried and grieved and wanted to run away, but she could not, because the house was enchanted. It let people enter, but no one could leave. There was plenty there to eat and drink, everything that even a princess could desire, but she did not want anything and did not take a single bite. She could neither see nor hear the poodle, but the birds sang wonderfully. There were deer grazing around and about, and they looked at the princess with their large eyes. The morning wind curled her golden locks and poured fresh color over her face. The princess sighed and said, "Oh, if only someone were here, even if it were the most miserable, dirty beggar woman. I would kiss her and hug her and love her and honor her!"

"Is that true?" screeched a harsh voice close behind her, startling the princess. She looked around, and there stood a bleary-eyed woman as old as the hills. She glared at the princess and said, "You called for a beggar woman, and a beggar woman is here! In the future do not despise beggar women. Now listen well! The poodle dog is an enchanted prince, this hut an enchanted castle, the forest an enchanted city, and all the animals enchanted people. If you are a genuine princess and are also kind to poor people, then you can redeem them all and become rich and happy. The poodle goes away every morning, because he has to, and every evening he returns home, because he wants to. At midnight he pulls off his rough hide and becomes an ordinary man. If he knocks on your bedroom door, do not let him in, however much he asks and begs, not the first night, not the second night, and especially not the third night. During the third night, after he has tired himself out talking and has fallen asleep, take the hide, make a large fire, and burn it. But first lock your bedroom door securely, so that he cannot get in, and do not open it when he scratches on the door, if you cherish your life. And on your wedding day say three times, don't forget it now, say three times:

> Old tongues,
> Old lungs!

and I will see you again." The princess took very careful notice of everything, and the old woman disappeared.

The first night the prince asked and begged her to open her door, but she answered, "No, I'll not do it," and she did not do it. The second night he asked her even more sweetly, but she did not answer at all. She buried her head in her pillow, and she did not open the door. The third night he asked her so touchingly and sang such beautiful melodies to her, that she wanted to jump up and open the door for him, but fortunately she remembered the old woman and her mother and father. She pulled the bedcovers over her head, and did not open the door. Complaining, the prince walked away, but she did not hear him leave. While he slept she built up the fire, crept out on tiptoe, picked up the rough hide from the corner where the poodle always put it, barred the bedroom door, and threw it into the flames. The poodle jumped up howling, gnawed and clawed at the door, threatened, begged, growled, and howled again. But she did not open the door, and he could not open the door, however fiercely he threw himself against it.

The fire flamed up brightly one last time, and there was an enormous bang, as if heaven and hell had exploded. Standing before her was the most handsome prince in the world. The hut was now a magnificent castle, the forest a great city full of palaces, and the animals were all kinds of people.

At their wedding ceremony, the prince and the princess were seated at the table with the old king and the old queen and the two sisters and many rich and important people, when the bride called out three times,

> Old tongues,
> Old lungs!

and the tattered old woman came in. The old queen scolded, and the two princesses scolded, and they wanted to chase her away, but the young queen stood up and let the old woman sit down at her place, eat from her plate, and drink from her goblet. When the old woman had eaten and drunk her fill, she looked at the old queen and the evil daughters, and they became crooked and lame. But she blessed the young queen, and she became seven times more beautiful, and no one ever saw or heard from the old woman again.[172]

Beauty and the Beast

Marie LePrince de Beaumont

There was once a very rich merchant, who had six children, three sons, and three daughters; being a man of sense, he spared no cost for their education, but gave them all kinds of masters. His daughters were extremely handsome, especially the youngest. When she was little everybody admired her, and called her "The little Beauty;" so that, as she grew up, she still went by the name of Beauty, which made her sisters very jealous. The youngest, as she was handsomer, was also better than her sisters. The two eldest had a great deal of pride, because they were rich. They gave themselves ridiculous airs, and would not visit other merchants' daughters, nor keep company with any but persons of quality. They went out every day to parties of pleasure, balls, plays, concerts, and so forth, and they laughed at their youngest sister, because she spent the greatest part of her time in reading good books. As it was known that they were great fortunes, several

---

[172]Type 425C. Source: Carl and Theodor Colshorn, *Märchen und Sagen aus Hannover* (Hannover, 1854), pp. 64-69.

eminent merchants made their addresses to them; but the two eldest said, they would never marry, unless they could meet with a duke, or an earl at least. Beauty very civilly thanked them that courted her, and told them she was too young yet to marry, but chose to stay with her father a few years longer.

All at once the merchant lost his whole fortune, excepting a small country house at a great distance from town, and told his children with tears in his eyes, they must go there and work for their living. The two eldest answered, that they would not leave the town, for they had several lovers, who they were sure would be glad to have them, though they had no fortune; but the good ladies were mistaken, for their lovers slighted and forsook them in their poverty. As they were not beloved on account of their pride, everybody said; they do not deserve to be pitied, we are very glad to see their pride humbled, let them go and give themselves quality airs in milking the cows and minding their dairy. But, added they, we are extremely concerned for Beauty, she was such a charming, sweet-tempered creature, spoke so kindly to poor people, and was of such an affable, obliging behavior. Nay, several gentlemen would have married her, though they knew she had not a penny; but she told them she could not think of leaving her poor father in his misfortunes, but was determined to go along with him into the country to comfort and attend him. Poor Beauty at first was sadly grieved at the loss of her fortune; "but," said she to herself, "were I to cry ever so much, that would not make things better, I must try to make myself happy without a fortune."

When they came to their country house, the merchant and his three sons applied themselves to husbandry and tillage; and Beauty rose at four in the morning, and made haste to have the house clean, and dinner ready for the family. In the beginning she found it very difficult, for she had not been used to work as a servant, but in less than two months she grew stronger and healthier than ever. After she had done her work, she read, played on the harpsichord, or else sung whilst she spun. On the contrary, her two sisters did not know how to spend their time; they got up at ten, and did nothing but saunter about the whole day, lamenting the loss of their fine clothes and acquaintance. "Do but see our youngest sister," said they, one to the other, "what a poor, stupid, mean-spirited creature she is, to be contented with such an unhappy dismal situation." The good merchant was of quite a different opinion; he knew very well that Beauty outshone her sisters, in her person as well as her mind, and admired her humility and industry, but above all her humility and patience; for her sisters not only left her all the work of the house to do, but insulted her every moment.

The family had lived about a year in this retirement, when the merchant received a letter with an account that a vessel, on board of which he had effects, was safely arrived. This news had liked to have turned the heads of the two eldest daughters, who immediately flattered themselves with the hopes of returning to town, for they were quite weary of a country life; and when they saw their father ready to set out, they begged of him to buy them new gowns, headdresses, ribbons, and all manner of trifles; but Beauty asked for nothing for she thought to herself, that all the money her father was going to receive, would scarce be sufficient to purchase everything her sisters wanted. "What will you have, Beauty?" said her father. "Since you have the goodness to think of me," answered she, "be so kind to bring me a rose, for as none grows hereabouts, they are a kind of rarity." Not that Beauty cared for a rose, but she asked for something, lest she should seem by her example to condemn her sisters' conduct, who would have said she did it only to look particular. The good man went on his journey, but when he came there, they went to law with him about the merchandise, and after a great deal of trouble and pains to no purpose, he came back as poor as before.

He was within thirty miles of his own house, thinking on the pleasure he should have in seeing his children again, when going through a large forest he lost himself. It rained and snowed terribly; besides, the wind was so high, that it threw him twice off his horse, and night coming on, he began to apprehend being either starved to death with cold and hunger, or else devoured by the wolves, whom he heard howling all round him, when, on a sudden, looking through a long walk of trees, he saw a light at some distance, and going on a little farther perceived it came from a place illuminated from top to bottom. The merchant returned God thanks for this happy discovery, and hastened to the place, but was greatly surprised at not meeting with any one in the outer courts. His horse followed him, and seeing a large stable open, went in, and finding both hay and oats, the poor beast, who was almost famished, fell to eating very heartily; the merchant tied him up to the manger, and walking towards the house, where he saw no one, but entering into a large hall, he found a good fire, and a table plentifully set out with but one cover laid. As he was wet quite through with the rain and snow, he drew near the fire to dry himself. "I hope," said he, "the master of the house, or his servants will excuse the liberty I take; I suppose it will not be long before some of them appear."

He waited a considerable time, until it struck eleven, and still nobody came. At last he was so hungry that he could stay no longer, but took a chicken, and ate it in two mouthfuls, trembling all the while. After this he drank a few glasses of wine, and growing more courageous he went out of the hall, and crossed through several grand apartments with magnificent furniture, until he came into a chamber, which had an exceeding good bed in it, and as he was very much fatigued, and it was past midnight, he concluded it was best to shut the door, and go to bed.

It was ten the next morning before the merchant waked, and as he was going to rise he was astonished to see a good suit of clothes in the room of his own, which were quite spoiled; certainly, said he, this palace belongs to some kind fairy, who has seen and pitied my distress. He looked through a window, but instead of snow saw the most delightful arbors, interwoven with the beautifullest flowers that were ever beheld. He then returned to the great hall, where he had supped the night before, and found some chocolate ready made on a little table. "Thank you, good Madam Fairy," said he aloud, "for being so careful, as to provide me a breakfast; I am extremely obliged to you for all your favors."

The good man drank his chocolate, and then went to look for his horse, but passing through an arbor of roses he remembered Beauty's request to him, and gathered a branch on which were several; immediately he heard a great noise, and saw such a frightful Beast coming towards him, that he was ready to faint away. "You are very ungrateful," said the Beast to him, in a terrible voice; "I have saved

261

your life by receiving you into my castle, and, in return, you steal my roses, which I value beyond any thing in the universe, but you shall die for it; I give you but a quarter of an hour to prepare yourself, and say your prayers." The merchant fell on his knees, and lifted up both his hands, "My lord," said he, "I beseech you to forgive me, indeed I had no intention to offend in gathering a rose for one of my daughters, who desired me to bring her one."

"My name is not My Lord," replied the monster, "but Beast; I don't love compliments, not I. I like people to speak as they think; and so do not imagine, I am to be moved by any of your flattering speeches. But you say you have got daughters. I will forgive you, on condition that one of them come willingly, and suffer for you. Let me have no words, but go about your business, and swear that if your daughter refuse to die in your stead, you will return within three months." The merchant had no mind to sacrifice his daughters to the ugly monster, but he thought, in obtaining this respite, he should have the satisfaction of seeing them once more, so he promised, upon oath, he would return, and the Beast told him he might set out when he pleased, "but," added he, "you shall not depart empty handed; go back to the room where you lay, and you will see a great empty chest; fill it with whatever you like best, and I will send it to your home," and at the same time Beast withdrew.

"Well," said the good man to himself, "if I must die, I shall have the comfort, at least, of leaving something to my poor children." He returned to the bedchamber, and finding a great quantity of broad pieces of gold, he filled the great chest the Beast had mentioned, locked it, and afterwards took his horse out of the stable, leaving the palace with as much grief as he had entered it with joy. The horse, of his own accord, took one of the roads of the forest, and in a few hours the good man was at home. His children came round him, but instead of receiving their embraces with pleasure, he looked on them, and holding up the branch he had in his hands, he burst into tears. "Here, Beauty," said he, "take these roses, but little do you think how dear they are like to cost your unhappy father," and then related his fatal adventure. Immediately the two eldest set up lamentable outcries, and said all manner of ill-natured things to Beauty, who did not cry at all.

"Do but see the pride of that little wretch," said they; "she would not ask for fine clothes, as we did; but no truly, Miss wanted to distinguish herself, so now she will be the death of our poor father, and yet she does not so much as shed a tear."

"Why should I," answered Beauty, "it would be very needless, for my father shall not suffer upon my account, since the monster will accept of one of his daughters, I will deliver myself up to all his fury, and I am very happy in thinking that my death will save my father's life, and be a proof of my tender love for him."

"No, sister," said her three brothers, "that shall not be, we will go find the monster, and either kill him, or perish in the attempt."

"Do not imagine any such thing, my sons," said the merchant, "Beast's power is so great, that I have no hopes of your overcoming him. I am charmed with Beauty's kind and generous offer, but I cannot yield to it. I am old, and have not long to live, so can only loose a few years, which I regret for your sakes alone, my dear children."

"Indeed father," said Beauty, "you shall not go to the palace without me, you cannot hinder me from following you." It was to no purpose all they could say. Beauty still insisted on setting out for the fine palace, and her sisters were delighted at it, for her virtue and amiable qualities made them envious and jealous.

The merchant was so afflicted at the thoughts of losing his daughter, that he had quite forgot the chest full of gold, but at night when he retired to rest, no sooner had he shut his chamber door, than, to his great astonishment, he found it by his bedside; he was determined, however, not to tell his children, that he was grown rich, because they would have wanted to return to town, and he was resolved not to leave the country; but he trusted Beauty with the secret, who informed him, that two gentlemen came in his absence, and courted her sisters; she begged her father to consent to their marriage, and give them fortunes, for she was so good, that she loved them and forgave heartily all their ill usage. These wicked creatures rubbed their eyes with an onion to force some tears when they parted with their sister, but her brothers were really concerned. Beauty was the only one who did not shed tears at parting, because she would not increase their uneasiness.

The horse took the direct road to the palace, and towards evening they perceived it illuminated as at first. The horse went of himself into the stable, and the good man and his daughter came into the great hall, where they found a table splendidly served up, and two covers. The merchant had no heart to eat, but Beauty, endeavoring to appear cheerful, sat down to table, and helped him. "Afterwards," thought she to herself, "Beast surely has a mind to fatten me before he eats me, since he provides such plentiful entertainment." When they had supped they heard a great noise, and the merchant, all in tears, bid his poor child, farewell, for he thought Beast was coming. Beauty was sadly terrified at his horrid form, but she took courage as well as she could, and the monster having asked her if she came willingly; "ye—e—es," said she, trembling.

The beast responded, "You are very good, and I am greatly obliged to you; honest man, go your ways tomorrow morning, but never think of coming here again."

"Farewell Beauty, farewell Beast," answered he, and immediately the monster withdrew. "Oh, daughter," said the merchant, embracing Beauty, "I am almost frightened to death, believe me, you had better go back, and let me stay here."

"No, father," said Beauty, in a resolute tone, "you shall set out tomorrow morning, and leave me to the care and protection of providence." They went to bed, and thought they should not close their eyes all night; but scarce were they laid down, than they fell fast asleep, and Beauty dreamed, a fine lady came, and said to her, "I am content, Beauty, with your good will, this good action of yours in giving up your own life to save your father's shall not go unrewarded." Beauty waked, and told her father her dream, and though it helped to comfort him a little, yet he could not help crying bitterly, when he took leave of his dear child.

As soon as he was gone, Beauty sat down in the great hall, and fell a crying likewise; but as she was mistress of a great deal of resolution, she recommended herself to God, and resolved not to be uneasy the little time she had to live; for she firmly believed Beast would eat her up that night.

However, she thought she might as well walk about until then, and view this fine castle, which she could not help admiring; it was a delightful pleasant place, and she was extremely surprised at seeing a door, over which was written, "BEAUTY'S APARTMENT." She opened it hastily, and was quite dazzled with the magnificence that reigned throughout; but what chiefly took up her attention, was a large library, a harpsichord, and several music books. "Well," said she to herself, "I see they will not let my time hang heavy upon my hands for want of amusement." Then she reflected, "Were I but to stay here a day, there would not have been all these preparations." This consideration inspired her with fresh courage; and opening the library she took a book, and read these words, in letters of gold:

> Welcome Beauty, banish fear,
> You are queen and mistress here.
> Speak your wishes, speak your will,
> Swift obedience meets them still.

"Alas," said she, with a sigh, "there is nothing I desire so much as to see my poor father, and know what he is doing." She had no sooner said this, when casting her eyes on a great looking glass, to her great amazement, she saw her own home, where her father arrived with a very dejected countenance. Her sisters went to meet him, and notwithstanding their endeavors to appear sorrowful, their joy, felt for having got rid of their sister, was visible in every feature. A moment after, everything disappeared, and Beauty's apprehensions at this proof of Beast's complaisance.

At noon she found dinner ready, and while at table, was entertained with an excellent concert of music, though without seeing anybody. But at night, as she was going to sit down to supper, she heard the noise Beast made, and could not help being sadly terrified. "Beauty," said the monster, "will you give me leave to see you sup?"

"That is as you please," answered Beauty trembling.

"No," replied the Beast, "you alone are mistress here; you need only bid me gone, if my presence is troublesome, and I will immediately withdraw. But, tell me, do not you think me very ugly?"

"That is true," said Beauty, "for I cannot tell a lie, but I believe you are very good-natured."

"So I am," said the monster, "but then, besides my ugliness, I have no sense; I know very well, that I am a poor, silly, stupid creature."

"'Tis no sign of folly to think so," replied Beauty, "for never did fool know this, or had so humble a conceit of his own understanding."

"Eat then, Beauty," said the monster, "and endeavor to amuse yourself in your palace, for everything here is yours, and I should be very uneasy, if you were not happy."

"You are very obliging," answered Beauty, "I own I am pleased with your kindness, and when I consider that, your deformity scarce appears."

"Yes, yes," said the Beast, "my heart is good, but still I am a monster."

"Among mankind," says Beauty, "there are many that deserve that name more than you, and I prefer you, just as you are, to those, who, under a human form, hide a treacherous, corrupt, and ungrateful heart."

"If I had sense enough," replied the Beast, "I would make a fine compliment to thank you, but I am so dull, that I can only say, I am greatly obliged to you."

Beauty ate a hearty supper, and had almost conquered her dread of the monster; but she had like to have fainted away, when he said to her, "Beauty, will you be my wife?"

She was some time before she dared answer, for she was afraid of making him angry, if she refused. At last, however, she said trembling, "no Beast." Immediately the poor monster went to sigh, and hissed so frightfully, that the whole palace echoed. But Beauty soon recovered her fright, for Beast having said, in a mournful voice, "then farewell, Beauty," left the room; and only turned back, now and then, to look at her as he went out.

When Beauty was alone, she felt a great deal of compassion for poor Beast. "Alas," said she, "'tis thousand pities, anything so good-natured should be so ugly."

Beauty spent three months very contentedly in the palace. Every evening Beast paid her a visit, and talked to her, during supper, very rationally, with plain good common sense, but never with what the world calls wit; and Beauty daily discovered some valuable qualifications in the monster, and seeing him often had so accustomed her to his deformity, that, far from dreading the time of his visit, she would often look on her watch to see when it would be nine, for the Beast never missed coming at that hour. There was but one thing that gave Beauty any concern, which was, that every night, before she went to bed, the monster always asked her, if she would be his wife. One day she said to him, "Beast, you make me very uneasy, I wish I could consent to marry you, but I am too sincere to make you believe that will ever happen; I shall always esteem you as a friend, endeavor to be satisfied with this."

"I must," said the Beast, "for, alas! I know too well my own misfortune, but then I love you with the tenderest affection. However, I ought to think myself happy, that you will stay here; promise me never to leave me."

Beauty blushed at these words; she had seen in her glass, that her father had pined himself sick for the loss of her, and she longed to see him again. "I could," answered she, "indeed, promise never to leave you entirely, but I have so great a desire to see my father, that I shall fret to death, if you refuse me that satisfaction."

"I had rather die myself," said the monster, "than give you the least uneasiness. I will send you to your father, you shall remain with him, and poor Beast will die with grief."

"No," said Beauty, weeping, "I love you too well to be the cause of your death. I give you my promise to return in a week. You have shown me that my sisters are married, and my brothers gone to the army; only let me stay a week with my father, as he is alone."

"You shall be there tomorrow morning," said the Beast, "but remember your promise. You need only lay your ring on a table before you go to bed, when you have a mind to come back. Farewell Beauty." Beast sighed, as usual, bidding her good night, and Beauty went to bed very sad at seeing him so afflicted. When she waked the next morning, she found herself at her father's, and having rung a little bell, that was by her bedside, she saw the maid come, who, the moment she saw her, gave a loud shriek, at which the good man ran up stairs, and thought he should have died with joy to see his dear daughter again. He held her fast locked in his arms above a quarter of an hour. As soon as the first transports were over, Beauty began to think of rising, and was afraid she had no clothes to put on; but the maid told her, that she had just found, in the next room, a large trunk full of gowns, covered with gold and diamonds. Beauty thanked good Beast for his kind care, and taking one of the plainest of them, she intended to make a present of the others to her sisters. She scarce had said so when the trunk disappeared. Her father told her, that Beast insisted on her keeping them herself, and immediately both gowns and trunk came back again.

Beauty dressed herself, and in the meantime they sent to her sisters who hastened thither with their husbands. They were both of them very unhappy. The eldest had married a gentleman, extremely handsome indeed, but so fond of his own person, that he was full of nothing but his own dear self, and neglected his wife. The second had married a man of wit, but he only made use of it to plague and torment everybody, and his wife most of all. Beauty's sisters sickened with envy, when they saw her dressed like a princess, and more beautiful than ever, nor could all her obliging affectionate behavior stifle their jealousy, which was ready to burst when she told them how happy she was. They went down into the garden to vent it in tears; and said one to the other, in what way is this little creature better than us, that she should be so much happier? "Sister," said the oldest, "a thought just strikes my mind; let us endeavor to detain her above a week, and perhaps the silly monster will be so enraged at her for breaking her word, that he will devour her."

"Right, sister," answered the other, "therefore we must show her as much kindness as possible." After they had taken this resolution, they went up, and behaved so affectionately to their sister, that poor Beauty wept for joy. When the week was expired, they cried and tore their hair, and seemed so sorry to part with her, that she promised to stay a week longer.

In the meantime, Beauty could not help reflecting on herself, for the uneasiness she was likely to cause poor Beast, whom she sincerely loved, and really longed to see again. The tenth night she spent at her father's, she dreamed she was in the palace garden, and that she saw Beast extended on the grass plat, who seemed just expiring, and, in a dying voice, reproached her with her ingratitude. Beauty started out of her sleep, and bursting into tears. "Am I not very wicked," said she, "to act so unkindly to Beast, that has studied so much, to please me in everything? Is it his fault if he is so ugly, and has so little sense? He is kind and good, and that is sufficient. Why did I refuse to marry him? I should be happier with the monster than my sisters are with their husbands; it is neither wit, nor a fine person, in a husband, that makes a woman happy, but virtue, sweetness of temper, and complaisance, and Beast has all these valuable qualifications. It is true, I do not feel the tenderness of affection for him, but I find I have the highest gratitude, esteem, and friendship; I will not make him miserable, were I to be so ungrateful I should never forgive myself." Beauty having said this, rose, put her ring on the table, and then laid down again; scarce was she in bed before she fell asleep, and when she waked the next morning, she was overjoyed to find herself in the Beast's palace.

She put on one of her richest suits to please him, and waited for evening with the utmost impatience, at last the wished-for hour came, the clock struck nine, yet no Beast appeared. Beauty then feared she had been the cause of his death; she ran crying and wringing her hands all about the palace, like one in despair; after having sought for him everywhere, she recollected her dream, and flew to the canal in the garden, where she dreamed she saw him. There she found poor Beast stretched out, quite senseless, and, as she imagined, dead. She threw herself upon him without any dread, and finding his heart beat still, she fetched some water from the canal, and poured it on his head. Beast opened his eyes, and said to Beauty, "You forgot your promise, and I was so afflicted for having lost you, that I resolved to starve myself, but since I have the happiness of seeing you once more, I die satisfied."

"No, dear Beast," said Beauty, "you must not die. Live to be my husband; from this moment I give you my hand, and swear to be none but yours. Alas! I thought I had only a friendship for you, but the grief I now feel convinces me, that I cannot live without you." Beauty scarce had pronounced these words, when she saw the palace sparkle with light; and fireworks, instruments of music, everything seemed to give notice of some great event. But nothing could fix her attention; she turned to her dear Beast, for whom she trembled with fear; but how great was her surprise! Beast was disappeared, and she saw, at her feet, one of the loveliest princes that eye ever beheld; who returned her thanks for having put an end to the charm, under which he had so long resembled a Beast. Though this prince was worthy of all her attention, she could not forbear asking where Beast was.

"You see him at your feet, said the prince. A wicked fairy had condemned me to remain under that shape until a beautiful virgin should consent to marry me. The fairy likewise enjoined me to conceal my understanding. There was only you in the world generous enough to be won by the goodness of my temper, and in offering you my crown I can't discharge the obligations I have to you."

Beauty, agreeably surprised, gave the charming prince her hand to rise; they went together into the castle, and Beauty was overjoyed to find, in the great hall, her father and his whole family, whom the beautiful lady, that appeared to her in her dream, had conveyed thither.

"Beauty," said this lady, "come and receive the reward of your judicious choice; you have preferred virtue before either wit or beauty, and deserve to find a person in whom all these qualifications are united. You are going to be a great queen. I hope the throne will not lessen your virtue, or make you forget yourself. As to you, ladies," said the fairy to Beauty's two sisters, "I know your hearts, and all the malice they contain. Become two statues, but, under this transformation, still retain your reason. You shall stand before your sister's palace gate, and be it your punishment to behold her happiness; and it will not be in your power to return to your former state, until you own your faults, but I am very much afraid that you will al-

267

ways remain statues. Pride, anger, gluttony, and idleness are sometimes conquered, but the conversion of a malicious and envious mind is a kind of miracle." Immediately the fairy gave a stroke with her wand, and in a moment all that were in the hall were transported into the prince's dominions. His subjects received him with joy. He married Beauty, and lived with her many years, and their happiness—as it was founded on virtue—was complete.[173]

Zelinda and the Monster

Italy

There was once a poor man who had three daughters; and as the youngest was the fairest and most civil, and had the best disposition, her other two sisters envied her with a deadly envy, although her father, on the contrary, loved her dearly. It happened that in a neighboring town, in the month of January, there was a great fair, and that poor man was obliged to go there to lay in the provisions necessary for the support of his family; and before departing he asked his three daughters if they would like some small presents in proportion, you understand, to his means. Rosina wished a dress, Marietta asked him for a shawl, but Zelinda was satisfied with a handsome rose. The poor man set out on his journey early the next day, and when he arrived at the fair quickly bought what he needed, and afterward easily found Rosina's dress and Marietta's shawl; but at that season he could not find a rose for his Zelinda, although he took great pains in looking everywhere for one. However, anxious to please his dear Zelinda, he took the first road he came to, and after journeying a while arrived at a handsome garden enclosed by high walls; but as the gate was partly open he entered softly. He found the garden filled with every kind of flowers and plants, and in a corner was a tall rosebush full of beautiful rosebuds. Wherever he looked no living soul appeared from whom he might ask a rose as a gift or for money, so the poor man, without thinking, stretched out his hand, and picked a rose for his Zelinda.

Mercy! scarcely had he pulled the flower from the stalk when there arose a great noise, and flames darted from the earth, and all at once there appeared a terrible Monster with the figure of a dragon, and hissed with all his might, and cried out, enraged at that poor Christian, "Rash man! what have you done? Now you must die at once, for you have had the audacity to touch and destroy my rosebush." The poor man, more than half dead with terror, began to weep and beg for mercy on his

---

[173]Type 425C. Source: *The Young Misses Magazine, Containing Dialogues between a Governess and Several Young Ladies of Quality Her Scholars*, by Madam Prince de Beaumont, 4th ed., v. 1 (London, 1783), pp. 45-67. Spelling and punctuation revised.

knees, asking pardon for the fault he had committed, and told why he had picked the rose; and then he added, "Let me depart; I have a family, and if I am killed they will go to destruction" But the Monster, more wicked than ever, responded, "Listen; one must die. Either bring me the girl that asked for the rose or I will kill you this very moment." It was impossible to move him by prayers or lamentations; the Monster persisted in his decision, and did not let the poor man go until he had sworn to bring him there in the garden his daughter Zelinda.

Imagine how downhearted that poor man returned home! He gave his oldest daughters their presents and Zelinda her rose; but his face was distorted and as white as though he had arisen from the dead; so that the girls, in terror, asked him what had happened and whether he had met with any misfortune. They were urgent, and at last the poor man, weeping bitterly, related the misfortunes of that unhappy journey and on what condition he had been able finally to return home. "In short," he exclaimed, "either Zelinda or I must be eaten alive by the Monster." Then the two sisters emptied the vials of their wrath on Zelinda. "Just see," they said, "that affected, capricious girl! She shall go to the Monster! She who wanted roses at this season. No, indeed! Papa must stay with us. The stupid creature!" At all these taunts Zelinda, without growing angry, simply said, "It is right that the one who has caused the misfortune should pay for it. I will go to the Monster's. Yes, Papa, take me to the garden, and the Lord's will be done."

The next day Zelinda and her sorrowful father began their journey and at nightfall arrived at the garden gate. When they entered they saw as usual no one, but they beheld a lordly palace all lighted and the doors wide open. When the two travelers entered the vestibule, suddenly four marble statues, with lighted torches in their hands, descended from their pedestals, and accompanied them up the stairs to a large hall where a table was lavishly spread. The travelers, who were very hungry, sat down and began to eat without ceremony; and when they had finished, the same statues conducted them to two handsome chambers for the night. Zelinda and her father were so weary that they slept like dormice all night.

At daybreak Zelinda and her father arose, and were served with everything for breakfast by invisible hands. Then they descended to the garden, and began to seek the Monster. When they came to the rosebush he appeared in all his frightful ugliness. Zelinda, on seeing him, became pale with fear, and her limbs trembled, but the Monster regarded her attentively with his great fiery eyes, and afterward said to the poor man, "Very well; you have kept your word, and I am satisfied. Now depart and leave me alone here with the young girl." At this command the old man thought he should die; and Zelinda, too, stood there half stupefied and her eyes full of tears; but entreaties were of no avail; the Monster remained as obdurate as a stone, and the poor man was obliged to depart, leaving his dear Zelinda in the Monster's power.

When the Monster was alone with Zelinda he began to caress her, and make loving speeches to her, and managed to appear quite civil. There was no danger of his forgetting her, and he saw that she wanted nothing, and every day, talking with her in the garden, he asked her, "Do you love me, Zelinda? Will you be my wife?" The young girl always answered him in the same way, "I like you, sir, but I will never be your wife." Then the monster appeared very sorrowful, and redoubled his caresses and attentions, and, sighing deeply, said, "But you see, Zelinda, if you should marry me wonderful things would happen. What they are I cannot tell you until you will be my wife."

Zelinda, although in her heart not dissatisfied with that beautiful place and with being treated like a queen, still did not feel at all like marrying the Monster, because he was too ugly and looked like a beast, and always answered his requests in the same manner. One day, however, the Monster called Zelinda in haste, and said, "Listen, Zelinda; if you do not consent to marry me it is fated that your father must die. He is ill and near the end of his life, and you will not be able even to see him again. See whether I am telling you the truth." And, drawing out an enchanted mirror, the Monster showed Zelinda her father on his deathbed. At that spectacle Zelinda, in despair and half mad with grief, cried, "Oh, save my father, for mercy's sake! Let me be able to embrace him once more before he dies. Yes, yes, I promise you I will be your faithful and constant wife, and that without delay. But save my father from death."

Scarcely had Zelinda uttered these words when suddenly the Monster was transformed into a very handsome youth. Zelinda was astounded by this unexpected change, and the young man took her by the hand, and said, "Know, dear Zelinda, that I am the son of the King of the Oranges. An old witch, touching me, changed me into the terrible Monster I was, and condemned me to be hidden in this rosebush until a beautiful girl consented to become my wife."[174]

The Enchanted Brahman's Son

The Panchatantra

In the city of Radschagriha there lived a Brahman by the name of Devasarman. His childless wife wept bitterly whenever she saw the neighbors' children. One day the Brahman said to her, "Dear one, stop your grieving. Behold, I was offering a sacrifice for the birth of a son when an invisible being said to me in the clearest words, 'Brahman, you shall be granted this son, and he shall surpass all men in beauty and virtue, and good fortune shall be his.'"

After hearing this, the Brahman's wife was overjoyed, and she said, "Such promises must come true." In the course of time she became pregnant and gave birth to a snake. When her attendants saw it, they all cried out, "Throw it away!" However, she paid no attention to them, but instead picked it up, had it bathed,

---

[174]Type 425C. Source: Thomas Frederick Crane, *Italian Popular Tales* (Boston and New York, 1885), no. 2.

and—filled with a mother's love toward her son—laid it in a large, clean container, fed it milk, fresh butter, and the like, so that within a few days it had reached its full growth.

Once when the Brahman's wife witnessed the wedding feast of a neighbor's son, her eyes clouded over with tears, and she said to her husband, "You treat me with contempt, because you are not making any effort at all to arrange a wedding for my dear child!"

When he heard this, the Brahman said, "Honored one! To achieve that I would have to go to the depths of hell and beseech Pasuki, the King of Snakes, for who else, you fool, would give his daughter in marriage to a snake?"

Having said this, he looked at his wife with her exceedingly sad face, and—for the sake of her love and in order to pacify her—he took some travel provisions and departed for a foreign land. After traveling about for several months he came to a place by the name of Kukutanagara. There, as evening fell, he was received by an acquaintance, a member of his caste. He was given a bath, food, and every necessity, and he spent the night there.

The next morning he took leave and was preparing to set forth once again, when his host said, "What brought you to this place, and where are you going now."

The Brahman answered, "I have come to seek an appropriate bride for my son."

After hearing this, the host said, "If that is the case, then I have a very appropriate daughter. I have only respect for you. Take her for your son!" Acting upon these words, the Brahman took the girl, together with her servants, and returned to his home city. However, when the inhabitants of this region saw the girl, who was beautiful, gifted, and charming beyond comparison, they opened their eyes wide with love for her, and said to her attendants, "How could you deliver such a jewel of a girl to a snake?"

After hearing this, all of her companions were horrified, and they said, "She must be rescued from the murderer set up by this old Brahman."

Hearing this, the maiden said, "Spare me from such deception, for behold:

> Kings speak but once. The virtuous speak but once. A girl is promised in marriage but once. These three things happen but once.

And further:

> Not even wise men and gods can change the decrees of fate.

And moreover, my father shall not be reproached for his daughter's falseness." Having said that, and with the permission of her attendants, she married the snake. She showed him proper respect, and served him milk and similar things.

One night the snake left his large basket, which was kept in the bedroom, and climbed into his wife's bed. She cried out, "Who is this creature, shaped like a man?" Thinking it was a strange man, she jumped up. Shaking all over, she tore open the door and wanted to rush away, when the snake said, "Dear one! Stay here! I am your husband!" To convince her of this, he once again entered the body that he had left in the basket, then left it again. He was wearing a magnificent diadem, rings, bands, and bracelets on his upper and lower arms. His wife fell at his feet. Then together they partook of the joys of love.

His father, the Brahman, had arisen earlier than his son, and saw everything. He took the snake skin, which was lying in the basket, and burned it in the fire, saying, "He shall not enter it again." Later that morning, filled with joy, he presented his son to his family. Vitalized by unending love, he became an ideal son.[175]

The Silk Spinster

Germany

Once upon a time there was a peasant. He worked in the woods and took his oldest daughter along to help him. When the day grew hot he took off his jacket and laid it in the grass. When his work was finished, he asked his daughter to fetch it for him. She went to it, but there was a worm lying on it. She did not want to pick it up, so she ran back to her father and asked him what she should do. He told her not to be afraid of the worm. She should just throw it aside and bring him his jacket. She did this, and they went home.

The next day the peasant again went to work in the woods, taking his second daughter along. Everything happened as before, and in the end she threw the worm aside, and she and her father returned home together.

On the third day, the first daughter was to go along again, but the third daughter asked the father to take her. She wanted to help out like the others. They laughed at her, and asked her just how she would be able to help. They had a low opinion of her and kept her at home like a Cinderella. But she begged her father so earnestly, that he finally said she might come along. When it was time to go home, her father told her to fetch his jacket. She went to it and found the worm on it. But she said to it, "Dear little worm, would you like a soft place to lie?"

The worm looked at her with bright and friendly eyes, as though it wanted to say "yes!" Therefore she gathered together some moss and made him a nice soft nest. As soon as she laid him in it, the worm began to speak, and asked her, "Would you like to enter my service? All you have to do is carry me about a few hours each day. For this you will receive a good wage and food and drink as well. If you do this for three years, I will be redeemed, because I am an enchanted prince, and then I will marry you!"

The girl said that she would do it, and the worm said, "Then come here tomorrow at the same time."

---

[175]Type 433. Source: *Pantschatantra: Fünf Bücher indischer Fabeln, Märchen und Erzählungen*, translated from the Sanskrit into German by Theodor Benfey (Leipzig, 1859), v. 2, book 1, story 8.

After that she went home with her father. Then she said, "I have lived at home long enough. I am going try my luck out in the world."

They all laughed at her, saying, "You, Cinderella, who would have any use for you?"

The girl replied, "I already have a position," and asked her father to allow her to leave. He did not want to give his permission, because even if she did not understand very much, she was still a good worker. Finally he gave in to her begging, and the next day she set forth.

She went into the woods and soon found the worm. He was very pleased that she had come, and he told her that she should now carry him around a little. That she did, and when the time was up, a splendid castle suddenly appeared. In the castle there was a great hall with a large table all decked out with food and drink, more beautiful than anything she had ever seen in her entire lifetime. She ate and drank her fill, and then went to bed. Every day she carried the worm about for an hour or two and then went to the castle, where everything was prepared for her, and where she was splendidly provided for.

After a year had passed she asked the worm for permission to visit her father. He agreed on the condition that she return promptly. She took gold and other precious things for her father and her sisters and went home. When she arrived with her treasures, her sisters wanted to know where she had gotten it all, and who her master was. But she told them nothing, for the worm had forbidden her to do so. They beat her and scolded her, but she said nothing.

The next day she went back into the woods to the worm, and again carried it about for an hour or two each day. At the end of the second year she once again visited her father and her sisters, and also at the end of the third year. When she left the worm, he ordered her also this last time to return promptly, and she promised to do so.

Her father and her sisters insisted that she tell them who her master was and where she worked, and they refused to let her go. Finally she tore herself away with force. When she returned to the woods, it was too late. The worm was no longer there. Sadly she looked everywhere, but that castle had disappeared, and the worm as well, for while she was away, his spell had lapsed, and he had turned back into a king, and he was now back at home in his own kingdom.

The girl decided to search for him throughout the world. On her way she came to a hut in the forest where an old woman lived, whom she asked for shelter for the night. The old woman received her in a friendly manner, and the next morning when she was about the leave, she gave her three apples. She told her there was a golden spindle in the first one, a golden yarn reel in the second one, and a golden spinning wheel in the third one, and told her whom she would meet and what she should do. The girl kindly thanked the friendly old woman and set forth.

Many days later and after she had walked a great distance, she came to a glass mountain. She did not know how she could cross over it, because it was so smooth that she always slid back down. Finally she saw a smithy not far away. She went there and had horseshoes attached to her hands and knees, and climbed over the mountain.

She came to a great city. This was where the king lived who had been the worm that she had carried about every day. He was already married. He had a beautiful wife and had long since forgotten the girl.

She disguised herself and went to the castle where she hired herself out as a silk spinster. On the first day she opened the first apple that the old woman in the woods had given her. She took out the golden spindle. When the queen saw it, she liked it very much and wanted to buy it from the girl. "No," she said. "It is not for sale, but I will give it to you if you will let me sleep with the king one night."

"Why not?," thought the queen, and gave her promise. As evening approached she gave the king a sleeping potion, and when he was fast asleep, she sent for the silk spinster and led her into the king's bedroom.

She sat next to his bed and cried bitterly, "Now I know that thanklessness is the way of the world," she said. "Three years I carried you about as a worm. For your sake I received blows and harsh words from my father and sisters. I had horseshoes attached to my hands and knees in order to climb over the glass mountain. Now you have forgotten everything and taken another wife." But the king was so fast asleep that he did not understand a thing. At dawn the queen came and led the silk spinster out again.

Sadly she took the second apple, broke it open, and took out the golden yarn reel. When the queen saw it, she admired it greatly and asked the girl to sell it to her. Once again she said that it was not for sale, but it could be earned if she were allowed to sleep with the king for another night. The queen gave her promise, and everything happened as during the first night. The king lay in knee-deep sleep, and no amount of crying and complaining could awaken him. However, one of the king's servants had seen the queen bring the spinster into the king's bedroom. He was curious, and listened to everything that the silk spinster said. The next day he told the king what he had seen and heard.

But that morning the queen had once again led the silk spinster out of the king's bedroom. In desperation, the girl opened her last apple, the one with the golden spinning wheel. When the queen saw it, she said she would let her sleep with the king yet another night, if she would give her the golden spinning wheel. The girl agreed, and that evening the queen once again gave her husband a sleeping potion, but he only pretended to drink it. He secretly poured it out, then lay down and pretended to be asleep. Then the queen fetched the silk spinster and led her into the king's bedroom. The girl sat sadly next to the king's bed and cried bitterly, "Now I know that thanklessness is the way of the world," she said. "Three years I carried you about as a worm. For your sake I received blows and harsh words from my father and sisters. I had horseshoes attached to my hands and knees in order to climb over the glass mountain. And you have forgotten everything and taken another wife."

The king listened silently to every word, but pretended to be asleep. The next day he ordered a large festive meal, and he invited the silk spinster to take her place at his right side. When everyone was seated, he said, "I want to present all of you with a question, and ask for your honest and open answer. Many years ago I lost the key to my chest, and therefore had a new one made. But now I have found the old one. Which one should I use from now on?"

"The old one," they all said as with one voice. "The old one always fits better."

"Now," said the king, "the silk spinster who is sitting here at my right side took care of me for three years while I was an enchanted worm. She suffered greatly on my behalf. Therefore, I would like to leave my wife for as long as the first one is alive, and marry her." And that is what he did. And thus the silk spinster became queen.[176]

The Girl and the Snake

Sweden

Once upon a time there was a girl who was supposed to go into the woods and bring home the cattle, but she could not find the herd. She got lost and came to a large mountain with gates and doors. She went inside. A table was standing there, set with all kinds of things to eat. There was also a bed there, and a large snake was lying on it. It said to the girl, "Have a seat, if you want to. Come and lie down in this bed, if you want to! But if you don't want to, it's all right!" The girl did not do any of this. Finally the snake said, "People are coming now who want to dance with you, but don't go with them." Soon afterward people did come, and they wanted to dance with the girl, but she would have nothing to do with them. Then they began to eat and drink. The girl left the mountain and went home again. The next day she went into the woods again to look for her herd, but she could not find what she was looking for. Instead, she got lost again and came to the same mountain. She went inside again and found everything the same as the first time: a set table and the bed with the snake. It said to her, as the time before, "Have a seat, if you want to! Eat, if you want to! Come and lie down in this bed, if you want to! But if you don't want to, it's all right. Now a lot more people are coming who want to dance with you, but do not go with them." The snake had barely finished talking when a lot more people came, and they began to dance and to eat and drink. The girl had nothing to do with them, but instead left the mountain and went home.

On the third day she went into the woods again, and the same thing happened to her as on the previous days. The snake invited her to eat and drink, which she did with a good appetite. After that the snake asked her to lie down next to it, and the girl did that as well. Then the snake said, "Hold me in your arm!" She did it.

---

[176]Types 433 and 425. Source: Adalbert Kuhn and Wilhelm Schwartz, *Norddeutsche Sagen, Märchen und Gebräuche* (Leipzig, 1848), pp. 347-352.

"Kiss me!" said the snake. "If you are afraid, just put your apron between us!" The girl did it, and in that instant the snake turned into a handsome young man. In reality he was a prince who had been bewitched into this form through magic, but the girl's courage had saved him. Of course, the two of them went away, and since then they have never been heard from again.[177]

King Lindorm

Denmark

Once upon a time there was a king who had a beautiful queen. On the first night of their marriage, nothing was written on their bed when they retired, but when they got up the next day, they read there that they would have no children. The king was very sad about this, and the queen even more so. She found it most unfortunate that there would be no heir for their kingdom.

One day, while deep in thought, she wandered to a remote spot. There she met an old woman who asked her why she was so sad. The queen looked up and said, "Oh, telling you will do no good. You can't help me."

"But perhaps I can," said the old woman, and asked the queen to tell her story. So the queen agreed, and told how on their wedding night a message had appeared on their bed that they would have no children. This was why she was so sad. The old woman told her that she could help her have children. That evening at sunset she should place a platter upside down in the northwest corner of the garden. The next morning at sunrise she should take it away. Beneath it she would find two roses, a red one and a white one. "Take the red one and eat it, and you shall have a boy; take the white one and it will be a girl. But do not eat them both," said the old woman.

The queen returned home and did what the old woman had told her to do. The next morning, just as the sun was coming up, she went to the garden and picked up the platter. There were two roses, a red one and a white one. Now she did not know which of the two she should take. If it were the red one, she would have a boy, and he might have to go to war and be killed, and then again she would have no child. So she decided to take the white one; then it would be a girl who would stay at home with her, and then get married and become queen in another kingdom. Thus she picked up the white rose and ate it. But it tasted so good that she picked up the red rose and ate it as well.

Now it so happened that at this time the king was away at war. When the queen noticed that she was pregnant she wrote to him to let him know, and he was very

---

[177]Type 433A. Retold from Klara Stroebe, *Nordische Volksmärchen* (Jena, 1915), v. 1, no. 8.

pleased. When the time for her delivery came, she gave birth to a lindorm.[178] As soon as he was born, he crawled under the bed in the bedroom, and stayed there. Sometime later a letter arrived from the king announcing that he soon would return home. When his carriage pulled up in front of the castle and the queen came out to receive him, the lindorm came too and wanted to greet him. He jumped up into the carriage, calling out, "Welcome home, father!"

"What!," said the king. "Am I your father?"

"Yes, and if you will not be my father, I shall destroy you and the castle as well!"

The king had to agree. They went into the castle together, and the queen had to confess what had happened between her and the old woman. Some days later the council and all the important people in the kingdom assembled to welcome the king back home and to congratulate him on the victory over his enemies. The lindorm came as well and said, "Father, it is time for me to get married!"

"What are you thinking? Who would have you?" said the king.

"If you do not find a wife for me, be she young or old, large or small, rich or poor, then I shall destroy you and the entire castle as well."

So the king wrote to all the kingdoms, asking if someone would not marry his son. A beautiful princess responded, but it seemed strange to her that she was not allowed to see her future husband before entering the hall where the wedding was to take place. Only then did the lindorm make his appearance, taking his place beside her. The wedding day came to an end, and it was time for them to retire to the bedroom. They were scarcely inside, when he ate her alive.

Sometime later, the king's birthday arrived. They were all seated at the dinner table when the lindorm appeared and said, "Father, I want to get married!"

"What kind of a woman would have you?" asked the king.

"If you do not find a wife for me, whoever she may be, I shall eat you up, and the entire castle as well!"

So the king wrote to all the kingdoms, asking if someone would not marry his son. Once again a beautiful princess came from far away. She too was not allowed to see her groom until she was in the hall where they were to be married. The lindorm entered and took his place beside her. When the wedding day was over and they went into the bedroom, the lindorm killed her.

Sometime later, on the queen's birthday, they were all seated at the dinner table when the lindorm came in and said once again, "Father, I want to get married!"

"I cannot get you another wife," answered the king. "The two kings whose daughters I gave to you are now waging war against me. What am I to do?"

"Just let them come! As long as I am on your side, just let them come, and even if there were ten of them! But if you do not find a wife for me, be she young or old, large or small, rich or poor, then I shall destroy you and the castle as well!"

---

[178]A lindorm (also spelled lindworm) was a mythological beast much feared in ancient northern Europe. It is depicted variously as a giant snake or a wingless dragon. The name derives from an Old Norse word for "serpent."

The king had to give in, but he was not happy about it. Now one of the king's shepherds, an old man who lived in a little house in the woods, had a daughter. The king went to him and said, "Listen, my dear man. Won't you give your daughter in marriage to my son?"

"No, I can't do that. I have only the one child to care for me when I am older, and further, if the prince can't take care of beautiful princesses he will not take care of my daughter, and that would be a sin." But the king insisted on having her, and the old man had to give in.

The old shepherd went home and told his daughter everything. She became very sad and, deep in thought, took a walk in the woods. There she met an old woman who had gone into the woods to pick berries and wild apples. She was wearing a red skirt and a blue jacket. "Why are you so sad?" she asked.

"I have every reason to be sad, but there is no purpose in my telling you about it, because you can't help me."

"But perhaps I can," she said. "Just tell me!"

"Well, I am supposed to marry the king's son, but he is a lindorm and has already killed two princesses, and I know for sure that he will kill me as well."

"If you just listen to me, I can help you," said the old woman.

The girl was eager to hear her advice. "When you go to the bedroom following the ceremony, you must have ten nightshirts on. If you don't have that many, then you must borrow some. Ask for a bucketful of lye water, a bucketful of sweet milk, and an armful of switches. All these things must be taken to the bedroom. When he comes in, he will say, 'Beautiful maiden, take off your nightshirt!' Then you must say, 'King Lindorm, take off your skin!' You will say that to each other until you have taken off nine nightshirts and he has taken off nine skins. By then he will not have another skin, but you will still have on a nightshirt. Then you must take hold of him. He will be nothing more than a clump of bloody meat. Dip the switches into the lye water and beat him with them until he has almost fallen to pieces. Then you must bathe him in the sweet milk, wrap him in the nine night-shirts, and hold him on your arm. You will then fall asleep, but only for a short time."

The girl thanked her for the good advice, but she was still afraid, for this was indeed a dangerous undertaking with such a sinister animal.

The wedding day arrived. A large and splendid carriage brought two ladies who prepared the girl for the wedding. Then she was taken to the castle and led into the hall. The lindorm appeared, took his place next to her, and they were married. When evening arrived, and it was time for them to go to bed, the bride asked for a bucketful of lye water, a bucketful of sweet milk, and an armful of switches. The men all laughed at her, saying that it was some kind of a peasant superstition and all in her imagination. But the king said that she should have what she asked for, and they brought it to her. Before going into the bedroom, she put nine nightshirts over the one she was already wearing.

When they both were in the bedroom the lindorm said, "Beautiful maiden, take off your nightshirt!"

She answered, "King Lindorm, take off your skin!"

And thus it continued until she had taken off nine nightshirts and he had taken off nine skins. She found new courage, for he was now lying and the floor with blood flowing freely from him and barely able to move. Then she took the switches, dipped them into the lye water, and beat him as hard as she could until there was scarcely a twig left among the sticks. Then she dipped him into the sweet milk and laid him on her arm. She fell asleep, for it was late, and when she awoke, she was lying in the arms of a handsome prince.

Morning came, and no one dared to look into the bedroom, because they all believed that the same thing had happened to her as to the two others. Finally the king wanted to look, and as he opened the door she called out, "Do come in! Everything is all right!" He went in and was filled with joy. He fetched the queen and the others, and there was a great celebration about the bridal bed unlike any that had ever been seen before. The bridal couple got up and went into another room where they got dressed, because the bedroom was in a horrible mess. Then the wedding was celebrated anew with pomp and joy. The king and queen liked the young queen very much. They could not treat her too well, for she had redeemed their lindorm.

Sometime later she became pregnant. There was another war, and the old king and King Lindorm had gone to the battlefield. Her time arrived, and she gave birth to two beautiful boys. At this time the Red Knight was at court. They asked him to take the king a letter announcing the birth of the two beautiful boys. He rode away a short distance and opened the letter, then changed it to read that she had given birth to two young dogs. The king received the letter and was very sad. He found it unbelievable that she had given birth to young dogs, although it would have not surprised him if it had been a lindorm or something like that. He wrote back that the creatures should be allowed to live until he returned home, that is if they could be kept alive at all. The Red Knight was to deliver this letter, but a short distance away he opened it as well and wrote that the queen and her children were to be burned alive.

The old queen was greatly saddened by this letter, for she liked the young queen very much. Soon thereafter another letter arrived, announcing the king's return home. The queen became frightened and did not know what to do. She could not bring herself to have them burned. She sent the two children to live with a wet nurse, for she hoped that the king might change his mind once he was back home. She gave the young queen some money and food and sent her into the forest.

She wandered about in the woods for two days and was in great need. She came to a high mountain, which she climbed without stopping. At the top there were three benches. She sat down on the middle one and squeezed the milk from her breasts, for she was in great distress, not having her children with her. Then two large birds, a swan and a crane, flew down and sat on either side of her, and she pressed her milk into their beaks. They were that close to her. And even as they sat there, they turned into the two most handsome princes that one can imagine, and the mountain turned into the most beautiful royal castle, with servants and animals and gold and silver and everything that there should be. They had been enchanted, and the spell would never have been broken if they had not drunk the milk from a queen who had just given birth to two boys. She went with them, with King Swan and King Crane. Each one wanted to marry her, for she had redeemed them both.

Meanwhile King Lindorm arrived home and asked about the queen. "Indeed!" Said the old queen. "You should be asking about her! Who do you think that you are! You paid no attention to the fact that she redeemed you from your curse. You just went ahead and wrote to me that she and the children should be burned alive. For shame!"

"No!" answered King Lindorm. "You wrote to me that she had given birth to two young dogs. And I wrote back that you should let the creatures live until I returned home."

They talked back and forth for a long time and finally realized that the Red Knight had been behind the treachery. He was captured, and he had to confess. They locked him in a barrel studded with nails, hitched it to four horses, and they ran with him over mountains and valleys.

The king was full of despair about his wife and children, when he discovered that they were two beautiful boys. The old queen said to him, "Don't worry, the boys are well cared for. They are staying with wet nurses, but I do not know how she is faring. I gave her some food and money and sent her into the woods, but since then we have heard nothing from her."

The king ordered that the children be brought back. Then he took some food and some money and went into the woods to look for her. He wandered about for two, then three days looking for her, but he could not find her. Finally he came to the castle in the woods. He asked if the people there had not seen a strange maiden in the woods, but they had not seen anyone. Then he wanted to enter the castle to see what kind of royalty lived there. He went inside. Just as he entered he saw her, but she was afraid, for she thought that he had come to burn her alive, and she ran away.

The two princes came in. They talked together and became good friends. They invited him to stay for dinner. He mentioned the beautiful maiden and asked where she was from. They answered that she was a lovely person and that she had freed them both. He wanted to know what she had freed them from, and they told him the entire story. Then he said that he liked her very much and asked them if they could not come to an agreement concerning her. He proposed that her dinner should be over salted, and that the person she would ask to drink to her health should receive her. The princes agreed to this arrangement, for this would enable them to determine which of the two of them would have her, for they did not believe that she would ask a stranger to drink to her health.

They went to dinner, and she said:

> The food is too salty for me,
> King Swan sits next to me,
> King Crane is good to me,
> King Lindorm drinks with me.

He picked up the silver tankard and drank to her health. The others drank to their own health, but then they had to drink to her health as well, even though they were not satisfied with the outcome. Then King Lindorm told how she had redeemed him before she had redeemed them. Therefore he was the closest one to her. After hearing this, the two princes stated that if he had told them this in the first place, they would have given her to him. But he said that he could not have known that for sure.

Then King Lindorm returned home with the queen. Meanwhile the children had also been taken back home. King Swan kept the castle in the woods and married a princess from another kingdom. And King Crane went to a different country where he got married. Thus each one of them had something. King Lindorm and his queen stood in high honor as long as they lived. They were very happy and had many children.

When I was there the last time, they offered me a tin sandwich in a sieve.[179]

The Water Snake

Russia

There was once an old woman who had a daughter; and her daughter went down to the pond one day to bathe with the other girls. They all stripped off their shifts, and went into the water. Then there came a snake out of the water, and glided on to the daughter's shift. After a time the girls all came out, and began to put on their shifts, and the old woman's daughter wanted to put on hers, but there was the snake lying on it. She tried to drive him away, but there he stuck and would not move. Then the snake said, "If you'll marry me, I'll give you back your shift."

Now she wasn't at all inclined to marry him, but the other girls said, "As if it were possible for you to be married to him! Say you will!"

So she said, "Very well, I will." Then the snake glided off from the shift, and went straight into the water. The girl dressed and went home. And as soon as she got there, she said to her mother, "Mammie, mammie, thus and thus, a snake got upon my shift, and says he, 'Marry me or I won't let you have your shift;' and I said, 'I will.'"

"What nonsense are you talking, you little fool! as if one could marry a snake!" And so they remained just as they were, and forgot all about the matter.

A week passed by, and one day they saw ever so many snakes, a huge troop of them, wriggling up to their cottage. "Ah, mammie, save me, save me!" cried the girl, and her mother slammed the door and barred the entrance as quickly as possi-

---

[179]Type 433B. Source: Sven Grundtvig, *Gamle danske Minder i Folkemunde* (Copenhagen, 1854-1861), v. 1, no. 216.

ble. The snakes would have rushed in at the door, but the door was shut; they would have rushed into the passage, but the passage was closed. Then in a moment they rolled themselves into a ball, flung themselves at the window, smashed it to pieces, and glided in a body into the room. The girl got upon the stove, but they followed her, pulled her down, and bore her out of the room and out of doors. Her mother accompanied her, crying like anything.

They took the girl down to the pond, and dived right into the water with her. And there they turned into men and women. The mother remained for some time on the dike, wailed a little, and then went home.

Three years went by. The girl lived down there, and had two children, a son and a daughter. Now she often entreated her husband to let her go to see her mother. So at last one day he took her up to the surface of the water, and brought her ashore. But she asked him before leaving him, "What am I to call out when I want you?"

"Call out to me, 'Osip, [Joseph] Osip, come here!' and I will come," he replied.

Then he dived under water again, and she went to her mother's carrying her little girl on one arm, and leading her boy by the hand. Out came her mother to meet her. She was so delighted to see her!

"Good day, mother!" said the daughter.

"Have you been doing well while you were living down there?" asked her mother.

"Very well indeed, mother. My life there is better than yours here."

They sat down for a bit and chatted. Her mother got dinner ready for her, and she dined. "What's your husband's name?" asked her mother.

"Osip," she replied.

"And how are you to get home?"

"I shall go to the dike, and call out, 'Osip, Osip, come here!' and he'll come."

"Lie down, daughter, and rest a bit," said the mother.

So the daughter lay down and went to sleep. The mother immediately took an ax and sharpened it, and went down to the dike with it. And when she came to the dike, she began calling out, "Osip, Osip, come here!"

No sooner had Osip shown his head than the old woman lifted her ax and chopped it off. And the water in the pond became dark with blood.

The old woman went home. And when she got home her daughter awoke. "Ah! mother," says she, "I'm getting tired of being here; I'll go home."

"Do sleep here tonight, daughter; perhaps you won't have another chance of being with me."

So the daughter stayed and spent the night there. In the morning she got up and her mother got breakfast ready for her; she breakfasted, and then she said good-bye to her mother and went away, carrying her little girl in her arms, while her boy followed behind her. She came to the dike, and called out, "Osip, Osip, come here!"

She called and called, but he did not come. Then she looked into the water, and there she saw a head floating about. Then she guessed what had happened.

"Alas! my mother has killed him!" she cried.

There on the bank she wept and wailed. And then to her girl she cried, "Fly about as a wren, henceforth and evermore!"

And to her boy she cried, "Fly about as a nightingale, my boy, henceforth and evermore!"

"But I," she said, "will fly about as a cuckoo, crying 'Cuckoo!' henceforth and evermore!"[180]

Bearskin

Hans Jakob Christoffel von Grimmelshausen

A soldier, having deserted his regiment in the thick of battle, took refuge in the woods. However, the foes of war were soon replaced by the enemies of cold, thirst, and hunger. With nowhere to turn for help, he was about to surrender to the powers of despair, when without warning an awful spirit appeared before him. He offered the poor soldier great wealth, if he would but serve this uncanny master for seven years. Seeing no other escape from his misery, the soldier agreed.

The terms of the pact were quickly stated: For seven years the soldier was to wear only a bearskin robe, both day and night. He was to say no prayers. Neither comb nor shears were to touch his hair and beard. He was not to wash, nor cut his nails, nor blow his nose, nor even wipe his behind. In return, the spirit would provide him with tobacco, food, drink, and an endless supply of money.

The soldier, who by his very nature was not especially fond of either prayers or of cleanliness, entered into the agreement. He took lodgings in a village inn, and discovered soon enough that his great wealth was ample compensation for his strange looks and ill smell.

A nobleman frequented this inn. Impressed by Bearskin's lavish and generous expenditures, he presented him with a proposal. "I have three beautiful daughters," he said. "If the terms are right, you may choose any one of them for a bride."

Bearskin named a sum that was acceptable to the nobleman, and the two set forth to the palace to make the selection. The two older daughters made no attempt to hide their repugnance of the strange suitor, but the youngest unhesitatingly accepted her father's will. Bearskin formalized the betrothal by removing a ring from his own finger and twisting it into two pieces. One piece he gave to his future bride; the other he kept. Saying that soon he would return, he departed.

---

[180]Type 433. Source: W. R. S. Ralston, *Russian* Folk-Tales (London, 1873), pp. 116-118. Ralston's source: A. A. Erlenvein.

The seven years were nearly finished, so a short time later Bearskin did indeed come back for his bride. Now freshly bathed, neatly shorn, elegantly dressed, and riding in a luxurious carriage, he was a suitor worthy of a princess. Identifying himself with his half of the twisted ring, he claimed his bride.

Beside themselves with envy, and furious that they had squandered their rights to this handsome nobleman, one of the bride's older sisters hanged herself from a tree and the other one drowned herself in a well. Thus the devil gained two souls for the one that he had lost.[181]

The Enchanted Head

Turkey

Once upon a time an old woman lived in a small cottage near the sea with her two daughters. They were very poor, and the girls seldom left the house, as they worked all day long making veils for the ladies to wear over their faces, and every morning, when the veils were finished, the mother took them over the bridge and sold them in the city. Then she bought the food that they needed for the day, and returned home to do her share of veil making.

One morning the old woman rose even earlier than usual, and set off for the city with her wares. She was just crossing the bridge when, suddenly, she knocked up against a human head, which she had never seen there before. The woman started back in horror; but what was her surprise when the head spoke, exactly as if it had a body joined on to it.

"Take me with you, good mother!" it said imploringly; "take me with you back to your house."

At the sound of these words the poor woman nearly went mad with terror. Have that horrible thing always at home? Never! Never! And she turned and ran back as fast as she could, not knowing that the head was jumping, dancing, and rolling after her. But when she reached her own door it bounded in before her, and stopped in front of the fire, begging and praying to be allowed to stay.

All that day there was no food in the house, for the veils had not been sold, and they had no money to buy anything with. So they all sat silent at their work, inwardly cursing the head which was the cause of their misfortunes.

When evening came, and there was no sign of supper, the head spoke, for the first time that day, "Good mother, does no one ever eat here? During all the hours I have spent in your house, not a creature has touched anything."

---

[181]Type 361. Retold from "Der erste Bärenhäuter" (1670). A variant of this tale is found in the Grimms' *Kinder- und Hausmärchen*, no. 101.

284

"No," answered the old woman, "we are not eating anything."

"And why not, good mother?"

"Because we have no money to buy any food."

"Is it your custom never to eat?"

"No, for every morning I go into the city to sell my veils, and with the few shillings I get for them I buy all we want. Today I did not cross the bridge, so of course I had nothing for food."

"Then I am the cause of your having gone hungry all day?" asked the head.

"Yes, you are," answered the old woman.

"Well, then, I will give you money and plenty of it, if you will only do as I tell you. In an hour, as the clock strikes twelve, you must be on the bridge at the place where you met me. When you get there call out 'Ahmed,' three times, as loud as you can. Then an African will appear, and you must say to him, 'The head, your master, desires you to open the trunk, and to give me the green purse which you will find in it.'"

"Very well, my lord," said the old woman, "I will set off at once for the bridge." And wrapping her veil round her she went out.

Midnight was striking as she reached the spot where she had met the head so many hours before. "Ahmed! Ahmed! Ahmed!" cried she, and immediately a huge African, as tall as a giant, stood on the bridge before her.

"What do you want?" asked he.

"The head, your master, desires you to open the trunk, and to give me the green purse which you will find in it."

"I will be back in a moment, good mother," said he. And three minutes later he placed a purse full of sequins in the old woman's hand.

No one can imagine the joy of the whole family at the sight of all this wealth. The tiny, tumble-down cottage was rebuilt, the girls had new dresses, and their mother ceased selling veils. It was such a new thing to them to have money to spend, that they were not as careful as they might have been, and by and by there was not a single coin left in the purse. When this happened their hearts sank within them, and their faces fell.

"Have you spent your fortune?" asked the head from its corner, when it saw how sad they looked. "Well, then, go at midnight, good mother, to the bridge, and call out "Mahomet!" three times, as loud as you can. An African will appear in answer, and you must tell him to open the trunk, and to give you the red purse which he will find there."

The old woman did not need twice telling, but set off at once for the bridge.

"Mahomet! Mahomet! Mahomet!" cried she, with all her might; and in an instant an African, still larger than the last, stood before her.

"What do you want?" asked he.

"The head, your master, bids you to open the trunk, and to give me the red purse which you will find in it."

"Very well, good mother, I will do so," answered the African, and, the moment after he had vanished, he reappeared with the purse in his hand.

This time the money seemed so endless that the old woman built herself a new house, and filled it with the most beautiful things that were to be found in the shops. Her daughters were always wrapped in veils that looked as if they were woven out of sunbeams, and their dresses shone with precious stones. The neighbors wondered where all this sudden wealth had sprung from, but nobody knew about the head.

"Good mother," said the head, one day, "this morning you are to go to the city and ask the sultan to give me his daughter for my bride."

"Do what?" asked the old woman in amazement. "How can I tell the sultan that a head without a body wishes to become his son-in-law? They will think that I am mad, and I shall be hooted from the palace and stoned by the children."

"Do as I bid you," replied the head; "it is my will."

The old woman was afraid to say anything more, and, putting on her richest clothes, started for the palace. The sultan granted her an audience at once, and, in a trembling voice, she made her request.

"Are you mad, old woman?" said the sultan, staring at her.

"The wooer is powerful, O sultan, and nothing is impossible to him."

"Is that true?"

"It is, O sultan; I swear it," answered she.

"Then let him show his power by doing three things, and I will give him my daughter."

"Command, O gracious prince," said she.

"Do you see that hill in front of the palace? asked the sultan.

"I see it," answered she.

"Well, in forty days the man who has sent you must make that hill vanish, and plant a beautiful garden in its place. That is the first thing. Now go, and tell him what I say."

So the old woman returned and told the head the sultan's first condition.

"It is well," he replied; and said no more about it.

For thirty-nine days the head remained in its favorite corner. The old woman thought that the task set before him was beyond his powers, and that no more would be heard about the sultan's daughter.

But on the thirty-ninth evening after her visit to the palace, the head suddenly spoke, "Good mother," he said, "you must go tonight to the bridge, and when you are there cry "Ali! Ali! Ali!" as loud as you can. An African will appear before you, and you will tell him that he is to level the hill, and to make, in its place, the most beautiful garden that ever was seen."

"I will go at once," answered she.

It did not take her long to reach the bridge which led to the city, and she took up her position on the spot where she had first seen the head, and called loudly "Ali! Ali! Ali!" In an instant an African appeared before her, of such a huge size that the old woman was half frightened; but his voice was mild and gentle as he said, "What is it that you want?"

"Your master bids you to level the hill that stands in front of the sultan's palace and in its place to make the most beautiful garden in the world."

"Tell my master he shall be obeyed," replied Ali; "it shall be done this moment." And the old woman went home and gave Ali's message to the head.

Meanwhile the sultan was in his palace waiting till the fortieth day should dawn, and wondering that not one spadeful of earth should have been dug out of the hill.

"If that old woman has been playing me a trick," thought he, "I will hang her! And I will put up a gallows tomorrow on the hill itself."

But when tomorrow came there was no hill, and when the sultan opened his eyes he could not imagine why the room was so much lighter than usual, and what was the reason of the sweet smell of flowers that filled the air.

"Can there be a fire?" he said to himself; "the sun never came in at this window before. I must get up and see." So he rose and looked out, and underneath him flowers from every part of the world were blooming, and creepers of every color hung in chains from tree to tree.

Then he remembered. "Certainly that old woman's son is a clever magician!" cried he; "I never met anyone as clever as that. What shall I give him to do next? Let me think. Ah! I know." And he sent for the old woman, who by the orders of the head, was waiting below.

"Your son has carried out my wishes very nicely," he said. "The garden is larger and better than that of any other king. But when I walk across it I shall need some place to rest on the other side. In forty days he must build me a palace, in which every room shall be filled with different furniture from a different country, and each more magnificent than any room that ever was seen." And having said this he turned round and went away.

"Oh! He will never be able to do that," thought she; "it is much more difficult than the hill." And she walked home slowly, with her head bent.

"Well, what am I to do next?" asked the head cheerfully. And the old woman told her story.

"Dear me! Is that all? Why it is child's play," answered the head; and troubled no more about the palace for thirty-nine days. Then he told the old woman to go to the bridge and call for Hassan.

"What do you want, old woman?" asked Hassan, when he appeared, for he was not as polite as the others had been.

"Your master commands you to build the most magnificent palace that ever was seen," replied she; "and you are to place it on the borders of the new garden."

"He shall be obeyed," answered Hassan. And when the sultan woke he saw, in the distance, a palace built of soft blue marble, resting on slender pillars of pure gold.

"That old woman's son is certainly all powerful," cried he, "what shall I bid him to do now?" And after thinking some time he sent for the old woman, who was expecting the summons.

"The garden is wonderful, and the palace the finest in the world," said he, "so fine, that my servants would cut but a sorry figure in it. Let your son fill it with forty slaves whose beauty shall be unequaled, all exactly like each other, and of the same height."

This time the king thought he had invented something totally impossible, and was quite pleased with himself for his cleverness.

Thirty-nine days passed, and at midnight on the night of the last the old woman was standing on the bridge.

"Bekir! Bekir! Bekir!" cried she. And an African appeared, and inquired what she wanted.

"The head, your master, bids you to find forty slaves of unequaled beauty, and of the same height, and place them in the sultan's palace on the other side of the garden."

And when, on the morning of the fortieth day, the sultan went to the blue palace, and was received by the forty slaves, he nearly lost his wits from surprise.

"I will assuredly give my daughter to the old woman's son," thought he. "If I were to search all the world through, I could never find a more powerful son-in-law."

And when the old woman entered his presence he informed her that he was ready to fulfill his promise, and she was to bid her son to appear at the palace without delay.

This command did not at all please the old woman, though, of course, she made no objections to the sultan.

"All has gone well so far," she grumbled, when she told her story to the head, "but what do you suppose the sultan will say, when he sees his daughter's husband?"

"Never mind what he says! Put me on a silver dish and carry me to the palace."

So it was done, though the old woman's heart beat as she laid down the dish with the head upon it.

At the sight before him the king flew into a violent rage. "I will never marry my daughter to such a monster," he cried.

But the princess placed her hand gently on his arm. "You have given your word, and you cannot break it," said she.

"But, my child, it is impossible for you to marry such a being," exclaimed the sultan.

"Yes, I will marry him. He has a beautiful head, and I love him already."

So the marriage was celebrated, and great feasts were held in the palace, though the people wept tears to think of the sad fate of their beloved princess. But when the merrymaking was done, and the young couple were alone, the head suddenly disappeared, or rather, a body was added to it, and one of the handsomest young men that ever was seen stood before the princess.

"A wicked fairy enchanted me at my birth," he said, "and for the rest of the world I must always be a head only. But for you, and you only, I am a man like other men."

"And that is all I care about," said the princess.[182]

---

[182]Type 444*. Source: Andrew Lang, *The Brown Fairy Book* (London, 1904), pp. 205-214. Lang's source: *Traditions populaires de toutes les nations (Asie Mineure)*.

Abandoned Women

The Twelve Huntsmen

Jacob and Wilhelm Grimm

Long ago and far away a prince and a princess fell in love with one another. He promised to marry her, sealing this promise with a kiss and a ring. But first, he said, he would have to return to his own country and make peace with his dying father. Back in his own kingdom, the prince learned that his father had arranged a marriage for him with another princess. Out of respect to the king, the prince agreed to the betrothal, and forgot the princess with the ring.

Meanwhile, the princess with the ring waited and wept, and waited and wept. Finally, in desperation, she asked her father to outfit her and eleven of her ladies-in-waiting as huntsmen. This he did, and the twelve women, disguised as men, rode to the faithless prince's castle, where they were installed as huntsmen at his court.

Now the prince suspected that the huntsmen were women in disguise, so he devised a test to learn the truth. He scattered hard peas across the floor, believing that the twelve, being women, would tiptoe this way and that way to avoid stepping on the peas. However, the huntsmen got wind of the trap, and when they entered the room they walked with sure steps and a firm gait, paying no attention to the peas.

The prince was still suspicious, so he invited the twelve to join him in a great hall containing a display of the most advanced spinning wheels as well as the best weapons of war. "If they are women," he thought, "they will surely be attracted to the spinning wheels."

Once again, the huntsmen got wind of the trap, and upon entering the hall they walked past the spinning wheels to examine and admire the weaponry. Satisfied at last that the huntsmen were what they appeared to be, the prince proceeded with plans for his marriage.

The prince was out hunting with the twelve when the wedding entourage approached. Hearing the drums and the trumpets, the princess with the ring grew faint and fell to the ground. The prince jumped to her aid, but in picking her up, he perceived that she was indeed a woman. Then he saw his ring on her finger, and his love for her returned.

The prince, with all due honor and respect, received the other bride with her family, friends, and servants. He then told them the parable of the lost key:

> A man lost the key to his treasure chest, so he had a new one made. After using the new key for some time, he found the old one. Which key should he use in the future: the new one or the old one?

The guests answered that the original key would work better and would thus be preferred to the new one. He then explained that he, like the man with two keys, had two brides, and that he was going to return to the original one. And that is what he did, and the two of them, together with her eleven ladies-in-waiting, lived happily ever after.[183]

Sweetheart Roland

Jacob and Wilhelm Grimm

Once upon a time there was a mother who loved her real daughter and hated her stepdaughter, who was a thousand times more beautiful and a thousand times better. Now it happened that the real daughter was envious of the stepdaughter's beautiful apron, and she insisted that her mother should get it for her. The mother said, "Don't worry; you shall have it. Your stepsister has long deserved to die. Tonight be sure to take the side of the bed against the wall. Push her to the front part of the bed, and after she is asleep, I shall come and chop off her head."

However, the stepsister was standing in a corner and overheard everything. She let her wicked stepsister get into bed first, against the wall, but after she had fallen asleep, she pushed her to the front side of the bed, and she herself lay down against the wall. The mother crept in during the night, felt to make sure that someone was asleep on the front side of the bed, then took an ax with both hands, and with one blow chopped off her own daughter's head.

As soon as she left, the girl got up and went to her sweetheart Roland, knocked on his door, and called out, "Listen, we must run away. My stepmother has killed her own child, thinking it was me. When morning comes, and she sees what she has done, she will kill me. I have taken her magic wand. We can make it work for us."

Sweetheart Roland got up, and they took the dead girl's head and dribbled three drops of blood, one in front of the bed, one in the kitchen, and one on the steps; and then they left.

The next morning the mother got up and called to her daughter, "Come! You can have the apron now!" But the daughter did not come. "Where are you?"

"Out here on the steps," said the one drop of blood, "I'm sweeping."

She went outside, but no one was there. "Where are you then?"

"Here in the kitchen. I'm getting warm by the fire," said the second drop of blood.

---

[183]Type 884. Retold from *Kinder- und Hausmärchen*, 1st ed. (Berlin, 1812/1815), no. 67.

She went into the kitchen, but saw no one. "Just where are you?"

"In the bedroom. I'm sleeping."

She ran into the bedroom, and there she saw her own child bathed with blood. Horrified, she saw that she had been deceived, and she became furious with anger. Now because she was a witch, she could see far into the world, and she saw her stepdaughter running away with her sweetheart, and they were already a long way off. She quickly put on her seven-league boots and pursued them, soon overtaking them.

The girl, through the magic wand, knew that they were being pursued, so she transformed herself into a lake and her sweetheart Roland into a duck, swimming on the lake. The stepmother sat down on the bank of the lake and tried to attract the duck to her with bread, but it was to no avail, and that evening she had to return home empty handed.

The two reassumed their human form and continued on their way, but at the break of day the witch again took up her pursuit. This time the girl transformed herself into a beautiful flower in the middle of a thorn hedge and her sweetheart into a violin player. When the old woman came by, she asked the musician if she might pluck the flower. "Of course," he answered, "and I'll play for you while you do it." She crept into the hedge trying to reach the flower. When she was in the middle, he began to play, and she was compelled to dance, to dance without stopping until the thorns ripped off her clothes and pricked her bloody, and she fell down dead.

Then the two were free. Roland said to the girl, "Now I shall go home to my father and make preparations for our wedding."

"In the meanwhile," she said, "I shall transform myself into a red boundary stone. I shall stay here and wait for you until you return." So she turned herself into a red stone and waited a long time for her sweetheart, but he did not return. He forgot her. And when she saw that he was not going to return, she became very sad, and turned herself into a flower, thinking that someone would trample her to death.

However, a shepherd found the flower, and because it was so beautiful, he took it home with him and put it into his cupboard. From now on strange things happened at the shepherd's house. When he awoke in the morning, the housework was all done. Everything was swept and cleaned, and the fire was already going. When he came home at midday, his food was cooked, the table was set, and everything was ready to eat. He could not understand how this happened, for he never saw anyone in his house.

Although he was very pleased with everything, in time he became frightened, and he asked a wise woman about it. She said it was magic, and told him to watch in the morning and see if anything moved. If he saw something move, he should throw a white cloth over it. That is what he did. The next morning he saw how the cupboard opened by itself and the flower emerged from it. He jumped up and threw a white cloth over it. The enchantment was broken, and the beautiful girl that had been forgotten by her sweetheart Roland stood before him.

The shepherd wanted to marry her, but she said no, that she only wanted to work for him and keep house for him. Soon she learned that Roland was about to marry someone else. In keeping with an old custom, everyone was supposed to sing a song at the wedding celebration. The faithful girl went to the celebration, but she did not want to sing. Finally, at last, she was compelled to sing, and as soon as she started, Roland recognized her at once. He jumped up and said that she was the true bride, and that he did not want any other one. Then he married her. That was the end of her suffering and the beginning of her happiness.[184]

The Mastermaid

Norway

Once upon a time there was a king who had several sons; I don't know exactly how many there were. The youngest had no rest at home, for nothing would please him but to go out into the world and try his luck. After a long time the king was had to let him go. After he had traveled some days, he came to a giant's house, and there he got a place in the giant's service. In the morning the giant went off to herd his goats, and as he left the yard he told the prince to clean out the stable; "After you have finished, you can have the rest of the day off, for you must know that you have come to an easy master. But when you are asked to do something, you must do it well, and don't even think of going into any of the rooms that are beyond the one where you slept last night, for if you do, it will cost you your life."

"I surely do have an easy master," said the prince to himself, as he walked up and down the room humming and singing, for he thought there was plenty of time to clean out the stable. "But it would be good to take just a peep into his other rooms, for there must be something in them that he doesn't want me to see, since he won't allow me to enter them."

He went into the first room, and there was a pot boiling on a hook by the wall, but the prince saw no fire underneath it. I wonder what is inside it, he thought. He dipped a lock of his hair into it, and the hair seemed to have turned to copper. "What a nice stew," he said. "If you tasted it, it would do something to your gullet." With that he went into the next room.

There, too, was a pot hanging by a hook. It, too, was bubbling and boiling, although there was also no fire under it. "I may as well try this too," said the prince. He put another lock into the pot, and it came out looking like silver. "We don't

---

[184]Type 1119, followed by type 313C. Source: *Kinder- und Hausmärchen*, 1st ed. (Berlin, 1812/1815), v. 1, no. 56.

have such expensive stew at my father's house," said the prince. "But the important thing is how it tastes." With that he went into the third room.

There, too, hung a pot, boiling just as he had seen in the two other rooms, and the prince wanted to test this one as well, so he dipped a lock of hair into it, and it came out looking like pure gold, so that the light gleamed from it. "This is getting worse and worse," said the old woman. "No, it's getting better and better," said the prince. "If he is cooking up gold in here, I wonder what he is cooking up in the next room."

He wanted to see; so he went through the door into the fourth room. Well, there was no pot to be seen in there, but there was a girl—she was certainly a princess—seated on a bench. Whoever she was, she was so beautiful that the prince had never seen anyone like her all his born days.

"Oh, in Jesus' name," she said, "what do you want here?"

"I entered service here yesterday," said the prince.

"Service indeed! May God help you out of it!" she said.

"Well, I think I've got an easy master; he hasn't given me much to do today. As soon as I have cleaned out the stable my day's work is over."

"Yes, but how will you do it?" she said; "for if you set to work to clean it like other people, ten pitchforks full will come back in for every one that you throw out. But I will teach you what to do. Turn the fork upside down, and throw with the handle, and then everything will fly out by itself."

He said that he would do it that way, and then he sat there the whole day, for he and the princess soon decided that they wanted to get married. Thus, the first day of his service with the giant went by very quickly indeed. As evening approached, she said that he should go and clean out the stable before the giant came home. He went out to the stable, and thought he would just see if what she had said were true, and so he began to work like he had seen the servants in his father's stable do; but he soon had to stop, for he hadn't worked a minute before the stable was so full of dung that he hadn't room to stand. Then he did what the princess had told him to do: He turned the fork upside down and worked with the handle. In an instant the stable was as clean as if it had been scoured. When he was finished he went back to the room that the giant had given him, and began to walk up and down, humming and singing. After a while, the giant came home with his goats.

"Have you cleaned the stable?" asked the giant.

"Yes, master, it's all spic-and-span," answered the prince.

"I'll soon see if it is," growled the giant, and strode off to the stable, where he found it just as the prince had said.

"You've been talking to my Mastermaid, I can see," said the giant; "for you didn't suck this knowledge out of your own breast."

"Mastermaid!" said the prince, playing dumb, "what sort of thing is that, master? I'd like to see one."

"Well!" said the giant, "you'll see her soon enough."

The next day the giant again went out with his goats. Before leaving he told the prince to bring in his horse, which was out grazing on the pasture, and when he had done that he could take the rest of the day off.

"For you must know that you have come to an easy master," said the giant; "but if you go into any of the rooms I spoke of yesterday, I'll rip your head off." Then off he went with his flock of goats.

"You are indeed an easy master," said the prince; "but I still I would like to have a chat with your Mastermaid. Maybe she'd just as soon mine as yours!" So he went to her, and she asked him what he had to do that day.

"Oh, nothing to be afraid of," he said. "I only have to go up to the pasture and bring in his horse."

"Very well, and how will you go about doing it?"

"Well, there's nothing very difficult about riding a horse home. I have ridden many a frisky horse before now," said the prince.

"This task will not be as easy as you think, "she said, "but I'll teach you how to do it. When you see it, it will come up to you breathing fire and flame out of its nostrils like a pitch torch. You must take the bit that is hanging behind the door over there. Throw it into his mouth, and he will grow so tame that you can do anything that you want to with him."

He said that he would do that and so he sat there the whole day, talking and chatting with the Mastermaid about one thing and another. But they talked about how happy they would be if they could only get married, and get away from the giant; and, to tell the truth, the prince would have forgotten both the horse and the pasture, if the Mastermaid hadn't reminded him of them as evening was approaching. She told him that he had better go out bring the horse in before the giant came home. So he set off. Taking the bit which hung in the corner, he ran up to the pasture, and it wasn't long before he met the horse, with fire and flame blowing out of its nostrils. But he took his time, and when the horse came up to him, with its jaws wide apart, he threw the bit into its mouth, and the horse became as quiet as a lamb. After that it was not at all difficult to ride it home and put it into the stable. Then the prince went to his room, and began to hum and sing.

When the giant came home that evening with his goats, the first words that he said were, "Have you brought my horse down from the pasture?"

"Yes, master, that I have," said the prince; "and although it is a wonderful riding horse, I rode it straight home to the stable."

"I'll just check on that," said the giant, and ran out to the stable. The horse was standing there just as the prince had said.

"You've been talking to my Mastermaid, you have!" said the giant again, for you haven't sucked this out of your own breast."

"Yesterday master talked of this Mastermaid, and today it's the same story. God bless you, master! Won't you show me the thing at once? I really would like to see it," said the prince, pretending to be simple minded and stupid.

"You'll get to see her soon enough," said the giant.

On the third day at dawn the giant went out into the woods again with his goats. Before leaving he said to the prince, "Today you must go to Hell and get my fire tax. When you have done that you can have the rest of the day off, for you must know that you have come to an easy master." And with that off he went.

"Easy master, indeed!" said the prince. "You may be easy, but you give me hard tasks all the same. I may as well see if I can find your Mastermaid. You claim that she belongs to you, but I'll see if she won't tell me what to do," and so he went to her once again.

The Mastermaid asked what the giant had asked him to do that day, and he told her how he was to go to Hell and fetch the fire tax.

"And how will you go about it?" asked the Mastermaid.

"You will have to tell me," said the prince, "for I have never been to Hell in my life. Even if I knew the way, I wouldn't know how much I am to ask for."

"Well, I'll tell you," said the Mastermaid. "Go to the steep cliff over there beyond the pasture. Take the club that is lying there and knock on the face of the cliff. Someone who is all glowing with fire will come out. Tell him about your errand. When he asks you how much you need, say, 'As much as I can carry.'"

He said that he would do just that, and then he sat there with the Mastermaid all that day too. Although evening was approaching, he would have sat there until now, if the Mastermaid had not reminded him that it was time to be off to Hell to fetch the giant's fire tax before he came home. So he went on his way, and did just as the Mastermaid had told him. When he reached the rock he picked up the club and gave a great thump. The cliff opened, and out came a person whose face was aglow, and from whose eyes and nostrils flew sparks of fire.

"What do you want?" he said.

"I've come from the giant to fetch his fire tax," said the prince.

"How much do you need?" said the other.

"I never ask for more than I am able to carry," said the prince.

"Lucky for you that you did not ask for a whole horseload," said the man from the cliff; "but come now into the cliff with me, and you shall have it."

So the prince went inside with him, and what heaps and heaps of gold and silver he saw lying in there, just like stones in a gravel pit. He got a load just as big as he was able to carry, and set off for home with it.

When the giant came home with his goats that evening, the prince went into his room, and began to hum and sing just as he had done the evenings before.

"Have you been to Hell after my fire tax?" roared the giant.

"Oh yes, that I have, master," answered the prince.

"Where did you put it?" said the giant.

"The sack is on the bench over there," said the prince.

"I'll check on that," said the giant, and went to the bench. There he saw that the sack was so full that the gold and silver dropped out on the floor as soon as he untied the string.

"You've been talking to my Mastermaid, that I can see," said the giant; "and if you have, I'll rip your head off."

"Mastermaid!" said the prince; "yesterday master talked of this Mastermaid, and today he talks of her again, and the day before yesterday it was the same story. I only wish I could see what sort of thing she is, I do!"

"Well, wait until tomorrow," said the giant, "and then I'll take you in to her myself."

"Thank you kindly, master," said the prince; "but I'll bet that master is only joking."

The next day the giant took him in to the Mastermaid, and said to her, "You must cut his throat, and boil him in the great big pot, you know the one I mean, and when the stew is ready just give me a call." Then he lay down on the bench to sleep, and began to snore so loud that it sounded like thunder in the mountains.

The Mastermaid took a knife and cut the prince in his little finger, and let three drops of blood fall on a stool; then she took all the old rags and soles of shoes, and all the rubbish she could lay her hands on, and put it all into the pot. She then filled a chest full of ground gold, and took a lump of salt, and a flask of water that hung behind the door, and she took, besides, a golden apple, and two golden chickens, and off she set with the prince from the giant's house as fast as they could. When they had gone a little way, they came to the sea, and after that they sailed over the sea; but I do not know where they got the ship from.

After the giant had slept a good bit, he began to stretch as he lay on the bench, and called out, "Will it soon be done?"

"Only just begun," answered the first drop of blood on the stool.

So the giant went back to sleep, and slumbered a long, long time. At last he began to toss about a little, and cried out, "Do you hear what I say? Will it soon be done?" but he did not look up this time any more than the first, for he was still half asleep.

"Half done," said the second drop of blood.

The giant again thought it was the Mastermaid, so he turned over on his other side, and fell asleep again; and when he had slept for many hours, he began to stir and stretch his old bones, and he called out, "Isn't it done yet?"

"Done to a turn," said the third drop of blood.

So the giant got up, and began to rub his eyes, but he couldn't see who it was that was talking to him. He searched and called for the Mastermaid, but no one answered.

"Ah, well! I dare say she's just gone outside for a bit," he thought, and took up a spoon and went up to the pot to taste the stew. There he found nothing but shoe soles, and rags, and such stuff, all boiled up together, so that he couldn't tell the thick from the thin. As soon as he saw this, he realized what had happened, and he became so angry that he barely knew which leg to stand upon. Away he went after the prince and the Mastermaid, until the wind whistled behind him; but he soon came to the water and couldn't cross it.

"Never mind," he said; "I can fix this. I'll just call on my stream sucker."

So he called on his stream sucker, and he came and stooped down, and took one, two, three, gulps; and then the water fell so much in the sea that the giant could see the Mastermaid and the prince sailing in their ship.

"Throw out the lump of salt!" said the Mastermaid.

So the prince threw it overboard, and it grew up into a mountain so high, right across the sea, that the giant couldn't pass it, and the stream sucker couldn't help him by swilling up any more water.

"Never mind," cried the giant; "there's a fix for this too." So he called on his hill borer to come and bore through the mountain, so the stream sucker might crawl through and take another swill; but just as they had made a hole through the hill, and the stream sucker was about to drink, the Mastermaid told the prince to pour a drop or two out of the flask into the sea, and then the sea was just as full as ever, and before the stream sucker could take another gulp, they reached the land and were saved from the giant.

So they made up their minds to go home to the prince's father; but the prince would not hear of the Mastermaid's walking, for he did not think it would be appropriate, neither for her nor for him.

"Just wait here ten minutes," he said, "while I go home after the seven horses which stand in my father's stall. It's not very far, and I won't be gone very long; I will not hear of my sweetheart walking to my father's palace."

"No!" said the Mastermaid, "please don't leave me, for once you are home in your palace you'll forget me outright; I know you will."

"Oh!" said the prince, "how can I forget you; you with whom I have gone through so much, and whom I love so dearly?"

There was no stopping him, he insisted on going home to fetch the coach and seven horses, and she was to wait for him by the seaside. Finally the Mastermaid gave in. "But when you get home," she warned, "don't even take the time to greet anyone, but go straight to the stable, hitch up the horses, and drive back as quickly as you can. They will all come to you, but you must pretend that you cannot see them; and above all else, do not eat a bite of food, for if you do, we shall both come to grief." The prince promised all of this.

Now, just as he came home to the palace, one of his brothers was preparing to get married. The bride, with all her relatives, had just arrived at the palace. They all thronged around him, and asked about this thing and that, and wanted him to go inside with them. He pretended that he could not see them, and went straight to the stall and began to hitch up the horses. When they saw they could not get him to go inside, they came out to him with food and drink, the best of everything they had prepared for the feast, but the prince would not taste a thing, but busied himself with the horses.

Finally the bride's sister rolled an apple across the yard to him, saying, "Well, if you won't eat anything else, at least take a bite of this, for you must be hungry and thirsty after your long journey." So he picked up the apple and took a bite out of it. He barely had the piece in his mouth before he forgot the Mastermaid, and that he was going to drive back for her.

"I must be crazy," he said. "What am I doing here with this coach and horses?"

So he put the horses back into the stable, and went along with the others into the palace, and it was soon settled that he should marry the bride's sister, who had rolled the apple to him.

The Mastermaid sat by the seashore, and waited and waited for the prince, but the prince did not come. Finally she left the shore, and walked a while until she came to a little hut, which stood by itself in a grove near the king's palace. She went in and asked if she might stay there. The hut belonged to an old woman, who was a disgusting and cranky old hag. At first she would not hear of the Master-maid's lodging in her house, but finally, in exchange for kind words and high rent, the Mastermaid was permitted to stay there.

The hut was as dark and dirty as a pigsty, so the Mastermaid said she would clean it up a little, so that their house might look like other people's. The old hag did not like this either, and complained and became angry; but the Mastermaid did not pay any attention to her. She took her chest of gold, and threw a handful or so into the fire. The gold melted and bubbled over out of the grate, spreading itself over the whole hut, until it was entirely plated with gold, both outside and in. But as soon as the gold began to bubble up, the old hag became so afraid that she ran out as if the evil one were after her. As she ran through the door, she forgot to stoop down, and she crushed her head against the door frame.

The next morning the constable passed that way. He could scarce believe his eyes when he saw the golden hut shining and glistening there in the grove; but he was still more astonished when he went in and saw the lovely maiden who was sitting there. He fell in love with her at once, and begged her on the spot to marry him.

"Very well, but do you have a lot of money?" asked the Mastermaid. He said that he had plenty, and he went home to fetch it. That evening he came back with a half-bushel sack filled with money, and set it down on the bench.

The Mastermaid said that he was rich enough and that she would have him. They went to bed together, but they had barely lain down before she said she must get up again, because she had forgotten to bank up the fire. "Please don't get up," said the constable; "I'll take care of it." He jumped out of bed, and ran to the hearth.

"Tell me as soon as you have taken hold of the poker," said the Mastermaid.

"I'm holding it now," said the constable.

Then the Mastermaid said, "God grant that you may hold the poker and that the poker may hold you, and may you heap hot burning coals over yourself until morning." So the constable had to stand there all night long, shoveling hot burning coals over himself. He begged, and prayed, and wept, but none of this made the coals a bit colder. As soon as day broke, and he finally was able to rid himself of the poker, he set off as though the bailiff or the devil were after him. Everyone who met him stared at him, for he acted like a madman, and looked like he had been flayed and tanned. They wondered what had happened to him, but he was too ashamed to tell anyone.

The next day the clerk passed by the place where the Mastermaid lived, and he too saw how it gleamed and glistened in the grove, and he went inside to find out who lived there. When he saw the beautiful maiden, he fell even more madly in love with her than had the constable, and he immediately began to woo her.

The Mastermaid responded to him, as she had responded to the constable, by asking if he had a lot of money. The clerk replied that he was wealthy enough, and to prove it he went home to fetch his money. That evening he came back with a large sack of money—I think that the sack held a whole bushel—and set it down on the bench. So she accepted him, and they went to bed. But the Mastermaid had forgotten to shut the outside door, and she would have to get up and lock it for the night.

"What! *You* should do that!" said the clerk. "No, you lie here, and I'll go and take care of it." He jumped up like a pea on a drumhead, and ran into the hallway.

"Tell me when you have hold of the door latch" said the Mastermaid.

"I've got hold of it now," said the clerk.

"Then may you hold the door, and may the door hold you, and may you go back and forth until morning!" said the Mastermaid.

And so the clerk had to dance the whole night through. He had never experienced such a waltz before, and would not want to experience such a waltz again. He pulled the door one way, and then the door pulled him back the other; and so it went on and on. First he was dashed into one corner of the hallway, and then into the other, until he was almost battered to death. At first he cursed and swore; then he begged and prayed, but the door cared for nothing but holding its own until the break of day. As soon as it let him go, the clerk ran off, leaving his money behind to pay for his night's lodging, and forgetting his courtship altogether, for—to tell the truth—he was afraid that the door might come dancing after him.

Everyone who met him stared and gaped at him, for he too acted like a madman, and he would not have looked worse if he had spent the whole night butting against a flock of rams.

On the third day the sheriff passed that way, and he too saw the golden hut, and went inside to find out who lived there. He had barely set eyes on the Mastermaid before he began to woo her. So she responded to him as she had with the other two. If he had lots of money she would have him; if not, he might as well go about his business. Well, the sheriff said that he wasn't so badly off, and that he would go home and fetch the money. When he came back that evening, he had a bigger sack even than the clerk had had—it must have been at least a bushel and a half—, and put it down on the bench. So it was soon settled that he was to have the Mastermaid, but they had barely gone to bed before the Mastermaid said she had forgotten to bring the calf home from the meadow, so she would have to get up and drive him into the stall.

"No!" swore the sheriff. He would go and take care of it. And stout and fat as he was, he jumped up as nimbly as a young boy.

"Tell me when you've got hold of the calf's tail," said the Mastermaid.

"I have hold of it now," said the sheriff.

"Then may you hold the calf's tail, and may the calf's tail hold you, and may you tour the world together until morning."

The race began at once. Away they went, he and the calf, over high and low, across hill and dale, and the more the sheriff cursed and swore, the faster the calf ran and jumped. By dawn the poor sheriff had nearly collapsed, and he was so glad to be able to let go of the calf's tail that he forgot his sack of money and everything else. He was a large man, and he went home a little slower than the clerk and the constable had done, and the slower he went the more time people had to gape and stare at him; and I must say they made good use of their time, for he was terribly tattered and torn from his dance with the calf.

299

The next day there was to be a wedding at the palace, the elder prince to be married. And the younger one, the one who had lived with the giant, was to marry the bride's sister. They had just got into the coach and were about to drive off, when one of the harness pins snapped off. They put in another, and then a third, but they all broke, whatever kind of wood they used to make them with. It all took a long time, and they couldn't get to church, and everyone became very unhappy. All at once the constable said—for he too had been invited to the wedding—that a maiden lived over there in the grove, "And if you can only get her to lend you her fireplace poker, I know very well that it will hold."

They sent a messenger at once, and he asked the maiden very politely if she would not mind lending them the poker that the constable had spoken of. The maiden said "yes," they might have it; so they got a harness pin which wasn't likely to break.

But just as they were driving off, the bottom of the coach fell apart. They set to work to make a new bottom as best they could; but however many nails they used nor whatever kind of wood they chose, as soon as they put a new bottom into the coach, it fell apart again as soon as they drove off, so they were even worse off than when they had broken the harness pin. Then the clerk said—for if the constable was there, you may be sure that the clerk was there too—"A maiden lives over there in the grove, and if you could only get her to lend you half of her outside door, I know it would hold together."

They sent another message to the grove, and he asked very politely if they couldn't borrow the golden door that the clerk had described; and they got it on the spot. They were just setting out, but now the horses were not strong enough to draw the coach, though there were six of them; then they put on eight, and ten, and twelve, but the more they put on, and the more the coachman whipped, the more the coach wouldn't stir an inch. By this time it was late in the day, and everyone about the palace was very unhappy; they had to make it to the church, and yet it looked as if they would never get there. Then the sheriff said that a maiden lived in the golden hut over there in the grove, and if they could only borrow her calf, "I know it can pull the coach, even if it were as heavy as a mountain."

Well, they all thought it would look silly to be drawn to church by a calf, but there was nothing they could do about it, so they had to send a third time, and ask very politely in the king's name, if he couldn't borrow the calf the sheriff had spoken of, and the Mastermaid let them have it on the spot, for she was not going to say "no" this time either. So they put the calf on before the horses, and waited to see if it would do any good, and away went the coach over high and low, and stock and stone, so that they could barely catch their breath; sometimes they were on the ground, and sometimes up in the air, and when they reached the church, the calf began to run around and around it like a spinning wheel, so that they had a hard time getting out of the coach, and into the church. On the way back home they went even faster, and they reached the palace almost before they knew they had set out.

Now when they sat down to dinner, the prince—the one who had been with the giant—said he thought they ought to ask the maiden who had lent them her poker, her door, and her calf, to come up to the palace. "For," he said he, "if we hadn't got these three things, we would still be stuck here."

The king thought that that was only right and fair, so he sent five of his best men down to the golden hut to greet the maiden from the king, and to ask her if she wouldn't be so good as to come and dine at the palace.

"Send the king my greetings," said the Mastermaid, "and tell him, if he's too good to come to me, then I am too good to go to him."

So the king had to go himself, and then the Mastermaid went with him without any more bother; and as the king thought she was more than she seemed to be, he sat her down in the highest seat by the side of the youngest bridegroom.

Now, when they had sat a little while at the table, the Mastermaid took out her golden apple, and the golden cock and hen, which she had carried off from the giant, and put them down on the table before her, and the cock and hen began at once to peck at one another, and to fight for the golden apple.

"Just look," said the prince; "and see how those two are struggling for the apple."

"Yes, just as we two had to struggle to escape from the cliff," said the Mastermaid.

Then the spell was broken, and the prince knew her again, and he was very glad indeed. But as for the witch who had rolled the apple over to him, he had her tied to twenty-four horses and torn to pieces, so that there was not a bit of her left. Then they celebrated the wedding for real. And even though they were still stiff and sore, the constable, the clerk, and the sheriff kept it up with the best of them.[185]

---

[185]Type 711. Source: Peter Christen Asbjørnsen and Jørgen Moe, *Norske Folkeeventyr* (Christiania [Oslo], 1842-1852), translated by George Webb Dasent (1859). Revised.

The Powerful and the Weak

Good and Evil

The Scorpion and the Tortoise

Bidpai

A scorpion and a tortoise became such fast friends that they took a vow that they would never separate. So when it happened that one of them was obliged to leave his native land, the other promised to go with him. They had traveled only a short distance when they came to a wide river. The scorpion was now greatly troubled.

"Alas," he said, "you, my friend, can easily swim, but how can a poor scorpion like me ever get across this stream?"

"Never fear," replied the tortoise; "only place yourself squarely on my broad back and I will carry you safely over."

No sooner was the scorpion settled on the tortoise's broad back, than the tortoise crawled into the water and began to swim. Halfway across he was startled by a strange rapping on his back, which made him ask the scorpion what he was doing.

"Doing?" answered the scorpion. "I am whetting my sting to see if it is possible to pierce your hard shell."

"Ungrateful friend," responded the tortoise, "it is well that I have it in my power both to save myself and to punish you as you deserve." And straightway he sank his back below the surface and shook off the scorpion into the water.[186]

---

[186]Source: *The Tortoise and the Geese and other Fables of Bidpai*, retold by Maude Barrows Dutton (Boston, 1908), pp. 12-13. In some versions, the odd couple is depicted as a scorpion and a frog who, against their natural inclinations, swear an oath of friendship. They too cross a river together, and in midstream the scorpion reverts to his natural self, stings the frog, and they both drown. Yet another version, classified as type 278, tells how a mouse and a frog tie themselves together in order to cross a stream. Half way across the defenseless duo is carried away by a falcon.

302

Dharmabuddhi and Pâpabuddhi

The Panchatantra

In a certain place there lived two friends, Dharmabuddhi, which means "having a just heart" and Pâpabuddhi, which means "having an unjust heart." One day Pâpabuddhi thought to himself, "I am a simpleton, plagued with poverty. I am going to travel abroad with Dharmabuddhi, and earn money with his help. Then I will cheat him out of it and thus gain a good situation for myself." One day he said to Dharmabuddhi, "Listen, friend! When you are old, which of your deeds will you be able to remember? You have never seen a foreign country, so what will you be able to tell the young people? After all, don't they say:

> His birth has borne no fruit, who knows not foreign lands, many languages, customs, and the like.

And also:

> One never properly grasps knowledge, wealth, and art, until joyfully one has wandered from one land to another.

Pâpabuddhi, as soon as he had heard these words, took leave from his parents with a joyful heart, and one happy day set forth for foreign lands. Through their diligence and skill, Dharmabuddhi and Pâpabuddhi acquired great wealth on their travels. Happy, but also filled with longing, they turned homeward with their great treasure. For it is also said:

> For those who gain wisdom, art, and wealth in foreign lands, the absence of one hour has the length of hundreds.

As they approached their city, Pâpabuddhi said to Dharmabuddhi, "Friend, it is not prudent for us to return home with our entire treasure, for our families and relatives will want part of it. Therefore let us bury it somewhere here in the thick of the forest and take only a small part home with us. When the need arises, we can come back and get as much as we need from here. For they also say:

> A smart man does not show off his money, not even in small amounts, for the sight of gold will agitate even a good heart.

And also:

> Like meat is devoured in the water by fish, on land by wild animals, and in the air by birds, he who owns money is everywhere at risk.

Upon hearing this, Dharmabuddhi said, "Yes, my friend, that is what we will do!" After having thus buried their treasure, they both returned home and lived happily together.

However, one day at midnight Pâpabuddhi went back into the forest, took the entire treasure, refilled the hole, and returned home. Then he went to Dharmabuddhi and said to him, "Friend, each of us has a large family, and we are suffering because we have no money. Therefore, let us go to that place and get some money."

303

Dharmabuddhi answered, "Yes, my friend, let us do it!" They went there and dug up the container, but it was empty. Then Pâpabuddhi struck himself on the head and cried out, "Aha! Dharmabuddhi! You and only you have taken the money, for the hole has been filled in again. Give me my half of what you have hidden, or I will bring action against you at the king's court."

Dharmabuddhi said, "Do not speak like that, you evildoer. I am in truth Dharmabuddhi, the one with a just heart! I would not commit such an act of thievery. After all, it is said:

> The person with a just heart treats another man's wife like his own mother, another man's property like a clod of earth, and all beings like himself.

Quarreling thus, they proceeded to the court where they told their stories and brought action against one another. The top judges decreed that they submit to an Ordeal of God, but Pâpabuddhi said, "No! Such an ordeal is not just. After all, it is written:

> In a legal action one should seek documents. If there are no documents, then one should seek witnesses. If there are no witnesses, then wise men should prescribe an Ordeal of God.

In this matter the goddess of the tree will serve as my witness. She will declare which one of us is a thief and which one an honest man."

To this they all replied, "What you say is right, for it is also written:

> An Ordeal of God is inappropriate where there is a witness, be he even a man of the lowest caste, to say nothing of the case where he is a god.

We too are very curious about this case. Tomorrow morning we shall go with you to that place in the forest."

In the meanwhile, Pâpabuddhi returned home and said to his father, "Father! I have stolen this money from Dharmabuddhi, and one word from you will secure it for us. Without your word, we shall lose it, and I shall lose my life as well."

The father said, "Child, just tell what I have to say in order to secure it!"

Pâpabuddhi said, "Father, in thus and such a place there is a large mimosa tree. It has a hollow trunk. Go hide yourself in it. When I swear an oath there tomorrow morning, then you must reply that Dharmabuddhi is the thief."

Having made these arrangements, the next morning Pâpabuddhi bathed himself, put on a clean shirt, and went to the mimosa tree with Dharmabuddhi and the judges. Once there, he spoke with a piercing voice, "Sun and moon, wind and fire, heaven and earth, heart and mind, day and night, sunrise and sunset, all of these, like dharma, know a man's deeds.
Sublime goddess of the forest, reveal which of us is the thief!"

Then Pâpabuddhi's father, who was standing in the hollow trunk of the mimosa tree, said, "Listen! Listen! The money was taken away by Dharmabuddhi!"

Having heard this, the king's servants, their eyes opened wide with amazement, searched in their law books for an appropriate punishment for Dharmabuddhi's theft of the money. While they were thus engaged, Dharmabuddhi himself surrounded the tree's opening with flammable material, and set it on fire. When it was well ablaze, Pâpabuddhi's father emerged from the hollow tree. His eyes streaming, he cried out bitterly.

"What is this?" they asked him.

He confessed everything, and then died. The king's servants forthwith hanged Pâpabuddhi from a branch of the mimosa tree, but they had only words of praise for Dharmabuddhi.[187]

The Gentile and the Jew

Jewish

Once a gentile and a Jew were walking along together, when the gentile remarked to the Jew, "My religion is better than yours."

"Not so," replied the Jew; "on the contrary, mine is better than yours, as it is said, 'what nation is there so great that has statutes and judgments so righteous as all this law.'"

The gentile then said, "Supposing it is decided my religion is better than yours, then I will take your money; but if it be decided that your religion is better than mine, then you shall take my money."

The Jew replied, "I agree to accept this condition."

As they were walking along, Satan appeared to them in the form of an old man. They thereupon asked him the question as to whose religion was the better; and he replied, "That of the gentile is the better."

After they had proceeded a little farther, Satan appeared to them again, in the form of a young man. They put the same question, and they received the same reply. When they had walked a little farther, he appeared to them again in the form of another old man. On asking the same question again, the identical reply was once more given. The gentile therefore took the Israelite's money.

The Israelite then journeyed on in fear of his life, and lodged in the open. When a third of the night had gone by, he heard some spirits speaking to each other. Two of them asked a third, "Where have you been today?" to which he replied, "I met a Jew and an Aramean, I laughed at them and gave evidence in favor of the gentile."

Then they asked another, "Where have you been today?" to which he replied, "I prevented the daughter of an emperor from giving birth, after she had suffered the pains of travail for seven days. But if they had taken some green leaves of the tree

---

[187]Type 613. Source: *Pantschatantra: Fünf Bücher indischer Fabeln, Märchen und Erzählungen*, translated from the Sanskrit into German by Theodor Benfey (Leipzig, 1859), v. 2, book 1, story 19.

overhanging their throne, and had squeezed them upon her nose, she would have given birth immediately."

They again addressed a third spirit, "Where have you been?"

He replied, "I stopped up the well of a certain province. But if they had taken a black ox and had slaughtered it over the water, the well would have been open again."

The Jew gave great heed to their conversation; and, rising up early in the morning, he went to the country of the emperor spoken of, and found his daughter in travail. He then told one to take some green leaves of the tree overhanging their throne, and to squeeze them upon her nose. This was done, and she immediately gave birth. The king thereupon presented the Jew with a large sum of money, because this was the only child he had.

The Jew then journeyed to the country in which the stopped wells were to be found, and told the people to take a black ox and slaughter it over the well, after which the water would flow as usual. They did so, and the water flowed. The inhabitants thereupon presented him with a large sum of money.

On the morrow he met the gentile who had taken his money, and the gentile expressed his surprise by saying, "Have I not already taken all your money from you; how is it that you are such a rich man?" He then related to him what had happened.

"Then I will also go," he said, "and inquire of the people of that place." He therefore journeyed on and lodged in that field; but the three spirits came and killed him, for it is said, "The righteous is delivered out of trouble, and the wicked cometh in his stead." (Proverbs, 11:8)[188]

True and Untrue

Norway

Once upon a time there were two brothers; one was called True, and the other Untrue. True was always upright and good towards all, but Untrue was bad and full of lies, so that no one could believe what he said. Their mother was a widow, and did not have much to live on; so when her sons had grown up, she was forced to send them away, that they might earn their bread in the world. Each received a little knapsack with some food in it, and then they went their way.

[188]Type 613. Source: M. Gaster, "Fairy Tales from Inedited Hebrew MSS. of the Ninth and Twelfth Centuries," *Folk-Lore: Transactions of the Folk-Lore Society*, v. 7, no. 3 (September 1896), pp. 231-232. Known generically as "The Two Travelers: Truth and Falsehood," this is one of the most enduring of all international folktales. It is found in *The Panchatantra*, one of ancient India's most important story collections, and in folklore versions from China to Norway.

They walked until evening and then sat down by a windfall in the woods, and took out their knapsacks, for they were hungry after walking the whole day, and thought that a bit of food would taste good.

"I think that you'll agree with me," said Untrue, "that we should eat out of your knapsack as long as there is anything in it, and after that we can eat from mine."

Yes, True was in agreement with this, so they started to eat, but Untrue stuffed himself with all the best things, while True got only the burnt crusts. The next morning they had their breakfast from True's food, and they ate dinner from it too, and then there was nothing left in his knapsack. They had walked until late that night, and when they were ready to eat again, True wanted to eat out from his brother's knapsack, but Untrue said "No," that this food was his, and that he had only enough for himself.

"Wait! You know that you ate from my knapsack as long as there was anything in it," said True.

"That is all well and good," answered Untrue; "but if you are such a fool to let others eat up your food right in front of you, then you must make the best of it. All you can do now is to sit here and starve."

"Very well," said True, "you're Untrue by name and untrue by nature. You have always been that way, and so you will be all the rest of your life."

Now when Untrue heard this, he flew into a rage, rushed at his brother, and plucked out both of his eyes. "Now, try to see whether people are untrue or not, you blind buzzard!" So saying, he ran away and left him.

Poor True! There he went walking along and feeling his way through the thick wood. Blind and alone, he barely knew which way to turn, when all at once he caught hold of the trunk of a great bushy linden tree. He thought, for fear of the wild beasts, that he would climb the tree and sit there until the night was over.

"When the birds begin to sing," he said to himself, "I shall know it is day, and I can try to grope my way farther on." So he climbed up into the linden tree. After he had sat there a little while, he heard how someone came and began to make a stir and clatter under the tree, and soon afterward others came. When they began to greet each other, he found out it was Bruin the bear, Graylegs the wolf, Slyboots the fox, and Longears the hare, all of whom had come to celebrate St. John's Eve[189] under the tree. They began to eat, drink, and be merry. When they were finished eating, they started to talk together. At last the fox said, "Let each of us tell a little story while we sit here."

The others had nothing against that. It would be good fun, they said, and the bear began; for he was the leader.

"The King of England," said Bruin, "has such bad eyesight, he can barely see a yard in front of him. If he would only come to this linden tree in the morning, while the dew is still on the leaves, and would rub his eyes with the dew, he would get back his sight as good as ever."

---

[189]The evening of June 23, leading to Midsummer Day, June 24, a time long associated with witchcraft, elf-lore, and all manner of supernatural happenings throughout northern Europe.

"Very true!" said Graylegs. "And the King of England has a daughter who is deaf and dumb. If he only knew what I know, he could soon cure her. Last year she went to communion. She let a crumb of the bread fall out of her mouth, and a large toad came and swallowed it down. If they would just dig up the chapel floor, they would find the toad sitting right under the altar, with the bread still sticking in his throat. If they were to cut the toad open, and give the bread to the princess, she would be able to hear and to speak again, just like other people."

"That's all very well," said the fox, "but if the King of England knew what I know, he would not be so badly off for water in his palace. Under the large stone in his palace yard there is a spring of the clearest water one could wish for, if he only knew to dig for it there."

"Ah!" said the hare in a small voice; "the King of England has the finest orchard in the whole land, but it does not bear so much as a green apple, for a heavy gold chain is buried, circling the orchard three times. If he would have it dug up, there would not be a garden like it in all his kingdom."

"Very true, I dare say," said the fox, "but now it's getting very late, and we should all go home."

So they all went away together.

After they were gone, True fell asleep, sitting there in the tree. When the birds began to sing at dawn, he woke up, and took the dew from the leaves, and rubbed his eyes with it, and thus he got his sight back as good as it was before Untrue plucked his eyes out.

Then he went straight to the King of England's palace, and begged for work, and got it on the spot. One day the king came out into the palace yard, and when he had walked about a bit, he wanted to drink out of his pump; for you must know the day was hot, and the king very thirsty; but when they poured him out a glass, it was so muddy, and nasty, and foul, that the king got quite upset.

"I don't think there's ever a man in my whole kingdom who has such bad water in his yard as I, and yet I bring it in pipes from far, over hill and dale," cried out the king.

"True enough, your majesty;" said True, "but if you would let me have some men to help me dig up this large stone which lies here in the middle of your yard, you would soon see good water, and plenty of it."

The king was willing enough. They barely had the stone out, and dug under it a while, before a jet of water sprang out high up into the air, as clear and full as if it came out of a conduit, and clearer water was not to be found in all England.

A little while after, the king was out in his palace yard again, and there came a great hawk flying after his chicken, and all the king's men began to clap their hands and bawl out, "There he flies! There he flies!" The king picked up his gun and tried to shoot the hawk, but he couldn't see that far, so he became very upset.

"Would to Heaven," he said, "there was anyone who could tell me a cure for my eyes; for I think I shall soon go quite blind!"

"I can tell you one soon enough," said True, and he told the king what he had done to cure his own eyes. The king set off that very afternoon to the linden tree, and his eyes were quite cured as soon as he rubbed them with the dew which was

308

on the leaves in the morning. From that time forth there was no one whom the king held so dear as True, and he had to be with him wherever he went, both at home and abroad.

One day they were walking together in the orchard, and the king said, "I don't know why, but there isn't a man in England who spends as much on his orchard as I, and yet I can't get one of the trees to bear as much as a green apple."

"Well," said True, "if I may have what is buried twisted three times around your orchard, and men to dig it up, your orchard will bear well enough."

Yes, the king was quite willing, so True got men and began to dig, and at last he dug up the whole gold chain. Now True was a rich man, far richer indeed than the king himself, but still the king was well pleased, for his orchard now bore so that the limbs of the trees hung down to the ground heavy with apples and pears sweeter than anyone had ever tasted.

The king and True were walking about and talking together on another day, when the princess passed them, and the king became quite downcast when he saw her.

"Isn't it a pity, now, that so lovely a princess as mine should not be able to speak or hear?" he said to True.

"Yes, but there is a cure for that," said True.

When the king heard that, he was so glad that he promised him the princess's hand in marriage, and half his kingdom as well, if he could cure her. So True took a few men, and went into the church, and dug up the toad which sat under the altar. Then he cut open the toad, took out the bread, and gave it to the king's daughter; and from that hour she got back her speech, and could talk like other people.

Now True was to have the princess, and they got ready for the bridal feast, and such a feast had never been seen before. It was the talk of the whole land. Just as they were dancing the bridal dance, in came a beggar lad, and begged for a morsel of food, and he was so ragged and wretched that they all crossed themselves when they looked at him. True knew him at once, and saw that it was Untrue, his brother.

"Do you recognize me?" asked True.

"Where would a person like me ever have seen so great a lord?" answered Untrue.

"You have seen me before," said True. "I was the one whose eyes you plucked out a year ago this very day. Untrue by name, and untrue by nature. I said it before, and I am saying it now. But you are still my brother, and so you shall have some food. After that, you may go to the linden tree where I sat last year. If you hear anything that can do you good, you will be lucky."

Untrue did not wait to be told twice. "If True has got so much good by sitting in the linden tree, that in one year he has come to be king over half England, what good may I get?" he thought. So he set off and climbed up into the linden tree. He had not sat there long, before all the beasts came as before, and ate and drank, and celebrated St. John's eve under the tree. When they were finished eating, the fox wished that they should begin to tell stories. Untrue got ready to listen with all his might, until his ears almost fell off. But Bruin the bear was cross. He growled and

309

said, "Someone has been chattering about what we said last year, and so this time we will hold our tongues about what we know." With that the beasts wished each other a good night, and parted. Untrue was just as wise as he was before, and the reason was, that his name was Untrue, and his nature untrue too.[190]

Resignation

Cat and Mouse in Partnership

Jacob and Wilhelm Grimm

A cat and a mouse wanted to live together and keep house as a partnership. They prepared for winter by buying a pot of fat, and because they had no safer spot for it, they placed it under the alter in the church until such time that they would need it. However, one day the cat took a longing for it, and approached the mouse. "Listen, little mouse, my cousin has invited me to serve as godfather. She has given birth to a brown and white spotted little son, and I am supposed to carry him to his baptism. Is it all right for me to leave you home alone with the housework today?"

"Go ahead," said the mouse, "and if they serve you something good, just think of me. I would certainly welcome a drop of good red christening wine." But the cat went straight to the church and ate the top off the fat and then went strolling about the town and did not return home until evening.

"You must have had a good time," said the mouse. "What name did they give the child?"

"Top-Off," answered the cat.

"Top-Off? That's a strange name, one that I've not yet heard."

Soon afterward the cat took another longing, went to the mouse, and said, "I've been asked to serve as godfather once again. The child has a white ring around its body. I can't say no. You'll have to do me a favor and take care of the house by yourself today."

---

[190]Type 613. Source: Peter Christen Asbjørnsen and Jørgen Moe, *Norske Folkeeventyr* (Christiania [Oslo], 1842-1852), translated by George Webb Dasent (1859). Revised. This ancient tale is found throughout Asia, India, the Arabic world, and Europe.

The mouse agreed, and the cat went and ate up half the fat. When she returned home, the mouse asked, "What name did this godchild receive?"

"Half-Gone."

"Half-Gone? What are you telling me? I've never heard that name. It certainly isn't in the almanac."

Now the cat could not take his mind off the pot of fat. "I've been invited to serve as godfather for a third time," he said. "The child is black and has white paws, but not another white hair on his entire body. That only happens once in a few years. You will let me go, won't you?"

"Top-Off, Half-Gone," said the mouse. "Those names are so curious that it makes me a bit suspicious, but go ahead."

The mouse took care of the house and cleaned up everything, while the cat finished off the pot of fat. Round and full, she did not return until nighttime.

"What is the third child's name?"

"All-Gone."

"All-Gone! That is a worrisome name!" said the mouse. "All-Gone. Just what does this mean? I've never seen that name in print," and she shook her head and went to bed.

No one invited the cat to serve as godfather a fourth time. Winter soon came, and when they could no longer find anything to eat outside, the mouse said to the cat, "Let's get the provisions that we've hid in the church under the altar." They went there, but the pot was empty.

"Now I see!" said the mouse. "You came here when you said you were invited to be a godfather. First came Top-Off, then it was Half-Gone, and then..."

"Be still," said the cat. "I'll eat you up, if you say another word."

"All-Gone" was already in the poor mouse's mouth, and she had scarcely said it before the cat jumped on her and swallowed her down.[191]

The Lion's Share

Aesop

The lion went once hunting along with the fox, the jackal, and the wolf. They hunted and they hunted until at last they surprised a stag, and soon took its life. Then came the question how the spoil should be divided. "Quarter me this stag," roared the lion; so the other animals skinned it and cut it into four parts. Then the lion took his stand in front of the carcass and pronounced judgment, "The first quarter is for me in my capacity as King of Beasts; the second is mine as

---

[191]Type 15. Source: *Kinder- und Hausmärchen*, 1st ed. (Berlin, 1812/1815), v. 1, no. 2.

arbiter; another share comes to me for my part in the chase; and as for the fourth quarter, well, as for that, I should like to see which of you will dare to lay a paw upon it."

"Humph," grumbled the fox, and walked away with his tail between his legs.

Moral: You may share the labors of the great, but you will not share the rewards.[192]

The Lion, the Fox, and the Donkey

Aesop

A lion, a fox, and a donkey went out hunting together. They had soon taken a large booty, which the lion requested the donkey to divide between them. The donkey divided it all into three equal parts, and modestly begged the others to take their choice; at which the lion, bursting with fury, sprang upon the donkey and tore him to pieces. Then, glaring at the fox, he asked him to make a fresh division. The fox gathered almost the whole in one great heap for the lion's share, leaving only the smallest possible morsel for himself. "My dear friend," said the lion, "how did you get the knack of it so well?"

The fox replied, "Me? Oh, the donkey was a good teacher."

Moral: Happy is he who learns from the misfortunes of others.[193]

The Wolf and the Lamb

Aesop

Once upon a time a wolf was lapping at a spring on a hillside, when, looking up, what should he see but a lamb just beginning to drink a little lower down. "There's my supper," thought he, "if only I can find some excuse to

---

[192]Type 51. Source: Joseph Jacobs, *The Fables of Aesop* (London, 1894), no. 4.

[193]Type 51. Source: *Aesop's Fables*, translated by V. S. Vernon Jones (London and New York, 1912), pp. 196-197. Slightly revised.

seize it." Then he called out to the lamb, "How dare you muddle the water from which I am drinking?"

"Nay, master, nay," said the lamb. "If the water is muddy up there, I cannot be the cause of it, for it runs down from you to me.

"Well, then," said the wolf, "why did you call me bad names this time last year?"

"That cannot be," said the lamb. "I am only six months old."

"Then it was your father!" snarled the wolf. And with that he rushed upon the poor little lamb and ate her all up.

Moral: Any excuse will serve a tyrant.[194]

Masters and Servants

The Elephant and His Keeper

India

There was an elephant which was accustomed to suffer most cruel treatment at the hands of his keeper; and the keeper knowing the sagacity of these animals, and being in fear of his life, used to sleep some little distance from the peg to which the elephant was tied. One night the elephant, taking up a long loose branch, chewed the end of it, in order to separate the fibers; and having twisted them in the long hair of the sleeping man, he dragged him within reach, and trampled him to death.[195]

---

[194]Type 111A. Source: Joseph Jacobs, *The Fables of Aesop* (London, 1894), no. 2.

[195]Source: Charles Swynnerton, *Indian Nights' Entertainment; or, Folk-Tales from the Upper Indus* (London, 1892), no. 25.

How the Man Taught the Tiger to Fly

India (Assam)

The tiger and the man met on the road. As they were chatting a hornbill flew overhead, and the tiger looking up said, "I wonder how that is done. I wish I could fly."

"I know all about it, and I can teach you, said the man. "I made that hornbill."

"Could you make wings for me?" asked the tiger.

"All right," said the man. So he made the tiger lie down and stretch out his four legs on a wooden frame. "This is for the wings," he said, as he tied the beast's legs to the frame with cane lashings. "You must stay like that all day, and tomorrow I will fetch you."

Next day when the man came the tiger said, "I am very stiff and it hurts."

But the man only tied him the tighter. Then he got some sharp spikes and drove them into the tiger's armpits. "This is how we make the wing bones," he said.

The tiger moaned, but the man said, "Don't cry, or the charm will not work." Then he drove a stake into his body to make a tail, and went off, saying, "I will come back in three days and finish the job." But while he was away, the flies and maggots devoured the tiger, and that was the end of him.[196]

The Cruel Merchant

India

Once upon a time there lived a merchant who was very cruel to his servants. When anybody applied to him for service, he agreed to employ him on the condition that the servant's nose should be cut off if he at any time showed himself abusive or angry. Now, since servants are no better than the majority of their masters, we are not surprised to hear that several servants quitted this merchant's service *minus* their noses.

One of these servants was a poor farmer, who had been obliged to take service on account of a failure in his crops. The man lived up in the hills, where nothing except maize can be grown; and that year but little rain had fallen, so that his labor and expense were all wasted. He was of a most amiable and willing disposition. If any man had a chance of continuing in the merchant's service, it was he. But, alas,

---

[196]Source: *Folk-Lore: A Quarterly Review of Myth, Tradition, Institution, and Custom*, v. 25 (London, 1914), p. 488.

he too failed. One day he was very much troubled about a matter, when something his master did or said—and the merchant used to say and do some very nasty things—provoked the farmer, so that he spoke angrily; whereupon the merchant rushed at him and cut off his nose.

This farmer had a brother, who grieved to see him in this noseless condition, and resolved to avenge him of this cruelty. So he went to the merchant and offered himself for employment.

"Very well," said the merchant. "I will give you work, but only on the condition that your nose is cut off if you ever show yourself abusive or angry."

"I will agree to this if you too will be bound by the like condition," said the man.

"All right," said the merchant.

"If the plan worked well for one party, it might also work well for the other," thought the man.

It did work well for a long time. Both master and servant were so very careful over their words and actions that they both preserved their temper. One day, however, the merchant ordered his servant to go and put on his son's clothes quickly. The man went, and while dressing the boy pulled him about here and there to make him run. The boy, naturally not liking such treatment, roared, "Oh father! Oh mother!"

"What are you doing?" asked the merchant.

"The boy will not run about while I am dressing him, but wants to sit down," he replied.

Now the master had ordered him to dress the child quickly, and thus he would have been understood by nineteen out of twenty people; but the words might possibly be construed to mean, "Run about quickly and dress the child;" so the servant chose to understand them thus, thinking thereby to provoke his master to anger; and he almost succeeded.

On another occasion the merchant, accompanied by all his family, went to stay for a few days in some place where a big religious festival was accustomed to be held. He left the house in charge of this servant, and before leaving, especially ordered him to keep his eye on the doors and windows. The man promised faithfully. His master, however, had not long departed when he too felt an intense desire to attend the festival. Accordingly he collected the furniture and things of the house and stored them away in a big pit. He then called several coolies, and loading them with the doors and windows of the place, started off for the festival. The astonishment of the merchant, when he saw his servant, followed by a long string of coolies bearing his doors and windows, will be imagined.

"You fool!" he exclaimed, "what have you done?"

"I have simply obeyed your order," replied the servant. "You told me to look after the doors and windows. So, when I wished to leave the house and come to the festival, I thought it would be safer to bring them with me. The furniture, too, is quite safe. I have hidden it all in a great pit."

"You consummate fool!" said the merchant, and struck him a blow across the face.

"Ha! Ha!" said the man, seizing him by the back of his neck and cutting off his nose, "we are quits now. I will go and tell my brother."[197]

Till Eulenspiegel

Germany

Till Eulenspiegel came to Braunschweig, where he presented himself as a journeyman baker, and was taken in by a master baker. On the second day, the master ordered Eulenspiegel to work late into the evening, and by himself at that. "What do you want me to bake?" asked Eulenspiegel.

The baker, who was impatient and short tempered, shouted back sarcastically, "Are you a journeyman baker or not? What do bakers make, anyway, owls or monkeys?" and he went to bed.

So Eulenspiegel cut the dough into the shape of owls and monkeys, and baked the whole lot.

The next morning when the baker found owls and monkeys instead of bread and rolls, he shouted, "May you be struck by the plague! What have you done?"

"I made owls and monkeys, just like you told me to," answered Eulenspiegel.

"I'll never sell this kind of bread!" shouted the baker. "Pay me for the ruined dough!"

So Eulenspiegel had to pay for the dough, but then the owls and monkeys belonged to him. He took them out onto the street and sold them for even more money than bread and rolls would have brought. When the baker heard of his success, he tried to get him to pay for the wood he had burned in baking them, but Eulenspiegel had already set forth for the next town.

Eulenspiegel came to Ascherleben in mid winter. Times were hard, but finally he found a furrier who was willing to take on an apprentice, and he was put to

---

[197]Type 1000. Source: J. Hinton Knowles, *Folk-Tales of Kashmir* (London, 1893), pp. 98-100. This story has circulated throughout India, the Middle East, and Europe since the middle ages, both in oral tales and in printed jest books. The penalty for losing one's temper in the European stories is typically to have a strip of skin cut from one's back. Popular episodes include a wide range of "misunderstandings," for example: The servant is told to give the master's grandmother a hot bath, so he scalds her to death. The servant is told to make a fire before the master returns home on an evening, so he sets the house afire. The servant is told to harvest apples as quickly as possible, so he cuts down the trees. The servant is told to keep on eye on something or another, so he digs an eye from one of the master's favorite animals. The tales often depend upon puns that are lost in translation, but they nearly all derive their popularity from showing how a harsh master is made to suffer by a servant who follows the master's orders to the letter.

work sewing pelts. Not being accustomed to the smell of the curing hides, he said, "Pew! Pew! You are as white as chalk, but stink like dung!"

The furrier said, "If you don't like the smell, then why are you a furrier's apprentice? It's a natural smell. It's only wool."

Eulenspiegel said nothing, but thought, "One bad thing can drive another bad thing away." Then he let such a sour fart that the furrier and his wife had to stop working.

The furrier said, "If you have to fart like that, then go out into the courtyard. There you can fart as much as you like."

Eulenspiegel answered, "A fart is more natural and healthier than the stench of your sheep pelts."

The furrier said, "Healthy or not, if you want to fart, then go outside."

Eulenspiegel said, "Master, it would do no good, because farts don't like the cold. They are used to being in a warm place. That's why if you let a fart it always rushes for your nose. It goes from one warm place to another."

The furrier said nothing, for he could see that Eulenspiegel knew nothing of the furrier trade and was a rogue at that. And he sent him on his way.

Eulenspiegel then went to Berlin, where he apprenticed himself to another furrier. His new master was from Swabia, and Swabians would rather drink than work, so their workshops are usually in disarray. Now the Swabian furrier had just received a large number of wolf pelts with an order to make them into coats.

"Can you make wolves?" asked the master, meaning "wolfskin coats."

"Yes, indeed," answered Eulenspiegel. "Just leave me alone with the pelts." The master, happy for the help in filling his large order, left him alone. Eulenspiegel then cut the pelts into pieces and sewed them together in the shape of wolves, stuffing them with hay and propping them up on wooden legs.

When the master returned and saw the fur animals, he said, "What have you done? I'll have you arrested for the damage you have caused!"

Eulenspiegel said, "Is this how you thank me for doing what you asked me to. I was only following your orders!"

And thus Eulenspiegel had to leave Berlin, without pay, and without recommendation.

After having played many such tricks, Eulenspiegel fell ill. Fearing that he might die, he sent for a priest to hear his confession. Before the priest arrived, Eulenspiegel filled a pot with human muck, which he covered with a thin layer of money.

"Eulenspiegel, my dear son," said the priest upon his arrival. "Think of your salvation, as life draws to a close. You have been an adventuresome fellow and have often sinned. Now if you will give me some money, I can prepare a way for you to enter the glory of God."

"Take a handful from this pot," said Eulenspiegel, "but do not reach in too deeply."

The priest consented, but his greed led him to push his hand to the bottom of the pot. Instead of hard money he felt something wet and soft. He pulled out his hand, filthy with muck.

"You rogue!" said the priest. "You lie and cheat even on your deathbed!"

317

"Don't blame me!" returned Eulenspiegel. I told you not to reach in too deeply." The priest walked away, leaving Eulenspiegel lying there.

"You forgot your money!" shouted Eulenspiegel. But the priest did not hear him.[198]

Clever Gretel

Jacob and Wilhelm Grimm

There was a cook whose name was Gretel. She wore shoes with red heels, and whenever she went out she would turn this way and that way, and was very cheerful, and thought, "You are a beautiful girl!" Then after returning home, because she was so happy, she drank a swallow of wine, and the wine gave her an appetite, so she tasted the best of what she had cooked, until she was quite full, and then said, "The cook has to know how the food tastes."

One day her master said to her, "Gretel, this evening a guest is coming. Prepare two chickens for me, the best way that you can."

"Yes indeed, my lord," answered Gretel. She killed the chickens, scalded them, plucked them, stuck them on the spit, and then, as evening approached, put them over the fire to roast. The chickens began to brown, and were nearly done, but the guest had not yet arrived. Gretel called to her master, "If the guest doesn't come, I'll have to take the chickens from the fire. And it will be a crying shame if they're not eaten soon, because they're at their juicy best right now."

The master answered, "You're right. I'll run and fetch the guest myself."

As soon as the master had turned his back, Gretel set the spit and the chickens aside and thought, "Standing here by the fire has made me sweaty and thirsty. Who knows when they will be back. I'll just run down into the cellar and take a swallow. So she ran down, lifted a jug to her lips, "God bless you, Gretel!" and took a healthy drink. "Wine belongs together," she said to herself. It's not good to keep it apart." Then she went back upstairs and placed the chickens over the fire again, basted them with butter, and cheerfully turned the spit. Because the roasting chicken smelled so good, she thought, "It could be lacking something. I'd better

---

[198]Source: Retold from *Ein kurtzweilig Lesen von Dyl Ulenspiegel* (Strasbourg, 1515). Till Eulenspiegel's pranks were known throughout northern Europe in the fifteenth and sixteenth centuries. The four jests above, gleaned from a collection of some ninety-five episodes are typical, not only of this well known work, but of a vast body of master-servant folk literature. These burlesque power-plays between master and apprentice reflect deeply rooted resentment and frustration. Eulenspiegel's main defense is either to follow his master's orders to the letter, or—bluntly stated—to fart and run.

taste it!" She tested them with her fingers, and said, "My, these chickens are good! It's a sin and a shame that they won't be eaten at once!"

She ran to the window, to see if her master and his guest were arriving, but she saw no one. Returning to the chickens, she said, "That one wing is burning. I'd better just eat it." So she cut it off and ate it, and it tasted so good, and when she had finished it, she thought, "I'd better eat the other one too, or the master will see that something is missing." When both wings had been eaten, she once again looked for her master, but could not see him. Then it occurred to her, "who knows, perhaps they've gone somewhere else and aren't coming here at all." Then she said, "Well, Gretel, be of good cheer! The one has already been cut into. Have another drink and eat the rest of it. When it's gone, you can rest! Why should this gift of God go to waste?"

So she ran to the cellar once again, downed a noble drink, and finished off the first chicken with pleasure. When it was gone, and still the master had not yet returned, she looked at the other chicken and said, "Where the one is, the other should follow. The two belong together. What is right for the one, can't be wrong for the other. I believe that if I have another drink, it will do me no harm." So she took another drink, and sent the second chicken running after the first one.

Just as she was making the most of it, her master returned, calling out, "Gretel, hurry up, the guest is right behind me."

"Yes, master, I'm getting it ready," answered Gretel. The master saw that the table was set, and he picked up the large knife that he wanted to carve the chickens with, and stood in the hallway sharpening it.

The guest arrived and knocked politely on the door. Gretel ran to see who it was, and when she saw that it was the guest, she held a finger before her mouth, and said, "Be quiet! Hurry and get away from here. If my master catches you, you'll be sorry. Yes, he invited you for an evening meal, but all he really wants is to cut off both of your ears. Listen, he's sharpening his knife for it right now."

The guest heard the whetting and ran down the steps as fast as he could. Then Gretel, who was not a bit lazy, ran to her master, crying, "Just what kind of a guest did you invite?"

"What do you mean, Gretel?"

"Why," she said, "he took both of the chickens off the platter, just as I was about to carry them out, and then ran away with them."

"Now that's a fine tune!" said the master, feeling sorry about the loss of the good chickens. "At the least, he could have left one of them, so I would have something to eat." He called out to him to stop, but the guest pretended not to hear. Therefore he ran after him, the knife still in his hand, shouting, "Just one! Just one!" But the guest thought that he wanted him to give up just one of his ears, so he ran as though there were a fire burning beneath him, in order to get home with both ears.[199]

---

[199]Type 1741. Source: *Kinder- und Hausmärchen*, 2nd ed. (Berlin, 1819), no. 77.

The Good Husband and the Bad Wife

India

In a remote village there lived a Brahman whose good nature and charitable disposition were proverbial. Equally proverbial also were the ill nature and uncharitable disposition of the Brahmani, his wife. But as Paramêsvara (God) had joined them in matrimony, they had to live together as husband and wife, though their temperaments were so incompatible. Every day the Brahman had a taste of his wife's ill temper, and if any other Brahman was invited to dinner by him, his wife, somehow or other, would manage to drive him away.

One fine summer morning a rather stupid Brahman friend of his came to visit our hero and was at once invited to dinner. He told his wife to have dinner ready earlier than usual, and went off to the river to bathe. His friend, not feeling very well that day, wanted a hot bath at the house, and so did not follow him to the river, but remained sitting in the outer verandah. If any other guest had come, the wife would have accused him of greediness to his face and sent him away, but this visitor seemed to be a special friend of her lord, so she did not like to say anything; but she devised a plan to make him go away of his own accord.

She proceeded to smear the ground before her husband's friend with cow dung, and placed in the midst of it a long pestle, supporting one end of it against the wall. She next approached the pestle most solemnly and performed worship (pûjâ) to it. The guest did not in the least understand what she was doing, and respectfully asked her what it all meant.

"This is what is called pestle worship," she replied. "I do it as a daily duty, and this pestle is intended to break the head of some human being in honor of a goddess, whose feet are most devoutly worshipped by my husband. Every day as soon as he returns from his bath in the river, he takes this pestle, which I am ordered to keep ready for him before his return, and with it breaks the head of any human being whom he has managed to get hold of by inviting him to a meal. This is his tribute (dakshinâ) to the goddess; today you are the victim."

The guest was much alarmed.

"What! break the head of a guest! I at any rate shall not be deceived today," thought he, and prepared to run away.

The Brahman's wife appeared to sympathize with his sad plight, and said, "Really, I do pity you. But there is one thing you can do now to save yourself. If you go out by the front door and walk down the street my husband may follow you, so you had better go out by the back door."

To this plan the guest most thankfully agreed, and hastily ran off by the back door.

Almost immediately our hero returned from his bath, but before he could arrive his wife had cleaned up the place she had prepared for the pestle worship, and when the Brahman, not finding his friend in the house, inquired of her as to what had become of him, she said in seeming anger, "The greedy brute! he wanted me to give him this pestle—this very pestle which I brought forty years ago as a dowry from my mother's house, and when I refused he ran away by the back yard in haste."

But her kind-hearted lord observed that he would rather lose the pestle than his guest, even though it was a part of his wife's dowry, and more than forty years old. So he ran off with the pestle in his hand after his friend, crying out, "Oh Brahman! Oh Brahman! Stop please, and take the pestle."

But the story told by the old woman now seemed all the more true to the guest when he saw her husband running after him, and so he said, "You and your pestle may go where you please. Never more will you catch me in your house," and ran away.[200]

The Gardener's Cunning Wife

India

In a certain village there lived with his wife a poor gardener who cultivated greens in a small patch in the backyard of his house. They were in thirty little beds, half of which he would water every day. This occupied him from the fifth to the fifteenth *ghatikâ*.[201]

His wife used to cut a basketful of greens every evening, and he took them in the mornings to sell in the village. The sale brought him a measure or two of rice, and on this the family lived! If he could manage any extra work of an evening he got a few coppers which served to meet their other expenses.

Now in that village there was a temple to Kâlî, before which was a fine tank with a mango tree on its bank. The fish in the tank and the mangoes from the tree were dedicated to the goddess, and were strictly forbidden to the villagers. If anyone was discovered cutting a mango or catching a fish, he was at once excommunicated from the village. So strict was the prohibition.

The gardener was returning home one morning after selling his greens and passed the temple. The mangoes, so carefully guarded by religious protection, were hanging on the tree in great numbers, and the gardener's eyes fell on them! His mouth watered. He look round about him, and fortunately there was no one by, at least, as far as his eyes could reach. So he hastily plucked one of the mangoes and with nimble feet descended into the tank to wash it. Just then a most charming shoal of fish met his eyes. These protected dwellers in the tank had no notion of danger, and so were frolicking about at their ease. The gardener looked

---

[200]Type 1741. Source: Georgiana Kingscote and Pandit Natesa Sástrî, *Tales of the Sun; or, Folklore of Southern India* (London, 1890), no. 11.

[201]A unit of time equal to twenty-four minutes.

about him first and finding no one by caught half a dozen stout fish at one plunge of his hand. He hid them and the mango underneath the rice in his basket and returned home, happy in the thought that he had not been caught. Now he had a special delight in fish, and when he reached his house he showed what he brought to his wife and asked her to prepare a dish with the newly caught fish and the never-till-then tasted mango.

Meanwhile he had to water his garden, and went to the backyard for the purpose. The watering was done by a *pikôta*. He used to run up and down the pole while a friend of his, the son of his neighbor, lifted the water and irrigated the garden.

Meanwhile his wife cooked the dish of mango and fish in a pan, and found the flavor so sweet that even while the fish was only half cooked she began to taste on bit of it after another till more than half had already gone down her throat! The dish was at last cooked, and the few remaining slices in the pan were taken off the fire, so she went into the verandah and from thence saw her husband running up and down the *pikôta*. She beckoned to him that the dish was ready and that he should come in and taste it. However, he never noticed her, but kept on running up and down the *pikôta*, and while running up and down he was obliged to wave his hand about, and this his wife mistook as an indication that she might eat up her portion of the dish. At any rate her imagination made her think so; and she went in and ate a slice, and then went out into the verandah again to call her husband who was still running up and down the *pikôta* Again, her husband, so she thought, waved his hands in permission to go on with her dinner. Again she went in and had another slice. Thus it went on for a full *ghatikâ* till the last slice was consumed.

"Alas!" thought she, "With what great eagerness my husband fetched the fish and the mango, and how sadly, out of greediness, have I disappointed him. Surely his anger will know no bounds when he comes in. I must soon devise some means to save myself."

So she brought the pan in which she cooked the fish and mango out of the house and covered it with another pan of similar size and sat down before it. Then she undid her hair and twisted it about her head until it was disheveled. She then began to make a great noise. This action by a woman in an illiterate family of low caste is always supposed to indicate a visitation from a goddess and a demon; so when her husband from the *pikôta* tree saw the state of his wife, his guilty conscience smote him. The change in his wife alarmed him, and he came down suddenly and stood before her.

As soon as she saw him she roared out at him, "Why have you injured me today by plundering my mango and fish? You shall soon see the results of your impertinence!"

"The goddess has come upon my wife most terribly," thought the poor man. "Her divine power may soon kill her! What shall I do?"

So he fell at the feet of the divine visitation as he thought it to be, and said, "My most holy goddess, your dog of a servant has this day deviated from the straight path. Excuse him this time, and he will never do so a second time."

"Run then with the pan which contains the fruits of you robbery and dip it deep into my tank. Then shall the fish become alive and the mango shall take its place in the tree."

The gardener received the order most submissively, and taking the pan in his hand flew to the tank. There he dipped it in the water and came back to his house fully believing that his sin that day had been forgiven, and that the cooked fish had become alive again and the mango a living one. Thus did the cunning wife save herself from her husband's wrath![202]

More Tricksters

The Monkey's Heart

The Jataka Tales

Once upon a time, while Brahmadatta was king of Benares, the Bodhisatta came to life at the foot of the Himalayas as a monkey. He grew strong and sturdy, big of frame, well to do, and lived by a curve of the river Ganges in a forest haunt. Now at that time there was a crocodile dwelling in the Ganges. The Crocodile's mate saw the great frame of the monkey, and she conceived a longing to eat his heart. So she said to her lord, "Sir, I desire to eat the heart of that great king of the monkeys!"

"Good wife," said the crocodile, "I live in the water and he lives on dry land. How can we catch him?"

"By hook or by crook," she replied, "he must be caught. If I don't get him, I shall die."

"All right," answered the crocodile, consoling her, "don't trouble yourself. I have a plan. I will give you his heart to eat."

So when the Bodhisatta was sitting on the bank of the Ganges, after taking a drink of water, the crocodile drew near, and said, "Sir Monkey, why do you live on bad fruits in this old familiar place? On the other side of the Ganges there is no end to the mango trees, and labuja trees, with fruit sweet as honey! Is it not better to cross over and have all kinds of wild fruit to eat?"

---

[202]Similar to type 1741. Source: Mrs. Howard Kingscote and Pandit Natêsá Sástrî, *Tales of the Sun; or, Folklore of Southern India* (London, 1890), no. 21.

"Lord Crocodile," the monkey answered. "The Ganges is deep and wide. How shall I get across?"

"If you want to go, I will let you sit upon my back, and carry you over."

The monkey trusted him, and agreed. "Come here, then," said the crocodile. "Up on my back with you!" and up the monkey climbed. But when the crocodile had swum a little way, he plunged the monkey under the water.

"Good friend, you are letting me sink!" cried the monkey. "What is that for?"

The crocodile said, "You think I am carrying you out of pure good nature? Not a bit of it! My wife has a longing for your heart, and I want to give it to her to eat!"

"Friend," said the monkey, "it is nice of you to tell me. Why, if our heart were inside us when we go jumping among the tree tops, it would be all knocked to pieces!"

"Well, where do you keep it?" asked the crocodile.

The Bodhisatta pointed out a fig tree, with clusters of ripe fruit, standing not far off. "See," said he, "there are our hearts hanging on yonder fig tree."

"If you will show me your heart," said the crocodile, "then I won't kill you."

"Take me to the tree, then, and I will point it out to you."

The crocodile brought him to the place. The monkey leapt off his back, and, climbing up the fig tree, sat upon it. "Oh silly crocodile!" said he. "You thought that there were creatures that kept their hearts in a treetop! You are a fool, and I have outwitted you! You may keep your fruit to yourself. Your body is great, but you have no sense." And then to explain this idea he uttered the following stanzas:

> Rose-apple, jack-fruit, mangoes, too, across the water there I see;
> Enough of them, I want them not; my fig is good enough for me!
>
> Great is your body, verily, but how much smaller is your wit!
> Now go your ways, Sir Crocodile, for I have had the best of it.

The crocodile, feeling as sad and miserable as if he had lost a thousand pieces of money, went back sorrowing to the place where he lived.[203]

The Lion and the Hare

Bidpai

In the neighborhood of Baghdad there was a beautiful meadow, which was the home of many wild animals. They would have lived very happily there had it not been for one mischief loving lion. Every day this lion wandered about,

---

[203]Type 91. Source: *The Jataka; or, Stories of the Buddha's Former Births*, edited by E. B. Cowell (Cambridge, 1895), book 2, no. 208.

killing many helpless creatures for the mere sport of the slaying. To put an end to this, the animals gathered in a body, and going to the lion, spoke to him in this manner, "King lion, we are proud to have such a brave and valiant beast to rule over us. But we do not think that it is fitting for one of your rank to hunt for his own food. We therefore wait upon you with this request: Henceforth do you remain quietly at home, and we your subjects will bring to your lair such food as it is fitting that a king should eat."

The lion, who was greatly flattered, immediately accepted their offer. Thus every day the animals drew lots to decide who among their number should offer himself for the lion's daily portion. In due time it came about that the lot fell upon the hare. Now the hare, when he learned that it was his turn to die, complained bitterly.

"Do you not see that we are still tormented by that lion?" he asked the other animals. "Only leave it to me, and I will release you for all time from his tyranny."

The other animals were only too glad at these words, and told the hare to go his way. The hare hid for some time in the bushes, and then hurried to the lion's lair. By this time the lion was as angry as he was hungry. He was snarling, and lashing his yellow tail on the ground. When he saw the hare, he called out loudly, "Who are you, and what are my subjects doing? I have had no morsel of food today!"

The hare besought him to calm his anger and listen to him. "The lot fell today," he began, "on another hare and myself. In good season we were on our way here to offer ourselves for your dinner, when a lion sprang out of the bushes and seized my companion. In vain I cried to him that we were destined for the king's table, and, moreover, that no one was permitted to hunt in these royal woods except your majesty. He paid no heed to my words save to retort, 'You do not know what you are saying. I am the only king here. That other lion, to whom you all bow down, is a usurper.' Dumb with fright, I jumped into the nearest bush."

The lion grew more and more indignant as he listened to the hare's tale.

"If I could once find that lion," he roared, "I would soon teach him who is king of these woods."

"If your majesty will trust me," answered the hare, humbly, "I can take you to his hiding place."

So the hare and the lion went out together. They crossed the woods and the meadow, and came to an ancient well, which was full of clear, deep water.

"Yonder is the home of your enemy," whispered the hare, pointing to the well. "If you go near enough, you can see him. But," he added, "perhaps you had better wait until he comes out before you attack him."

These words only made the lion more indignant. "He shall not live a moment after I have laid eyes upon him," he growled.

So the hare and the lion approached stealthily to the well. As they bent over the edge and looked down into the clear water, they saw themselves reflected there. The lion, thinking that it was the other lion with the other hare, leaped into the well, never to come out again.[204]

---

[204]Type 92. Source: *The Tortoise and the Geese and other Fables of Bidpai*, retold by Maude

The Cat and the Mice

Tibet

Once upon a time there was a cat who lived in a large farm house in which there was a great number of mice. For many years the cat found no difficulty in catching as many mice as she wanted to eat, and she lived a very peaceful and pleasant life. But as time passed on she found that she was growing old and infirm, and that it was becoming more and more difficult for her to catch the same number of mice as before; so after thinking very carefully what was the best thing to do, she one day called all the mice together, and after promising not to touch them, she addressed them as follows:

"Oh! mice," said she, "I have called you together in order to say something to you. The fact is that I have led a very wicked life, and now, in my old age, I repent of having caused you all so much inconvenience and annoyance. So I am going for the future to turn over a new leaf. It is my intention now to give myself up entirely to religious contemplation and no longer to molest you, so henceforth you are at liberty to run about as freely as you will without fear of me. All I ask of you is that twice every day you should all file past me in procession and each one make an obeisance as you pass me by, as a token of your gratitude to me for my kindness."

When the mice heard this they were greatly pleased, for they thought that now, at last, they would be free from all danger from their former enemy, the cat. So they very thankfully promised to fulfill the cat's conditions, and agreed that they would file past her and make a salaam twice every day.

So when evening came the cat took her seat on a cushion at one end of the room, and the mice all went by in single file, each one making a profound salaam as it passed.

Now the cunning old cat had arranged this little plan very carefully with an object of her own; for, as soon as the procession had all passed by with the exception of one little mouse, she suddenly seized the last mouse in her claws without anybody else noticing what had happened, and devoured it at her leisure. And so twice every day, she seized the last mouse of the series, and for a long time lived very comfortably without any trouble at all in catching her mice, and without any of the mice realizing what was happening.

Now it happened that amongst these mice there were two friends, whose names were Rambé and Ambé, who were very much attached to one another. Now these two were much cleverer and more cunning than most of the others, and after a few days they noticed that the number of mice in the house seemed to be decreasing very much, in spite of the fact that the cat had promised not to kill any more. So they laid their heads together and arranged a little plan for future processions. They agreed that Rambé was always to walk at the very front of the procession of the mice, and the Ambé was to bring up the rear, and that all the time the procession was passing, Rambé was to call to Ambé, and Ambé to answer Rambé at frequent

Barrows Dutton (Boston, 1908), pp. 90-94.

326

intervals. So next evening, when the procession started as usual, Rambé marched along in front, and Ambé took up his position last of all. As soon as Rambé had passed the cushion where the cat was seated and had made his salaam, he called out in a shrill voice, "Where are you, Brother Ambé?"

"Here I am, Brother Rambé," squeaked the other from the rear of the procession. And so they went on calling out and answering one another until they had all filed past the cat, who had not dared to touch Ambé as long as his brother kept calling to him.

The cat was naturally very much annoyed at having to go hungry that evening, and felt very cross all night. But she thought it was only an accident which had brought the two friends, one in front and one in rear of the procession, and she hoped to make up for her enforced abstinence by finding a particularly fat mouse at the end of the procession next morning. What, then, was her amazement and disgust when she found that on the following morning the very same arrangement had been made, and that Rambé called to Ambé, and Ambé answered Rambé until all the mice had passed her by, and so, for the second time, she was foiled of her meal. However, she disguised her feelings of anger and decided to give the mice one more trial; so in the evening she took her seat as usual on the cushion and waited for the mice to appear.

Meanwhile, Rambé and Ambé had warned the other mice to be on the lookout, and to be ready to take flight the moment the cat showed any appearance of anger. At the appointed time the procession started as usual, and as soon as Rambé had passed the cat he squeaked out, "Where are you, Brother Ambé?"

"Here I am, Brother Rambé," came the shrill voice from the rear.

This was more than the cat could stand. She made a fierce leap right into the middle of the mice, who, however, were thoroughly prepared for her, and in an instant they scuttled off in every direction to their holes. And before the cat had time to catch a single one the room was empty and not a sign of a mouse was to be seen anywhere.

After this the mice were very careful not to put any further trust in the treacherous cat, who soon after died of starvation owing to her being unable to procure any of her customary food; but Rambé and Ambé lived for many years, and were held in high honor and esteem by all the other mice in the community.[205]

---

[205]Type 113B. Source: W. F. O'Connor, *Folk Tales from Tibet* (London, 1906), no. 5.

The Wolf in Sheep's Clothing

Aesop

A wolf found great difficulty in getting at the sheep owing to the vigilance of the shepherd and his dogs. But one day he found the skin of a sheep that had been flayed and thrown aside, so he put it on over his own pelt and strolled down among the sheep. The lamb that belonged to the sheep, whose skin the wolf was wearing, began to follow him; so, leading the lamb a little apart, he soon made a meal off her, and for some time he succeeded in deceiving the sheep, and enjoying hearty meals.

Moral: Appearances are deceptive.[206]

The Reward of Good Deeds

Denmark

There was once a man who went into the woods to cut some firewood. He went from one tree to another, but they were all too good for his purpose, as they would make good timber if allowed to stand. At last he found a tree which seemed good for nothing; it was gnarled and partly decayed, so he began to hew away at it. But just as he began to cut, he heard a voice calling to him, "Help me out, my good man." And as he turned he saw a large viper that was caught in a cleft of the tree and could not free itself.

"No, I will not help you," said the man, "for you would harm me."

But the viper said that it would not hurt him, if he would only free it. Then the man put his ax into the cleft under the snake, and so freed it. But hardly was it free, when it coiled itself up, hissed, put out its tongue and prepared to strike him.

"Did I not tell you," said the man, "that you were a rascal who would reward good with evil!"

"Yes," answered the viper, "you may well say that; but so it is in the world, that all good deeds are rewarded with evil."

"That is not true," said the man, "good deeds are rewarded with good."

"You will not find anybody to agree with you there," said the viper. "I know better how it goes in the world."

"Let us inquire about it," said the man.

---

[206]Type 123B. Source: Joseph Jacobs, *The Fables of Aesop* (London, 1894), no. 39.

"Very well," said the viper. So it did not bite him, but went with him through the forest until they came to an old, worn out horse that was grazing. It was lame, and blind in one eye, and had only a few broken teeth in its mouth. They asked him whether good deeds were rewarded with good, or with evil. "They are rewarded with evil," said the horse. "For twenty years I have served my master faithfully; I have carried him on my back, and drawn his wagon, and have taken care not to stumble lest he fall. As long as I was young and strong, I had kind treatment; I had a good stall, and plenty of food, and was well curried. But now that I am old and weak, I must work in the treadmill the livelong day; I never have a roof to cover me, and all the food I have is what I get for myself. No, indeed, good deeds are rewarded only with evil."

"There now, you hear," said the viper, "Now I shall bite you."

"Oh, no! wait a moment," said the man, "there comes the fox; let us ask him for his opinion." The fox came up and stopped and looked at them, for he saw that the man was in serious trouble. Then the viper asked the fox whether good deeds were rewarded with evil or with good.

"Say 'with good,'" whispered the man, "and I will give you two fat geese."

Then the fox said, "Good deeds are rewarded with good," and as he said that he jumped on the viper and bit its neck so that it fell to the ground. But as it was dying it insisted, "No, good deeds *are* rewarded with evil; that I have experienced, I, who spared the man's life, who has now cheated me out of mine."

Now the viper was dead and the man was free. Then he said to the fox, "Come home with me and get your geese."

"No, I thank you," said the fox, "I will not go to town, for there the dogs would get me."

"Then wait here until I come with the geese," said the man. He ran home and said to his wife, "Hasten and put two fat geese into a sack, for I have promised them to the fox for his breakfast today."

The woman took a sack and put something into it; but it was not geese she put in, but two fierce dogs.

The man then ran out with the bag to the fox, and said, "Here you have your reward."

"Thank you," said the fox, "then it was not a lie after all, what I said first—that good deeds are rewarded with good." Then taking the bag on his back he ran off into the woods.

"That sack is heavy," said the fox, so he sat down and tore it open with his sharp teeth. But as he did so the two dogs leaped from the bag and fixed their teeth in his throat. There was no escape from them, so he was bitten to death, but not until he had said, "No, what I said first was a lie, after all; good deeds *are* rewarded with evil."[207]

---

[207]Type 154. Source: Sven Grundtvig, *Danish Fairy Tales*, translated by J. Grant Cramer (Boston, 1919), no. 14.

The Camel Driver and the Adder

Bidpai

A camel driver, crossing the plains, stopped to rest where a caravan had halted and built a fire the night before; in the morning they had moved on before it had died out. As the night wind arose, it fanned the sparks and soon set all the brushwood around on fire. In the midst of the brushwood lay coiled an adder, fast asleep. The flames, however, soon awoke him, but not until he was completely encircled by the fire. He was about to despair of his life, when he saw the camel driver and called upon him for aid. At first the camel driver hesitated, for he remembered the poisonous sting of the adder. Still, he could not bear to see any living creature suffer, so he promised to help the adder. He had a bag beneath his saddle. This he now drew forth and tied to the end of his spear. He then reached it over into the midst of the burning brush; the adder crawled inside, and the camel driver drew him safely out of the fire.

"Now go your way," said the camel driver, loosening the neck of the bag so that the adder could glide out. "Only remember the kindness which I have shown to you, and do you hereafter be kind to men in your turn."

"I confess," replied the adder, slipping out on the ground, "that you have been kind to me, and yet I shall not go away until I have stung both you and your camel. I only leave it to you to decide whether I shall sting you first or the camel."

"What a monster of ingratitude you are!" cried the camel driver. "Is it right to return evil for good?"

Such is the custom of men," said the adder.

"You are not only ungrateful, but untruthful as well," the camel driver made reply. "It would be hard indeed for you to prove these words of yours. There is no other creature in the world, I venture to say, who will agree with you. If you can find out one other, I will allow you to sting me."

"Very well," responded the adder; "let us put the question to yonder cow."

The cow stopped chewing her cud. "If you mean what is man's custom," she began, in answer to their question, "I must answer to my sorrow that he is wont to repay evil for good. For many years I have been the faithful servant of a farmer. Every day I have supplied him with milk to drink and rich cream for his butter. Now I am old and no longer able to serve him. So he has put me out in this pasture that I may grow fat, and only yesterday he brought the butcher to see me. Tomorrow I am to be sold for beef. Surely this is repaying my kindness with evil."

"You see," said the adder to the camel driver, "that what I said is true. Get ready for me to sting you. Shall it be you or the camel first?"

"Hold," replied the camel driver. "In court a decree is not passed without the testimony of two witnesses. Bring another witness, and if he agrees with the cow, you may do with me as you please."

The adder looked about him and saw that they were standing beneath a huge palm tree. "Let us put the question to the tree," he said.

When the palm had heard their question, he shook his great branches sadly. "Experience has taught me," he moaned, "that for every favor you do to men, you must expect some injury in return. I stand here in the desert, doing harm to none and good to many. Every traveler who comes by can rest beneath my shade. I bear dates for his refreshment, and gladly give my sap to quench his thirst. Yet when the traveler has eaten and slept beneath my shade, he looks up into my branches and says to himself, 'That branch would make me a good cane, or handle for my ax,' or 'What splendid wood there is in this tree! I must cut off a limb to make some new doors for my house.' And I must consent to this without a murmur. Thus is my kindness returned by men."

"The two witnesses have now testified," spoke the adder, "and agree. Which shall I bite first, you or the camel?"

But just at that moment a fox ran by, and the camel driver pleaded that they might hear one more testimony. The adder was so pleased with what the cow and the tree had said, that he readily agreed to listen to the fox.

When the camel driver had finished telling the whole tale to the fox, the fox laughed out loud. "You seem to be a clever fellow," he replied to the camel driver. "Why do you tell me such a falsehood?"

"Indeed, he is telling you nothing but the truth," the adder hastened to assure the fox.

Again the fox laughed outright. "Do you mean to tell me," he asked scornfully, "that such a large adder as you could possibly get into such a small bag?"

"If you do not believe it, I will crawl in again and show you," answered the adder.

"Well," responded the fox, thoughtfully, "if I see you in there with my own eyes, then I will consent to give my answer to your question."

The camel driver straightway held the bag open, and the adder crept in and coiled up in the bottom.

"Be quick now," cried the fox, "and draw the string. Any creature so lacking in gratitude as this adder deserves nothing but death."[208]

---

[208]Type 155. Source: *The Tortoise and the Geese and other Fables of Bidpai*, retold by Maude Barrows Dutton (Boston, 1908), pp. 118-125.

Of Nature and the Returns of Ingratitude

Gesta Romanorum

An emperor rode out in the afternoon to hunt. Happening to pass a certain wood, he heard a serpent, which some shepherds had caught and bound firmly to a tree, making a most horrible clamor. Moved by pity, he loosed it, and warmed its frozen body in his own bosom. No sooner, however, did the animal find itself recovered, than it began to bite its benefactor, and shot a flood of poison into the wound. "What have you done?" said the emperor. "Wherefore have you rendered evil for good?"

The serpent, like the ass of Balaam, being suddenly endowed with voice, replied, "The propensities which nature has implanted no one can destroy. You have done what you could; and I have only acted according to my nature. You exhibited towards me all the kindness in your power, and I have recompensed you as well as I might. I offered poison, because, except poison, I had nothing to offer. Moreover, I am an enemy to man; for through him I became punished with a curse."

As they thus contended, they entreated a philosopher to judge between them, and to state which was in the wrong. "I know this matter," answered the umpire, "only by your relation; but I should like to see the thing itself upon which I am to pronounce judgment. Let the serpent, therefore, be bound to the tree, as he was in the first instance, and let my lord the emperor remain unbound; I shall then determine the matter between you." This was done accordingly. "Now you are bound," said the philosopher, addressing the serpent, loose yourself if you can."

"I cannot," said the serpent; "I am bound so fast that I can scarcely move."

"Then die," rejoined the philosopher, "by a just sentence. You were always ungrateful to man, and you always will be. My lord, you are now free; shake the venom from your bosom, and go your way. Do not repeat your folly. Remember that the serpent is only influence by his natural propensities." The emperor thanked the philosopher for his assistance and advice, and departed.

> Application: My beloved, the emperor is any good ecclesiastic, the wood is the world, and the serpent is the devil. The shepherds are the prophets, patriarchs, Christian preachers, etc. The philosopher is a discreet confessor.[209]

---

[209]Type 155. Source: *Gesta Romanorum*, translated by Charles Swan (London, 1877), no. 174.

The Hedgehog and the Hare

Leo Tolstoy

The hare was belittling the hedgehog about his lack of speed and grace. "It's because of your short legs," he said. "And they are crooked as well."

The hedgehog bristled up with anger and pride. "My legs are as good as yours!" he said. And he challenged him to a race. The hare, always eager to show off his speed, accepted. The time was set for the next day; the place for a nearby field.

When the hedgehog told his wife about the race, she at first thought that he was mad. But then he explained his plan. What he lacked in strength, he would make up in wit. But his wife would have to help.

The next day hare and hedgehog put their toes against a line drawn in the dirt, and with a shout took off for the opposite side of the field. The rabbit, his eyes on the goal, ran ahead at full speed. The hedgehog, however, ducked into a burrow. His wife, who looked exactly like her prickly mate, was hidden in a burrow near the goal. As the hare approached, sure of victory, she jumped up and shouted, "I've beaten you!"

Not believing his eyes, the hare demanded that they run again, and darted off toward the starting line. This time the hedgehog wife crouched down in her burrow, and the husband greeted the hare with a jeer, "I've beaten you."

The hare demanded yet another trial, but the outcome was the same. And another trial. And another. And another. However fast he ran, a jeering hedgehog was always at the finish line when he arrived. Finally he fell exhausted to the ground. He never again belittled the hedgehog's crooked legs.[210]

The Mongoose Boy

India

Once upon a time there was a raja who had two wives. By his first wife he had six sons, but the second wife bore only one son and he was born as a mongoose. When the six sons of the elder wife grew up, they used to jeer at their mongoose brother and his mother, so the raja sent his second wife to live in

---

[210]Type 275A*. Retold from *Second Reader* (1872). This variation of the Aesop fable "The Tortoise and the Hare" is found throughout Europe (especially in Germany and England) and northern Africa. Other printed sources include the Grimms' *Kinder- und Hausmärchen*, no. 186, and Joel Chandler Harris's *Uncle Remus*, no. 18.

a separate house. The mongoose boy could talk like any man but he never grew bigger than an ordinary mongoose and his name was Lelsing.

One day the raja called all his sons to him and said that he wished, before he died, to divide his property among them. But the sons said that they had rather he did not do so then; they wished to go abroad and see the world, and if he would give each of them some capital to start with, they would go abroad and trade and even if they did not make much profit they would have the advantage of seeing the world.

So the raja gave his six sons twenty rupees each to start business with; but when Lelsing also asked for some money, his brothers jeered at him and declared that he certainly could not go with them, for he would only get eaten up by some dog. Lelsing made no answer at the time but afterwards he went to his father alone and begged again for some money. At last the raja, though he scarcely believed that Lelsing would really go out trading, gave him ten rupees.

The six brothers made everything ready and one morning set out on their travels, without saying anything to Lelsing. But Lelsing saw them start and followed after them, and as the brothers were resting in the middle of the day they looked back and saw Lelsing galloping along to overtake them. So they all traveled together for three or four days, until they came to a great jungle and camped on its outskirts. There they debated how long they should stay away from home and they decided that they would trade for six months and then go back.

The next morning they entered the jungle, and as they traveled through it, the six brothers managed to give Lelsing the slip, so that when they came out of the forest they found themselves at Nilam bazaar, but Lelsing after wandering about for some time came out at Sujan bazaar.

The six brothers bought sun-horses at Nilam bazaar, and began to trade. But Lelsing at Sujan bazaar looked about for someone who would engage him as a servant. No one would employ a mongoose, and Lelsing was in despair, for he had very little money. At last he began to inquire whether anyone would sell him a cheap horse, and learned that the horse market was at Nilam bazaar; so he went to Nilam bazaar and there found his brothers trading, but he did not make himself known to them. He tried to buy a horse but they were all too highly priced for him, so at last he had to be content with buying a donkey for three rupees and some articles to trade with.

When the six months expired, the brothers went home; and a little after them came Lelsing, leading his donkey. His brothers laughed at him, but the raja did not laugh; and Lelsing showed his father and mother what profits he had made by his trading, which his brothers declined to do. The raja was pleased with Lelsing for this and declared that, in spite of his shape, he was a man and a raja. It only made his brothers more angry with him to hear Lelsing praised.

Two or three years later there was a famine in the land. Lelsing foresaw it and he dug a large hole in the floor of his house and buried in it all the grain on which he could lay his hand. The famine grew severe, but Lelsing and his mother always had enough to eat from their private store. But his brothers were starving and their children cried from want of food. Lelsing had pity on them and sent his mother with some rice for them to eat. The raja and his sons were amazed that Lelsing should have rice to give away, and they went to his house to see how much he had; but they found the house apparently empty, for they did not know of the store buried in the ground. Puzzled and jealous, the brothers made up their minds to burn down Lelsing's house. So one night they set fire to it, and it was burnt to ashes. The store buried in the ground was however uninjured.

Lelsing put the ashes of his house into sacks and, loading them on his donkey, set out to sell them. As he found no buyers, he rested for the night under a tree by the road side. Presently a band of merchants with will loaded pack bullocks came to the place. "You must not camp here," called out Lelsing to them, "I have two sacks of gold coin here and you may take an opportunity to steal them. If you are honest men, you will go to a distance." So the merchants camped a little way off, but in the middle of the night they came and carried off Lelsing's sacks, leaving two of their own in their place, and hurried on their way. In the morning Lelsing made haste to carry home the sacks which had been changed, and when he came to open them he found them full of rice and rupees. He sent his mother to borrow a measure from his brothers with which to measure the rupees; and when he returned it, he sent it to them full of rupees.

His brothers came running to know where he had found so much money. "I got it by selling the ashes of my house," said Lelsing, "and it is a pity that I had only one house; if I had had more houses, I should have had more ashes, and should have got more money still." On hearing this the brothers at once made up their mind to burn their own houses, and take the ashes for sale. But when they did so and took the ashes for sale from village to village they were only laughed at for their pains, and in the end had to throw away the ashes and come back empty handed. They were very angry at the trick which Lelsing had played on them and decided to kill him and his mother; but when they went to the house to do the murder, Lelsing happened to be away from home and so they were only able to kill his mother.

When Lelsing came home he found his mother lying dead. He placed the body on his donkey and carried it off to burn it on the banks of the Ganges. As he went, he saw a large herd of bullocks coming along the road. He quickly propped the body of his mother against a tree which grew by the road and himself climbed into its branches, and when the bullocks came up he began to call out, "Take care, take care. You will have my sick mother trampled to death." But the drivers were too far behind to hear what he said. When they came up, he climbed down from the tree and charged them with having allowed their bullocks to kill his mother. The drivers had no wish to face a charge of murder; and in the end, to secure their release, they made over to Lelsing all their bullocks, with the merchandise which they were carrying.

Lelsing threw his mother's corpse into some bushes, and drove the laden bullocks home. Naturally his brothers wanted to know where he had got such wealth from, and he explained that it was by selling the dead body of his mother and he was sorry that he had only one to dispose of. At once his brothers went and killed all their wives, and took the corpses away to sell; but no one would buy and they had to return disappointed.

Another trick that Lelsing played on his brothers was this: He used to mix rupees in the food he gave his donkey, and these passed out in the droppings; and Lelsing took care that his brothers should know of it. They found no rupees in the dung of their horses, and consulted Lelsing as to the reason why. He told them that if they gave their horses a blow with an ax while they ate their grain, they would find rupees in the dung. The brothers did as they were advised, but the only result was that they killed all their horses.

More and more angry, the brothers resolved to kill Lelsing by guile. So they went to him and said that they had found a wife for him, and would take him to be married. When the procession was ready, Lelsing got into a palki.[211] His brothers made the doors of the palki fast and carried him off towards a deep river, into which they meant to throw him, palki and all.

When they reached the river, they put the palki down and went to look for a suitably deep pool. Lelsing found that he was outwitted, and began to weep and wail. Just then a shepherd came by, driving a flock of sheep and asked what was the matter. Lelsing cried out that they were going to marry him against his will, but that anyone who would take his place in the palki could marry his bride. The shepherd thought that this would be a great opportunity to get a wife without spending any money on the marriage, and readily changed places with Lelsing, who drove away the flock of sheep. The brothers soon came back and, picking up the palki, threw it into the river and went home, thinking that they had at last got rid of Lelsing.

But four or five days later Lelsing appeared, driving a large flock of sheep. His brothers asked him, in amazement, where he had come from. "You threw me," said Lelsing, "into a shallow pool of the river where there were only sheep, but in the deeper parts there are cattle and buffaloes as well. I can take you to fetch some of them if you like. You take your palkis to the bank of the river—for I cannot carry you all—and then shut yourselves inside and I will push you into the water." So the brothers took their palkis to the riverside and shut themselves in, and each called out "Let me have the deepest place, brother." Then Lelsing pushed them in one by one and they were all drowned. Then he went home rejoicing at the revenge which he had taken for their ill treatment of him.[212]

---

[211]An enclosed litter used to carry persons of high rank.

[212]Type 1535. Source: Cecil Henry Bompas, *Folklore of the Santal Parganas* (London, 1909), no. 67.

Big Peter and Little Peter

Norway

Once there were two brothers, both named Peter; the older one was called Big Peter, and the younger one Little Peter. When their father died, Big Peter took over the farm and found himself a wealthy wife. Little Peter, however, stayed at home with his mother, and lived from her pension until he came of age. Then he received his inheritance, and Big Peter said that he could stay in the old house no longer, living from his mother. It would be better for him to go out into the world and do something for himself.

Little Peter agreed; so he bought himself a fine horse and a load of butter and cheese, and set off to the town. With the money he got for his goods he bought brandy and other drinks, and as soon as he arrived home, he threw a great feast, inviting all of his relatives and acquaintances. They in turn invited him for drinking and merrymaking. Thus he lived in fun and frolic so long as his money lasted. But when his last farthing was spent, and Little Peter found himself sitting high and dry, he went back home again to his old mother, and there he had nothing but one calf. When spring came he turned out the calf and let it graze on Big Peter's meadow. But this made Big Peter angry, and he struck the calf, killing it. Little Peter skinned the calf, and hung the hide up in the bathroom until it was thoroughly dry; then he rolled it up, stuffed it into a sack, and went about the area trying to sell it; but wherever he went, people only laughed at him, saying that they had no need of smoked calfskin. After walking a long way, he came to a farm, where he asked for a night's lodging.

"No," said the old woman of the house, "I can't give you lodging, for my husband is at the hut in the upper pasture, and I'm alone in the house. You will have to ask for shelter at the next farm; but if they won't take you in, you may come back, because you can't spend the night out of doors."

As Peter passed by the living-room window, he saw that there was a priest in there, whom the woman was entertaining. She was serving him ale and brandy, and a large bowl of custard. But just as the priest had sat down to eat and drink, the husband came back home. The woman heard him in the hallway, and she was not slow; she put the bowl of custard under the fireplace mantel, the ale and brandy into the cellar, and as for the priest, she locked him inside a large chest that was there. Little Peter was standing outside the whole time and saw everything. As soon as the husband had entered, Little Peter went to the door and asked if he might have a night's lodging.

"Yes," said the man, "you can stay here," and he asked Little Peter to sit down at the table and eat. Little Peter sat down, taking his calfskin with him, which he laid under his feet.

When they had sat a while, Little Peter began to step on the skin.

"What are you saying now? Can't you be quiet?" said Little Peter.

"Who are you talking to?" asked the man.

"Oh," answered Little Peter, "it's only the fortuneteller that I have here in my calfskin."

"And what does she foretell?" asked the man.

"Why, she says that there is a bowl of custard under the fireplace mantel," said Little Peter.

"Her prediction is wrong," answered the man. "We haven't had custard in this house for a year and a day."

But Peter asked him to take a look; he did so and found the custard. So they proceeded to enjoy it, but just as they were eating, Peter stepped on the calfskin again.

"Hush!" he said, "can't you hold your mouth?"

"What is the fortuneteller saying now?" asked the man.

"Oh, she says there is probably some ale and brandy just under the cellar door," answered Peter.

"Well, if she never predicted wrong in her life, she's predicting wrong now," said the man. "Ale and brandy! We have never had such things in the house!"

"Just take a look," said Peter. The man did so, and there, sure enough, he found the drinks, and was very pleased indeed.

"How much did you pay for that fortuneteller?" said the man, "for I must have her, whatever you ask for her."

"I inherited her from my father, and never thought that she was worth much," answered Peter. "Of course, I am not eager to part with her, but you may have her nonetheless, if you'll give me that old chest in the living room."

"The chest is locked and the key is lost," cried the old woman.

"Then I'll take it without the key," said Peter, and he and the man quickly struck the bargain.

Peter got a rope instead of the key. The man helped him load the chest onto his back, and off he stumbled with it. After he had walked a while, he came to a bridge. Beneath the bridge ran a raging stream, foaming, gurgling, and roaring until the bridge shook.

"That brandy, that brandy!" said Peter. Now I can tell that I've had too much. Why should I be dragging this chest about? If I hadn't been drunk and crazy, I would not have traded my fortuneteller for it. But now this chest is going into the river, and quickly!"

And with that he began to untie the rope.

"Au! Au! For God's sake save me. It is the priest that you have in the chest," screamed someone from inside.

"That must be the devil himself," said Peter, "and he wants to make me believe he has become a priest; but whether he claims to be a priest or a sexton, into the river he goes!"

"Oh, no! Oh no! I am in truth the parish priest. I was visiting the woman for her soul's health, but her husband is rough and wild, so she had to hide me in the chest. I have a silver watch and a gold watch with me. You can have them both, and eight hundred dollars beside, if you will only let me out," cried the priest.

"Oh, no!" said Peter. "Is it really your reverence after all?" With that he picked up a stone, and knocked the lid of the chest into pieces. The priest got out and ran home to his parsonage quickly and lightly, for he no longer had his watches and money to weigh him down.

Then Little Peter went home and said to Big Peter, "Today at the market there was a good price for calfskins."

"What did you get for your shabby one?" asked Big Peter.

"Shabby as it was, I got eight hundred dollars for it, but those from larger and fatter calves were bringing twice as much," said Little Peter, and showed his money.

"It is good that you told me this," answered Big Peter. He then slaughtered all his cows and calves, and set off to town with their skins and hides. When he arrived at the market, and the tanners asked what he wanted for his hides, Big Peter said "eight hundred dollars for the small ones, and more for the big ones." But they all laughed at him and made fun of him, and said he should not have come there, that he could get a better bargain at the madhouse. Thus he soon found out that Little Peter had tricked him.

But when he got home again he was not very gentle; he swore and cursed, threatening to strike Little Peter dead that very night. Little Peter stood and listened to all this. After he had gone to bed with his mother, and the night had worn on a little, he asked her to change sides with him, saying that he was cold and that it would be warmer next to the wall. Yes, she did that, and a little later Big Peter came with an ax in his hand, crept up to the bedside, and with one blow chopped off his mother's head.

The next morning, Little Peter went into Big Peter's room.

"Heaven help you," he said. "You have chopped our mother's head off. The sheriff will not be pleased to hear that you are paying mother's pension in this way."

Then Big Peter became terribly frightened, and he begged Little Peter, for God's sake, to say nothing about what he knew. If he would only keep still, he should have eight hundred dollars.

Well, Little Peter swept up the money; set his mother's head on her body again; put her on a sled, and pulled her to market. There he set her up with an apple basket on each arm, and an apple in each hand. By and by a skipper came walking along; he thought she was a market woman, and asked if she had apples to sell, and how many he might have for a penny. But the old woman did not answer. So the skipper asked again. No! She said nothing.

"How many may I have for a penny?" he cried the third time, but the old woman sat there, as though she neither saw nor heard him. Then the skipper flew into a rage and slapped her, causing her head to roll across the marketplace. At that moment, Little Peter came running. Weeping and wailing, and threatened to make trouble for the skipper, for having killed his old mother.

"Dear friend, keep still about what you know," said the skipper, "and I'll give you eight hundred dollars," and thus they made a deal.

When Little Peter got home again, he said to Big Peter, "Old women were bringing a good price at the market today; I got eight hundred dollars for our mother," and he showed him the money.

"It is good that I came to know this," said Big Peter. He had an old mother-in-law, and he killed her, and then set forth to sell her. But when people heard how he was trying to sell dead bodies, they wanted to hand him over to the sheriff, and it was all he could do to escape.

When Big Peter arrived home again, he was so angry with Little Peter, that he threatened to strike him dead there and then, without mercy.

"Yes, indeed" said Little Peter, "we must all go this way, and between today and tomorrow there is only the night. But if I must set off now, I've only one thing to ask; put me into that sack that's hanging over there, and carry me to the river."

Big Peter had nothing against that; he stuffed him into the sack, and set off. But he hadn't gone far before it came into his mind that he had forgotten something which he had to go back and fetch; meanwhile, he set the sack down by the side of the road. Just then came a man driving a big flock of fine sheep,

> To the Kingdom of Heaven, to Paradise.
> To the Kingdom of Heaven, to Paradise!

cried out Little Peter from inside the sack, and he kept mumbling and muttering the same words over and over.

"May I not go with you?" asked the man with the sheep.

"Of course you may," said Little Peter. "Just untie the sack, and trade places with me, and you'll get there enough. I can wait until next time. But you must keep on calling out what I was saying, or you'll not go to the right place."

Then the man untied the sack, and took Little Peter's place. Peter tied the sack up again, and the man began to cry out,

> To the Kingdom of Heaven, to Paradise.
> To the Kingdom of Heaven, to Paradise!

and repeated the saying over and over again.

After Peter got him positioned in the sack, he wasn't slow; off he went with the flock of sheep, making a broad turn. Meantime, Big Peter, returned, took the sack on his shoulders, and carried it to the river, and all the while he went, the shepherd sat inside crying:

> To the Kingdom of Heaven, to Paradise!

"Yes, indeed! Now try now to find the way for yourself," said Big Peter, and with that he tossed him out into the stream.

When Big Peter had done that, and was going back home, he met his brother, who was driving the flock of sheep before him. Big Peter could hardly believe his eyes, and asked how Little Peter had gotten out of the river, and where he had found the fine flock of sheep.

"That was an act of brotherly love that you did for me when you threw me into the river," answered Little Peter. I sank right down to the bottom like a stone, and there I saw flocks of sheep, believe me. Down there they go about by the thousands; each flock is finer than the others. And just see what splendid wool they have!"

That is good of you to tell me that, said Big Peter. Then he ran home to his wife; made her come with him to the river; crept into a sack, and asked her to quickly tie it up, and throw him over the bridge.

"I'm going after a flock of sheep," he said. "If I stay too long, it's because I can't manage the flock by myself; then you'll have to jump in and help me."

"Well, don't stay too long," said his wife, "for I am looking forward to those sheep."

She stood there and waited a while, but then she thought that her husband couldn't gather the flock together, and so she jumped in after him.

Now Little Peter was rid of them all, and he inherited their farm and fields, and horses and tools too; and besides, he had money enough to buy cattle as well.[213]

The Countryman and the Merchant

Georgia

A countryman caught a pheasant, and was carrying it home to cook it for himself and his wife. Suddenly the pheasant spoke like a man, and said, "Let me go, my good man, and I shall repay you."

The countryman was astonished, and asked, "What could you do for me?"

The pheasant replied, "You are an old man, and must soon die; when you are dead, I shall gather together all the birds of the air, and follow you to the grave. Since the world began, no king ever had such an honor paid to him at his funeral."

The countryman was pleased at the offer, and set the pheasant free. When he reached home, he told his wife what had happened, and, although she scolded him at first for letting the bird go, yet she was pleased when the pheasant sent, every morning, birds to ask after the old man's health.

A happy thought soon occurred to the wife, and she said to her husband, "Listen to me, we are almost dying of hunger, and we have a good chance of getting plenty of food. Pretend that you are dead; I shall begin to cry, and all the birds will come to your funeral. I shall entice them into our cottage, shut the doors and windows.

---

[213]Type 1535. Source: Peter Christen Asbjørnsen and Jørgen Moe, *Norske Folkeeventyr* (Christiania [Oslo], 1842-1852), translated by George Webb Dasent (1859). Revised. This classical trickster story, known generically as "Unibos" (One-Ox), is told around the world. It was especially popular among the writers of renaissance jest books.

We can knock them down with sticks, and thus lay in a store of food to last us for a long time."

So the countryman covered himself with a sheet, and lay down, while his wife went outside and wept loudly.

A hoopoe flew down, and asked after her husband's health. When the wife announced his death, the hoopoe at once flew away, and, within an hour, there flew into the yard, in long lines, some thousands of pheasants, the same number of doves, snipe, quails, woodcocks, etc., and even eagle kites, hawks, etc.

Some of the birds settled in the cottage, some in the barn, some in the stable, some in the yard, and the rest, for which there was no room remained in serried ranks in the air.

Then the wife shut the doors, and, with her husband, set about killing the birds; only those that were outside escaped.

In the evening there came a merchant, and asked to be allowed to spend the night in the cottage. At supper, the merchant saw a great abundance of game of all kinds, and asked the countryman how such luxury was within the reach of a poor man. The countryman replied, "I have a cat of a famous breed, which has never yet failed me. When I want game for my table, I tell her what kind of birds I should like, and how many, and she goes into the forest and gets them. I do not know what was the matter with her last night, but see! she went into the wood of her own will, and killed all the birds in the neighborhood, and brought them to us." The countryman then showed a whole heap of dead game.

The merchant at once began to bargain with the countryman for the cat, and finally purchased it for a large sum.

When the merchant reached home, he went about his business, and told his wife that he would not leave her any money for housekeeping, for she had only to give her orders, and the cat would bring all sorts of game for food. But when he came in, he was astonished to find that his wife had eaten nothing. The cat had brought no birds, but had even stolen what was in the house already. So he went back to ask the countryman about it.

The countryman saw him coming, filled a pot with millet, and hung it over the fire. He then sat down near it, put a grain of millet in the palm of his hand, and began to wash it. The merchant came in and stood by him; the countryman pretended not to see the merchant, muttered an incantation, and dropped the grain into the pot. Then he stirred it with a spoon, and behold the pot was full. The merchant did not know whether to quarrel with the countryman or to get this magic pot from him.

"What is this you have done to me?" said he. "Your cat is useless. It brings nothing, and steals what we have."

"Have you been feeding it with roast meat? I forgot to warn you that you must not do this."

"Well, it is my fault then," said the merchant. "But will you sell me that pot?"

"I have already lost my famous cat. It is not likely that I shall now let you have this pot, in which I can make a dish of porridge with only one grain."

However, they began bargaining, and at last the countryman sold his pot for a large sum. When the merchant reached home, he consoled his wife by telling her that from one barleycorn she could now make as much porridge as she wanted. He then set out again. When he returned, his wife complained that the pot was of no use. So he called again on the countryman, to ask for an explanation.

The countryman, foreseeing that the merchant would come, got two hares exactly alike, and tied ribbons of the same color around their necks. He left one hare at home, and took the other out into the fields with him. He told his wife that if the merchant came, she was to send him out to the field, and in an hour bring him a dinner consisting of two boiled fowls, a roast turkey, ten eggs, wine, and bread.

The merchant came, and the woman sent him to the field where her husband was working. In reply to the reproaches of the merchant, the countryman said, "You have probably made the same stupid mistake with the pot as you did with the cat. But let us sit down and dine while we talk it over, for I cannot allow you to come to me without feeding you."

The merchant looked around and said, "How can we get anything to eat out here in the fields?"

The peasant went to a bush, untied the hare, and said to it, "Run at once, little hare, to my wife, and tell her to come with you and bring us a pair of fowls, a roast turkey, ten eggs, wine, and bread."

The hare ran off as fast as it could. It is easy to understand the astonishment of the merchant when the woman came with the hare, bringing all that the man had ordered. When they had eaten, the merchant said, "You have cheated me about the cat and the pot, but I forgive you if you let me have the hare." The countryman refused at first, but finally agreed to sell the hare for a large sum.

On his way home with the hare, the merchant met some friends whom he asked to sup with him, but seeing that he would not arrive until it was late, he ordered the hare to run and tell his wife that he was coming with some guests, and that she was to prepare supper. When he and his friends reached home, they found the house quite dark, and had difficulty in rousing the wife from her sleep. She told him that no hare had been there, and that she did not know what he was talking about.

The merchant was now furious, and determined to punish the countryman severely. But the countryman guessed what would happen, and arranged with his wife what should be done. He took the intestine of a small calf, filled it with blood, and tied it around his wife's neck, telling her to cover it up with a kerchief. The merchant came in, and without saying a word rushed at the countryman, who, in his turn, attacked his wife, accusing her of being the guilty party, and with a knife pierced the intestine under her throat. She fell on the ground, and pretended that she was dying.

The merchant was alarmed, and cried, "What have you done, you wretched man? I would willingly have lost the money rather than have this innocent blood shed."

The countryman answered, "That is my affair. Though I have killed my wife, I can raise her to life again."

"I believe you no longer," said the merchant, "but if you perform this miracle I shall forgive you all."

343

The countryman approached his wife with the knife in his hand, muttered something, and his wife opened her eyes, and, to the surprise of the merchant, rose up.

The merchant bought the wonderful knife, saying that his wife, too, needed a lesson sometimes. When the merchant reached home, his wife asked where he had been. He told her to be silent and mind her own business. "If you are not quiet I will cut your throat." The woman looked at him with astonishment, and wondered whether he had gone out of his mind. The merchant threw down his wife, and cut her throat. All the neighbors flocked in, and raised a great cry. The merchant said, "What if I have killed my wife? I can bring her to life again." The neighbors stood by while he muttered the invocations he had learned, but he could not raise her.

Then he flew to the countryman, tied his hands, and dragged him into the forest, saying, "I wish to prolong your sufferings, and will not kill you at once. I shall starve you, drag you about in the woods, and, when I have worn you out with tortures, I shall throw you into the sea."

On the road there was a town, in which a king had just died, and his funeral was then taking place. Having bound the countryman to a tree in the depths of the forest, the merchant returned to the town to see the royal funeral. Just then, a shepherd happened to drive his flock near the tree to which the countryman was tied. Seeing the shepherd a little way off, the countryman began to shout "I will not be king! I will not be king! No! No! No!" The shepherd came up and asked what was wrong. The countryman replied, "You know, brother, that the king is dead in town. They want me to take his place, but I will not, for I have been king twice, and know what it is. Ah, brother! one has so many cares, so much work, that one's head swims. I had rather be tied to this tree than consent to be king."

The shepherd thought for a moment, and replied, "I, brother, would give anything in the world to have a trial of the life of a king."

"I gladly give you my place, but, so that people may not know, put on my clothes, and I shall bind you to the tree, and by tomorrow you shall be king." The shepherd gladly gave him his flock, and took his place at the tree.

As soon as the countryman was free, he drove away the flock. When it was quite dark, the merchant appeared, loosed his victim, and drove him on. When they came to the steep seashore, the shepherd saw that the merchant wished to drown him, and cried, "Do not drown me! I would rather consent to be king." The merchant thought his prisoner had lost his wits through fatigue and ill treatment. Without more ado he threw him into the sea.

A fortnight later, the merchant was traveling on business, when he met on the road the same countryman whom he, as he thought, had drowned, and who was now driving a flock. "What do I see!" cried the merchant. "Are you there? Did I not drown you in the sea?"

"My benefactor!" replied the countryman. "I wish you would drown me again. You cannot imagine what a quantity of cattle there is down there at the bottom of the sea. It is a pity I had no stick with me, for I could not drive out more than these with my hands."

The merchant besought the countryman, saying, "You have ruined me. The cat, the pot, the hare, the knife, have all cost money. Thanks to you, I am a beggar and

344

a widower. If you remember the place where I threw you into the sea, drown me there, but let me have a stick, so that I may repair my fortune."

To get rid of the troublesome merchant, the countryman agreed to fulfill his request, and so drowned him with a very long switch in his hand."[214]

Miracle upon Miracle

The Panchatantra

In a certain place there once lived a merchant by the name of Nanduka, which means "cheerful one" and a merchant by the name of Lakschmana, which means "fortunate one." The latter, who had lost all his wealth, decided to travel abroad. For it is said:

> A person who has lived well in a particular place, but who stays there after he has lost his wealth, is of common mind.

And further:

> A person who, reduced to misery, remains at a place where he once was happy, is worthy of reproach.

In his house there was a large set of heavy iron scales that had been acquired by his ancestors. He gave these to the guild-master Nanduka for safekeeping, and set forth for foreign lands. After he had pursued his desires for a long time abroad, he returned to his homeland, and said to the guild-master Nanduka, "Guild-master, give me back the scales that I left here for safekeeping."

Nanduka replied, "Oh, your scales are no longer here. The mice ate them up."

When he heard this, Lakschmana said, "Well, Nanduka, if the mice ate them up, then it is through no fault of yours. That is the way of the world. Nothing in it is eternal. But now I would like to bathe myself in the river. Send your child with me, the boy named Dhanadeva, to carry my bathing things."

Nanduka, fearing Lakschama because of the theft he had committed against him, said to his son, "Child, your uncle Lakschmana wants to take a bath in the river. Go with him and carry his bathing things." Yes, with truth they say:

> No one does a favor for another, unless driven by fear, greed, or some other purpose.

And further:

> If someone shows you unusual courtesy, be cautious, lest it lead to a bad end.

---

[214]Type 1539. Source: Marjory Wardrop, *Georgian Folk Tales* (London, 1894), pp. 153-159.

345

Nanduka's son, carrying the bathing things, set forth happily with Lakschmana. After taking his bath, Lakschmana threw Nanduka's son Dhanadeva into a cave on the bank of the river, and sealed the opening with a large stone. Then he rushed back to Nanduka's house. The merchant asked him, "Speak up, Lakschmana! Tell me, where is my child who went to the river with you?"

Lakschmana said, "He was taken away from the river's bank by a falcon."

The merchant cried, "You liar! How in the world can a falcon steal a boy? Give me back my son, or I will bring action against you at the king's court."

Lakschmana said, "Oh, you who always speak the truth! A falcon can carry away a boy, if mice can eat a large set of heavy iron scales. If you want your son back, then give me my scales!"

Thus quarreling one with another, they went to the king's gate, where Nanduka cried out loudly, "A dastardly crime has happened here! This thief has robbed me of my child!"

Hearing this, the judges said to Lakschmana, "Return the guild-master's son to him!"

Lakschmana answered, "What can I do? Before my very eyes a falcon carried him away from the bank of the river."

Hearing this, they said, "You do not tell the truth. How could a falcon be capable of carrying off a fifteen-year-old boy?"

Lakschmana answered, laughing, "Ha! Listen to this proverb:

> When mice can eat a thousand pounds of iron, then a falcon can carry away an elephant, to say nothing of a little boy."

The judges said, "What do you mean by that?"

Then Lakschmana told the whole story about the scales. After hearing this, they laughed at what Nanduka and Lakschmana had done, reconciled the two with each other, and made them respectively return the scales and the boy.[215]

The Merchant and His Iron

Bidpai

A merchant, who was about to set out on a journey, went to the house of a friend, taking with him two hundred tons of iron. "I beg of you," he said to his friend, "that you will kindly keep this iron for me. I am about to set out

---

[215]Type 1592. Source: *Pantschatantra: Fünf Bücher indischer Fabeln, Märchen und Erzählungen*, translated from the Sanskrit into German by Theodor Benfey (Leipzig, 1859), v. 2, book 1, story 21.

on a long journey, and it may be that ill luck will befall me. If so, then I can return home and sell this iron for a large price."

The friend took the iron, and even as the merchant feared, it came to pass. Misfortune overtook him on the way, and he was obliged to return home.

Straightway he went to the house of his friend and demanded the iron. In the meantime the friend had sold the iron to pay his own debts, for he believed that the merchant would never return home. However, he put on a bold face and replied, "Truly, friend, I have sad news for you. I locked the iron in a room, thinking that it was as safe there as is my own gold. But, unknown to me, there was a rat hole in the wall, and the rats have stolen into the room and eaten all of the iron."

The merchant, pretending that he believed this untruth, answered promptly, "That is, indeed, sad news for me, for the iron was all that I had left. Still, I know of old that rats delight in chewing upon iron bars. I have lost much iron in this same way before, so I shall know how to bear my present ill luck."

This answer was very pleasing to the friend, who now was sure that the merchant believed that the rats had eaten his iron. To avoid any further suspicion, he invited the merchant to dine with him on the morrow. The merchant accepted and went his way. As he was passing through the city, he met one of his friend's sons, whom he quietly took home and locked up in a room.

The next day he went to his friend's to dine. His friend came to the door with tears streaming down his face. "You must pardon me my distress," he said to the merchant, "but yesterday one of my children disappeared, and nothing has been heard of him since. The town crier has been through the streets, but no trace of the child is to be found."

"I am, indeed, sorry to hear this news," replied the merchant, "for last evening I saw a sparrow hawk flying over the city with a child in its claws. The child certainly looked very much like one of your children."

"You senseless fellow," retorted the friend, "why do you mock me in my trouble! How could a sparrow hawk carry off a child weighing fifty pounds?"

"Ah," replied the merchant, "you must not be surprised that a sparrow hawk should carry off a child of fifty pounds in our city where rats eat up two hundred tons of iron. My friend, give me back my iron, and I will gladly restore your boy."[216]

---

[216]Type 1592. Source: *The Tortoise and the Geese and other Fables of Bidpai*, retold by Maude Barrows Dutton (Boston, 1908), pp. 69-72.

Crab

Italy

There was once a king who had lost a valuable ring. He looked for it everywhere, but could not find it. So he issued a proclamation that if any astrologer could tell him where it was he would be richly rewarded.

A poor peasant by the name of Crab heard of the proclamation. He could neither read nor write, but took it into his head that he wanted to be the astrologer to find the king's ring. So he went and presented himself to the king, to whom he said, "Your majesty must know that I am an astrologer, although you see me so poorly dressed. I know that you have lost a ring and I will try by study to find out where it is."

"Very well," said the king, "and when you have found it, what reward must I give you?"

"That is at your discretion, your majesty."

"Go, then, study, and we shall see what kind of an astrologer you turn out to be."

He was conducted to a room, in which he was to be shut up to study. It contained only a bed and a table on which were a large book and writing materials. Crab seated himself at the table and did nothing but turn over the leaves of the book and scribble the paper so that the servants who brought him his food thought him a great man. They were the ones who had stolen the ring, and from the severe glances that the peasant cast at them whenever they entered, they began to fear that they would be found out. They made him endless bows and never opened their mouths without calling him "Mr. Astrologer."

Crab, who, although illiterate, was, as a peasant, cunning, all at once imagined that the servants must know about the ring, and this is the way his suspicions were confirmed. He had been shut up in his room turning over his big book and scribbling his paper for a month, when his wife came to visit him. He said to her, "Hide yourself under the bed, and when a servant enters, say, "That is one." When another comes, say, "That is two," and so on.

The woman hid herself. The servants came with the dinner, and hardly had the first on entered when a voice from under the bed said, "That is one." The second one entered; the voice said, "That is two," and so on.

The servants were frightened at hearing that voice, for they did not know where it came from, and held a consultation. One of them said, "We are discovered. If the astrologer denounces us to the king as thieves, we are lost."

"Do you know what we must do?" said another.

"Let us hear."

"We must go to the astrologer and tell him frankly that we stole the ring, and ask him not to betray us, and present him with a purse of money. Are you willing?"

"Perfectly."

So they went in harmony to the astrologer, and making him a lower bow than usual, one of them began, "Mr. Astrologer, you have discovered that we stole the ring. We are poor people and if you reveal it to the king, we are undone. So we beg you not to betray us, and accept this purse of money."

Crab took the purse and then added, "I will not betray you, but you must do what I tell you, if you wish to save your lives. Take the ring and make that turkey in the courtyard swallow it, and leave the rest to me."

The servants were satisfied to do so and departed with a low bow. The next day Crab went to the king and said to him, "Your majesty must know that after having toiled over a month I have succeeded in discovering where the ring has gone to."

"Where is it, then?" asked the king.

"A turkey has swallowed it."

"A turkey? Very well, let us see."

They went for the turkey, opened it, and found the ring inside. The king, amazed, presented the astrologer with a large purse of money and invited him to a banquet. Among the other dishes, there was brought on the table a plate of crabs. Crabs must then have been very rare, because only the king and a few others knew their name. Turning to the peasant the king said, "You, who are an astrologer, must be able to tell me the name of these things which are in this dish."

The poor astrologer was very much puzzled, and, as if speaking to himself, but in such a way that the others heard him, he muttered, "Ah! Crab, Crab, what a plight you are in!" All who did not know that his name was Crab rose and proclaimed him the greatest astrologer in the world.[217]

Harisarman

India

There was a certain Brahman in a certain village, named Harisarman. He was poor and foolish and in evil case for want of employment, and he had very many children, that he might reap the fruit of his misdeeds in a former life. He wandered about begging with his family, and at last he reached a certain city, and entered the service of a rich householder called Sthuladatta. His sons became keepers of Sthuladatta's cows and other property, and his wife a servant to him, and he himself lived near his house, performing the duty of an attendant. One day there was a feast on account of the marriage of the daughter of Sthuladatta, largely attended by many friends of the bridegroom, and merrymakers. Harisarman hoped that he would be able to fill himself up to the throat with ghee and flesh and other

---

[217]Type 1641. Source: Thomas Frederick Crane, *Italian Popular Tales* (Boston and New York, 1885), no. 109.

dainties, and get the same for his family, in the house of his patron. While he was anxiously expecting to be fed, no one thought of him.

Then he was distressed at getting nothing to eat, and he said to his wife at night, "It is owing to my poverty and stupidity that I am treated with such disrespect here; so I will pretend by means of an artifice to possess a knowledge of magic, so that I may become an object of respect to this Sthuladatta; so, when you get an opportunity, tell him that I possess magical knowledge." He said this to her, and after turning the matter over in his mind, while people were asleep he took away from the house of Sthuladatta a horse on which his master's son-in-law rode. He placed it in concealment at some distance, and in the morning the friends of the bridegroom could not find the horse, though they searched in every direction. Then, while Sthuladatta was distressed at the evil omen, and searching for the thieves who had carried off the horse, the wife of Harisarman came and said to him, "My husband is a wise man, skilled in astrology and magical sciences; he can get the horse back for you; why do you not ask him?"

When Sthuladatta heard that, he called Harisarman, who said, "Yesterday I was forgotten, but today, now the horse is stolen, I am called to mind," and Sthuladatta then propitiated the Brahman with these words, "I forgot you, forgive me," and asked him to tell him who had taken away their horse. Then Harisarman drew all kinds of pretended diagrams, and said, "The horse has been placed by thieves on the boundary line south from this place. It is concealed there, and before it is carried off to a distance, as it will be at close of day, go quickly and bring it." When they heard that, many men ran and brought the horse quickly, praising the discernment of Harisarman. Then Harisarman was honored by all men as a sage, and dwelt there in happiness, honored by Sthuladatta.

Now, as days went on, much treasure, both of gold and jewels, had been stolen by a thief from the palace of the king. As the thief was not known, the king quickly summoned Harisarman on account of his reputation for knowledge of magic. And he, when summoned, tried to gain time, and said, "I will tell you tomorrow," and then he was placed in a chamber by the king, and carefully guarded. And he was sad because he had pretended to have knowledge. Now in that palace there was a maid named Jihva (which means tongue), who, with the assistance of her brother, had stolen that treasure from the interior of the palace. She, being alarmed at Harisarman's knowledge, went at night and applied her ear to the door of that chamber in order to find out what he was about. And Harisarman, who was alone inside, was at that very moment blaming his own tongue, that had made a vain assumption of knowledge. He said, "Oh tongue, what is this that you have done through your greediness? Wicked one, you will soon receive punishment in full." When Jihva heard this, she thought, in her terror, that she had been discovered by this wise man, and she managed to get in where he was, and falling at his feet, she said to the supposed wizard, "Brahman, here I am, that Jihva whom you have discovered to be the thief of the treasure, and after I took it I buried it in the earth in a garden behind the palace, under a pomegranate tree. So spare me, and receive the small quantity of gold which is in my possession."

When Harisarman heard that, he said to her proudly, "Depart, I know all this; I know the past, present and future; but I will not denounce you, being a miserable creature that has implored my protection. But whatever gold is in your possession you must give back to me." When he said this to the maid, she consented, and departed quickly. But Harisarman reflected in his astonishment, "Fate brings about, as if in sport, things impossible, for when calamity was so near, who would have thought chance would have brought us success? While I was blaming my jihva, the thief Jihva suddenly flung herself at my feet. Secret crimes manifest themselves by means of fear." Thus thinking, he passed the night happily in the chamber. And in the morning he brought the king, by some skillful parade of pretended knowledge into the garden, and led him up to the treasure, which was buried under the pomegranate tree, and said that the thief had escaped with a part of it. Then the king was pleased, and gave him the revenue of many villages.

But the minister, named Devajnanin, whispered in the king's ear, "How can a man possess such knowledge unattainable by men, without having studied the books of magic; you may be certain that this is a specimen of the way he makes a dishonest livelihood, by having a secret intelligence with thieves. It will be much better to test him by some new artifice."

Then the king of his own accord brought a covered pitcher into which he had thrown a frog, and said to Harisarman, "Brahman, if you can guess what there is in this pitcher, I will do you great honor today." When the Brahman Harisarman heard that, he thought that his last hour had come, and he called to mind the pet name of "Froggie" which his father had given him in his childhood in sport, and, impelled by luck, he called to himself by his pet name, lamenting his hard fate, and suddenly called out, "This is a fine pitcher for you, Froggie; it will soon become the swift destroyer of your helpless self." The people there, when they heard him say that, raised a shout of applause, because his speech chimed in so well with the object presented to him, and murmured, "Ah! a great sage, he knows even about the frog!" Then the king, thinking that this was all due to knowledge of divination, was highly delighted, and gave Harisarman the revenue of more villages, with gold, an umbrella, and state carriages of all kinds. So Harisarman prospered in the world.[218]

---

[218]Type 1641. Source: Jacobs, *Indian Fairy* Tales (London, 1892), no. 11. Jacobs' source: Somadeva, *Katha-Sarit-Sagara* (Calcutta, 1880).

Fools

Ethnic Fools

The Seven Wise Men of Buneyr

India

Seven men of Buneyr once left their native wilds for the purpose of seeking their fortunes. When evening came they all sat down under a tree to rest, when one of them said, "Let us count to see if we are all here." So he counted, "One, two, three, four, five, six," but, quite omitting to reckon himself, he exclaimed, "There's one of us missing, we are only six!"

"Nonsense!" cried the others, and the whole company of seven began counting with uplifted forefingers, but they all forgot to count themselves.

Fearing some evil, they now rose up, and at once set out to search for their missing comrade. Presently they met a shepherd, who greeted them civilly and said, "Friends, why are you in such low spirits?"

"We have lost one of our party," answered they; "we started this morning seven in number, and now we are only six. Have you seen any one of us hereabouts?"

"But," said the shepherd, "seven you are, for I have found your lost companion; behold: one, two, three, four, five, six, *seven!*"

"Ah," answered the wise men of Buneyr, "you have indeed found our missing brother." We owe you a debt of gratitude. Because you have done us this service, we insist on doing a month's free labor for you."

So the shepherd, overjoyed with his good fortune, took the men home with him.

Now, the shepherd's mother was a very old woman, in her dotage, utterly feeble and unable to help herself. When the morning came he placed her under the care of one of the Buneyris, saying to him, "You will stay here and take care of my old mother."

To another Buneyri he said, "You take out my goats, graze them on the hills by day, and watch over them by night."

To the other five he said, "As for you, I shall have work for you tomorrow."

The man who was left in charge of the old crippled mother found that his time was fully occupied in the constant endeavor to drive off the innumerable flies which

352

in that hot season kept her in a state of continual excitement and irritation. When, however, he saw that all his efforts were fruitless, and that he flapped the wretches away in vain, he became desperate, and, lifting up a large stone, he aimed it deliberately at a certain fly which had settled on the woman's face. Hurling it with all his might, he of course missed the fly, but, alas! he knocked the woman prone on her back. When the shepherd saw this he wrung his hands in despair. "Ah," cried he, "what has your stupidity done for me? The fly has escaped, but as for my poor old mother, you have killed her dead."

Meanwhile, the second Buneyri led his flock of goats up and down among the hills, and when midday came he rested to eat his bread, while many of the assembled goats lay down beside him. As he was eating he began to observe how the goats were chewing the cud and occasionally looking at him So he foolishly imagined that they were mocking him, and waxed wroth. "So," cried he, "because I am taking my food, you must needs crowd round and make game of me, must you?" And, seizing his hatchet, he made a sudden rush at the poor animals, and he had already struck off the heads of several of them, when the shepherd came running to the spot, bemoaning his bad luck and crying to the fellow to desist from slaughter.

That night was a sorrowful one for the trustful shepherd, and bitterly he repented his rashness. In the morning the remaining five wise men of Buneyr came to him, and said, "It is now our turn. Give us some work to do, too!"

"No, no, my friends," answered he; "you have amply repaid me for the trifling favor I did for you in finding your missing companion; and now, for God's sake, go your way and let me see you no more."

Hearing these words, the wise men of Buneyr resumed their journey.[219]

The Baneyrwal and the Thief

India

Once upon a time a little Baneyrwal, holding his two fingers to his mouth, happened to look into a tub, and there perceived his own image reflected in the water. "Mother, mother," cried he, "there is a child in this tub begging for bread."

"Listen to that now," said the mother to her husband. "Look into the tub, man, and see if there is anyone there."

---

[219]Types 1287, 1586. Source: Charles Swynnerton, *Indian Nights' Entertainment; or, Folk-Tales from the Upper Indus* (London, 1892), no. 74.

So the husband looked in and at once exclaimed, "Wife, wife, there is no child, but I see an old villain of a thief, and when we are all asleep he will certainly jump out and murder us in our beds!"

Picking up a stone in the utmost alarm, the man hurled it into the tub, intending to strike the robber dead. Then he cautiously approached the tub once more, but failing to see anything but the tossing water, he said to his wife, "That thief must have been a very cunning rascal. He has escaped I don't know where, but he is not likely to trouble *this* house again."[220]

The Baneyr Man and the Mill

India

A Baneyrwal came down to the Indus, where he saw a water mill at work. Said he to himself, "People say that God is known by His wonderful ways. Now, here is a wonderful thing with wonderful ways, though it has neither hands nor feet. It must be God." So he went forward and kissed the walls, but he merely cut his face with the sharp stones.[221]

The Twelve Men of Gotham

England

On a certain day there were twelve men of Gotham that went to fish, and some stood on dry land; and in going home one said to the other, "We have ventured wonderfully in wading. I pray God that none of us come home and be drowned."

"Nay, marry," said one to the other, "let us see that; for there did twelve of us come out." Then they counted themselves, and every one counted eleven.

---

[220]Type 1336A. Source: Charles Swynnerton, *Indian Nights' Entertainment; or, Folk-Tales from the Upper Indus* (London, 1892), no. 2.

[221]Type 1319A* (variant). Source: Charles Swynnerton, *Indian Nights' Entertainment; or, Folk-Tales from the Upper Indus* (London, 1892), no. 10.

Said one to the other, "There is one of us drowned." They went back to the brook where they had been fishing, and sought up and down for him that was wanting, making great lamentation. A courtier, coming by, asked what it was they sought for, and why they were sorrowful.

"Oh," said they, "this day we went to fish in the brook; twelve of us came out together, and one is drowned."

Said the courtier, "Count how many there be of you."

One of them said, "Eleven," and he did not count himself.

"Well," said the courtier, "what will you give me, and I will find the twelfth man?"

"Sir," said they, "all the money we have got."

"Give me the money," said the courtier, and began with the first, and gave him a stroke over the shoulders with his whip, which made him groan, saying, "Here is one," and so served them all, and they all groaned at the matter. When he came to the last, he paid him well, saying, "Here is the twelfth man."

"God's blessing on your heart," said they, "for thus finding our dear brother!"[222]

The Foolish German

Russia

The German steward didn't understand the Russian saints and their holy days. So, after he had forced them to work on St. Nicholas' Day, the peasants decided to play a trick on him.

"Mein Herr," the village elder said, "we cannot work tomorrow, for it is the venerable St. Hornet's Day."

"Show him to me!" said the German, so they led him to a hollow tree, where the hornets had built a nest.

"He's drunk too much vodka!" shouted the German, upon hearing the buzzing inside the tree. "I'm not afraid of him! You'll have to work, Saint Hornet's Day or not!" But even as he spoke, the hornets attacked the German, stinging him dreadfully.

"I repent!" he cried out. "Take off the whole day! No! Take off the entire week!"[223]

---

[222]Type 1287. Source: W. A. Clouston, *The Book of Noodles: Stories of Simpletons; or, Fools and Their Follies* (London, 1888), pp. 28-29.

[223]Similar to types 49A and 1321C. Retold from a Russian folktale by Aleksandr Afanasyev (1826-1871).

Russian Soldiers

Austria

This friend of mine had Russian soldiers quartered in his house during the occupation, and they had never seen a bathroom. They thought the toilet was a well, and drew water from it for drinking, and they used the bathtub for a coal bin. But the funniest thing was to watch one of them try to ride a bicycle. Not a one of them could keep his balance, and they were always getting their hands and feet caught in the spokes.[224]

An East Frisian Wedding Custom

Germany

Do you know why they always have a manure wagon at an East Frisian wedding?
    No. Why?
    To draw the flies away from the bride.[225]

---

[224]Source: Personal recollection, Steyr, Austria, 1958-1960.

[225]Source: Personal recollection, Braunschweig, Germany, 1964.

More Fools

Lawyer and Doctor

Egypt

A man had two sons. When they grew up, he saw the sons, one was a thief and the other a murderer. He did not know what to do. A neighbor said to him, "Send them to school." So to school they went, and the one became a lawyer and the other a doctor.[226]

The Man, the Boy, and the Donkey

Aesop

A man and his son were once going with their donkey to market. As they were walking along by is side a countryman passed them and said, "You fools, what is a donkey for but to ride upon?" So the man put the boy on the donkey, and they went on their way.

But soon they passed a group of men, one of whom said, "See that lazy youngster, he lets his father walk while he rides." So the man ordered his boy to get off, and got on himself.

But they hadn't gone far when they passed two women, one of whom said to the other, "Shame on that lazy lout to let his poor little son trudge along." Well, the man didn't know what to do, but at last he took his boy up before him on the donkey.

By this time they had come to the town, and the passersby began to jeer and point at them. The man stopped and asked what they were scoffing at. The men said, "Aren't you ashamed of yourself for overloading that poor donkey of yours—you and your hulking son?" The man and boy got off and tried to think what to do. They thought and they thought, until at last they cut down a pole, tied the donkey's feet to it, and raised the pole and the donkey to their shoulders. They

---

[226]Source: A. H. Sayce, "Cairene and Upper Egyptian Folk-Lore," *Folk-Lore: Transactions of the Folk-Lore Society*, v. 31, no. 3 (September 1920), p. 177.

went along amid the laughter of all who met them until they came to a bridge, when the donkey, getting one of his feet loose, kicked out and caused the boy to drop his end of the pole. In the struggle the donkey fell over the bridge, and his forefeet being tied together, he was drowned.

Moral: Try to please everyone, and you will please no one.[227]

The Two Weavers and the Grasshoppers

India

Two weavers took guns, and went out for a day's sport. As they passed through the fields, one of them espied an immense grasshopper sitting on a madâr plant, which, as they approached, flew on to the shoulder of his companion. "See, see, there he is!" cried he, and, leveling his piece, he shot his friend through the heart.[228]

The Broken Pot

The Panchatantra

In a certain place there lived a Brahman by the name of Svabhâvakripana, which means "luckless by his very nature." By begging he acquired a quantity of rice gruel, and after he had eaten what he wanted, there was still a potful left. He hung this pot on a nail in the wall above his bed. As night progressed, he could not take his eyes from the pot. All the while he was thinking, "This pot is filled to overflowing with rice gruel. If a famine should come to the land, then I could sell it for a hundred pieces of silver. Then I could buy a pair of goats. They have kids every six months, so I would soon have an entire herd of goats. Then I would trade the goats for cattle. As soon as the cows had calved, I would sell the calves. Then I would trade the cattle for buffalo. And the buffalo for horses. And when the horses foaled, I would own many horses. From their sale I would gain a large

---

[227]Type 1215. Source: Joseph Jacobs, *The Fables of Aesop* (London, 1894), no. 63.

[228]Type 1321. Source: Charles Swynnerton, *Indian Nights' Entertainment; or, Folk-Tales from the Upper Indus* (London, 1892), no. 49.

amount of gold. With this gold I would buy a house with four buildings in a rectangle. Then a Brahman would enter my house and give me a very beautiful girl with a large dowry for my wife. She will give birth to a son, and I will give him the name Somasarman. When he is old enough to be bounced on my knee, I will take a book, sit in the horse stall, and read. In the meantime, Somasarman will see me and want to be bounced on my knee. He will climb down from his mother's lap and walk toward me, coming close to the horses hooves. Then, filled with anger, I will shout at my wife, "Take the child! Take the child!" But she, busy with her housework, will not hear me. So I will jump up and give her a kick!" And, buried in his thoughts, he struck out with his foot, breaking the pot, and painting himself white with the rice gruel that had been in it. Therefore I say:

> He who dreams about unrealistic projects for the future will have the same fate as Somasarman's father: He will find himself lying there painted white with rice gruel.[229]

The Poor Man and the Flask of Oil

Bidpai

There was once a poor man, who lived in a house next to a wealthy merchant who sold oil and honey. As the merchant was a kind neighbor, he one day sent a flask of oil to the poor man. The poor man was delighted, and put it carefully away on the top shelf. One evening, as he was gazing at it, he said half aloud, "I wonder how much oil there is in that bottle. There is a large quantity. If I should sell it, I could buy five sheep. Every year I should have lambs, and before long I should own a flock. Then I should sell some of the sheep, and be rich enough to marry a wife. Perhaps we might have a son. And what a fine boy he would be! So tall, strong, and obedient! But if he should disobey me," and he raised the staff which he held in his hand, "I should punish him thus!" And he swung the staff over his head and brought it heavily to the ground, knocking, as he did so, the flask off the shelf so that the oil ran over him from head to foot.[230]

---

[229]Type 1430. Source: *Pantschatantra: Fünf Bücher indischer Fabeln, Märchen und Erzählungen*, translated from the Sanskrit into German by Theodor Benfey (Leipzig, 1859), v. 2, book 5, story 9.

[230]Type 1430. Source: *The Tortoise and the Geese and other Fables of Bidpai*, retold by Maude Barrows Dutton (Boston, 1908), pp. 8-9.

The Barber's Tale of His Fifth Brother

1001 Nights

When our father died, he left each of us one hundred dirhams. My fifth brother invested his inheritance in glassware, hoping to resell it at a handsome profit. He exhibited the glassware on a large tray, then fell to musing:

"These pieces will bring me two hundred dirhams, which I can use to buy more glass, which I will then sell for four hundred dirhams. With this money I can buy more glass and other merchandise to sell, and so on and so on until I have amassed a hundred thousand dirhams. Then I will purchase a fine house with slaves and eunuchs, and when my capital has grown to a hundred thousand dinars, I will demand to marry the Prime Minister's eldest daughter, and if he refuses consent, I will take her by force.

"On my wedding night I will don my finest attire and seat myself on a cushion of gold brocade to receive my bride. She will present herself in her most beautiful clothing, lovely as the full moon, but I will not even glance at her until her attendants kiss the ground before me and beg me to look at her, and then I will cast at her one single glance.

"When they leave us alone I will neither look at her nor speak to her, but will show my contempt by lying beside her with my face to the wall. Presently her mother will come into the chamber and beg of me, 'Please, my lord, your handmaid longs for your favor.' I will give no answer. Then she will kiss my feet and say, 'My lord, my daughter is truly a beautiful maid who has never before been with a man. Do speak to her and soothe her mind and spirit.' Then she will bring a cup of wine, hand it to her daughter, saying, 'Take this to your lord.'

"I will say nothing, leaning back so that she may see in me a sultan and a mighty man. She will say to me, 'My lord, do not refuse to take this cup from the hand of your servant.' I will say nothing, and she will insist, 'You must drink it,' and press the cup to my lips. Then I will shake my fist in her face and kick her with my foot."

With that he struck out, catching the tray of glassware with his foot. It crashed to the ground and everything broke to pieces, and thus my brother lost both his capital and his profit.[231]

---

[231]Type 1430. Source: *The Book of the Thousand Nights and a Night*, translated by Richard F. Burton (Privately printed, 1885), v. 1, pp. 335-338. Revised and abridged.

The Milkmaid and Her Pail

Aesop

A farmer's daughter had been out to milk the cows, and was returning to the dairy carrying her pail of milk upon her head. As she walked along, she fell a-musing after this fashion, "The milk in this pail will provide me with cream, which I will make into butter and take to market to sell. With the money I will buy a number of eggs, and these, when hatched, will produce chickens, and by and by I shall have quite a large poultry yard. Then I shall sell some of my fowls, and with the money which they will bring in I will buy myself a new gown, which I shall wear when I go to the fair; and all the young fellows will admire it, and come and make love to me, but I shall toss my head and have nothing to say to them." Forgetting all about the pail, and suiting the action to the word, she tossed her head. Down went the pail, all the milk was spilled, and all her fine castles in the air vanished in a moment!

Moral: Do not count your chickens before they are hatched.[232]

The Mosquito and the Carpenter

The Jataka Tales

Once on a time when Brahmadatta was reigning in Benares, the Bodhisatta gained his livelihood as a trader. In these days in a border village in Kasi there dwelt a number of carpenters. And it chanced that one of them, a bald gray-haired man, was planing away at some wood with his head glistening like a copper bowl, when a mosquito settled on his scalp and stung him with its dart like sting.

Said the carpenter to his son, who was seated hard by, "My boy, there's a mosquito stinging me on the head. Do drive it away."

"Hold still then father," said the son. "One blow will settle it."

(At that very time the Bodhisatta had reached that village in the way of trade, and was sitting in the carpenter's shop.)

"Rid me of it!" cried the father.

---

[232]Type 1430. Source: *Aesop's Fables*, translated by V. S. Vernon Jones (London and New York, 1912), pp. 25-26.

"All right, father," answered the son, who was behind the old man's back, and, raising a sharp ax on high with intent to kill only the mosquito, he cleft his father's head in two. So the old man fell dead on the spot.

Thought the Bodhisatta, who had been an eye witness of the whole scene, "Better than such a friend is an enemy with sense, whom fear of men's vengeance will deter from killing a man." And he recited these lines:

> Sense-lacking friends are worse than foes with sense;
> Witness the son that sought the gnat to slay,
> But cleft, poor fool, his father's skull in two.

So saying, the Bodhisatta rose up and departed, passing away in after days to fare according to his deserts. And as for the carpenter, his body was burned by his kinsfolk.[233]

The Gardener and the Bear

Bidpai

In the eastern part of Persia there lived at one time a gardener whose one joy in life was his flowers and fruit trees. He had neither wife, nor children, nor friends; nothing except his garden. At length, however, the good man wearied of having no one to talk to. He decided to go out into the world and find a friend. Scarcely was he outside the garden before he came face to face with a bear, who, like the gardener, was looking for a companion. Immediately a great friendship sprang up between these two.

The gardener invited the bear to come into his garden, and fed him on quinces and melons. In return for this kindness, when the gardener lay down to take his afternoon nap, the bear stood by and drove off the flies.

One afternoon it happened that an unusually large fly alighted on the gardener's nose. The bear drove it off, but it only flew to the gardener's chin. Again the bear drove it away, but in a few moments it was back once more on the gardener's nose. The bear now was filled with rage. With no thought beyond that of punishing the fly, he seized a huge stone, and hurled it with such force at the gardener's nose that he killed not only the fly, but the sleeping gardener.

It is better to have a wise enemy than a foolish friend.[234]

---

[233]Type 1586. Source: *The Jataka; or, Stories of the Buddha's Former Births*, edited by E. B. Cowell (Cambridge, 1895), book 1, no. 44.

[234]Type 1586. Source: *The Tortoise and the Geese and other Fables of Bidpai*, retold by Maude Barrows Dutton (Boston, 1908), pp. 22-23.

The King's New Turban

Turkey

Of old time there was a great king. One day a man came before him and said, "My king, I shall weave a turban such that one born in wedlock will see it, while the bastard will see it not." The king marveled and ordered that that weaver should weave that turban; and the weaver received an allowance from the king and tarried a long while. One day he folded up this side and that side of a paper and brought it and laid it before the king and said, "Oh king, I have woven that turban." So the king opened the paper and saw that there was nothing; and all the viziers and nobles who stood there looked on the paper and saw nothing. Then the king said in his heart, "Do you see? I am then a bastard"; and he was sad. And he thought, "Now, the remedy is this, that I say it is a goodly turban and admire it, else will I be put to shame before the folk." And he said, "Blessed by God! Oh master, it is a goodly turban, I like it much."

Then that weaver youth said, "Oh king, let them bring a cap that I may wind the turban for the king." They brought a cap, and the weaver youth laid that paper before him and moved his hands as though he wound the turban, and he put it on the king's head. All the nobles who were standing there said, "Blessed be it! Oh king, how fair, how beautiful a turban!" and they applauded it much.

Then the king rose and went with two viziers into a private room and said, "Oh viziers, I am then a bastard; I see not the turban."

The viziers said, "Oh king, we too see it not." At length they knew of a surety that the turban had not existence, and that that weaver had thus played a trick for the sake of money.[235]

The Emperor's New Clothes

Hans Christian Andersen

Many years ago there lived an emperor who loved beautiful new clothes so much that he spent all his money on being finely dressed. His only interest was in going to the theater or in riding about in his carriage where

---

[235]Type 1620. Source: Sheykh-Zada, *The History of the Forty Vezirs; or, the Story of the Forty Morns and Eves*, translated by E. J. W. Gibb (London, 1886), pp. 148-149. The tale's original title is "The Lady's Twelfth Story."

he could show off his new clothes. He had a different costume for every hour of the day. Indeed, where it was said of other kings that they were at court, it could only be said of him that he was in his dressing room!

One day two swindlers came to the emperor's city. They said that they were weavers, claiming that they knew how to make the finest cloth imaginable. Not only were the colors and the patterns extraordinarily beautiful, but in addition, this material had the amazing property that it was be invisible to anyone who was incompetent or stupid.

"It would be wonderful to have clothes made from that cloth," thought the emperor. "Then I would know which of my men are unfit for their positions, and I'd also be able to tell clever people from stupid ones." So he immediately gave the two swindlers a great sum of money to weave their cloth for him.

They set up their looms and pretended to go to work, although there was nothing at all on the looms. They asked for the finest silk and the purest gold, all of which they hid away, continuing to work on the empty looms, often late into the night.

"I would really like to know how they are coming with the cloth!" thought the emperor, but he was a bit uneasy when he recalled that anyone who was unfit for his position or stupid would not be able to see the material. Of course, he himself had nothing to fear, but still he decided to send someone else to see how the work was progressing.

"I'll send my honest old minister to the weavers," thought the emperor. He's the best one to see how the material is coming. He is very sensible, and no one is more worthy of his position than he.

So the good old minister went into the hall where the two swindlers sat working at their empty looms. "Goodness!" thought the old minister, opening his eyes wide. "I cannot see a thing!" But he did not say so.

The two swindlers invited him to step closer, asking him if it wasn't a beautiful design and if the colors weren't magnificent. They pointed to the empty loom, and the poor old minister opened his eyes wider and wider. He still could see nothing, for nothing was there. "Gracious" he thought. "Is it possible that I am stupid? I have never thought so. Am I unfit for my position? No one must know this. No, it will never do for me to say that I was unable to see the material."

"You aren't saying anything!" said one of the weavers.

"Oh, it is magnificent! The very best!" said the old minister, peering through his glasses. "This pattern and these colors! Yes, I'll tell the emperor that I am very satisfied with it!"

"That makes us happy!" said the two weavers, and they called the colors and the unusual pattern by name. The old minister listened closely so that he would be able say the same things when he reported back to the emperor, and that is exactly what he did.

The swindlers now asked for more money, more silk, and more gold, all of which they hid away. Then they continued to weave away as before on the empty looms.

The emperor sent other officials as well to observe the weavers' progress. They too were startled when they saw nothing, and they too reported back to him how wonderful the material was, advising him to have it made into clothes that he could wear in a grand procession. The entire city was alive in praise of the cloth. "Magnifique! Nysseligt! Excellent!" they said, in all languages. The emperor awarded the swindlers with medals of honor, bestowing on each of them the title Lord Weaver.

The swindlers stayed up the entire night before the procession was to take place, burning more than sixteen candles. Everyone could see that they were in a great rush to finish the emperor's new clothes. They pretended to take the material from the looms. They cut in the air with large scissors. They sewed with needles but without any thread. Finally they announced, "Behold! The clothes are finished!"

The emperor came to them with his most distinguished cavaliers. The two swindlers raised their arms as though they were holding something and said, "Just look at these trousers! Here is the jacket! This is the cloak!" and so forth. "They are as light as spider webs! You might think that you didn't have a thing on, but that is the good thing about them."

"Yes," said the cavaliers, but they couldn't see a thing, for nothing was there.

Would his imperial majesty, if it please his grace, kindly remove his clothes." said the swindlers. "Then we will fit you with the new ones, here in front of the large mirror."

The emperor took off all his clothes, and the swindlers pretended to dress him, piece by piece, with the new ones that were to be fitted. They took hold of his waist and pretended to tie something about him. It was the train. Then the emperor turned and looked into the mirror.

"Goodness, they suit you well! What a wonderful fit!" they all said. "What a pattern! What colors! Such luxurious clothes!"

"The canopy to be carried above your majesty awaits outside," said the grandmaster of ceremonies.

"Yes, I am ready!" said the emperor. "Don't they fit well?" He turned once again toward the mirror, because it had to appear as though he were admiring himself in all his glory.

The chamberlains who were to carry the train held their hands just above the floor as if they were picking up the train. As they walked they pretended to hold the train high, for they could not let anyone notice that they could see nothing.

The emperor walked beneath the beautiful canopy in the procession, and all the people in the street and in their windows said, "Goodness, the emperor's new clothes are incomparable! What a beautiful train on his jacket. What a perfect fit!" No one wanted it to be noticed that he could see nothing, for then it would be said that he was unfit for his position or that he was stupid. None of the emperor's clothes had ever before received such praise.

"But he doesn't have anything on!" said a small child.

"Good Lord, let us hear the voice of an innocent child!" said the father, and whispered to another what the child had said.

"A small child said that he doesn't have anything on!"

Finally everyone was saying, "He doesn't have anything on!"

The emperor shuddered, for he knew that they were right, but he thought, "The procession must go on!" He carried himself even more proudly, and the chamberlains walked along behind carrying the train that wasn't there.[236]

Peter Ox

Denmark

There were once upon a time a peasant and his wife who lived in Jutland, but they had no children. They often lamented that fact and were also sad to think that they had no relatives to whom to leave their farm and other possessions. So the years went by and they became richer and richer, but there was no one to inherit their wealth.

One year the farmer bought a fine calf which he called Peter, and it was really the finest animal that he had ever seen, and so clever that it seemed to understand nearly everything that one said to it. It was also very amusing and affectionate, so that the man and his wife soon became as fond of it as if it were their own child.

One day the farmer said to his wife, "Perhaps the sexton of our church could teach Peter to talk then we could not do better than to adopt him as our child, and he could then inherit all our property."

"Who can tell?" said the wife, "Our sexton is a learned man and perhaps he might be able to teach Peter to talk, for Peter is really very clever. Suppose you ask the sexton."

So the farmer went over to the sexton and asked him whether he did not believe that he could teach his calf to talk, because he wanted to make the animal his heir. The crafty sexton looked around to see that no one was near, and then said that he thought he could do so. "Only you must not tell anybody," he said, "for it must be a great secret, and the minister in particular must not know anything about it, or I might get into serious trouble as such things are strictly forbidden. Moreover it will cost a pretty penny as we shall need rare and expensive books." The farmer said that he did not mind, and handing the sexton a hundred dollars to buy books with, promised not to say a word about the arrangement to anyone.

That evening the man brought his calf to the sexton who promised to do his best. In about a week the farmer returned to see how his calf was getting on, but the sexton said that he did not dare let him see the animal, else Peter might become homesick and forget all that he had already learned. Otherwise he was making good progress, but the farmer must pay another hundred dollars, as Peter needed

---

[236]Type 1620. Source: "Kejserens nye klæder" (1836). Andersen's source was a Spanish story recorded by Don Juan Manuel (1282-1348).

366

more books. The peasant happened to have the money with him, so he gave it to the sexton and went home filled with hope and pleasant anticipations.

At the end of another week the man again went to make inquiry about Peter, and was told by the sexton that he was doing fairly well. "Can he say anything?" asked the farmer.

"Yes, he can say 'Ma,'" answered the sexton.

"The poor animal is surely ill," said the peasant, "and he probably wants mead. I will go straight home and bring him a jug of it." So he fetched a jug of good, old mead and gave it to the sexton for Peter. The sexton, however, kept the mead and gave the calf some milk instead.

A week later the farmer came again to find out what Peter could say now. "He still refuses to say anything but 'Ma,'" said the sexton.

"Oh! he is a cunning rogue;" said the peasant, "so he wants more mead, does he? Well, I'll get him some more, as he likes it so much. But what progress has he made?"

"He is doing so well," answered the sexton, "that he needs another hundred dollars' worth of books, for he cannot learn anything more from those that he has now."

"Well then, if he needs them he shall have them." So that same day the farmer brought another hundred dollars and a jug of good, old mead for Peter.

Now the peasant allowed a few weeks to elapse without calling on Peter, for he began to be afraid that each visit would cost him a hundred dollars. In the meantime the calf had become as fat as he would ever be, so the sexton killed him and sold the meat carefully at a distance from the village. Having done that he put on his black clothes and went to call on the farmer and his wife. As soon as he had bid them good day he asked them whether Peter had reached home safe and sound.

"Why no," said the farmer, "he has not run away, has he?"

"I hope," said the sexton, "that after all the trouble I have taken he has not been so tricky as to run away and to abuse my confidence so shamefully. For I have spent at least a hundred dollars of my own money to pay for books for him. Now Peter could say whatever he wanted, and he was telling me only yesterday that he was longing to see his dear parents. As I wanted to give him that pleasure, but feared that he would not be able to find his way home alone, I dressed myself and started out with him. We were hardly in the street when I suddenly remembered that I had left my stick at home, so I ran back to get it. When I came out of the house again, I found that Peter had run on alone. I thought, of course, that he had gone back to your house. If he is not there, I certainly do not know where he can be."

Then the people began to weep and lament that Peter was lost, now especially when they might have had such pleasure with him, and after paying out so much money for his education. And the worst of it was that they were again without an heir. The sexton tried to comfort them and was also very sorry that Peter had deceived them so. But perhaps he had only lost his way, and the sexton promised that he would ask publicly in church next Sunday whether somebody had not seen the calf. Then he bade the farmer and his wife good-bye and went home and had some good roast veal for dinner.

One day the sexton read in the paper that a new merchant, named Peter Ox, had settled in the neighboring town. He put the paper into his pocket and went straight to the farmer and read this item of news to him. "One might almost believe," he said, "that this is your calf."

"Why yes," said the farmer, "who else should it be?" Then his wife added, "Yes father, go at once to see him, for I feel sure that it can be no other than our dear Peter. But take along plenty of money for he probably needs it now that he has become a merchant."

On the following morning the farmer put a bag of money on his shoulder, took with him some provisions, and started to walk to the town where the merchant lived. Early next morning he arrived there and went straight to the merchant's house. The servants told the man that the merchant had not gotten up yet. "That does not make any difference for I am his father; just take me up to his room."

So they took the peasant up to the bedroom where the merchant lay sound asleep. And as soon as the farmer saw him, he recognized Peter. There were the same thick neck and broad forehead and the same red hair, but otherwise he looked just like a human being. Then the man went to him and bade him good morning and said, "Well, Peter, you caused your mother and me great sorrow when you ran away as soon as you had learned something. But get up now and let me have a look at you and talk with you."

The merchant, of course, believed that he had a crazy man to deal with, so he thought it best to be careful. "Yes I will get up," he said, and jumped out of bed into his clothes as quickly as possible.

"Ah!" said the peasant, "now I see what a wise man our sexton was; he has brought it to pass that you are like any other man. If I were not absolutely certain of it, I should never dream that you were the calf of our red cow. Will you come home with me?" The merchant said that he could not as he had to attend to his business. "But you could take over my farm and I would retire. Nevertheless if you prefer to stay in business, I am willing. Do you need any money?"

"Well," said the merchant, "a man can always find use for money in his business."

"I thought so," said the farmer, "and besides you had nothing to start with, so I have brought you some money." And with that he poured out on the table the bright dollars that covered it entirely.

When the merchant saw what kind of a man his new found acquaintance was, he chatted with him in a very friendly manner and begged him to remain with him for a few days.

"Yes indeed," said the farmer, "but you must be sure to call me father from now on."

"But I have neither father nor mother living," answered Peter Ox.

"That I know perfectly well," the peasant replied, "for I sold your real father in Copenhagen last Michaelmas, and your mother died while calving. But my wife and I have adopted you as our child and you will be our heir, so you must call me father."

The merchant gladly agreed to that and kept the bag of money; and before leaving town the farmer made his will and bequeathed all his possessions to Peter after his death. Then the man went home and told his wife the whole story, and she was delighted to learn that the merchant Peter Ox was really their own calf.

"Now you must go straight over to the sexton and tell him what has happened;" she said, "and be sure to refund to him the hundred dollars that he paid out of his own pocket for Peter, for he has earned all that we have paid him, because of the joy that he has caused us in giving us such a son and heir."

Her husband was of the same opinion and went to call on the sexton, whom he thanked many times for his kindness and to whom he also gave two hundred dollars.

Then the farmer sold his farm, and he and his wife moved into the town where the merchant was, and lived with him happily until their death.[237]

The Fool's Good Fortune

Georgia

A certain man died and left three sons. One was altogether a fool, another was fairly intelligent, and the third was rather clever. This being so, it was of course difficult for them to live together. In dividing the inheritance among them, the fool was cheated, and in regard to the cattle he was thus duped: There were three entrances to the pen, two open and one very narrow. The two clever brothers proposed to drive the beasts out of all three at once; those that issued from the small gap were to belong to the fool. In this way the latter's share was only one young bull out of the whole flock. But to his feeble mind the division seemed fair enough, so he contentedly drove his bull out into the forest, and tied it with a stout rope to a young tree, whilst he himself wandered aimlessly about.

Three days later, the fool went to see his beast. It had eaten and drunk nothing, but had pulled the tree up by the roots, and laid bare a jar full of old gold coins. The fool was delighted, and played with the money for a time. Then he resolved to take the jar and present it to the king. As he passed along the road, every wayfarer looked into the pot, took out the gold in handfuls, and so that he should not notice their thefts, filled it up with stones and blocks of wood. On reaching the palace, the fool asked for an audience of the king, and it was granted. He emptied out the

---

[237]Type 1675. Source: Sven Grundtvig, *Danish Fairy Tales*, translated by J. Grant Cramer (Boston, 1919), no. 2.

contents of the jar at the feet of the king. When the courtiers saw the wrath of the king, they took the fool away and beat him. When he had recovered himself he asked why he had been thrashed. One of the bystanders, for fun, cried to him, "You have been beaten because you labor in vain."

The fool went his way, muttering the words, "You labor in vain." As he passed a peasant who was reaping, he repeated his phrase again and again, until the peasant grew angry, and thrashed him. The fool asked why he had been beaten, and what he ought to have said. "You ought to have said, 'God give you a good harvest!'"

The fool went on, saying "God give you a good harvest!" and met a funeral. Again he was beaten, and again he asked what he should say. They replied that he should have said, "Heaven rest your soul!" He then came to a wedding, and saluted the newly married couple with this funereal phrase. Again he was beaten, and then told that he should say, "Be fruitful and multiply!"

His next visit was to a monastery, and he accosted every monk with his new salutation. They too gave him a thrashing, with such vigor that the fool determined to have his revenge by stealing of the bells from their belfry. So he hid himself until the monks had gone to rest, and then carried oft a bell of moderate size.

He went into the forest, climbed a tree, and hung the bell on the branches, ringing it from time to time, partly to amuse himself and partly to frighten away wild beasts. In the forest there was a gang of robbers, who were assembled to share their booty, and had just ended a merry banquet. Suddenly they heard the sound of the bell, and were much afraid. They took counsel as to what was to be done, and most of them were for flight, but the oldest of the band advised them to send a scout to see what was wrong. The bravest among them was sent to get information, and the rest remained as quiet as possible.

The brigand went on tiptoe through the bushes to the tree where the fool was, and respectfully asked, "Who are you? If you are an angel sent by God to punish our wickedness, pray spare us and we shall repent. If you are a devil from hell, come and share with us."

The fool was not so stupid that he did not see he had to deal with robbers, so he took out a knife, tolled the bell, and then said with a grave air, "If you wish to know who I am, climb the tree and show me your tongue, so that I may mark on it who I am and what I ask of you."

The robber obediently climbed the tree, and put out his tongue as far as he could. The fool cut off his tongue, and kicked him to the ground. The robber, mad with pain, and frightened by his sudden fall, ran off howling. His comrades had come out to meet him, and when they saw the plight he was in, they ran off in terror, leaving their wealth. Next morning the fool found the booty, and without saying anything to anybody, took it home and became much richer than his brothers. The fool built three palaces: one for himself, one for me, and one for you. There is merrymaking in the fool's palace. Come and be one of the guests![238]

---

[238]Types 1696 and 1653. Source: Marjory Wardrop, *Georgian Folk Tales* (London, 1894), pp. 165-167.

The Traveler and the Farmer

North America

A traveler came upon an old farmer hoeing in his field beside the road. The wanderer hailed the countryman, who looked up from his work.

"How long will it take me to get to the next town?" asked the stranger.

"I can't rightly say," was the farmer's curt reply.

Insulted, the traveler strode off.

"About an hour," shouted the farmer after him.

"Why didn't you say so when I first asked?"

"Because I didn't know how fast you were walking."[239]

---

[239]Source: Personal recollection, Idaho, ca. 1950.

Husband and Wife

Wife Beaters

The Bull, the Donkey, and the Husbandman

1001 Nights

Once Allah endowed a wealthy husbandman with the ability to understand the language of every kind of beast and bird, commanding him, under pain of death, never to divulge this gift. Fearing for his life, the husbandman guarded the secret well.

One day while observing his animals, he heard a bull say to a donkey, "Lucky one, you enjoy the best of care, while I suffer all manner of ill treatment. I toil under the yoke by day, receive but a meager ration of beans and straw, and must lie at night in a filthy stall. You, by comparison, eat well and lie about at ease unless the master chooses to ride you into town, which happens seldom enough, and even then he returns with you straight-away."

"You fool," replied the donkey. "You could have an easier life, if you would only feign illness. When they next take you to your stall, fall to the ground, puff out your belly, and refuse to eat. This will surely bring a reprieve from your accustomed blows and toil."

The bull did as the donkey recommended and pretended to be sick. However, the master, who had overheard their conversation, responded by binding the wily donkey to the plow and forcing him to do the bull's work. The donkey, unaccustomed to such labor, suffered greatly under the yoke and the plowman's stick, while the bull enjoyed a day of rest. At day's end, the donkey, nearly dead from exertion and blows, came quickly to a new plan. "My friend," he said to the bull, "you have a bleak future if you do not soon recover your strength. I heard the master say that he intends to deliver you to the butcher, who will turn your flesh into meat for the poor and your hide into a leather mat." The husbandman heard this all.

The next morning the husbandman, accompanied by his wife, approached the bull in his stall. The beast gave a great show of health and vigor, whisking his tail, farting, and frisking lustily about. The master, greatly amused at the turn of events, broke into laughter.

"Why do you laugh?" asked his wife.

"I cannot tell you, lest I die." replied the man.

"So be it," answered the woman, "but I must know why you laughed." She continued to wheedle and to beg, until he, sensing that he could not forever resist her unrelenting pleas, resigned himself to his fate. He brought his affairs to order, then prepared to reveal his secret and to die.

Now the husbandman had some fifty hens, all serviced by one cock. The cock, lustily mounting one hen after the other, was interrupted by one of the farm dogs, who said, "For shame, that you thus satisfy your lust on this day that our master is to die."

The cock replied, "What sort of master do we have, who cannot manage a single wife? I control fifty hens."

"And what should the master do?" asked the dog.

"He should cut a branch from yonder mulberry tree then use it on her back and ribs until she repents. Then let him give her another beating for good measure, and henceforth he will sleep well and enjoy life."

The husbandman heard this conversation between the dog and the cock, and he took it to heart. He cut a branch from the mulberry tree and proceeded with it to his wife's room. Locking the door behind him, he announced that he was about to reveal his secret to her, but then began to beat her soundly about her back, shoulders, ribs, arms, and legs, all the while saying, "Are you ever again going to ask questions about matters that do not concern you?" Nearly senseless, she finally cried out, "I repent! With Allah as a witness, I will never again question you." She then kissed his hands and his feet, and he led her from the room as submissive as a wife should be. Her parents and other members of the family rejoiced at the turn of events.

Thus the husbandman learned family discipline from his cock, and he and his wife lived together the happiest of lives until they died.[240]

---

[240]Types 207A (the bull and the ass) and 670 (the man who understood the language of animals). Source: *The Book of the Thousand Nights and a Night*, translated by Richard F. Burton (Privately printed, 1885), v. 1, pp. 16-23. Revised and abridged.

The Language of Beasts

Andrew Lang

Once upon a time a man had a shepherd who served him many years faithfully and honestly. One day, whilst herding his flock, this shepherd heard a hissing sound, coming out of the forest nearby, which he could not account for. So he went into the wood in the direction of the noise to try to discover the cause. When he approached the place he found that the dry grass and leaves were on fire, and on a tree, surrounded by flames, a snake was coiled, hissing with terror.

The shepherd stood wondering how the poor snake could escape, for the wind was blowing the flames that way, and soon that tree would be burning like the rest. Suddenly the snake cried, "Oh shepherd! for the love of heaven save me from this fire!"

Then the shepherd stretched his staff out over the flames and the snake wound itself round the staff and up to his hand, and from his hand it crept up his arm, and twined itself about his neck. The shepherd trembled with fright, expecting every instant to be stung to death, and said, "What an unlucky man I am! Did I rescue you only to be destroyed myself?" But the snake answered, "Have no fear; only carry me home to my father who is the King of the Snakes." The shepherd, however, was much too frightened to listen, and said that he could not go away and leave his flock alone; but the snake said, "You need not be afraid to leave your flock, no evil shall befall them; but make all the haste you can."

So he set off through the wood carrying the snake, and after a time he came to a great gateway, made entirely of snakes intertwined one with another. The shepherd stood still with surprise, but the snake round his neck whistled, and immediately all the arch unwound itself.

"When we are come to my father's house," said his own snake to him, "he will reward you with anything you request—silver, gold, jewels, or whatever on this earth is most precious; but take none of all these things, ask rather to understand the language of beasts. He will refuse it to you a long time, but in the end he will grant it to you."

Soon after that they arrived at the house of the King of the Snakes, who burst into tears of joy at the sight of his daughter, as he had given her up for dead. "Where have you been all this time?" he asked, directly he could speak, and she told him that she had been caught in a forest fire, and had been rescued from the flames by the shepherd. The King of the Snakes, then turning to the shepherd, said to him, "What reward will you choose for saving my child?"

"Make me to know the language of beasts," answered the shepherd, "that is all I desire."

The king replied, "Such knowledge would be of no benefit to you, for if I granted it to you and you told anyone of it, you would immediately die; ask me rather for whatever else you would most like to possess, and it shall be yours."

But the shepherd answered him, "Sir, if you wish to reward me for saving your daughter, grant me, I pray you, to know the language of beasts. I desire nothing else." And he turned as if to depart.

Then the king called him back, saying, "If nothing else will satisfy you, open your mouth." The man obeyed, and the king spat into it, and said, "Now spit into my mouth." The shepherd did as he was told, then the King of the Snakes spat again into the shepherd's mouth. When they had spat into each other's mouths three times, the king said, "Now you know the language of beasts, go in peace; but, if you value your life, beware lest you tell anyone of it, else you will immediately die."

So the shepherd set out for home, and on his way through the wood he heard and understood all that was said by the birds, and by every living creature. When he got back to his sheep he found the flock grazing peacefully, and as he was very tired he laid himself down by them to rest a little. Hardly had he done so when two ravens flew down and perched on a tree nearby, and began to talk to each other in their own language, "If that shepherd only knew that there is a vault full of gold and silver beneath where that lamb is lying, what would he not do?" When the shepherd heard these words he went straight to his master and told him, and the master at once took a wagon, and broke open the door of the vault, and they carried off the treasure. But instead of keeping it for himself, the master, who was an honorable man, gave it all up to the shepherd, saying, "Take it, it is yours. The gods have given it to you." So the shepherd took the treasure and built himself a house. He married a wife, and they lived in great peace and happiness, and he was acknowledged to be the richest man, not only of his native village, but of all the countryside. He had flocks of sheep, and cattle, and horses without end, as well as beautiful clothes and jewels.

One day, just before Christmas, he said to his wife, "Prepare everything for a great feast, tomorrow we will take things with us to the farm that the shepherds there may make merry." The wife obeyed, and all was prepared as he desired. Next day they both went to the farm, and in the evening the master said to the shepherds, "Now come, all of you, eat, drink, and make merry. I will watch the flocks myself tonight in your stead." Then he went out to spend the night with the flocks.

When midnight struck the wolves howled and the dogs barked, and the wolves spoke in their own tongue, saying, "Shall we come in and work havoc, and shall you too eat flesh?" And the dogs answered in their tongue, "Come in, and for once we shall have enough to eat."

Now amongst the dogs there was one so old that he had only two teeth left in his head, and he spoke to the wolves, saying, "So long as I have my two teeth still in my head, I will let no harm be done to my master."

All this the master heard and understood, and as soon as morning dawned he ordered all the dogs to be killed excepting the old dog. The farm servants wondered at this order, and exclaimed, "But surely, sir, that would be a pity?"

The master answered, "Do as I bid you"; and made ready to return home with his wife, and they mounted their horses, her steed being a mare. As they went on their way, it happened that the husband rode on ahead, while the wife was a little way

375

behind. The husband's horse, seeing this, neighed, and said to the mare, "Come along, make haste; why are you so slow?" And the mare answered, "It is very easy for you, you carry only your master, who is a thin man, but I carry my mistress, who is so fat that she weighs as much as three." When the husband heard that he looked back and laughed, which the wife perceiving, she urged on the mare until she caught up with her husband, and asked him why he laughed. "For nothing at all," he answered; "just because it came into my head." She would not be satisfied with this answer, and urged him more and more to tell her why he had laughed. But he controlled himself and said, "Let me be, wife; what ails you? I do not know myself why I laughed." But the more he put her off, the more she tormented him to tell her the cause of his laughter. At length he said to her, "Know, then, that if I tell it you I shall immediately and surely die." But even this did not quiet her; she only besought him the more to tell her.

Meanwhile they had reached home, and before getting down from his horse the man called for a coffin to be brought; and when it was there he placed it in front of the house, and said to his wife, "See, I will lay myself down in this coffin, and will then tell you why I laughed, for as soon as I have told you I shall surely die."

So he lay down in the coffin, and while he took a last look around him, his old dog came out from the farm and sat down by him, and whined. When the master saw this, he called to his wife, "Bring a piece of bread to give to the dog." The wife brought some bread and threw it to the dog, but he would not look at it.

Then the farm cock came and pecked at the bread; but the dog said to it, "Wretched glutton, can you eat like that when you see that your master is dying?"

The cock answered, "Let him die, if he is so stupid. I have a hundred wives, which I call together when I find a grain of corn, and as soon as they are there I swallow it myself; should one of them dare to be angry, I would give her a lesson with my beak. He has only one wife, and he cannot keep her in order."

As soon as the man understood this, he got up out of the coffin, seized a stick, and called his wife into the room, saying, "Come, and I will tell you what you so much want to know"; and then he began to beat her with the stick, saying with each blow, "It is that, wife, it is that!" And in this way he taught her never again to ask why he had laughed.[241]

---

[241]Type 670. Source: Andrew Lang, *The Crimson Fairy Book* (London, 1903), pp. 55-61. Lang does not list his source, but the tale is widely distributed throughout Europe.

The Lark and the Taming of Women

Romania

A man was once plowing his field. In the midst of it a lark had made her nest and was hatching her young. When the cock lark saw what the man was doing, and that he was coming nearer and nearer with the plow, he feared that the nest would be destroyed. So he turned to the man and said, "Please, spare my nest; go around it with your plow and do not touch it, for I might also do you some good."

The man, surprised at hearing the lark speak to him, said, "What good can you do to me?"

"Oh," replied the lark, "you never know what I can do. Just bide your time, there might be a chance."

"Well," said the man, "I do not mind going with my plow around that piece of ground. It will not make much difference, but you see I have a very bad-tempered wife, and should she come out and see what I have done, and that I have left a part of the field without plowing it, I shall come in for a good hiding."

"What," said the lark, "you a man, and your wife, a woman, beating you. How can that be?"

"Oh," replied the man, "you do not know her; from morning until evening she does nothing but strike and beat me. I have not a minute's rest and peace."

"I can help you," replied the lark, "if only you will do what I tell you."

"If you will help me I shall be forever grateful to you."

"Well then, this is what you have to do. You get yourself a stout stick, and should she come and start chiding you, you just lay out and go for her without mercy. You will see it will be all right."

While they were thus speaking, the woman came out, with one jaw on earth and the other in heaven, spitting fire and fury; and when she saw that the man had left a part of the field not plowed she started to go for him with her fists and to give him a good beating. But before she had time to get to him, remembering the advice which the lark had given him he got hold of the stick, and there was a great change. The woman did not know what it was that happened to her; the blows fell upon her fast and thick over her head, face, shoulders, hands. At last she got frightened, and ran away vowing vengeance. After she had gone, the lark said to the man, "Don't be a fool. I know she awaits you at home with a long stick, but you get yourself a short, stout stick, and just slip into the house before she has time to use her long rod; and then you go for her, hitting as fast as you can and as hard as you can, for, being in the house, the woman will not be able to use the long rod to any advantage."

The man did as the lark had taught him, and the woman came in for a drubbing she never expected. The tables were now turned, and instead of beating the husband the woman got it now, and twice over.

That was the first case of the men beating their women, instead of the men being beaten by the women; for the neighbors, seeing how things had changed with this

377

man, soon followed his example, and there was yelling and shouting and cursing as never before, the women getting the worst.

When the women saw that the men got the upper hand, they all gathered together in the marketplace and held a conference under the leadership of the head woman of the town. After a long consultation and discussion, they all decided to leave their husbands alone and to get across the Danube to the other side.

So they did; they gathered themselves together and, led by the head woman, left the town to go across the Danube. When the men saw what the women were doing, and that they were in earnest, they turned on the first man who had set the example and threatened to kill him, for he had brought all that trouble upon them. And the man got frightened and ran out into the field, and going to the lark told all that was going on and that he was in danger of his life.

The lark laughed and said, "Oh, you are worse than a set of old women. Do not be afraid. Nothing will happen to you. You just wait and see. I am going to bring the women home again."

So saying, the lark rose up in the air, and flying over the heads of the women who were standing by the banks of the Danube waiting to cross, it sang out, "Tsirli, tsirli, on the other side of the Danube there are no men."

One of the women, hearing the bird's song, said to her neighbor, "Did you hear what that bird was singing?"

"Oh, yes, we can all hear it saying that across the Danube there are no men, and if that be true I think we had better return to our own husbands. Never mind whether they beat us or not."

And they all returned home quite meekly to their houses; and ever since then the men beat their wives, but the women never beat their husbands. And you should know that if a woman does beat her husband, he is not a man, but a donkey.[242]

Two in a Sack

Russia

What a life that poor man led with his wife, to be sure! Not a day passed without her scolding him and calling him names, and indeed sometimes she would take the broom from behind the stove and beat him with it. He had no peace or comfort at all, and really hardly knew how to bear it. One day, when his wife had been particularly unkind and had beaten him black and blue, he

---

[242]Similar to type 670. Source: M. Gaster, *Rumanian Bird and Beast Stories* (London, 1915), no. 96.

strolled slowly into the fields, and as he could not endure to be idle, he spread out his nets.

What kind of bird do you think he caught in his net? He caught a crane, and the crane said, "Let me go free, and I'll show myself grateful."

The man answered, "No, my dear fellow. I shall take you home, and then perhaps my wife won't scold me so much."

Said the crane, "You had better come with me to my house," and so they went to the crane's house.

When they got there, what do you think the crane took from the wall? He took down a sack, and he said, "Two out of a sack!" Instantly two pretty lads sprang out of the sack. They brought in oak tables, which they spread with silken covers, and placed all sorts of delicious dishes and refreshing drinks on them. The man had never seen anything so beautiful in his life, and he was delighted.

Then the crane said to him, "Now take this sack to your wife."

The man thanked him warmly, took the sack, and set out.

His home was a good long way off, and as it was growing dark, and he was feeling tired, he stopped to rest at his cousin's house by the way. The cousin had three daughters, who laid out a tempting supper, but the man would eat nothing, and said to his cousin, "Your supper is bad."

"Oh, make the best of it," said she, but the man only said, "Clear away!" and taking out his sack he cried, as the crane had taught him, "Two out of the sack!"

And out came the two pretty boys, who quickly brought in the oak tables, spread the silken covers, and laid out all sorts of delicious dishes and refreshing drinks. Never in their lives had the cousin and her daughters seen such a supper, and they were delighted and astonished at it. But the cousin quietly made up her mind to steal the sack, so she called to her daughters, "Go quickly and heat the bathroom. I am sure our dear guest would like to have a bath before he goes to bed."

When the man was safe in the bathroom she told her daughters to make a sack exactly like his, as quickly as possible. Then she changed the two sacks, and hid the man's sack away.

The man enjoyed his bath, slept soundly, and set off early next morning, taking what he believed to be the sack the crane had given him. All the way home he felt in such good spirits that he sang and whistled as he walked through the wood, and never noticed how the birds were twittering and laughing at him.

As soon as he saw his house he began to shout from a distance, "Hallo, old woman! Come out and meet me!"

His wife screamed back, "You come here, and I'll give you a good thrashing with the poker!"

The man walked into the house, hung his sack on a nail, and said, as the crane had taught him, "Two out of the sack!"

But not a soul came out of the sack. Then he said again, exactly as the crane had taught him, "Two out of the sack!"

His wife, hearing him chattering goodness knows what, took up her wet broom and swept the ground all about him. The man took flight and rushed off into the

379

field, and there he found the crane marching proudly about, and to him he told his tale.

"Come back to my house," said the crane, and so they went to the crane's house, and as soon as they got there, what did the crane take down from the wall? Why, he took down a sack, and he said, "Two out of the sack!"

And instantly two pretty lads sprang out of the sack, brought in oak tables, on which they laid silken covers, and spread all sorts of delicious dishes and refreshing drinks on them.

"Take this sack," said the crane.

The man thanked him heartily, took the sack, and went. He had a long way to walk, and as he presently got hungry, he said to the sack, as the crane had taught him, "Two out of the sack!"

And instantly two rough men with thick sticks crept out of the bag and began to beat him well, crying as they did so:

> Don't boast to your cousins of what you have got,
> One—two—
> Or you'll find you will catch it uncommonly hot,
> One—two—"

And they beat on until the man panted out, "Two into the sack."

The words were hardly out of his mouth, when the two crept back into the sack.

Then the man shouldered the sack, and went off straight to his cousin's house. He hung the sack up on a nail, and said, "Please have the bathroom heated, cousin."

The cousin heated the bathroom, and the man went into it, but he neither washed nor rubbed himself, he just sat there and waited.

Meantime his cousin felt hungry, so she called her daughters, and all four sat down to table. Then the mother said, "Two out of the sack."

Instantly two rough men crept out of the sack, and began to beat the cousin as they cried:

> Greedy pack! Thievish pack!
> One—two—
> Give the peasant back his sack!
> One—two—

And they went on beating until the woman called to her eldest daughter, "Go and fetch your cousin from the bathroom. Tell him these two ruffians are beating me black and blue."

"I've not finished rubbing myself yet," said the peasant.

And the two ruffians kept on beating as they sang:

> Greedy pack! Thievish pack!
> One—two—
> Give the peasant back his sack!
> One—two—

Then the woman sent her second daughter and said, "Quick, quick, get him to come to me."

"I'm just washing my head," said the man.

Then she sent the youngest girl, and he said, "I've not done drying myself."

At last the woman could hold out no longer, and sent him the sack she had stolen.

Now he had quite finished his bath, and as he left the bathroom he cried, "Two into the sack."

And the two crept back at once into the sack. Then the man took both sacks, the good and the bad one, and went away home. When he was near the house he shouted, "Hallo, old woman, come and meet me!"

His wife only screamed out, "You broomstick, come here! Your back shall pay for this."

The man went into the cottage, hung his sack on a nail, and said, as the crane had taught him, "Two out of the sack."

Instantly two pretty lads sprang out of the sack, brought in oak tables, laid silken covers on them, and spread them with all sorts of delicious dishes and refreshing drinks.

The woman ate and drank, and praised her husband. "Well, now, old man, I won't beat you any more," said she. When they had done eating, the man carried off the good sack, and put it away in his storeroom, but hung the bad sack up on the nail. Then he lounged up and down in the yard.

Meantime his wife became thirsty. She looked with longing eyes at the sack, and at last she said, as her husband had done, "Two out of the sack."

And at once the two rogues with their big sticks crept out of the sack, and began to belabor her as they sang:

> Would you beat your husband true?
> Don't cry so!
> Now we'll beat you black and blue!
> Oh! Oh!"

The woman screamed out, "Old man, old man! Come here, quick! Here are two ruffians pummeling me fit to break my bones."

Her husband only strolled up and down and laughed, as he said, "Yes, they'll beat you well, old lady."

And the two thumped away and sang again:

> Blows will hurt, remember, crone,
> We mean you well, we mean you well;
> In future leave the stick alone,
> For how it hurts, You now can tell.
> One—two—

At last her husband took pity on her, and cried, "Two into the sack." He had hardly said the words before they were back in the sack again. From this time the man and his wife lived so happily together that it was a pleasure to see them, and so the story has an end.[243]

The Wife Who Would Not Be Beaten

India

There was once a raja's son who announced that he would marry no woman who would not allow him to beat her every morning and evening. The raja's servants hunted high and low in vain for a bride who would consent to these terms. At long last, they found a maiden who agreed to be beaten morning and evening if the prince would marry her. So the wedding took place, and for two or three days the prince hesitated to begin the beating; but one morning he got up and, taking a stick from the corner, went to his bride and told her that she must have her beating.

"Wait a minute," said she, "there is one thing I want to point out to you before you beat me. It is only on the strength of your father's position that you play the fine gentleman like this. Your wealth is all your father's, and it is on his wealth that you are relying. When you have earned something for yourself, and made a position for yourself, then I am willing that you should beat me and not before."

The prince saw that what his bride said was true and held his hand. Then, in order to earn wealth for himself, he set out on a trading expedition, taking quantities of merchandise loaded in sacks; and he had a large band of retainers with him, mounted on horses and elephants, and altogether made a fine show. The princess sent one of her own servants with the prince and gave him secret instructions to watch his opportunity, and if ever, when the prince was bathing, he should throw away a loin cloth, to take possession of it without the prince knowing anything about it and bring it to her. The prince journeyed on till he came to the country called Lutia.

The Raja of Lutia was walking on the roof of his palace and he saw the cavalcade approaching, and he sent a *sipahi*[244] to meet the prince and ask him this question: "Have you the secret of prosperity for ever or of prosperity for a day?" When this question was put to the prince he answered that he had the secret of prosperity for ever. When the Lutia raja was told of this answer, he ordered his men to stop the prince's train; so they surrounded them and seized all the merchandise and the prince's retainers fled on their horses and elephants and left him alone and penni-

---

[243]Type 564.   Source: Andrew Lang, *The Violet Fairy Book* (London, 1901), pp. 153-159. Lang's source: Aleksandr Afanasyev.

[244]An armed guard or messenger.

less. In his distress the prince was forced to take service with a rich Hindu, and he had nothing to live on but what his master chose to give him, and all he had to wear was a loin cloth like the poorest laborer.

The only man who did not desert him was the servant whom the princess had sent; and one day he saw that the prince had thrown away an old loin cloth while bathing; this he picked up and took home to his mistress, who put it away. When she heard all that had happened to her husband, she set out in her turn to the Lutia country, and all she took with her was a mouse and a shawl. When she reached the Lutia country the raja as before sent a messenger to ask whether she knew the secret of prosperity for ever or of prosperity for a day.

She answered, "prosperity for a day." Thereupon the raja had her sent for and also all the retainers who had deserted the prince and who had collected together in the neighborhood. When they had all come the raja said that he would now decide who should have all the wealth which had been taken from the prince. He produced a cat and said that the person towards whom the cat jumped should have all the wealth. So they all sat round the raja, and the princess had her mouse hidden under her shawl, and every now and then she kept uncovering its head and covering it up again. The cat soon caught sight of the mouse and, when the raja let it go, it jumped straight to the princess in hopes of catching the mouse. The raja at once adjudged all the merchandise to her, and she loaded it on the horses and elephants and took it home accompanied by her husband's retainers.

A few days afterwards her husband came home, having got tired of working as a servant, and, putting a bold face on it, he went up to her and said that now he was going to beat her; all the retainers who had accompanied him when he set out to trade and also the servant whom the princess had sent with him were present. Then, before them all, the princess took up the old loin cloth and asked him if he knew to whom it had belonged. At this reminder of his poverty the prince was dumb with shame. "Ask your retainers," continued the princess, "to whom all the merchandise with which you set out now rightfully belongs; ask them whether it is yours or mine, and then say whether you will beat me."

The prince had no answer to give her, and after this lesson gave up all idea of beating his wife.[245]

---

[245]Type 888A. Source: Cecil Henry Bompas, *Folklore of the Santal Parganas* (London, 1909), no. 28.

Bluebeards

Sulasa and Sattuka

The Jataka Tales

Once upon a time when Brahmadatta was reigning in Benares, there was a beautiful woman of the town, called Sulasa, whose price was a thousand pieces a night. There was in the same city a robber named Sattuka, as strong as an elephant, who used to enter rich men's houses at night and plunder at will. One day he was captured. Sulasa was standing at her window when the soldiers led Sattuka, his hands bound behind his back, down the street toward the place of execution.

She fell in love with him on sight, and said, "If I can free that stout fighting man, I will give up this bad life of mine and live respectably with him." She sent a thousand pieces to the chief constable, and thus gained his freedom. They lived together in delight and harmony for some time, but after three or four months, the robber thought, "I shall never be able to stay in this one place. But one can't go empty handed. Her ornaments are worth a hundred thousand pieces. I will kill her and take them."

So he said to her one day, "Dear, when I was being hauled along by the king's men, I promised an offering to a tree deity on a mountain top, who is now threatening me because I have not paid it. Let us make an offering."

She consented to accompany her husband to the mountain top to make the offering. She should, he said, to honor the deity, wear all of her ornaments.

When they arrived at the mountain top, he revealed his true purpose: "I have not come to present the offering. I have come with the intention of killing you and going away with all your ornaments. Take them all off and make a bundle of them in your outer garment."

"Husband, why would you kill me?"

"For your money."

"Husband, remember the good I have done you. When you were being hauled along in chains, I paid a large sum and saved your life. Though I might get a thousand pieces a day, I never look at another man. Such a benefactress I am to you. Do not kill me. I will give you much money and be your slave."

But instead of accepting her entreaties, he continued his preparations to kill her.

"At least let me salute you," she said. "I am going to make obeisance to you on all four sides." Kneeling in front of him, she put her head to his foot, repeated the act at his left side, then at his right side, then from behind. Once behind him, she took hold of him, and with the strength of an elephant threw him over a cliff a hundred times as high as a man. He was crushed to pieces and died on the spot. Seeing this deed, the deity who lived on the mountain top spoke this stanza:

> Wisdom at times is not confined to men;
> A woman can show wisdom now and then.

So Sulasa killed the robber. When she descended from the mountain and returned to her attendants, they asked where her husband was. "Don't ask me," she said, and mounting her chariot she went on to the city.[246]

The Brahman Girl That Married a Tiger

India

In a certain village there lived an old Brahman who had three sons and a daughter. The girl being the youngest was brought up most tenderly and become spoilt, and so whenever she saw a beautiful boy she would say to her parents that she must be wedded to him. Her parents were, therefore, much put about to devise excuses for taking her away from her youthful lovers. Thus passed on some years, until the girl was very nearly grown up, and then the parents, fearing that they would be driven out of their caste if they failed to dispose of her hand in marriage before she came to the years of maturity, began to be eager about finding a bridegroom for her.

Now near their village there lived a fierce tiger, that had attained to great proficiency in the art of magic, and had the power of assuming different forms. Having a great taste for Brahman's food, the tiger used now and then to frequent temples and other places of public refreshment in the shape of an old famished Brahman in order to share the food prepared for the Brahmans. The tiger also wanted, if possible, a Brahman wife to take to the woods, and there to make her cook his meals after her fashion. One day, when he was partaking of his meals in Brahman shape at a public feeding place, he heard the talk about the Brahman girl who was always falling in love with every beautiful Brahman boy.

Said he to himself, "Praised be the face that I saw first this morning. I shall assume the shape of a Brahman boy, and appear as beautiful as can be, and win the heart of the girl."

Next morning he accordingly assumed the form of a Brahman teacher proficient in the Ramayana near the landing of the sacred river of the village. Scattering holy ashes profusely over his body he opened the Ramayana and began to read.

---

[246]Source: *The Jataka; or, Stories of the Buddha's Former Births*, edited by E. B. Cowell (Cambridge, 1897), book 8, no. 419. Slightly shortened.

"The voice of the new teacher is most enchanting. Let us go and hear him," said some women among themselves, and sat down before him to hear him expound the great book. The girl for whom the tiger had assumed this shape came in due time to bathe at the river, and as soon as she saw the new teacher fell in love with him, and bothered her old mother to speak to her father about him, so as not to lose her new lover. The old woman too was delighted at the bridegroom whom fortune had thrown in her way, and ran home to her husband, who, when he came and saw the teacher, raised up his hands in praise of the great god Mahesvara. The teacher was now invited to take his meals with them, and as he had come with the express intention of marrying the daughter, he, of course, agreed.

A grand dinner followed in honor of the teacher, and his host began to question him as to his parentage, etc., to which the cunning tiger replied that he was born in a village beyond the adjacent wood. The Brahman had no time to wait for further inquiries, and as the boy was very fair he married his daughter to him the very next day. Feasts followed for a month, during which time the bridegroom gave every satisfaction to his new relatives, who supposed him to be human all the while. He also did full justice to the Brahman dishes, and swallowed everything that was placed before him.

After the first month was over the tiger bridegroom yearned for his accustomed prey, and hankered after his abode in the woods. A change of diet for a day or two is all very well, but to renounce his own proper food for more than a month was hard. So one day he said to his father-in-law, "I must go back soon to my old parents, for they will be pining at my absence. But why should we have to bear the double expense of my coming all the way here again to take my wife to my village? So if you will kindly let me take the girl with me I shall take her to her future home, and hand her over to her mother-in-law, and see that she is well taken care of."

The old Brahman agreed to this, and replied, "My dear son-in-law, you are her husband, and she is yours, and we now send her with you, though it is like sending her into the wilderness with her eyes tied up. But as we take you to be everything to her, we trust you to treat her kindly."

The mother of the bride shed tears at the idea of having to send her away, but nevertheless the very next day was fixed for the journey. The old woman spent the whole day in preparing cakes and sweetmeats for her daughter, and when the time for the journey arrived, she took care to place in her bundles and on her head one or two margosa leaves to keep off demons. The relatives of the bride requested her husband to allow her to rest wherever she found shade, and to eat wherever she found water, and to this he agreed, and so they began their journey.

The boy tiger and his human wife pursued their journey for an hour or so in free and pleasant conversation, when the girl happened to see a fine pond, around which the birds were warbling their sweet notes. She requested her husband to follow her to the water's edge and to partake of some of the cakes and sweetmeats with her.

But he replied, "Be quiet, or I shall show you my original shape."

This made her afraid, so she pursued her journey in silence until she saw another pond, when she asked the same question of her husband, who replied in the same tone.

Now she was very hungry, and not liking her husband's tone, which she found had greatly changed ever since they had entered the woods, said to him, "Show me your original shape."

No sooner were these words uttered than her husband's form changed from that of a man. Four legs, striped skin, a long tail, and a tiger's face came over him suddenly and, horror of horrors! a tiger and not a man stood before her! Nor were her fears stilled when the tiger in human voice began as follows: "Know henceforth that I, your husband, am a tiger—this very tiger that now speaks to you. If you have any regard for your life you must obey all my orders implicitly, for I can speak to you in human voice, and understand what you say. In an hour or so we shall reach my home, of which you will become the mistress. In the front of my house you will see half a dozen tubs, each of which you must fill up daily with some dish or other, cooked in your own way. I shall take care to supply you with all the provisions you want." So saying the tiger slowly conducted her to his house.

The misery of the girl may more be imagined than described, for if she were to object she would be put to death. So, weeping all the way, she reached her husband's house. Leaving her there he went out and returned with several pumpkins and some flesh, of which she soon prepared a curry and gave it to her husband. He went out again after this and returned in the evening with several vegetables and some more flesh, and gave her an order, "Every morning I shall go out in search of provisions and prey, and bring something with me on my return; you must keep cooked for me whatever I leave in the house."

So next morning as soon as the tiger had gone away she cooked everything left in the house and filled all the tubs with food. At the fourth hour the tiger returned and growled out, "I smell a man! I smell a woman in my wood." And his wife for very fear shut herself up in the house.

As soon as the tiger had satisfied his appetite he told her to open the door, which she did, and they talked together for a time, after which the tiger rested awhile, and then went out hunting again. Thus passed many a day, until the tiger's Brahman wife had a son, which also turned out to be only a tiger.

One day, after the tiger had gone out to the woods, his wife was crying all alone in the house, when a crow happened to peck at some rice that was scattered near her, and seeing the girl crying, began to shed tears.

"Can you assist me?" asked the girl.

"Yes," said the crow.

So she brought out a palmyra leaf and wrote on it with an iron nail all her sufferings in the wood, and requested her brothers to come and relieve her. This palmyra leaf she tied to the neck of the crow, which, seeming to understand her thoughts, flew to her village and sat down before one of her brothers. He untied the leaf and read the contents of the letter and told them to his other brothers. All the three then started for the wood, asking their mother to give them something to eat on the way. She had not enough rice for the three, so she made a big ball of clay and stuck it over with what rice she had, so as to make it look like a ball of rice. This she gave to the brothers to eat on their way, and started them off to the woods.

They had not proceeded long before they caught sight of a donkey. The youngest, who was of a playful disposition, wished to take the donkey with him. The two elder brothers objected to this for a time, but in the end they allowed him to have his own way. Further on they saw an ant, which the middle brother took with him. Near the ant there was a big palmyra tree lying on the ground, which the eldest took with him to keep off the tiger.

The sun was now high in the horizon and the three brothers became very hungry. So they sat down near a tank and opened the bundle containing the ball of rice. To their utter disappointment they found it to be all clay, but being extremely hungry they drank all the water in the pond and continued their journey. On leaving the tank they found a big iron tub belonging to the washerman of the adjacent village. This they took also with them in addition to the donkey, the ant, and the palmyra tree. Following the road described by their sister in her letter sent by the crow, they walked on and on until they reached the tiger's house.

The sister, overjoyed to see her brothers again, ran out at once to welcome them, "My dearest brothers, I am so glad to see that you have come here to relieve me after all, but the time for the tiger's coming home is approaching, so hide yourselves in the loft, and wait until he is gone." So saying, she helped her brothers to ascend into the loft.

By this time the tiger returned, and perceived the presence of human beings by the peculiar smell. He asked his wife whether anyone had come to their house. She said, "No." But when the brothers, who with their trophies of the way—the donkey, the ant, and so on—were sitting upon the loft, saw the tiger dallying with their sister, they were greatly frightened; so much so that the youngest, through fear, began to quake, and they all fell on the floor.

"What is all this?" said the terrified tiger to his wife.

"Nothing," said she, "but your brothers-in-law. They came here three hours ago, and as soon as you have finished your meals they want to see you."

"How can my brothers-in-law be such cowards?" thought the tiger to himself. He then asked them to speak to him, whereon the youngest brother put the ant which he had in his hand into the ear of the donkey, and as soon as the latter was bitten, it began to bawl out most horribly.

"How is it that your brothers have such a hoarse voice?" said the tiger to his wife.

He next asked them to show him their legs. Taking courage at the stupidity of the tiger on the two former occasions, the eldest brother now stretched out the palmyra tree.

"By my father, I have never seen such a leg," said the tiger, and asked his brothers-in-law to show their bellies. The second brother now showed the tub, at which the tiger shuddered, and saying, "such a harsh voice, so stout a leg, and such a belly, truly I have never heard of such persons as these!" He ran away.

It was already dark, and the brothers, wishing to take advantage of the tiger's terror, prepared to return home with their sister at once. They ate up what little food she had, and ordered her to start. Fortunately for her, her tiger child was

388

asleep. So she tore it into two pieces and suspended them over the hearth, and, thus getting rid of the child, she ran off with her brothers towards home.

Before leaving she bolted the front door from inside, and went out at the back of the house. As soon as the pieces of the cub, which were hung up over the hearth, began to roast, they dripped, which made the fire hiss and sputter; and when the tiger returned at about midnight, he found the door shut and heard the hissing of the fire, which he mistook for the noise of cooking muffins.

"I see," said he to himself, "how very cunning you are; you have bolted the door and are cooking muffins for your brothers. Let us see if we can't get your muffins."

So saying, he went around to the back door and entered his house, and was greatly perplexed to find his cub torn in two and being roasted, his house deserted by his Brahman wife, and his property plundered; for his wife, before leaving, had taken with her as much of the tiger's property as she could conveniently carry.

The tiger now discovered all the treachery of his wife, and his heart grieved for the loss of his son, that was now no more. He determined to be revenged on his wife, and to bring her back into the wood, and there tear her into many pieces in place of only two. But how to bring her back? He assumed his original shape of a young bridegroom, making, of course, due allowance for the number of years that had passed since his marriage, and next morning went to his father-in-law's house. His brothers-in-law and his wife saw from a distance the deceitful form he had assumed, and devised means to kill him. The younger ones too ran here and there to bring provisions to feed him sumptuously, and the tiger was highly pleased at the hospitable way in which he was received.

There was a ruined well at the back of the house, and the eldest of the brothers placed some thin sticks across its mouth, over which he spread a fine mat. Now it is usual to ask guests to have an oil bath before dinner, and so his three brothers-in-law requested the tiger to take his seat on the fine mat for his bath. As soon as he sat on it, the thin sticks being unable to bear his weight, gave way, and down fell the cunning tiger with a heavy crash! The well was at once filled in with stones and other rubbish, and thus the tiger was effectually prevented from doing any more mischief.

But the Brahman girl, in memory of her having married a tiger, raised a pillar of the well and planted a *tulasi* shrub on the top of it. Morning and evening, for the rest of her life, she used to smear the pillar with sacred cow dung, and water the tulasi shrub.

This story is told to explain the Tamil proverb, "Be quiet, or I shall show you my original shape."[247]

[247]Type 312A. Source: Mrs. Howard Kingscote and Pandit Natêsá Sástrî, *Tales of the Sun; or, Folklore of Southern India* (London, 1890), no. 10.

The Tiger's Bride

India

One day a woman went to cut thatching grass and she cut such a quantity that when she tied it up, the bundle was too big for her to lift onto her head; so she stood and called for someone to help her, but no one was within hearing and no one came. She called and called and at last began to promise that she would give her daughter in marriage to anyone who would help her.

After she had called out this a few times, a tiger suddenly appeared and asked what she wanted; she explained her difficulty, and the tiger undertook to lift the load onto her head, if she would really give him her daughter in marriage. She promised, and with the help of the tiger took up the bundle and went home.

Two or three days after, the tiger presented himself at her house and was duly married to the daughter. After the wedding the couple started for the tiger's home; all the way the unhappy bride wept and sang:

> How far off is our home, big head?

"You can just see the mouth of the cave," answered the tiger, and in a short time they came to a large cave. Then the tiger told her to set to work and cook a feast while he went off and invited his friends to come and share it. But the bride, when left alone, caught a cat and killed it and hung it over the fire, so that its blood dropped slowly into the pan and made a fizzling noise, as if cooking were going on; and then she ran off to her mother's house and climbed a tree which grew near it, and began to sing:

> You married me to a ti-ti-tiger;
> You threw me to a bear;
> Take back the necklace you gave me;
> Take back the bracelet and the diamonds and the coral.

Meanwhile the tiger returned with his friends and sat down outside the cave and told his wife to be quick with the cooking of the cakes, for he heard the hissing over the fire and thought that she was cooking. At last, as she did not come out, he got tired of waiting and went in to fetch her; then he saw that she had disappeared and had to go and tell his friends. They were very angry at being cheated out of a feast, and fell upon the tiger and beat him till he ran away and was seen no more. But his bride was left to flit from tree to tree singing:

> You married me to a ti-ti-tiger;
> You threw me to a bear;
> Take back the necklace you gave me;
> Take back the bracelet and the diamonds and the coral.[248]

---

[248]Type 311. Source: Cecil Henry Bompas, *Folklore of the Santal Parganas* (London, 1909),

Your Hen Is in the Mountain

Norway

Once upon a time there was an old widow who lived, with her three daughters, far away from the rest of the world, next to a mountain. She was so poor that her only animal was a single hen, which she prized as the apple of her eye. It was always cackling at her heels, and she was always running to look after it. One day, all at once, the hen was gone. The old woman went out, and walked around and around the cottage, looking and calling for her hen, but it was gone, and could not be found.

So the woman said to her oldest daughter, "You must just go out and see if you can find our hen, for we must have it back, even if we have to fetch it out of the mountain."

The daughter was ready enough to go, so she set off and walked up and down, and looked and called, but she could not find the hen. Suddenly, just as she was about to give up the hunt, she heard someone calling out from a cleft in the rock:

> Your hen is in the mountain!
> Your hen is in the mountain!

So she went into the cleft to see what it was, but she had barely set foot inside, when she fell through a trapdoor, deep, deep down, into an underground cavern. When she got to the bottom she went through many rooms, each finer than the one before it; but in the innermost room of all, a large ugly troll came to her and asked, "Will you be my sweetheart?"

"No! I will not," she said. She wouldn't have him for any price! All she wanted was to get above ground again as fast as ever she could, and to find her lost hen. Then the troll got so angry that he picked her up, twisted her head off, and then threw both the head and body into the cellar.

While this was going on, her mother sat at home waiting and waiting, but no daughter came. After she had waited a bit longer, and neither heard nor saw anything of her daughter, she told her middle daughter to go out and look for her sister, and, she added, "Give our hen a call at the same time."

So the second sister had to set off, and the very same thing happened to her. She was looking and calling, and suddenly she too heard a voice calling from the cleft in the rock:

> Your hen is in the mountain!
> Your hen is in the mountain!

She thought that this was strange, and went to see what it was. She too fell through the trapdoor, deep, deep down, into the cavern. She too went from room to room, and in the innermost one the troll came to her and asked if she would be his sweetheart? No, she would not. All she wanted was to get above ground

no. 45.

391

again, and hunt for her lost hen. The troll got angry, and picked her up, twisted her head off, and threw both head and body into the cellar.

Now, when the old woman had sat and waited seven lengths and seven breadths for her second daughter, and could neither see nor hear anything of her, she said to the youngest, "Now, you must go out and look for your sisters. It was silly to lose the hen, but it would be sillier still to lose both your sisters. Of course, you can give the hen a call at the same time." You see, the old woman's heart was still set on her hen.

Yes, the youngest was ready to go, and she walked up and down, hunting for her sisters and calling the hen, but she could neither see nor hear anything of them. She too came to the cleft in the rock, and heard something say:

> Your hen is in the mountain!
> Your hen is in the mountain!

She thought that this was strange, so she too went to see what it was, and she too fell through the trapdoor, deep, deep down, into a cavern. When she reached the bottom she went from one room to another, each grander than the one before it; but she wasn't at all afraid, and took time to look carefully about her. As she was peeping into this and that, she saw the trapdoor into the cellar, and looked down it, and what should she see there but her dead sisters. She barely had time to slam to the trapdoor before the troll came to her and asked, "Will you be my sweetheart?"

"With all my heart," answered the girl, for she saw very well how it had gone with her sisters. When the troll heard that, he brought her the finest clothes in the world. Indeed, she had only to ask, and she got whatever she wanted, because the troll was so glad that someone would be his sweetheart.

One day, after she had been there a little while, she was looking very gloomy and downcast, so the troll asked her what was the matter, and why she was so sad.

"Ah!" said the girl, "it's because I can't get home to my mother. I know that she has very little to eat and drink, and she has no one with her."

"Well!" said the troll, "I can't let you go to see her; but just stuff some meat and drink into a sack, and I'll carry it to her."

With many thanks, she said that she would do that. However, she put a lot of gold and silver into the bottom of the sack, then laid a little food on top. She told the ogre the sack was ready, but that he must be sure not to look into it. He gave his word not to look inside, and set off. As the troll walked off, she peeped out at him through a chink in the trapdoor. When he had gone a little way, he said, "This sack is very heavy. I'll just see what is inside." He was about to untie the sack, when the girl called out to him, "I can still see you! I can still see you!"

"The devil you can!" said the troll; "you must have mighty sharp eyes!" And the troll did not try to look into it again. When he reached the widow's cottage, he threw the sack in through the cottage door, saying, "Here you have meat and drink from your daughter; she doesn't want for anything."

After the girl had been in the mountain a good bit longer, one day a billy goat fell down the trapdoor.

392

"Who sent for you, you long-bearded beast!" said the troll, in an awful rage, and he picked up the goat, twisted his head off, and threw him into the cellar.

"Oh!" said the girl, "why did you do that? I might have had the goat to play with down here."

"Well!" said the troll, "you don't need to be so down in the mouth about it. I can bring the billy goat back to life again."

So saying, he took down a flask that was hanging on the wall, put the billy goat's head on his body again, and smeared it with some ointment from flask, and he was as well and as lively as before.

"Aha!" said the girl to herself; "that flask is worth something—that it is."

When she had been in the mountain some time longer, on a day when the troll was away, she took her oldest sister, put her head on her shoulders, smeared her with some of the ointment from the flask, just as she had seen the troll do with the billy goat, and in an instant her sister came to life again.

The girl stuffed her into a sack, laid a little food over her, and when the troll came home, she said to him, "Dear friend! Now do go home to my mother with a morsel of food again. I'm certain that the poor thing is both hungry and thirsty, and besides that, she's all alone in the world. But you must not look into the sack."

He said that he would carry the sack, and that he would not look into it. But when he had gone a little way, he thought that the sack was getting very heavy; and when he had gone a bit further he said to himself, "Come what will, I must see what's inside this sack, for however sharp her eyes may be, she can't see me all this way off."

But just as he was about to untie the sack, the girl inside the sack called out, "I can still see you! I can still see you!"

"The devil you can!" said the ogre; "then you must have mighty sharp eyes," for he thought it was the girl inside the mountain who was speaking. So he didn't dare so much as to peep into the sack again, but carried it straight to her mother as fast as he could, and when he got to the cottage door he threw it in through the door, and cried out, "Here you have meat and drink from your daughter; she wants for nothing."

When the girl had been in the mountain a while longer, she did the very same thing with her other sister. She put her head on her shoulders, smeared her with ointment from the flask, brought her to life, and put her into the sack. This time she crammed in also as much gold and silver as the sack would hold, laying just a little food on top.

"Dear friend," she said to the troll, "you really must run home to my mother with a little food again; and don't look into the sack."

Yes, the troll was eager to do as she wished, and he gave his word too that he wouldn't look into the sack; but when he had gone a little way he began to think that the sack was getting very heavy, and when he had gone a bit further, he could scarce stagger along under it, so he set it down, and was just about to untie the string and look into it, when the girl inside the sack cried out, "I can still see you! I can still see you!"

"The devil you can," said the troll, "then you must have mighty sharp eyes."

Well, he did not dare to try to look into the sack, but hurried straight to the girl's mother. When he got to the cottage he threw the sack in through the door, and roared out, "Here you have food from your daughter; she wants for nothing!"

After the girl had been there a good while longer, on a day when the troll had decided to go out for the day, the girl pretended to be sick. She moaned and complained. "There's no need for you to come home before twelve o'clock tonight," she said, "for I won't be able to have supper ready before then. I'm just too sick!"

As soon as the troll was out of the house, she stuffed some of her clothes with straw, and stood this straw girl in the corner by the chimney, with a broom in her hand, so that it looked just as though she herself were standing there. After that she stole off home, and got a marksman to stay in the cottage with her mother.

So when the clock struck twelve, or thereabouts, the troll came home, and the first thing he said to the straw girl was, "Give me something to eat."

But she did not answer him.

"Give me something to eat, I say!" called out the troll, "for I am almost starved."

But she did not have a word for him.

"Give me something to eat!" roared out the ogre the third time. "I think you'd better open your ears and hear what I say, or else I'll wake you up, I will!"

But the girl stood just as still as ever; so he flew into a rage, and gave her such a slap in the face, that the straw flew all about the room. When he saw that he had been tricked, he began to hunt everywhere. When he came to the cellar, and found both the girl's sisters missing, he soon figured out what had happened, and ran off to the cottage, saying, "I'll soon pay her for this!"

But when he reached the cottage, the marksman fired off his piece. The troll did not dare go into the house, for he thought it was thunder. So he set off for home again as fast as he could run; but just as he reached the trapdoor, the sun rose and he exploded.

There's a lot of gold and silver down there still, if you only knew where the trapdoor is![249]

Fitcher's Bird

Jacob and Wilhelm Grimm

Once upon a time there was a sorcerer who was a thief. He disguised himself as a poor man and went begging from house to house. A girl came to the door and brought him a piece of bread. He touched her, and she was forced

---

[249]Type 311. Source: Peter Christen Asbjørnsen and Jørgen Moe, *Norske Folkeeventyr* (Christiania [Oslo], 1842-1852), translated by George Webb Dasent (1859). Revised.

to jump into his pack basket. Then he carried her to his house where everything was splendid, and he gave her everything that she wanted.

One day he said, "I have to take care of something away from home. I will be away for a while. Here is an egg. Take good care of it. Carry it with you at all times. And here is a key, but at the risk of your life, do not go into the room that it opens. But as soon as he had gone, she unlocked the door and went into the room. In the middle there was a large basin. In it there were dead and dismembered people. She was so terrified that she dropped the egg, which she was holding in her hand, into the basin. She quickly took it out again and wiped off the blood, but it reappeared in an instant. She could not get the egg clean, no matter how much she wiped and scrubbed.

When the man returned, he asked for the egg and the key. He looked at them and knew that she had been in the blood chamber. "You did not heed my words," he said angrily, "and now you are going into the chamber against your will." With that he seized her, led her into the room, cut her up in pieces, and threw her into the basin with the others.

Sometime later the man went begging again. He captured the second daughter from the house, and the same thing happened to her as to the first one. She too opened the forbidden door, dropped the egg into the blood, and was cut to pieces and thrown into the basin.

Then the sorcerer wanted to have the third daughter. He captured her in his pack basket, carried her home, and at his departure gave her the egg and the key. However, the third sister was clever and sly. First of all, she put the egg in a safe place, and then she went into the secret chamber. When she saw her sisters in the basin, she found all of their parts and put each one back in its right place: head, body, arm, and leg. The parts started to move, and then they joined together, and the two sister came back to life. She took them both out of the room and hid them.

When the man returned and found that the egg was free of blood, he asked her to become his bride. She said yes, but told him that first he would have to carry a basket filled with gold on his back to her parents, and that meanwhile she would be getting ready for the wedding. Then she told her sisters to get help from home. She put them into the basket and covered them over with gold. Then she said to the man, "Carry this away. And don't you dare stop to rest. If you do, I'll be able to see through my window." He lifted the basket onto his back and started off, but it was so heavy that the weight nearly killed him. He wanted to rest a little, but one of the girls inside the basket called out, "I can see through my window that you are resting. Walk on at once!" He thought it was his bride calling out, so he got up and walked on. Every time he wanted to rest, he heard the call, and had to continue on.

Meanwhile, back at his house, his bride dressed up a skull and placed it in the attic window. Then she invited all the sorcerer's friends to the wedding. Then she dipped herself in a barrel of honey, cut open the bed, and rolled in the feathers so that no one would be able to recognize her. In this strange disguise, she left the house and started down the path. Soon she met some of the guests, who said, "You, Fitcher's bird, where are you coming from?"

395

"I'm coming from Fitcher's house."

"And what is his young bride doing?"

"She's cleaning the house from bottom to top. Right now she is looking out of the attic window."

Then she also met the bridegroom, who was returning home.

"You, Fitcher's bird, where are you coming from?"

"I'm coming from Fitcher's house."

"And what is my young bride doing?"

"She's cleaning the house from bottom to top. Right now she is looking out of the attic window."

The bridegroom looked up, and saw the disguised skull. Thinking it was his bride, he waved to it. But after he arrived home, and all his friends were there as well, the help came that the sisters had sent. They closed up the house and set it afire, and because no one could get out, they all perished in the flames.[250]

How the Devil Married Three Sisters

Italy

Once upon a time the Devil was seized with a desire to marry. He therefore left hell, took the form of a handsome young man, and built a fine large house. When it was completed and furnished in the most fashionable style he introduced himself to a family where there were three pretty daughters, and paid his addresses to the eldest of them. The handsome man pleased the maiden, her parents were glad to see a daughter so well provided for, and it was not long before the wedding was celebrated.

When he had taken his bride home, he presented her with a very tastefully arranged bouquet, led her through all the rooms of the house, and finally to a closed door. "The whole house is at your disposal," said he, "only I must request one thing of you; that is, that you do not on any account open this door."

Of course the young wife promised faithfully; but equally, of course, she could scarcely wait for the moment to come when she might break her promise. When the Devil had left the house the next morning, under pretense of going hunting, she ran hastily to the forbidden door, opened it, and saw a terrible abyss full of fire that shot up towards her, and singed the flowers on her bosom. When her husband came home and asked her whether she had kept her promise, she unhesitatingly said "Yes." But he saw by the flowers that she was telling a lie, and said, "Now I will not put your curiosity to the test any longer. Come with me. I will show you

[250]Type 311. Source: *Kinder- und Hausmärchen*, 1st ed. (Berlin, 1812/1815), v. 1, no. 46.

myself what is behind the door." Thereupon he led her to the door, opened it, gave her such a push that she fell down into hell, and shut the door again.

A few months after he wooed the next sister for his wife, and won her; but with her everything that had happened with the first wife was exactly repeated.

Finally he courted the third sister. She was a prudent maiden, and said to herself, "He has certainly murdered my two sisters; but then it is a splendid match for me, so I will try and see whether I cannot be more fortunate than they." And accordingly she consented. After the wedding the bridegroom gave her a beautiful bouquet, but forbade her, also, to open the door which he pointed out.

Not a whit less curious than her sisters, she, too, opened the forbidden door when the Devil had gone hunting, but she had previously put her flowers in water. Then she saw behind the door the fatal abyss and her sisters therein. "Ah!" she exclaimed, "poor creature that I am; I thought I had married an ordinary man, and instead of that he is the Devil! How can I get away from him?" She carefully pulled her two sisters out of hell and hid them. When the Devil came home he immediately looked at the bouquet, which she again wore on her bosom, and when he found the flowers so fresh he asked no questions; but reassured as to his secret, he now, for the first time, really loved her.

After a few days she asked him if he would carry three chests for her to her parents' house, without putting them down or resting on the way. "But," she added, "you must keep your word, for I shall be watching you."

The Devil promised to do exactly as she wished. So the next morning she put one of her sisters in a chest, and laid it on her husband's shoulders. The Devil, who is very strong, but also very lazy and unaccustomed to work, soon got tired of carrying the heavy chest, and wanted to rest before he was out of the street on which he lived; but his wife called out to him, "Don't put it down; I see you!"

The Devil went reluctantly on with the chest until he had turned the corner, and then said to himself, "She cannot see me here; I will rest a little."

But scarcely had he begun to put the chest down when the sister inside cried out, "Don't put it down; I see you still!" Cursing, he dragged the chest on into another street, and was going to lay it down on a doorstep, but he again heard the voice, "Don't lay it down, you rascal; I see you still!"

"What kind of eyes must my wife have," he thought, "to see around corners as well as straight ahead, and through walls as if they were made of glass!" and thus thinking he arrived, all in a perspiration and quite tired out, at the house of his mother-in-law, to whom he hastily delivered the chest, and then hurried home to strengthen himself with a good breakfast.

The same thing was repeated the next day with the second chest. On the third day she herself was to be taken home in the chest. She therefore prepared a figure which she dressed in her own clothes, and placed on the balcony, under the pretext of being able to watch him better; slipped quickly into the chest, and had the maid put it on the Devil's back. "The deuce!" said he; "this chest is a great deal heavier than the others; and today, when she is sitting on the balcony, I shall have so much the less chance to rest." So by dint of the greatest exertions he carried it, without stopping, to his mother-in-law, and then hastened home to breakfast, scolding, and with his back almost broken.

But quite contrary to custom, his wife did not come out to meet him, and there was no breakfast ready. "Margerita, where are you?" he cried, but received no answer. As he was running through the corridors, he at length looked out of a window and saw the figure on the balcony. "Margerita, have you gone to sleep? Come down. I am as tired as a dog, and as hungry as a wolf." But there was no reply. "If you do not come down instantly I will go up and bring you down," he cried, angrily; but Margerita did not stir. Enraged, he hastened up to the balcony, and gave her such a box on the ear that her head flew off, and he saw that the head was nothing but a milliner's form, and the body, a bundle of rags. Raging, he rushed down and rummaged through the whole house, but in vain; he found only his wife's empty jewel box. "Ha!" he cried; "she has been stolen from me and her jewels, too!" and he immediately ran to inform her parents of the misfortune. But when he came near the house, to his great surprise he saw on the balcony above the door all three sisters, his wives, who were looking down on him with scornful laughter.

Three wives at once terrified the Devil so much that he took his flight with all possible speed.

Since that time he has lost his taste for marrying.[251]

Blue Beard

Charles Perrault

There was once a man who had fine houses, both in town and country, a deal of silver and gold plate, embroidered furniture, and coaches gilded all over with gold. But this man was so unlucky as to have a blue beard, which made him so frightfully ugly that all the women and girls ran away from him.

One of his neighbors, a lady of quality, had two daughters who were perfect beauties. He desired of her one of them in marriage, leaving to her choice which of the two she would bestow on him. Neither of them would have him, and they sent him backwards and forwards from one to the other, not being able to bear the thoughts of marrying a man who had a blue beard. Adding to their disgust and aversion was the fact that he already had been married to several wives, and nobody knew what had become of them.

---

[251]Type 311. Source: Thomas Frederick Crane, *Italian Popular Tales* (Boston and New York, 1885), no. 16.

Blue Beard, to engage their affection, took them, with their mother and three or four ladies of their acquaintance, with other young people of the neighborhood, to one of his country houses, where they stayed a whole week.

The time was filled with parties, hunting, fishing, dancing, mirth, and feasting. Nobody went to bed, but all passed the night in rallying and joking with each other. In short, everything succeeded so well that the youngest daughter began to think that the man's beard was not so very blue after all, and that he was a mighty civil gentleman.

As soon as they returned home, the marriage was concluded. About a month afterwards, Blue Beard told his wife that he was obliged to take a country journey for six weeks at least, about affairs of very great consequence. He desired her to divert herself in his absence, to send for her friends and acquaintances, to take them into the country, if she pleased, and to make good cheer wherever she was.

"Here," said he," are the keys to the two great wardrobes, wherein I have my best furniture. These are to my silver and gold plate, which is not everyday in use. These open my strongboxes, which hold my money, both gold and silver; these my caskets of jewels. And this is the master key to all my apartments. But as for this little one here, it is the key to the closet at the end of the great hall on the ground floor. Open them all; go into each and every one of them, except that little closet, which I forbid you, and forbid it in such a manner that, if you happen to open it, you may expect my just anger and resentment."

She promised to observe, very exactly, whatever he had ordered. Then he, after having embraced her, got into his coach and proceeded on his journey.

Her neighbors and good friends did not wait to be sent for by the newly married lady. They were impatient to see all the rich furniture of her house, and had not dared to come while her husband was there, because of his blue beard, which frightened them. They ran through all the rooms, closets, and wardrobes, which were all so fine and rich that they seemed to surpass one another.

After that, they went up into the two great rooms, which contained the best and richest furniture. They could not sufficiently admire the number and beauty of the tapestry, beds, couches, cabinets, stands, tables, and looking glasses, in which you might see yourself from head to foot; some of them were framed with glass, others with silver, plain and gilded, the finest and most magnificent that they had ever seen.

They ceased not to extol and envy the happiness of their friend, who in the meantime in no way diverted herself in looking upon all these rich things, because of the impatience she had to go and open the closet on the ground floor. She was so much pressed by her curiosity that, without considering that it was very uncivil for her to leave her company, she went down a little back staircase, and with such excessive haste that she nearly fell and broke her neck.

Having come to the closet door, she made a stop for some time, thinking about her husband's orders, and considering what unhappiness might attend her if she was disobedient; but the temptation was so strong that she could not overcome it. She then took the little key, and opened it, trembling. At first she could not see anything plainly, because the windows were shut. After some moments she began to perceive that the floor was all covered over with clotted blood, on which lay the bodies of several dead women, ranged against the walls. (These were all the wives whom Blue Beard had married and murdered, one after another.) She thought she should have died for fear, and the key, which she, pulled out of the lock, fell out of her hand.

After having somewhat recovered her surprise, she picked up the key, locked the door, and went upstairs into her chamber to recover; but she could not, so much was she frightened. Having observed that the key to the closet was stained with blood, she tried two or three times to wipe it off; but the blood would not come out; in vain did she wash it, and even rub it with soap and sand. The blood still remained, for the key was magical and she could never make it quite clean; when the blood was gone off from one side, it came again on the other.

Blue Beard returned from his journey the same evening, saying that he had received letters upon the road, informing him that the affair he went about had concluded to his advantage. His wife did all she could to convince him that she was extremely happy about his speedy return.

The next morning he asked her for the keys, which she gave him, but with such a trembling hand that he easily guessed what had happened.

"What!" said he, "is not the key of my closet among the rest?"

"I must," said she, "have left it upstairs upon the table."

"Fail not," said Blue Beard, "to bring it to me at once."

After several goings backwards and forwards, she was forced to bring him the key. Blue Beard, having very attentively considered it, said to his wife, "Why is there blood on the key?"

"I do not know," cried the poor woman, paler than death.

"You do not know!" replied Blue Beard. "I very well know. You went into the closet, did you not? Very well, madam; you shall go back, and take your place among the ladies you saw there."

Upon this she threw herself at her husband's feet, and begged his pardon with all the signs of a true repentance, vowing that she would never more be disobedient. She would have melted a rock, so beautiful and sorrowful was she; but Blue Beard had a heart harder than any rock!

"You must die, madam," said he, "at once."

"Since I must die," answered she (looking upon him with her eyes all bathed in tears), "give me some little time to say my prayers."

"I give you," replied Blue Beard, "half a quarter of an hour, but not one moment more."

When she was alone she called out to her sister, and said to her, "Sister Anne" (for that was her name), "go up, I beg you, to the top of the tower, and look if my brothers are not coming. They promised me that they would come today, and if you see them, give them a sign to make haste."

Her sister Anne went up to the top of the tower, and the poor afflicted wife cried out from time to time, "Anne, sister Anne, do you see anyone coming?"

And sister Anne said, "I see nothing but a cloud of dust in the sun, and the green grass."

In the meanwhile Blue Beard, holding a great saber in his hand, cried out as loud as he could bawl to his wife, "Come down instantly, or I shall come up to you."

"One moment longer, if you please," said his wife; and then she cried out very softly, "Anne, sister Anne, do you see anybody coming?"

And sister Anne answered, "I see nothing but a cloud of dust in the sun, and the green grass."

"Come down quickly," cried Blue Beard, "or I will come up to you."

"I am coming," answered his wife; and then she cried, "Anne, sister Anne, do you not see anyone coming?"

"I see," replied sister Anne, "a great cloud of dust approaching us."

"Are they my brothers?"

"Alas, no my dear sister, I see a flock of sheep."

"Will you not come down?" cried Blue Beard.

"One moment longer," said his wife, and then she cried out, "Anne, sister Anne, do you see nobody coming?"

"I see," said she, "two horsemen, but they are still a great way off."

"God be praised," replied the poor wife joyfully. "They are my brothers. I will make them a sign, as well as I can for them to make haste."

Then Blue Beard bawled out so loud that he made the whole house tremble. The distressed wife came down, and threw herself at his feet, all in tears, with her hair about her shoulders.

"This means nothing," said Blue Beard. "You must die!" Then, taking hold of her hair with one hand, and lifting up the sword with the other, he prepared to strike off her head. The poor lady, turning about to him, and looking at him with dying eyes, desired him to afford her one little moment to recollect herself.

"No, no," said he, "commend yourself to God," and was just ready to strike.

At this very instant there was such a loud knocking at the gate that Blue Beard made a sudden stop. The gate was opened, and two horsemen entered. Drawing their swords, they ran directly to Blue Beard. He knew them to be his wife's brothers, one a dragoon, the other a musketeer; so that he ran away immediately to save himself; but the two brothers pursued and overtook him before he could get to the steps of the porch. Then they ran their swords through his body and left him dead. The poor wife was almost as dead as her husband, and had not strength enough to rise and welcome her brothers.

Blue Beard had no heirs, and so his wife became mistress of all his estate. She made use of one part of it to marry her sister Anne to a young gentleman who had loved her a long while; another part to buy captains' commissions for her brothers, and the rest to marry herself to a very worthy gentleman, who made her forget the ill time she had passed with Blue Beard.

> Moral: Curiosity, in spite of its appeal, often leads to deep regret. To the displeasure of many a maiden, its enjoyment is short lived. Once satisfied, it ceases to exist, and always costs dearly.

Another moral: Apply logic to this grim story, and you will ascertain that it took place many years ago. No husband of our age would be so terrible as to demand the impossible of his wife, nor would he be such a jealous malcontent. For, whatever the color of her husband's beard, the wife of today will let him know who the master is.[252]

Mr. Fox

England

Once upon a time there was a young lady called Lady Mary, who had two brothers. One summer they all three went to a country seat of theirs, which they had not before visited. Among the other gentry in the neighborhood who came to see them was a Mr. Fox, a bachelor, with whom they, particularly the young lady, were much pleased. He used often to dine with them, and frequently invited Lady Mary to come and see his house. One day that her brothers were absent elsewhere, and she had nothing better to do, she determined to go thither, and accordingly set out unattended. When she arrived at the house and knocked at the door, no one answered.

At length she opened it and went in; over the portal of the door was written: "Be bold, be bold, but not too bold." She advanced; over the staircase was the same inscription. She went up; over the entrance of a gallery, the same again. Still she went on, and over the door of a chamber found written:

Be bold, be bold, but not too bold,
Lest that your heart's blood should run cold!

She opened it; it was full of skeletons and tubs of blood. She retreated in haste, and, coming downstairs, saw from a window Mr. Fox advancing towards the house with a drawn sword in one hand, while with the other he dragged along a young lady by her hair. Lady Mary had just time to slip down and hide herself under the stairs before Mr. Fox and his victim arrived at the foot of them. As he pulled the young lady upstairs, she caught hold of one of the banisters with her hand, on which was a rich bracelet. Mr. Fox cut it off with his sword. The hand and bracelet fell into Lady Mary's lap, who then contrived to escape unobserved, and got safe home to her brothers' house.

---

[252]Type 312. Source: Andrew Lang, *The Blue Fairy Book* (London, ca. 1889), pp. 290-295. Lang's source: Charles Perrault, *Histoires ou contes du temps passé, avec des moralités: Contes de ma mère l'Oye* (Paris, 1697).

A few days afterwards Mr. Fox came to dine with them as usual. After dinner the guests began to amuse each other with extraordinary anecdotes, and Lady Mary said she would relate to them a remarkable dream she had lately had. I dreamt, said she, that as you, Mr. Fox, had often invited me to your house, I would go there one morning. When I came to the house I knocked at the door, but no one answered. When I opened the door, over the hall I saw written, "Be bold, be bold, but not too bold." But, said she, turning to Mr. Fox, and smiling, "It is not so, nor it was not so." Then she pursued the rest of the story, concluding at every turn with, "It is not so, nor it was not so," until she came to the room full of skeletons, when Mr. Fox took up the burden of the tale, and said:

> It is not so, nor it was not so,
> And God forbid it should be so!

which he continued to repeat at every subsequent turn of the dreadful story, until she came to the circumstance of his cutting off the young lady's hand, when, upon his saying, as usual:

> It is not so, nor it was not so,
> And God forbid it should be so!

Lady Mary retorts by saying:

> But it is so, and it was so,
> And here the hand I have to show!

at the same moment producing the hand and bracelet from her lap, whereupon the guests drew their swords, and instantly cut Mr. Fox into a thousand pieces.[253]

---

[253]Type 955. Source: Edwin Sidney Hartland, *English Fairy and Other Folk Tales* (London, ca. 1890), pp. 25-27. Hartland's source is Malone's *Shakspeare* (1821), v. 7, p. 163. Additional note by Hartland: This story was contributed to Malone's *Shakspeare* by Blakeway, in elucidation of Benedict's speech in "Much Ado about Nothing," Act 1, Scene 1— "Like the old tale, my Lord: it is not so, nor 'twas not so; but indeed, God forbid it should be so!" Blakeway adds that this is evidently an allusion to the tale of "Mr. Fox," "which Shakspeare may have heard, as I have, related by a great-aunt in childhood."

Shrewish Wives

Haaken Grizzlebeard

Norway

Once upon a time there was a princess who was so haughty and proud that no suitor was good enough for her. She made fun of them all, and sent them about their business, one after the other. But in spite of this, new suitors kept on coming to the palace, for she was a beauty, the wicked hussy!

One day a prince came to woo her, and his name was Haaken Grizzlebeard. The first night he was there, the princess commanded the king's jester to cut off the ears of one of the prince's horses, and to slit the jaws of the other up to the ears. The next day when the prince went out for a ride, the princess stood on the porch and watched him.

"Well!" she cried, "I never saw the like of this in all my life; the sharp north wind that blows here has taken the ears off one of your horses, while the other stood by gaping at what was going on until his jaws split right up to his ears."

With that she broke into a roar of laughter, ran in, slammed the door, and let him drive off.

He returned home; but as he went, he thought to himself that he would pay her off one day. After a bit, he put on a great beard of moss, threw a large fur cloak over his clothes, and dressed himself up like a beggar. He went to a goldsmith and bought a golden spinning wheel, and sat down with it under the princess's window and began to file away at his spinning wheel, and to turn it this way and that, for it wasn't quite in order, and besides, it did not have a stand.

So when the princess got up in the morning, she came to the window and opened it, and asked the beggar if he would sell his golden spinning wheel.

"No, it isn't for sale," said Haaken Grizzlebeard; "but if I may sleep outside your bedroom door tonight, I'll give it you."

The princess thought that that was a good bargain; there could be no danger in letting him sleep outside her door.

So she got the wheel and that night Haaken Grizzlebeard lay down outside her bedroom. But as the night wore on he began to freeze.

"Huttetuttetuttetu! It is so cold; "let me in," he cried.

"I think that you're out of your mind," said the princess.

"Oh, Huttetuttetuttetu! It is so bitter cold, please let me in," said Haaken Grizzlebeard again.

Be quiet! Hold your tongue!" said the princess. "If my father were to know that there was a man in the house, I should be in serious trouble."

404

"Oh, Huttetuttetuttetu! I'm almost frozen to death. Just let me come inside and lie on the floor," said Haaken Grizzlebeard.

There was nothing she could do about it. She had to let him in, and when he was inside, he lay on the ground and fell sound asleep.

Some time afterward, Haaken came again with the stand to the spinning wheel and sat down under the princess's window, and began to file at it, for it was not quite in order. When she heard him filing, she opened the window and began to talk to him, and to ask what he had.

"Oh, only the stand to that spinning wheel which your royal highness bought. I thought that because you had the wheel you might like to have the stand as well."

"What do you want for it?" asked the princess. It was not for sale any more than the wheel had been, but she might have it if she would let him sleep on the floor of her bedroom the next night.

She agreed, but only if he would to be sure to lie still, and not to shiver and call out "huttetu," or any such stuff. Haaken Grizzlebeard promised fair enough, but as the night wore on he began to shiver and shake, and to ask whether he might not come nearer, and lie on the floor alongside the princess's bed.

She couldn't do anything about it; she had to let him, or the king would hear the noise he was making. So Haaken Grizzlebeard lay alongside the princess's bed, and fell sound asleep.

It was a long while before Haaken Grizzlebeard came again, this time with him a golden yarn reel, and he sat down and began to file away at it under the princess's window. Then came the old story over again. When the princess heard what was going on, she came to the window and asked him how he was, and whether he would sell the golden yarn reel?

"It is not to be had for money; but I'll give it to you for nothing, if you'll let me sleep in your bedroom tonight, with my head on your bedstead."

She agreed, but only if he would give his word to be quiet and make no noise. He said he would do his best to be still; but as the night wore on he again began to shiver and shake until his teeth chattered.

"Huttetuttetuttetu! It is so bitter cold! Do let me get into bed and warm myself a little," said Haaken Grizzlebeard.

"Get into bed!" said the princess; "why, you must be out of your mind."

"Huttetuttetuttetu!" said Haaken; "do let me get into bed. Huttetuttetuttetu!"

"Hush! Hush! For God's sake, be quiet!" said the princess." If father knows there is a man in here, I shall be in serious trouble. I'm sure he'll kill me on the spot."

"Huttetuttetuttetu! Let me get into bed," said Haaken Grizzlebeard, who kept on shivering so that the whole room shook. Well, there was nothing she could do about it. She had to let him get into bed. He slept soundly and gently, but a little while later the princess gave birth to a child. The king grew so wild with rage that he very nearly made an end of both mother and baby.

Just after this happened, Haaken Grizzlebeard came tramping that way once more, as if by chance, and took his seat down in the kitchen, like any other beggar.

When the princess came out and saw him, she cried, "Ah, God have mercy on me, for the bad luck you have brought me. Father is ready to fly into a rage. Let me go home with you."

"You're too well bred to follow me," said Haaken, "for I have nothing but a log hut to live in; and I don't know how I would ever feed you, for it's all I can do just to find food for myself."

"I don't care how you get it, or whether you get it at all," she said; "only let me be with you, for if I stay here any longer, my father will surely kill me."

So she got permission to go with the beggar, as she called him, and they walked a long, long way, even though she was not a good walker. When she left her father's land and entered into another, she asked whose it was?

"Oh! This is Haaken Grizzlebeard's, if you must know," he said.

"Indeed!" said the princess. "I could have married him if I had wanted to, and then I would not have had to walk about like a beggar's wife."

They came to grand castles, and woods, and parks, and when she asked whose they were, the beggar's answer was always the same, "Oh! They are Haaken Grizzlebeard's." The princess was very sad that she had not chosen the man who had such broad lands. Last of all they came to a palace, where he said he was known, and where he thought he could get work for her, so that they might have something to live on. He built a cabin at the edge of the woods for them to live in. Every day he went to the king's palace, as he said, to chop wood and draw water for the cook, and when he came back he brought a few scraps of food; but they did not go very far.

One day, when he came home from the palace, he said, "Tomorrow I will stay at home and look after the baby, but you must get ready to go to the palace, for the prince said you were to come and try your hand at baking."

"Bake!" said the princess; "I can't bake, for I never did such a thing in my life."

"Well, you must go," said Haaken, "since the prince has said it. If you can't bake, you can learn; you have only got to look how the rest bake; and as you leave, you must steal some bread for me."

"I can't steal," said the princess.

"You can learn that too," said Haaken; "you know that we are very short of food. But take care that the prince doesn't see you, for he has eyes everywhere."

When she was on her way, Haaken ran by a shortcut and reached the palace long before her, and took off his rags and beard, and put on his princely robes.

The princess took her turn in the bakehouse, and did as Haaken had asked her, for she stole bread until her pockets were crammed full. That evening, when she was about to go home, the prince said, "We don't know very much about this old vagabond woman. I think we'd best see if she is taking anything away with her."

He thrust his hand into all her pockets, and felt her all over, and when he found the bread, he became very angry, and raised a great stir.

She began to moan and cry, and said, "The beggar made me do it, and I couldn't help it."

"Well," said the prince at last, "it ought to have gone hard with you; but for the beggar's sake I will forgive you this time."

When she was on her way home, he took off his robes, put on his skin cloak, and his false beard, and reached the cabin before her. When she came home, he was busy tending the baby.

"You made me go against my own conscience. Today was the first time I ever stole, and it will be the last;" and with that she told him how it had gone with her, and what the prince had said.

A few days later, Haaken Grizzlebeard came home in the evening and said, "Tomorrow I will stay at home and tend the baby, for they are going to kill a pig at the palace, and you must help them make sausages."

"I make sausages!" said the princess; "I can't do any such thing. I have eaten sausages often enough, but I have never made one in my life."

But there was nothing that she could do about it; the prince had said it, and she had to go. As for not knowing how, she only had to do what the others did, and at the same time Haaken asked her to steal some sausages for him.

"No, I can't steal," she said; "you know how it went last time."

"Well, you can learn to steal. Who knows? You may have better luck this time," said Haaken Grizzlebeard.

When she was on her way, Haaken ran by a shortcut, reached the palace long before her, took off his skin cloak and false beard, and stood in the kitchen with his royal robes as she came in. So the princess stood by when the pig was killed. She made sausages with the others, and she did as Haaken had told her to, and stuffed her pockets full of sausages. That evening, when she was about to go home, the prince said, "This beggar's wife was long fingered last time; we had better see that she isn't carrying anything off."

So he began to thrust his hands into her pockets, and when he found the sausages he was again very angry, and made a great to do, threatening to send for the constable and have her thrown into jail.

"Oh, God bless your royal highness; do let me off! The beggar made me do it," she said, and cried bitterly.

"Well," said Haaken, "you ought to be punished for it; but for the beggar's sake I forgive you."

When she was gone, he changed his clothes again, ran by the shortcut, and when she reached the cabin, there he was before her. She told him the whole story, and swore it was the last time he would get her to do such a thing.

Now a little later the man came home from the palace and said, "Our prince is going to be married, but the bride is sick, so the tailor can't measure her for her wedding gown. The prince wants you to go to the palace and be measured instead of the bride; for he says that you are just the same height and shape. But after you have been measured, don't just leave. You can stand about, and when the tailor cuts out the gown, you can pick up the largest scraps, and bring them home for a vest for me."

"No, I can't steal," she said; "besides, you know how it went last time."

"You can learn then," said Haaken, "and you may have better luck this time."

She thought it bad, but still she went and did as she was told. She stood by while the tailor was cutting out the gown, and she swept up all the biggest scraps, and stuffed them into her pockets; and when she was on her way out, the prince said, "We may as well see if this old girl has not been long fingered this time too."

So he began to feel and search her pockets, and when he found the pieces he became very angry, and began to stamp and scold furiously, while she cried and said, "Please forgive me; the beggar made me do it, and I couldn't help it."

"Well, you ought to be punished for it," said Haaken; "but for the beggar's sake I forgive you."

So it went now just as it had gone before, and when she got back to the cabin, the beggar was there before her. "Oh, Heaven help me," she said; "you will be the death of me by making me wicked. The prince was so angry that he threatened me both with the constable and jail."

One evening, some time later, Haaken came home to the cabin and said, "The prince wants you to go up to the palace and stand in for the bride, for the bride is still sick in bed. He won't put off the wedding, and he says, that you are so like her, that no one could tell one from the other; so tomorrow you must get ready to go to the palace."

"I think that you are out of your mind, both you and the prince," she said. "Do you think I look fit to stand in the bride's place? Look at me! Can any beggar's wench look worse than I?"

"Well, the prince said you were to go, and so you have to go," said Haaken Grizzlebeard.

There was nothing that she could do about it. She had to go; and when she reached the palace, they dressed her out so finely that no princess ever looked so beautiful.

The bridal procession went to church, where she stood in for the bride, and when they came back, there was dancing and merriment in the palace. But just as she was dancing with the prince, she saw a gleam of light through the window, and behold, the cabin at the edge of the woods was all one bright flame.

"Oh! The beggar, and the baby, and the cabin," she screamed out, and was just about to faint.

"Here is the beggar, and there is the baby, and so let the cabin burn away," said Haaken Grizzlebeard.

She recognized him again, and then the joy and celebration began for real. Since that time, I have heard nothing more about them.[254]

[254]Type 900. Source: Peter Christen Asbjørnsen and Jørgen Moe, *Norske Folkeeventyr* (Christiania [Oslo], 1842-1852), translated by George Webb Dasent (1859). Revised.

Women Who Rule Their Husbands

The Man and His Two Wives

Aesop

A middle-aged man had two wives, one who was old and one who was young. Each one desired to see him like herself. Now the man's hair was turning gray, which the young wife did not like, as it made him look too old for her husband. So every night she used to comb his hair and pull out the white ones. But the elder wife saw her husband growing gray with great pleasure, for she did not like to be mistaken for his mother. So every morning she used to arrange his hair and pull out as many of the black ones as she could. In consequence the man soon found himself entirely bald.

> Moral: Yield to all and you will soon have nothing to yield.[255]

The Too Particular Wife

India

There was once a man with a large tumor on his forehead, and his wife was so ashamed of it that she would never go about with him anywhere for fear of being laughed at. One day she went with a party of friends to see the *Charak Puja*.[256] Her husband wished to go with her, but she flatly declined to allow him. So when she had gone, he went to a friend's house and borrowed a complete set of new clothes and a large pagri.[257] When he had rigged himself out in these he could hardly be recognized; but his forehead with the tumor was quite visible. Then he too went off to the fair and found his wife busy dancing. After watching

---

[255]Type 1215A. Source: Joseph Jacobs, *The Fables of Aesop* (London, 1894), no. 63.

[256]A festival at which men are swung by hooks from a pole.

[257]A turban.

her for some time he borrowed one of the drums and began to play for the dancers; and in particular he played and danced just in front of his wife.

When he saw that his wife was preparing to go home, he started off ahead, got rid of his fine clothes, and took the cattle out to graze. Presently he went back to the house and asked his wife whether she had enjoyed the fun. "You should have come to see it for yourself," said she.

"But you would not let me! Otherwise I should have gone."

"Yes," answered his wife, "I was ashamed of the lump on your forehead, but other people do not seem to mind, for there was a man there with a lump just like yours who was playing the drum and taking a leading part in the fun, and no one seemed to laugh at him. So in the future I shall not mind going about with you."[258]

The Two-Headed Weaver

The Panchatantra

In a certain place there lived a weaver by the name of Mantharaka, which means "the simpleton." One day, while weaving cloth, the wooden pieces on his loom broke. He took an ax, and set forth to find some wood. He found a large sissoo tree at the ocean's shore, and said aloud, "Now this is a large tree. If I fell it, I will have wood enough for all my weaving tools."

Having thus thought it through, he raised his ax to begin cutting. However, a spirit lived in this tree, and he said, "Listen! This tree is my home, and it must be spared in any event, because I like it here where my body can be stroked by the cool breezes that blow in from the ocean's waves.

The weaver said, "Then what am I to do? If I don't find a good tree, then my family will starve. You will have to go somewhere else. I am going to cut it down."

The spirit answered, "Listen, I am at your service. Ask whatever you would like, but spare this tree!"

The weaver said, "If that is what you want, then I will go home and ask my friend and my wife, and when I return, you must give me what I ask for."

The spirit promised, and the weaver, beside himself with joy, returned home. Upon his arrival in his city, he saw his friend, the barber, and said, "Friend, I have gained control over a spirit. Tell me what I should demand from him!"

The barber said, "My dear friend, if that is so, then you should demand a kingdom. You could be king, and I would be your prime minister, and we two would first enjoy the pleasures of this world and then those of the next one. For they say:

[258]Source: Cecil Henry Bompas, *Folklore of the Santal Parganas* (London, 1909), no. 142.

A prince who piously gives to others, achieves fame in this world, and through these good deeds, he will arrive in heaven, equal to the gods themselves."

The weaver spoke, "Friend, so be it! But let us also ask my wife."

The barber said, "One should never ask women for advice. They also say:

A wise man gives women food, clothing, jewelry, and above all the duties of marriage, but he never asks for their advice.

And further:

That house must perish where a woman, a gambler, or a child is listened to,

And:

A man will advance and be loved by worthy people as long as he does not secretly listen to women. Women think only of their own advantage, of their own desires. Even if they love only their own son, still, he will serve their wishes."

The weaver spoke, "Even though this is true, she nonetheless must be asked, because she is subservient to her husband."

Having said this, he went quickly to his wife and said to her, "Dear one, today I have gained control over a spirit, who will grant me one wish. Hence I have come to ask for your advice. Tell me, what should I ask for? My friend the barber thinks that I should request a kingdom."

She answered, "Oh, son of your excellence, what do barbers understand? You should never do what they say. After all, it is stated:

A reasonable person will no sooner take advice from dancers, singers, the low born, barbers, or children than from beggars.

Furthermore, a king's life is an unending procession of annoyances. He must constantly worry about friendships, animosities, wars, servants, defense alliances, and duplicity. He never gets a moment's rest, because:

Anyone who wants to rule must prepare his spirit for misfortune. The same container that is used for salve can also be used to pour out bad luck. Never envy the life of a king."

The weaver said, "You are right. But what should I ask for?"

She answered, "You can now work on only one piece of cloth at a time. That is barely enough to pay for the necessities. You should ask for another pair of arms and a second head, so that you can work on two pieces of cloth at once, one in front of you, and one behind you. We can sell the one for household necessities, and you can use the money from the second one for other things. You will thus gain the praise of your relatives, and you will make gains in both worlds."

After hearing his, he spoke with joy, "Good, you faithful wife! You have spoken well, and I will do what you say. That is my decision." With that he went to the spirit and let his will be known, "Listen, if you want to fulfill my wish, then give me another pair of arms and another head." He had barely spoken before he was two-headed and four-armed. Rejoicing, he returned home, but the people there

411

thought that he was a demon and beat him with sticks and stones, until he fell over dead.

And that is why I say:

He who cannot think for himself and will not follow the advice of friends, he will push himself into misfortune, just like the weaver Mantharaka.[259]

The Three Wishes

1001 Nights

A certain man had longed all his life to look upon the Night of Power, and one night it befell that he gazed at the sky and saw the angels, and Heaven's gates thrown open; and he beheld all things prostrating themselves before their Lord, each in its several stead. So he said to his wife, "Harkye, such an one, verily Allah hath shown me the Night of Power, and it hath been proclaimed to me, from the invisible world, that three prayers will be granted unto me; so I consult thee for counsel as to what shall I ask."

Quoth she, "Oh man, the perfection of man and his delight is in his prickle; therefore do thou pray Allah to greaten thy yard and magnify it."

So he lifted up his hands to heaven and said, "Oh Allah, greaten my yard and magnify it." Hardly had he spoken when his tool became as big as a column and he could neither sit nor stand nor move about nor even stir from his stead; and when he would have carnally known his wife, she fled before him from place to place. So he said to her, "Oh accursed woman, what is to be done? This is thy list, by reason of thy lust."

She replied, "No, by Allah, I did not ask for this length and huge bulk, for which the gate of a street were too strait. Pray Heaven to make it less."

So he raised his eyes to Heaven and said, "Oh Allah, rid me of this thing and deliver me therefrom." And immediately his prickle disappeared altogether and he became clean smooth.

When his wife saw this she said, "I have no occasion for thee, now thou art become pegless as a eunuch, shaven and shorn."

And he answered her, saying, "All this comes of thine ill-omened counsel and thine imbecile judgment. I had three prayers accepted of Allah, wherewith I might have gotten me my good, both in this world and in the next, and now two wishes are gone in pure waste, by thy lewd will, and there remaineth but one."

---

[259]Similar to type 750A. Source: *Pantschatantra: Fünf Bücher indischer Fabeln, Märchen und Erzählungen*, translated from the Sanskrit into German by Theodor Benfey (Leipzig, 1859), v. 2, book 5, story 8.

Quoth she, "Pray Allah the Most High to restore thee thy yard as it was."

So he prayed to his Lord and his prickle was restored to its first estate. Thus the man lost his three wishes by the lack of wit in the woman.[260]

The Sausage

Sweden

There was once an old woman, who was all alone one evening in her cottage, occupied with her household affairs. While she was waiting for her husband, who was away at work over in the forest, and while she was bustling about, a fine, grand lady came in, and so the woman began to curtsy and curtsy, for she had never seen such a grand person before.

"I should be so much obliged if you would lend me your brewing pan," said the lady, "for my daughter is going to be married, and I expect guests from all parts."

Oh, dear, yes! That she might have, said the woman, although she could not remember whether she had ever seen her before, and so she went to fetch the pan.

The lady took it, and thanked the woman, saying that she would pay her well for the loan of it, and so she went her way.

Two days afterwards the lady came back with it, and this time she also found the woman alone.

"Many thanks for the loan," said the lady. "and now in return you shall have three wishes."

And with this the lady left, and vanished so quickly that the old woman had not even time to ask her name or where she lived. But that did not matter, she thought, for now she had three wishes, and she began to think what she should wish for. She expected her husband back soon, and she thought it would be best to wait until he came home and could have a say in the matter. But the least they could wish for must be a fine big farm—the best in the parish, and a box full of money, and just fancy how happy and comfortable they would be then, for they had worked so hard all their days! Ah, yes, then the neighbors would have something to wonder at, for you may guess how they would stare at all the fine things she would have.

But since they were now so rich it was really a shame that there should be nothing but some blue, sour milk and some hard crusts of bread in the cupboard for her husband when he came home tired and weary, he who was fond of hot food. She

---

[260]Type 750A. Source: *The Book of the Thousand Nights and a Night*, translated by Richard F. Burton (Privately printed, 1885), v. 6, pp. 180-181. The full title of this story is "The Three Wishes, or the Man who Longed to see the Night of Power." Although I usually find Burton's translation style too florid for twentieth-century taste, his linguistic ornamentation seems to fit this tale, so I have let it stand.

had just been to her neighbor's and there she had seen a fine big sausage, which they were going to have for supper.

"Ah, deary me, I wish I had that sausage here!" sighed the old woman; and the next moment a big sausage lay on the table right before her.

She was just going to put it in the pan when her husband came in.

"Father, father!" cried the woman, "it's all over with our troubles and hard work now. I lent my brewing pan to a fine lady, and when she brought it back she promised we should have three wishes. And now you must help me to wish for something really good, for you're so clever at hitting upon the right thing—and it's all true, for just look at the sausage, which I got the moment I wished for it!"

"What do you mean, you silly old woman?" shouted the husband, who became angry. "Have you been wishing for such a paltry thing as a sausage, when you might have had anything you liked in the world? I wish the sausage were sticking to your nose, since you haven't any better sense."

All at once the woman gave a cry, for sure enough there was the sausage sticking to her nose; and she began tearing and pulling away at it, but the more she pulled the firmer it seemed to stick. She was not able to get it off.

"Oh, dear! oh, dear!" sobbed the woman. "You don't seem to have any more sense than I, since you can wish me such ill luck. I only wanted something nice for you, and then—, oh dear! oh, dear!" and the old woman went on crying and sobbing.

The husband tried, of course, to help his wife to get rid of the sausage; but for all he pulled and tugged away at it he did not succeed, and he was nearly pulling his wife's head off her body.

But they had one wish left, and what were they now to wish?

Yes, what were they to wish? They might, of course, wish for something very find and grand; but what could they do with all the finery in the world, as long as the mistress of the house had a long sausage sticking to the end of her nose? She would never be able to show herself anywhere!

"You wish for something," said the woman in the midst of her crying.

"No, you wish," said the husband, who also began crying when he saw the state his wife was in, and saw the terrible sausage hanging down her face.

So he thought he would make the best use he could of the last wish, and said, "I wish my wife was rid of that sausage."

And the next moment it was gone! They both became so glad that they jumped up and danced round the room in great glee—for you must know that although a sausage may be ever so nice when you have it in your mouth, it is quite a different thing to have one sticking to your nose all your life.[261]

---

[261]Type 750A. Source: Gabriel Djurklou, *Fairy Tales from the Swedish*, translated by H. L. Brækstad (New York, 1901), pp. 27-32.

414

The Bullock's Balls

The Panchatantra

In a certain place there lived a large bullock by the name of Tîkschnabrischana, which means "having substantial balls." Because of his excessive pride, he left his herd and wandered about in the forest, tearing up the banks as he pleased and devouring the emerald-colored grass.

In this same forest there lived a jackal by the name of Pralobhaka, which means "the greedy one." One day he was sitting pleasantly with his wife on an island in the river. Tîkschnabrischana came up to this island to have a drink of water. When the jackal's wife saw the balls, she said to her husband, "Master, just look! This bullock has two pieces of meat hanging down. They will be falling off immediately, at the least in a few hours. Take heed of this, and follow him."

The jackal answered, "Loved one, there is nothing certain about their falling off. Why do you ask me to set forth on such a futile task? Let me stay here with you, and together we can eat the mice that come here to drink. This is their pathway. If I leave you to follow the bullock, then someone else will come here and take over this spot. It is not a good idea, for it is said:

> He who gives up a sure thing for an uncertainty will lose the sure thing, and the uncertainty will remain just that."

The jackal's wife said, "Oh, you are a low-spirited creature. You are satisfied with the worst things that you can find. They also say:

> It is easy to fill a little brook and also the paws of a little mouse. Ordinary people are easily satisfied. They are pleased with the smallest things.

For this reason a good man must always be active. They also say:

> With every beginning there is a will to act. Avoid idleness, and join the community of the intelligent and the powerful. Think not that fate alone rules. Cease not to work. Without effort the sesame seed will not give up its oil.

And further:

> A foolish man is happy with little. His heart is satisfied just thinking of wealth.

It is thus not appropriate for you to say, 'It is uncertain, whether or not they will fall off.' It is also said:

> Active people deserve praise. Those with pride will be praised. What sort of scoundrel will wait until Indra brings him water?

Furthermore, I am mightily tired of eating mouse meat. These two pieces of meat look as though they will soon fall off. You must follow him. Nothing else will do!"

After hearing all this, the jackal left his mouse catching, and followed after Tîkschnabrischana. They rightly say:

415

A man is master in all things, until he lets his will be turned by a woman's words.

And further:

The impossible seems possible, the unachievable easily achieved, and the inedible edible to the man who is spurred on by a woman's words.

Thus, together with his wife, he followed the bullock a long time, but the two balls did not fall off. In the fifteenth year, the jackal finally said wearily to his wife, "Fifteen years, my love, I have kept my eyes on those hanging things to see whether or not they are going to fall off, but they still hold fast. Nor will they fall off in the future. Let us return to catching mice!"[262]

The Fisherman and His Wife

Jacob and Wilhelm Grimm

There was once upon a time a fisherman and his wife who lived together in a piss pot[263] near the sea. Everyday the fisherman went out fishing, and he fished a long time. Once he was sitting there fishing and looking into the clear water when his hook went to the bottom, deep down, and when he pulled it out, he had caught a large flounder. Then the flounder said to him, "I beg you to let me live. I am not an ordinary flounder, but an enchanted prince. Put me back into the water, and let me swim."

"Well," said the man, "there's no need to say more. I can certainly let a fish swim away who knows how to talk." Then he put it back into the water, and the flounder quickly disappeared to the bottom, leaving a long trail of blood behind him.

The man then went home to his wife in the piss pot and told her that he had caught a flounder that had told him he was an enchanted prince, and that he had let it swim away.

"Didn't you ask for anything first?" said the woman.

"No," said the man. What should I have asked for?"

---

[262]Type 115. Source: *Pantschatantra: Fünf Bücher indischer Fabeln, Märchen und Erzählungen*, translated from the Sanskrit into German by Theodor Benfey (Leipzig, 1859), v. 2, book 2, story 6.

[263]The couple's place of residence, in the originally published Low German, is called a "Pisputt." Most translators give this unambiguously earthy word a figurative meaning in English. Thus, one sees "shack," "pigsty," "miserable little hovel," "dirty hovel," and "chamber pot" in various English translations. I have chosen to keep with the low road, and call a Pisputt a piss pot.

"Oh," said the woman. "It is terrible living in this piss pot. It is filled with stench and filth. Go back and ask for a little hut for us."

The man did not want to, but he went back to the sea, and when he arrived it was all yellow and green, and he stood next to the water and said:

> Mandje! Mandje! Timpe Te!
> Flounder, flounder, in the sea!
> My wife, my wife Ilsebill,
> Wants not, wants not, what I will

The flounder swam up and said, "What does she want then?"

"Oh," said the man, "I did catch you, and my wife says that I really should have asked for something. She doesn't want to live in a piss pot any longer. She would like to have a hut."

"Go home," said the flounder. "She already has it."

The man went home, and his wife was standing in the door of a hut, and she said to him, "Come in. See, now isn't this much better." And there was a parlor and a bedroom and a kitchen; and outside there was a little garden with all kinds of vegetables, and a yard with hens and ducks.

"Oh," said the man. "Now we can live well."

"Yes," said the woman, "we'll give it a try."

Everything went well for a week or two, and then the woman said, "Husband. This hut is too small. The yard and the garden are too little. I want to live in a large stone castle. Go back to the flounder and tell him to get a castle for us."

"Oh, wife," said the man. The flounder has just given us the hut. I don't want to go back so soon. It may make the flounder angry."

"I know he can do it," said the woman, "and he won't mind. Just go!"

So, with a heavy heart, the man went back, and when he came to the sea, the water was quite purple and gray and dark blue, but it was still, and he stood there and said:

> Mandje! Mandje! Timpe Te!
> Flounder, flounder, in the sea!
> My wife, my wife Ilsebill,
> Wants not, wants not, what I will

"What does she want then?" said the flounder.

"Oh," said the man sadly, "my wife wants to live in a stone castle."

"Go home. She's already standing before the door," said the flounder.

So the man went home, and his wife was standing in front of a large palace.

"See, husband," she said. "Isn't this beautiful?" And with that they went inside together. There were many servants inside, and the walls were all white, and there were golden chairs and tables in the parlor, and outside the castle there was a garden and a forest a half mile long, and there were elk and deer and rabbits, and there were cow and horse stalls in the yard.

"Oh," said the man, "now we can stay in this beautiful castle and be satisfied."

"We'll think about it," said the woman. "Let's sleep on it." And with that they went to bed.

The next morning the woman awoke. It was daylight. She poked her husband in the side with her elbow and said, "Husband, get up. We should be king over all this land."

"Oh, wife," said the man, "why do you want to be king? I don't want to be king."

"Well, I want to be king."

"Oh, wife," said the man, "how can you be king? The flounder won't want to do that."

"Husband," said the woman, "Go there immediately. I want to be king."

So the man, saddened because his wife wanted to be king, went back. And when he arrived at the sea it was dark gray, and the water heaved up from below. He stood there and said:

> Mandje! Mandje! Timpe Te!
> Flounder, flounder, in the sea!
> My wife, my wife Ilsebill,
> Wants not, wants not, what I will

"What does she want then," said the flounder.

"Oh," said the man, "my wife wants to be king."

"Go home. She's already king," said the flounder.

Then the man went home, and when he arrived at the palace, there were so many soldiers, and drums, and trumpets, and his wife was sitting on a high throne of gold and diamonds, and she was wearing a large golden crown and on either side of her there stood a line of maidens-in-waiting, each one a head shorter than the other.

"Oh," said the man, "are you king now?"

"Yes," she said, "I am king."

And after he had looked at her awhile, he said, "It is nice that you are king. Now we don't have to wish for anything else."

"No, husband," she said, "I have been king too long. I can't stand it any longer. I am king, but now I would like to become emperor."

"Oh," said the man, "why do you want to become emperor?"

"Husband," she said, "go to the flounder. I want to be emperor."

"Oh, wife," said the man, "he can't make you emperor. I can't tell him to do that."

"I am king," said the woman, "and you are my husband. Now go there immediately!"

So the man went, and on his way he thought, "This is not going to end well. To ask to be emperor is shameful. The flounder is going to get tired of this." With that he arrived at the sea. The water was entirely black and dense, and a strong wind blew over him that curdled the water. He stood there and said:

Mandje! Mandje! Timpe Te!
Flounder, flounder, in the sea!
My wife, my wife Ilsebill,
Wants not, wants not, what I will

"What does she want then," said the flounder.

"Oh," he said, "my wife wants to become emperor."

"Go home," said the flounder. "She's already emperor."

Then the man went home, and when he arrived, his wife was sitting on a very high throne made of one piece of gold, and she was wearing a large golden crown that was two yards high, and guards were standing at her side, each one smaller than the other, beginning with the largest giant and ending with the littlest dwarf, who was no larger than my little finger. Many princes and counts were standing in front of her. The man went and stood among them and said, "Wife, are you emperor now?"

"Yes," she said, "I am emperor."

"Oh," said the man, taking a good look at her. "Wife, it's good that you are emperor."

"Husband," she said. "Why are you standing there? I'm emperor now, and I want to become pope as well."

"Oh, wife!" said the man. "Why do you want to become pope. There is only one pope in all Christendom."

"Husband," she said, "I want to become pope before the day is done."

"No, wife," he said, "the flounder cannot make you pope. It's not good."

"Husband, what nonsense! If he can make me emperor, then he can make me pope as well. Now go there immediately!"

Then the man went, and he felt sick all over, and his knees and legs were shaking, and the wind was blowing, and the water looked like it was boiling, and ships, tossing and turning on the waves, were firing their guns in distress. There was a little blue in the middle of the sky, but on all sides it had turned red, as in a terrible lightning storm. Full of despair he stood there and said:

Mandje! Mandje! Timpe Te!
Flounder, flounder, in the sea!
My wife, my wife Ilsebill,
Wants not, wants not, what I will

"What does she want then?" said the flounder.

"Oh," said the man, "my wife wants to become pope."

"Go home," said the flounder. "She's already pope."

Then he went home, and when he arrived there, his wife was sitting on a throne that was two miles high, and she was wearing three large crowns. She was surrounded with church-like splendor, and at her sides there were two banks of candles. The largest was as thick and as tall as the largest tower, down to the smallest kitchen candle. "Wife," said the man, giving her a good look, "are you pope now?"

"Yes," she said, "I am pope."

"Oh," said the man. "It is good that you are pope. Wife, we can be satisfied, now that you are pope. There's nothing else that you can become."

"I have to think about that," said the woman. Then they both went to bed, but she was not satisfied. Her desires would not let her sleep. She kept thinking what she wanted to become next. Then the sun came up. "Aha," she thought, as she watched the sunrise through her window. "Couldn't I cause the sun to rise?" Then she became very grim and said to her husband, "Husband, go back to the flounder. I want to become like God."

The man, who was still mostly asleep, was so startled that he fell out of bed. "Oh, wife," he said, "go on as you are and remain pope."

"No," said the woman, tearing open her bodice. "I will not be quiet. I can't stand it when I see the sun and the moon coming up, and I can't cause them to rise. I want to become like God!"

"Oh, wife," said the man. "The flounder can't do that. He can make you emperor and pope, but he can't do that."

"Husband," she said, looking very gruesome, "I want to become like God. Go to the flounder right now!"

The man trembled with fear at every joint. Outside there was a terrible storm. Trees and mountains were shaking. The heaven was completely black, and there was thunder and lightning. In the sea he could see black waves as high as mountains, and they were capped with white crowns of foam. He said:

> Mandje! Mandje! Timpe Te!
> Flounder, flounder, in the sea!
> My wife, my wife Ilsebill,
> Wants not, wants not, what I will

"What does she want then," said the flounder.
"Oh," he said, "she wants to become like God."
"Go home. She is sitting in her piss pot again."
And they are sitting there even today.[264]

---

[264]Type 555. Source: *Kinder- und Hausmärchen*, 1st ed. (Berlin, 1812/1815), v. 1, no. 19. The Grimms' source for this tale, recorded in wonderfully simple, but poetic Low German, was the romantic painter Philipp Otto Runge (1777-1810).

The Queen's Whim

Georgia

A certain queen wished to have a palace built of the bones of all kinds of birds. The king ordered birds to be caught, and the building was begun. Bones of all kinds were brought and cleaned, and the walls were rising, but they could not find a hedge sparrow, and, as the queen wanted all sorts of birds, a search was made for the missing one. At last the hedge sparrow was found, and brought before the king, who asked where she had been.

"Mighty monarch! I have been flying all over the kingdom counting the men and women; unfortunately there are twice as many women as men." The king ordered the bird to be punished for telling him such a shameless falsehood.

"King of kings," said the hedge sparrow, "perhaps I did not count in the same way as you do."

"How did you count, then?"

"I counted all those men who are under the slipper of women as old women."

The hedge sparrow thus hinted that the king himself was an old woman because he had not strength of mind enough to resist the foolish whims of his wife.[265]

The Black Mare Is a Better Horse

Denmark

There was once a man who was traveling about in the world with a string of horses and a wagon full of eggs. He gave an egg to those households where the wife ruled the husband, and he intended to give a horse to any household where the husband ruled the wife. Until now he had only given out eggs. Finally he came to a house where it appeared that the husband was in charge, and he decided to spend the night.

The next morning he wanted to be on his way. He thanked for the lodging and the good hospitality and told the husband to take his pick of two horses, a brown one and a black one. "I'll take the brown one," said the husband.

"No, don't be a fool," cried the wife. "The black mare is a better horse."

"All right," said the husband. "Little woman, if you say so, I'll take the black one." Then the stranger took an egg from his wagon, gave it to him, and drove off. And they could only gaze longingly after the brown horse and the black horse.[266]

---

[265]Type 1365. Source: Marjory Wardrop, *Georgian Folk Tales* (London, 1894), p. 164.

The Baneyrwal and His Drowned Wife

India

There was once a sudden flood in the Indus, which washed away numbers of people, and, among others, the wife of a certain Baneyrwal. The distracted husband was wandering along the banks of the river, looking for the dead body, when a countryman accosted him thus, "Oh friend, if, as I am informed, your wife has been carried away in the flood, she must have gone down the stream with the rest of the folk; yet you are going up the stream."

"Ah, sir," answered the wretched Baneyrwal, "you did not know that wife of mine. Her perversity was such that she always went clean contrary to everyone else, and, even now that she is drowned, I know full well that, if other bodies have floated down the river, hers *must* have floated up!"[267]

Scissors

Joseph Jacobs

Once upon a time, though it was not in my time nor in your time nor in anybody else's time, there lived a cobbler named Tom and his wife named Joan. And they lived fairly happily together, except that whatever Tom did Joan did the opposite, and whatever Joan thought Tom thought quite contrariwise. When Tom wanted beef for dinner Joan liked pork, and if Joan wanted to have chicken Tom would like to have duck. And so it went on all the time.

Now it happened that one day Joan was cleaning up the kitchen and, turning suddenly, she knocked two or three pots and pans together and broke them all. So Tom, who was working in the front room, came and asked Joan, "What's all this? What have you been doing?" Now Joan had got the pair of scissors in her hand, and sooner than tell him what had really happened she said, "I cut these pots and pans into pieces with my scissors."

"What," said Tom, "cut pottery with your scissors, you nonsensical woman; you can't do it!" "I tell you I did with my scissors!"

---

[266]Type 1366A. Retold from Sven Grundtvig, *Gamle danske Minder i Folkemunde* (Copenhagen, 1854-1861), v. 2, no. 121. Essentially the same story is told in England, except that there the color of the better horse is gray.

[267]Type 1365A. Source: Charles Swynnerton, *Indian Nights' Entertainment; or, Folk-Tales from the Upper Indus* (London, 1892), no. 35.

"You couldn't."

"I did."

"You couldn't."

"I did."

"Couldn't."

"Did."

"Couldn't."

"Did."

"Couldn't."

"Did."

At last Tom got so angry that he seized Joan by the shoulders and shoved her out of the house and said, "If you don't tell me how you broke those pots and pans I'll throw you into the river." But Joan kept on saying, "It was with the scissors"; and Tom got so enraged that at last he took her to the bank of the river and said, "Now for the last time, will you tell me the truth; how did you break those pots and pans?"

"With the scissors."

And with that he threw her into the river, and she sank once, and she sank twice, and just before she was about to sink for the third time she put her hand up into the air, out of the water, and made a motion with her first and middle finger as if she were moving the scissors. So Tom saw it was no use to try to persuade her to do anything but what she wanted. So he rushed up the stream and met a neighbor who said, "Tom, Tom, what are you running for?"

"Oh, I want to find Joan; she fell into the river just in front of our house, and I am afraid she is going to be drowned."

"But," said the neighbor, "you're running up stream."

"Well," said Tom, "Joan always went contrariwise whatever happened." And so he never found her in time to save her.[268]

The Merry Wives

Denmark

Once there stood three houses in a row, wall to wall. In one lived a tailor, in the next, a carpenter, and in the third, a smith. The three men were married, and their wives were the best of friends. They often told each other what

---

[268]Types 1365A, 1365B. Source: Joseph Jacobs, *European Folk and Fairy Tales* (New York, 1916), no. 4. This widespread tale often opens with a man and wife arguing over whether something should be cut with a knife (the husband's position) or with scissors (favored by the wife). The husband, in desperation, pushes his wife into the river, but she still gets the last word, making a scissors sign with her fingers as she drowns.

stupid men their husbands were, but they never could agree as to which one of them was the most stupid man; for each one of the women was sure that her husband must be the most stupid.

The three women used to go to church together every Sunday, and on the way they had a good opportunity to chat and gossip together. After the service they always stopped at a little tavern where they had a measure of brandy together. Now at that time a measure cost three shillings, so each woman had to pay one shilling. After a time the price of spirits went up so that a measure cost four shillings. That they did not like at all, as there were only three of them, and no one of them wanted to pay the extra shilling.

So one day on the way home from church they talked the matter over and agreed that the woman whose husband was the most stupid and allowed the worst trick to be played on him, need not pay for her drink thereafter.

The next day the tailor's wife said to her husband, "I have engaged some girls to come here tomorrow to card wool, for there is much to be done and we have to hurry. Now in the evening the young men will be sure to come, and the young people will want to have their fun together, so, of course, no work will be done then. If only we had a rather vicious dog we could easily keep the fellows away."

"Yes," said her husband, "that is very true."

"Listen," she continued, "you could act as watchdog and frighten the young men away from the house."

The man hardly thought that he could; nevertheless, he yielded to his wife's entreaties. So towards evening, she fastened some woolly skins about him, drew a wool cap over his head, and fastened him with a chain to their kennel. There he stood and growled and barked at everybody that approached, and his neighbors' wives amused themselves famously with him.

On the following day when the carpenter came home from his work, his wife clasped her hands and exclaimed, "For heaven's sake, husband dear, what is the matter with you? You are certainly sick." But he had not the faintest idea that anything was the matter with him; all that he knew was that he was very hungry. So he seated himself at the table and began to eat; but his wife who sat opposite him, shook her head and looked very sad.

"Dear, you are looking worse and worse; you are very pale, and I can see clearly that something serious is the matter with you." Now the man began to become uneasy himself, and to think that he was not well. "It is really high time that you should go to bed," said his wife; at last she succeeded in getting him to go to bed. She covered him up well and gave him hot drinks, and finally the man said that he really felt wretched. "You will certainly never recover from this illness, my poor husband," said the woman, "I am sure that you are going to die." Soon after that she said, "Now we shall have to bid each other farewell, for death has set his seal upon you, and now I must close your eyes for you are dead." And as she spoke, she did so. The foolish carpenter, who believed all that his wife said, believed that he was dead and lay perfectly quiet, letting his wife do what she wished.

She then called in her neighbors, and they helped her put her husband in a coffin—it was one that he had made himself. This the woman had prepared very comfortably; she had bored holes in the lid, so that her husband might have air, made a soft bed for him to lie on, and then covered him up with a warm blanket. She folded his hands on his breast, but instead of putting a bible or a hymnbook in them, she gave him a bottle of brandy. After the man had lain there a short time, he took a swallow of the liquor, then another and yet another, until he fell into a deep sleep and dreamed that he was in heaven.

In the meantime all the people of the village had learned that the carpenter had died and was to be buried on the following day. Meanwhile what did the smith's wife do? Her husband had come home intoxicated, and had fallen asleep. While he was sleeping, his wife daubed him with pitch from top to toe, and let him sleep until late the next forenoon, when the pallbearers and the funeral procession were already on the way to the church with the coffin. Then the smith's wife rushed in to her husband and woke him, saying that he had overslept himself and must hurry if he wanted to reach the church in time to pay his last respects to his friend. The smith was confused for he knew nothing about a funeral, but his wife hurried him, explaining to him the while that the carpenter had died the day before.

"But," said the smith, "I must put on my black suit."

"You fool," said the wife, "you have it on already, do hurry up and go."

So the smith ran and as he approached the procession, he called to the people to wait for him. They looked around and seeing the black figure running toward them, thought it was the devil. That frightened them nearly to death, so that they threw down the coffin and ran away as fast as they could. As it crashed to the ground the lid flew off, and the carpenter awoke and sat up to look out and see what was going on. Then he remembered what had taken place, and knew that he was dead and had to be buried. He recognized the smith, and said in a feeble voice, "Dear neighbor, if I were not already dead I should certainly laugh myself to death, to see you come to my corpse in that guise."

From that time on, the carpenter's wife never had to pay for her measure of brandy, for they all had to acknowledge that she had made the worst fool of her husband.[269]

---

[269]Type 1406. Source: Sven Grundtvig, *Danish Fairy Tales*, translated by J. Grant Cramer (Boston, 1919), no. 6.

Talkative Wives

The Telltale Wife

India

Once upon a time a man was setting out in his best clothes to attend a village meeting. As he was passing at the back of the house his maidservant happened to throw a basket of cow dung on the manure heap and some of it accidentally splashed his clothes. He thought that he would be laughed at if he went to the meeting in dirty clothes so he went back to change them; and he put the dirty cloth he took off in an earthen pot and covered the mouth with leaves and hung it to the roof of the room in which he and his wife slept.

Two or three days later his wife began to question him as to what was in the pot hanging from the roof. At first he refused to tell her; but every time she set eyes on it she renewed her questioning; for a time he refused to gratify her curiosity, saying that no woman could keep a secret, but she protested that she would tell no one; her husband's secrets were her own; at last he pretended that his patience was worn out and having made her promise never to tell a soul, he said, "I have killed a man, and to prevent the murder being traced I cut off his head and hid it in that pot; mind you do not say a word or my life will be forfeit."

For a time nothing more was said, but one day husband and wife had a quarrel; high words and blows passed between them and at last the woman ran out of the house, crying, "You have struck me, I shall let it be known that you are a murderer." She went to the village headman and told him what was hidden in the pot; the villagers assembled and bound the supposed murderer with ropes and took him to the police. The police officer came and took down the pot and found in it nothing but a stained cloth. So he fined the headman for troubling him with false information and went away. Then the man addressed his fellow villagers in these words, "Listen to me: Never tell a secret to a woman and be careful in your conversation with them; they are sure to let out a secret and one day will turn your accusers."

From that time we have learned the lesson that anything which you tell to a woman will become known.[270]

---

[270]Type 1381C. Source: Cecil Henry Bompas, *Folklore of the Santal Parganas* (London, 1909), no. 88.

426

How a Fish Swam in the Air and a Hare in the Water

Andrew Lang

Once upon a time an old man and his wife lived together in a little village. They might have been happy if only the old woman had had the sense to hold her tongue at proper times. But anything which might happen indoors, or any bit of news which her husband might bring in when he had been anywhere, had to be told at once to the whole village, and these tales were repeated and altered until it often happened that much mischief was made, and the old man's back paid for it.

One day, he drove to the forest. When he reached the edge of it he got out of his cart and walked beside it. Suddenly he stepped on such a soft spot that his foot sank in the earth.

"What can this be?" thought he. "I'll dig a bit and see."

So he dug and dug, and at last he came on a little pot full of gold and silver.

"Oh, what luck! Now, if only I knew how I could take this treasure home with me—but I can never hope to hide it from my wife, and once she knows of it she'll tell all the world, and then I shall get into trouble."

He sat down and thought over the matter a long time, and at last he made a plan. He covered up the pot again with earth and twigs, and drove on into the town, where he bought a live pike and a live hare in the market.

Then he drove back to the forest and hung the pike up at the very top of a tree, and tied up the hare in a fishing net and fastened it on the edge of a little stream, not troubling himself to think how unpleasant such a wet spot was likely to be to the hare.

Then he got into his cart and trotted merrily home.

"Wife!" cried he, the moment he got indoors. "You can't think what a piece of good luck has come our way."

"What, what, dear husband? Do tell me all about it at once."

"No, no, you'll just go on and tell everyone."

"No, indeed! How can you think such things! For shame! If you like I will swear never to—"

"Oh, well! If you are really in earnest then, listen."

And he whispered in her ear, "I've found a pot full of gold and silver in the forest! Hush!—"

"And why didn't you bring it back?"

"Because we'll drive there together and bring it carefully back between us."

So the man and his wife drove to the forest.

As they were driving along the man said, "What strange things one hears, wife! I was told only the other day that fish will now live and thrive in the tree tops and that some wild animals spend their time in the water. Well, well! Times are certainly changed."

"Why, you must be crazy, husband! Dear, dear, what nonsense people do talk sometimes."

"Nonsense, indeed! Why, just look. Bless my soul, if there isn't a fish, a real pike I do believe, up in that tree."

"Gracious!" cried his wife. "How did a pike get there? It *is* a pike—you needn't attempt to say it's not. Can people have said true—"

But the man only shook his head and shrugged his shoulders and opened his mouth and gaped as if he really could not believe his own eyes.

"What are you standing staring at there, stupid?" said his wife. "Climb up the tree quick and catch the pike, and we'll cook it for dinner."

The man climbed up the tree and brought down the pike, and they drove on.

When they got near the stream he drew up.

"What are you staring at again?" asked his wife impatiently. "Drive on, can't you?"

"Why, I seem to see something moving in that net I set. I must just go and see what it is."

He ran to it, and when he had looked in it he called to his wife, "Just look! Here is actually a four-footed creature caught in the net. I do believe it's a hare."

"Good heavens!" cried his wife. "How did the hare get into your net? It *is* a hare, so you needn't say it isn't. After all, people must have said the truth—"

But her husband only shook his head and shrugged his shoulders as if he could not believe his own eyes.

"Now what are you standing there for, stupid?" cried his wife. "Take up the hare. A nice fat hare is a dinner for a feast day."

The old man caught up the hare, and they drove on to the place where the treasure was buried. They swept the twigs away, dug up the earth, took out the pot, and drove home again with it.

And now the old couple had plenty of money and were cheery and comfortable. But the wife was very foolish. Every day she asked a lot of people to dinner and feasted them, until her husband grew quite impatient. He tried to reason with her, but she would not listen.

"You've got no right to lecture me!" said she. "We found the treasure together, and together we will spend it."

Her husband took patience, but at length he said to her, "You may do as you please, but I shan't give you another penny."

The old woman was very angry. "Oh, what a good-for-nothing fellow to want to spend all the money himself! But just wait a bit and see what I shall do."

Off she went to the governor to complain of her husband.

"Oh, my lord, protect me from my husband! Ever since he found the treasure there is no bearing him. He only eats and drinks, and won't work, and he keeps all the money to himself."

The governor took pity on the woman, and ordered his chief secretary to look into the matter.

The secretary called the elders of the village together, and went with them to the man's house.

"The governor," said he, "desires you to give all that treasure you found into my care."

The man shrugged his shoulders and said, "What treasure? I know nothing about a treasure."

"How? You know nothing? Why your wife has complained of you. Don't attempt to tell lies. If you don't hand over all the money at once you will be tried for daring to raise treasure without giving due notice to the governor about it."

"Pardon me, your excellency, but what sort of treasure was it supposed to have been? My wife must have dreamt of it, and you gentlemen have listened to her nonsense."

"Nonsense, indeed," broke in his wife. "A kettle full of gold and silver, do you call that nonsense?"

"You are not in your right mind, dear wife. Sir, I beg your pardon. Ask her how it all happened, and if she convinces you I'll pay for it with my life."

"This is how it all happened, Mr. Secretary," cried the wife. "We were driving through the forest, and we saw a pike up in the top of a tree—"

"What, a *pike?*" shouted the secretary. "Do you think you may joke with me, pray?"

"Indeed, I'm not joking, Mr. Secretary! I'm speaking the bare truth."

"Now you see, gentlemen," said her husband, "how far you can trust her, when she chatters like this."

"Chatter, indeed? I! Perhaps you have forgotten, too, how we found a live hare in the river?"

Everyone roared with laughter; even the secretary smiled and stroked his beard, and the man said, "Come, come, wife, everyone is laughing at you. You see for yourself, gentlemen, how far you can believe her."

"Yes, indeed," said the village elders, "it is certainly the first time we have heard that hares thrive in the water or fish among the tree tops."

The secretary could make nothing of it all, and drove back to the town. The old woman was so laughed at that she had to hold her tongue and obey her husband ever after, and the man bought wares with part of the treasure and moved into the town, where he opened a shop, and prospered, and spent the rest of his days in peace.[271]

---

[271]Type 1381. Source: Andrew Lang, *The Violet Fairy Book* (London, 1901), pp. 148-152.

The Treasure

Denmark

There was once a poor peasant who tilled a small field that belonged to a rich landowner. One day while he was plowing, his plow struck something so violently that it could not be moved. At first the man thought that it was a stone, but when he looked more carefully he found that it was a large chest full of old coins. It was gold and silver money that had probably been hidden there many hundred years ago in war times.

The peasant filled a bag with the money and dragged it home, for he thought that he had as good a right to keep the money as anyone else. The original owner had, of course, died many generations ago. In spite of that, he feared that the landowner would claim and seize the money when he learned that it had been found in his field. So the peasant said nothing to anybody except his wife about the find, and he begged her to keep silent about it.

But she could not keep the secret, and had to tell some of her friends about the good fortune. To be sure she asked each one separately not to tell anybody; but as they could not keep the secret either, at last the news of the discovery of the treasure came to the ears of the landowner.

Soon after that he rode out to the peasant's cottage, which lay far out on a lonely heath. There was, however, nobody at home except the woman, for her husband had just gone to town to get some money changed. So when the landowner asked the woman about the matter, she told him all that she knew—that her husband had found a chest full of money out in the field, and that he was not at home now, and that she did not know where he had put the money. The owner then said that he would return another time, and make further inquiry about the money.

When the peasant came home, his wife told him all that had happened; nevertheless, he did not reproach her. The next day he took his horses and wagon and asked his wife to accompany him to the town. There he exchanged all his old money for new coins, and invested the proceeds carefully and to good advantage. Then be bought a bushel of little rolls, which he put into a large bag. The man and his wife ate and drank to their hearts content, and towards evening they started on their homeward journey.

It was late in the autumn, and it was raining and blowing hard as they drove home in the dark. But the wine she had drunk had gone to the head of the wife, and she slept soundly on the back seat. After they had gone for some distance, she was awakened by a roll that fell on her head, and immediately after that another one fell into her lap; and as soon as she fell asleep, rolls again began to rain down upon her. These her husband was throwing into the air so that they should fall upon her.

"But what is happening?" the woman called to her husband, "it seems to me that it is raining rolls."

"Yes," said her husband, "that is just what it is doing; we are having terrible weather."

430

As they were passing the landowner's house, the woman was awakened by the braying of a donkey.

"What was that?" she exclaimed, feeling very uneasy.

"Well, I hardly like to say," replied her husband, "but if I must tell the truth, it was the devil who once loaned our landlord some money, and is now tormenting him because he will not pay the interest; he is thrashing him with a horsewhip."

"Hurry up," said the woman, "and get away from here as fast as you can." So the man whipped up his horses, and at last they reached home safe and sound.

But when they were home the husband said, "Listen, wife, I heard some bad news when we were in town. The enemy is in our land and this night he will be in our neighborhood. So you must crawl into the potato cellar in order to be out of danger, while I shall stay up stairs and protect our property as well as I can."

So the peasant's wife went down into the cellar, while her husband took his gun and went outside, and shot and cried out and made a great noise. This he kept up all night, and towards morning he told his wife that she could come up. "Fortunately," he said, "I was able to hold my own. I shot down many of the enemy, who at last were compelled to retire, taking with them their dead and wounded."

"Thank God," she said, "that everything has turned out well; I was frightened nearly to death."

A few days after that the landowner rode out and found the peasant standing before his cottage. "Where is the treasure that you found in my field?" he asked him. The man answered that he did not know anything about a treasure.

"Oh, nonsense," said the landowner, "it will not do you any good to deny it, for your wife told me all about it herself."

"That is quite possible," said the man, "for my wife is sometimes a little queer, and one can not always believe all that she says." And he touched his forehead as he spoke.

Then the landowner called the woman and asked whether it were not true that she had confessed to him that her husband had found a chest full of money in the field.

"Certainly," she said, "and I was with him in town when he exchanged the old money for new coins."

"When was that?" asked the landlord.

"Why that was the time we had the frightful storm when it rained bread rolls."

"Nonsense," said he; "when was that?"

"It was on the day of the great battle that was fought on our field, after the enemy had invaded our country."

"What battle, and what enemy?" said the landlord, "I think that the woman is crazy. But tell me at once, when was it that you were in town to exchange the money?"

Then the woman wept, and much as she disliked to do so, she had to say it, "It was the same evening that the devil was tormenting you and beating you because you would not pay him what you owed him."

"What are you saying?" screamed the landowner, in a rage; "I'll thrash you for your lying nonsense." And with that he gave her a blow with his whip and dashed out of the door and rode away, and never again asked about the treasure. The peasant, however, bought a large farm in another part of the country and lived there happily with his wife.[272]

Of Women, Who Lie Fearfully

Gesta Romanorum

There were two brothers, of whom one was a layman and the other a parson. The former had often heard his brother declare that there never was a woman who could keep a secret. He had a mind to put this maxim to the test in the person of his own wife, and one night he addressed her in the following manner, "My dear wife, I have a secret to communicate to you, if I were certain that you would reveal it to nobody. Should you divulge it, it would cause me the greatest uneasiness and vexation."

"My lord," answered his wife, "fear not; we are one body, and your advantage is mine. In like manner, your injury must deeply affect me."

"Well, then," said he, "know that, my bowels being oppressed to an extraordinary degree, I fell very sick. My dear wife, what will you think? I actually voided a huge black crow, which instantly took wing, and left me in the greatest trepidation and confusion of mind."

"Is it possible?" asked the innocent lady; "but, husband, why should this trouble you? You ought rather to rejoice that you are freed from such a pestilent tenant." Here the conversation closed; in the morning, the wife hurried off to the house of a neighbor. "My best friend," said she, "may I tell you a secret?"

"As safely as to your own soul," answered the fair auditor.

"Why," replied the other, "a marvelous thing has happened to my poor husband. Being last night extremely sick, he voided two prodigious black crows, feathers and all, which immediately flew away. I am much concerned."

The other promised very faithfully—and immediately told her neighbor that *three* black crows had taken this most alarming flight. The next edition of the story made it *four*; and in this way it spread, until it was very credibly reported that *sixty* black crows had been evacuated by one unfortunate varlet. But the joke had gone further than he dreamt of; he became much disturbed, and assembling his busy neighbors, explained to them that having wished to prove whether or not his wife could keep a secret, he had made such a communication. Soon after this, his wife,

---

[272]Type 1381. Source: Sven Grundtvig, *Danish Fairy Tales*, translated by J. Grant Cramer (Boston, 1919), no. 7.

dying, he ended his days in a cloister, where he learned three letters; of which one was black; the second, red; and the third, white.

> Application: My beloved, the layman is any worldly minded man who, thinking to do one foolish thing without offense, falls into a thousand errors. But he assembles the people—that is, past and present sins—and by confession expurgates his conscience.[273]

Foolish Wives

Admann and His Wife

Germany

Admann sends his wife out to weed the flax. In the field she asks herself the question, "Should I weed or should I eat?" and decides to do the latter. Then, having refreshed herself with food and drink she asks, "Should I weed or should I sleep?" and once again decides to do the latter. Thus it continues day in and day out. Then one day her husband follows her, and when he discovers her asleep he cuts off her long skirts. Awakening, she bewilderedly asks herself, "Is this me, or not?" Finally she goes to her house in order to convince herself, knocks on the window, and asks, "Admann, is your wife at home?" When he answers, "yes," she replies, "Then it's not me," and walks away, never to be seen again.[274]

---

[273]Type 1381D. Source: *Gesta Romanorum*, translated by Charles Swan (London, 1877), no. 75. The spiritual "application" or moral given to this very earthy jest seems, by the secular standards of the twentieth century, to be as strained as the poor man's bowel movement. Swan offers the following explanation of the tale's final sentence: "This seems merely introduced to tell us, in the application, that the black letter is recollection of our sins; the red, Christ's blood; and the white, the desire of heaven."

[274]Type 1383. Source: Karl Bartsch, *Sagen, Märchen und Gebräuche aus Meklenburg* (Vienna, 1879), v. 1, p. 507.

A Visitor from Paradise

Joseph Jacobs

There was once a woman, good but simple, who had been twice married. One day when her husband was in the field—of course that was her second husband, you know—a weary tramp came trudging by her door and asked for a drink of water. When she gave it to him, being rather a gossip, she asked where he came from.

"From Paris," said the man.

The woman was a little bit deaf, and thought the man said from Paradise. "From Paradise! Did you meet there my poor dear husband, Lord rest his soul?"

"What was his name?" asked the man.

"Why, John Goody, of course," said the woman. "Did you know him in Paradise?"

"What, John Goody!" said the man. "Him and me was as thick as thieves."

"Does he want for anything?" said the woman. "I suppose up in Paradise you get all you want."

"All we want! Why, look at me," said the man pointing to his rags and tatters. "They treat some of us right shabby up there."

"Dear me, that's bad. Are you likely to go back?"

"Go back to Paradise, marm; I should say. We have to be in every night at ten."

"Well, perhaps you wouldn't mind taking back some things for my poor old John," said the woman.

"Of course, marm, delighted to help my old chum John."

So the woman went indoors and got a big pile of clothes and a long pipe and three bottles of beer, and a beer jug, and gave them to the man. "But," he said, "please marm, I can't carry all these by my own self. Ain't you got a horse or a donkey that I can take along with me to carry them? I'll bring him back tomorrow."

Then the woman said, "There's our old Dobbin in the stable; I can't lend you mare Juniper 'cause my husband's plowing with her just now."

"Ah, well, Dobbin'll do as it's only until tomorrow."

So the woman got out Dobbin and saddled him, and the man took the clothes and the beer and the pipe and rode off with them.

Shortly afterwards her husband came home and said, "What's become of Dobbin? He's not in the stable." So his wife told him all that had happened. And he said, "I don't like that. How do we know that he is going to Paradise? And how do we know that he'll bring Dobbin back tomorrow? I'll saddle Juniper and get the things back. Which way did he go?"

So he saddled Juniper and rode after the man, who saw him coming afar off and guessed what had happened. So he got off from Dobbin and drove him into a clump of trees near the roadside, and then went and laid down on his back and looked up to the sky. When the farmer came up to him he got down from Juniper and said, "What are you doing there?"

434

"Oh, such a funny thing," said the man; "a fellow came along here on a horse with some clothes and things, and when he got to the top of the hill here he simply gave a shout and the horse went right up into the sky; and I was watching him when you came up."

"Oh, it's all right then," said the farmer. "He's gone to Paradise, sure enough," and went back to his wife.

Next day they waited, and they waited for the man to bring back Dobbin; but he didn't come that day nor the next day, nor the next. So the farmer said to his wife, "My dear, we've been done. But I'll find that man if I have to trudge through the whole kingdom. And you must come with me, as you know him."

"But what shall we do with the house?" said the wife. "You know there have been robbers around here, and while we are away they'll come and take my best china."

"Oh, that's all right," said the farmer. "He who minds the door minds the house. So we'll take the door with us and then they can't get in."

So he took the door off its hinges and put it on his back and they went along to find the man from Paradise. So they went along, and they went along, and they went along until night came, and they didn't know what to do for shelter. So the man said, "That's a comfortable tree there; let us roost in the branches like the birds." So they took the door up with them and laid down to sleep on it as comfortable, as comfortable can be.

Now it happened that a band of robbers had just broken into a castle nearby and taken out a great lot of plunder; and they came under the very tree to divide it. And when they began to settle how much each should have they began to quarrel and woke up the farmer and his wife. They were so frightened when they heard the robbers underneath them that they tried to get up farther into the tree, and in doing so let the door fall down right on the robbers' heads.

"The heavens are falling," cried the robbers, who were so frightened that they all rushed away. And the farmer and his wife came down from the tree and collected all the booty and went home and lived happy ever afterwards.

It was and it was not.[275]

---

[275]Types 1540, 1653. Source: Joseph Jacobs, *European Folk and Fairy Tales* (New York, 1916), no. 19. This tale of the swindler from Paradise often appeared (frequently in verse) in renaissance jest books. A particularly successful version is that of Hans Sachs (1494–1576).

The Good Wife and the Bad Husband

India

In a remote village there lived a man and his wife, who was a stupid little woman and believed everything that was told her. Whenever people wanted anything from her they used to come and flatter her; but this had to be done in the absence of her husband, because he was a very miserly man, and would never part with any of his money, for all he was exceedingly rich. Nevertheless, without his knowledge cunning beggars would now and then come to his wife and beg of her, and they used generally to succeed, as she was so amenable to flattery. But whenever her husband found her out he would come down heavily upon her, sometimes with words and sometimes with blows. Thus quarrels arose, until at last, for the sake of peace, the wife had to give up her charitable propensities.

Now there lived in the village a rogue of the first water, who had many a time witnessed what took place in the rich miser's family. Wishing to revive his old habit of getting what he wanted from the miser's wife he watched his opportunity and one day, when the miser had gone out on horseback to inspect his land, he came to his wife in the middle of the day and fell down at the threshold as if overcome by exhaustion. She ran up to him at once and asked him who he was.

"I am a native of Kailâsa," said he, "sent down by an old couple living there, for news of their son and his wife."

"Who are those fortunate dwellers on Siva's mountain? said she.

On this the rogue gave the names of her husband's deceased parents, which he had taken good care, of course, to learn from the neighbors.

"Do you really come from them?" said she. "Are they doing well there? Dear old people. How glad my husband would be to see you, were he here! Sit down please, and take rest awhile until he returns. How do they live there? Have they enough to eat and to dress themselves?"

These and a thousand other questions she put to the rogue, who, for his part, wanted to get away as quick as possible, as he knew full well how he would be treated if the miser should return while he was there, so he said, "Mother, language has no words to describe the miseries they are undergoing in the other world. They have not a rag to cover themselves, and for the last six days they have eaten nothing, and have lived on water only. It would break your heart to see them."

The rogue's pathetic words fully deceived the good woman, who firmly believed that he had come down from Kailâsa, sent by the old couple to her.

"Why should they suffer so?" said she, "when their son has plenty to eat and to dress himself, and when their daughter-in-law wears all sorts of costly ornaments?"

With that she went into the house and came out with two boxes containing all the clothes of herself and her husband, and gave the whole lot to the rogue, with instructions to take them to her poor old people in Kailâsa. She also gave him her jewel box for her mother-in-law.

"But dress and jewels will not fill their hungry stomachs," said he.

436

Requesting him to wait a little, the silly woman brought out her husband's cash chest and emptied the contents into the rogue's coat, who now went off in haste, promising to give everything to the good people in Kailâsa. Our good lady in accordance with etiquette, conducted him a few hundred yards along the road and sent news of herself through him to her relatives, and then returned home. The rogue now tied up all his booty in his coat and ran in haste towards the river and crossed over it.

No sooner had our heroine reached home than her husband returned after his inspection of his lands. Her pleasure at what she had done was so great, that she met him at the door and told him all about the arrival of the messenger from Kailâsa, and how she had sent clothes, and jewels, and money through him to her husband's parents. The anger of her husband knew no bounds. But he checked himself for a while, and asked her which road the messenger from Kailâsa had taken, as he said he wanted to follow him and send some more news to his parents. To this she willingly agreed and pointed out the direction the rogue had gone. With rage in his heart at the trick played upon his stupid wife, our hero rode on in hot haste, and after a ride of two *ghatikâs* he caught sight of the departing rogue, who, finding escape hopeless, climbed up into a big *pîpal* tree. Our hero soon reached the bottom of the tree and shouted to the rogue to come down.

"No, I cannot, this is the way to Kailâsa," said the rogue, and climbed up on the top of the tree.

Seeing no chance of the rogue's coming down, and as there was no third person present to whom he could call for help, our hero tied his horse to an adjacent tree and began climbing up the *pîpal* tree himself. The rogue thanked all his gods when he saw this, and waited until his enemy had climbed nearly up to him, and then, throwing down his bundle of booty, leapt quickly from branch to branch until he reached the bottom. He then got upon his enemy's horse, and with his bundle rode into a dense forest in which no one was likely to find him.

Our hero being much older in years was no match for the rogue. So he slowly came down, and cursing his stupidity in having risked his horse to recover his property, returned home at his leisure. His wife, who was waiting his arrival, welcomed him with a cheerful countenance and said, "I thought as much, you have sent away your horse to Kailâsa to be used by your father."

Vexed as he was at his wife's words, our hero replied in the affirmative to conceal his own stupidity.

Thus, some there are in this world, who, though they may not willingly give away anything, pretend to have done so when, by accident, or stupidity, they happen to lose it.[276]

---

[276]Type 1540. Source: Mrs. Howard Kingscote and Pandit Natêsá Sástrî, *Tales of the Sun; or, Folklore of Southern India* (London, 1890), no. 12.

The Serb from the Other World

Serbia

A Turk and his wife halted in the shadow of a tree. The Turk went to the river to water his horse, and his wife remained to await his return. Just then an Era[277] passed by and saluted the Turkish woman, "Allah help you, noble lady!"

"May God aid you," she returned; "where are you coming from?"

"I come from the other world, noble lady."

"As you have been in the other world, have you not, perchance, seen there my son Mouyo, who died a few months ago?"

"Oh, how could I help seeing him? He is my immediate neighbor."

"Happy me! How is he, then?"

"He is well, may God be praised! But he could stand just a little more tobacco and some more pocket money to pay for black coffee."

"Are you going back again? And if so, would you be so kind as to deliver to him this purse with his parent's greetings?"

The Era took the money protesting that he would be only too glad to convey so pleasant a surprise to the youth, and hurried away. Soon the Turk came back, and his wife told him what had transpired. He perceived at once that she had been victimized and without stopping to reproach her, he mounted his horse and galloped after the Era, who, observing the pursuit, and guessing at once that the horseman was the husband of the credulous woman, made all the speed that he could.

There was a mill nearby, and making for it, the Era rushed in and addressed the miller with, "For Goodness' sake, brother, fly! There is a Turkish horseman coming with drawn sword. He will kill you. I heard him say so and have hurried to warn you in time." The miller had no time to ask for particulars. He knew how cruel the Turks were, and without a word he dashed out of the mill and fled up the adjacent rocks.

Meantime the Era placed the miller's hat upon his own head and sprinkled flour copiously over his clothes, that he might look like a miller. No sooner was this done than the Turk came up. Alighting from his horse, he rushed into the mill and hurriedly asked the Era where he had hidden the thief. The Era pointed indifferently to the fleeing miller on the rock, whereupon the Turk requested him to take care of his horse while he ran and caught the swindler. When the Turk had gone some distance up the hill, our Era brushed his clothes, swiftly mounted the horse, and galloped away. The Turk caught the real miller, and demanded, "Where is the money you took from my wife, swindler?"

---

[277]In the original text the Serb is identified as an *Era*, a name given to the peasants of the district of Ouzitze in western Serbia. They, according to Woislav M. Petrovitch, "are supposed to be very witty and shrewd, and might be called the Irishmen of Serbia."

The poor miller made the sign of the cross and said, "God forbid! I never saw your noble lady, still less did I take her money."

After about half an hour of futile discussion, the Turk was convinced of the miller's innocence, and returned to where he had left his horse. But lo! There was no sign of a horse! He walked sadly back to his wife, and she, seeing that her husband had no horse, asked in surprise, "Where did you go, and what became of your horse?"

The Turk replied, "You sent money to our darling son; so I thought I had better send him the horse that he need not go on foot in the other world!"[278]

Christmas

Italy

Once upon a time there was a husband who had a wife who was a little foolish. One day he said to her, "Come, put the house in order, for Christmas is coming." As soon as he left the house his wife went out on the balcony and asked everyone who passed if his name was Christmas. All said, "No"; but finally, one—to see why she asked—said, "Yes." Then she made him come in, and gave him everything that she had (in order to clean out the house). When her husband returned he asked her what she had done with things. She responded that she had given them to Christmas, as he had ordered. Her husband was so enraged at what he heard that he seized her and gave her a good beating.

Another time she asked her husband when he was going to kill the pig. He answered, "At Christmas." The wife did as before, and when she spied the man called Christmas she called him and gave him the pig, which she had adorned with her earrings and necklace, saying that her husband had so commanded her. When her husband returned and learned what she had done, he gave her a sound thrashing; and from that time he learned to say nothing more to his wife.[279]

---

[278]Type 1540. Source: Woislav M. Petrovitch, *Hero Tales and Legends of the Serbians* (London, 1917), pp. 364-366.

[279]Type 1541. Source: Thomas Frederick Crane, *Italian Popular Tales* (Boston and New York, 1885), no. 94.

Stone Soup

Europe

A tramp knocked at the farmhouse door. "I can't let you in, for my husband is not at home," said the woman of the house. "And I haven't a thing to offer you," she added. Her voice showed unmasked scorn for the man she held to be a beggar.

"Then you could make use of my soup stone," he replied, pulling from his pocket what appeared to be an ordinary stone.

"Soup stone?" said she, suddenly showing interest in the tattered stranger.

"Oh yes," he said. "If I just had a potful of water and a fire, I'd show you how it works. This stone and boiling water make the best soup you've ever eaten. Your husband would thank you for the good supper, if you'd just let me in and put my stone to use over your fire."

The woman's suspicions yielded to her desire for an easy meal, and she opened the door. A pot of water was soon brought to a boil. The tramp dropped in his stone, then tasted the watery gruel. "It needs salt, and a bit of barley," he said. "And some butter, too, if you can spare it." The woman obliged him by adding the requested ingredients. He tasted it again. "Much better!" he said. "But a good soup needs vegetables and potatoes. Are there none in your cellar?"

"Oh yes," she said, her enthusiasm for the miracle soup growing, and she quickly found a generous portion of potatoes, turnips, carrots, and beans.

After the mixture had boiled awhile, the man tasted it again. "It's almost soup," he said. "The stone has not failed us. But some chicken broth and chunks of meat would do it well."

The woman, recognizing the truth of his claim, ran to the chicken yard, returning soon with a freshly slaughtered fowl. "Soup stone, do your thing!" she said, adding the chicken to the stew.

When their noses told them that the soup was done, the woman dished up a healthy portion for her guest and for herself. They ate their fill, and—thanks to the magic stone—there was still a modest bowlful left over for her husband's supper.

"My thanks for the use of your pot and your fire," said the tramp as evening approached, and he sensed that the husband soon would be arriving home. He fished his stone from the bottom of the pot, licked it clean, and put it back into his pocket.

"Do come again," said the thankful woman.

"I will indeed," said the tramp, and disappeared into the woods.[280]

---

[280]Type 1548. Retold from various European sources. Sometimes the "magic" soup ingredient is a nail.

Division of Labor

The Farmer, His Wife, and the Open Door

India

Once upon a time a poor farmer and his wife, having finished their day's labor and eaten their frugal supper, were sitting by the fire, when a dispute arose between them as to who should shut the door, which had been blown open by a gust of wind.

"Wife, shut the door!" said the man.

"Husband, shut it yourself!" said the woman.

"I will not shut it, and you shall not shut it," said the husband; "but let the one who speaks the first word shut it."

This proposal pleased the wife exceedingly, and so the old couple, well satisfied, retired in silence to bed.

In the middle of the night they heard a noise, and, peering out, they perceived that a wild dog had entered the room, and that he was busy devouring their little store of food. Not a word, however, would either of these silly people utter, and the dog, having sniffed at everything, and having eaten as much as he wanted, went out of the house.

The next morning the woman took some grain to the house of a neighbor in order to have it ground into flour.

In her absence the barber entered, and said to the husband, "How is it you are sitting here all alone?"

The farmer answered never a word. The barber then shaved his head, but still he did not speak; then he shaved off half his beard and half his mustache, but even then the man refrained from uttering a syllable. Then the barber covered him all over with a hideous coating of lampblack, but the stolid farmer remained as dumb as a mute. "The man is bewitched!" cried the barber, and he hastily quitted the house.

He had hardly gone when the wife returned from the mill. She, seeing her husband in such a ghastly plight, began to tremble, and exclaimed, "Ah! wretch, what have you been doing?"

"You spoke the first word," said the farmer, "so begone, woman, and shut the door."[281]

---

[281]Type 1351. Source: Charles Swynnerton, *Indian Nights' Entertainment; or, Folk-Tales from the Upper Indus* (London, 1892), no. 11.

441

The Wager

Italy

There was once a husband and a wife. The former said one day to the latter, "Let us have some fritters."

She replied, "What shall we do for a frying pan?"

"Go and borrow one from my godmother."

"You go and get it; it is only a little way off."

"Go yourself; I will take it back when we are done with it."

So she went and borrowed the pan, and when she returned said to her husband, "Here is the pan, but you must carry it back."

So they cooked the fritters, and after they had eaten, the husband said, "Now let us go to work, both of us, and the one who speaks first shall carry back the pan." Then she began to spin and he to draw his thread—for he was a shoemaker—and all the time keeping silence, except that when he drew his thread he said, "*Leulerò, leulerò;*" and she, spinning, answered, "*Picicì, picicì, piciciò.*" And they said not another word.

Now there happened to pass that way a soldier with a horse, and he asked a woman if there was any shoemaker in that street. She said that there was one nearby, and took him to the house. The soldier asked the shoemaker to come and cut his horse a girth, and he would pay him. The latter made no answer but, "*Leulerò, leulerò;*" and his wife, "*Picicì, picicì, piciciò.*" Then the soldier said, "Come and cut my horse a girth, or I will cut your head off!" The shoemaker only answered, "*Leulerò, leulerò;*" and his wife, "*Picicì, picicì, piciciò.*"

Then the soldier began to grow angry, and seized his sword and said to the shoemaker, "Either come and cut my horse a girth, or I will cut your head off!" But to no purpose. The shoemaker did not wish to be the first to speak, and only replied, "*Leulerò, leulerò;*" and his wife, "*Picicì, picicì, piciciò.*"

Then the soldier got mad in good earnest, seized the shoemaker's head, and was going to cut it off. When his wife saw that, she cried out, "Ah! don't, for mercy's sake!"

"Good!" exclaimed her husband. "Now you go and carry the pan back to my godmother, and I will go and cut the horse's girth." And so he did, and won the wager.[282]

---

[282]Type 1351. Source: Thomas Frederick Crane, *Italian Popular Tales* (Boston and New York, 1885), no. 95.

The Husband Who Was to Mind the House

Norway

Once upon a time there was a man who was so bad tempered and cross that he never thought his wife did anything right in the house. One evening, in hay-making time, he came home, scolding and swearing, and showing his teeth and making a commotion.

"Dear love, don't be so angry; that's a good man," said his wife; "tomorrow let's change jobs. I'll go out with the mowers and mow, and you can mind the house at home."

Yes, the husband thought that would do very well. He was quite willing, he said.

So early the next morning, his wife took a scythe over her neck, and went out into the hay field with the mowers and began to mow; but the man was to mind the house, and do the work at home.

First of all he wanted to churn the butter; but when he had churned awhile, he got thirsty, and went down to the cellar to tap a barrel of ale. He had just knocked in the bung, and was putting in the tap, when he heard the pig come into the kitchen above. As fast as he could, he ran up the cellar steps, with the tap in his hand, to keep the pig from upsetting the churn; but when he got there, he saw that the pig had already knocked the churn over, and was standing there, routing and grunting in the cream which was running all over the floor. He got so angry that he quite forgot the ale barrel, and ran at the pig as hard as he could. He caught it, too, just as it ran out of doors, and gave it such a powerful kick that he killed it on the spot. Then he remembered he had the tap in his hand; but when he got down to the cellar, all the ale had run out of the barrel.

Then he went into the milk shed and found enough cream left to fill the churn again, and so he began to churn, for they had to have butter at dinner. When he had churned a bit, he remembered that their milk cow was still shut up in the barn, and hadn't had a bit to eat or a drop to drink all morning, although the sun was high. It occurred to him that it was too far to take her down to the meadow, so he'd just get her up on the roof, for it was a sod roof, and a fine crop of grass was growing there. The house was close against a steep hill, and he thought if he laid a plank across to the back of the roof he'd easily get the cow up.

But he couldn't leave the churn, for his little baby was crawling about on the floor. "If I leave it," he thought, "the child will tip it over." So he took the churn on his back, and went out with it; but then he thought he'd better first water the cow before he put her on the roof; so he picked up a bucket to draw water out of the well; but, as he stooped over the edge of the well, all the cream ran out of the churn over his shoulder, and down into the well.

Now it was near dinner time, and he hadn't even got the butter yet; so he thought he'd best boil the porridge, and filled the pot with water, and hung it over the fire. When he had done that, it occurred to him that the cow might fall off the roof and break her legs or her neck. So he climbed up on the house to tie her up. He tied

443

one end of the rope to the cow's neck. He slipped the other end down the chimney and tied it around his own leg. Then he had to hurry, for the water was now boiling in the pot, and he had still to grind the oatmeal.

He began to grind away; but while he was hard at it, the cow fell off the roof, dragging the man up the chimney by the rope. There he stuck fast; and as for the cow, she hung halfway down the wall, swinging between heaven and earth, for she could neither get down nor up.

Now the wife waited seven lengths and seven breadths for her husband to come and call her home to dinner; but he never came. At last she thought she'd waited long enough, and went home. But when she got home and saw the cow hanging there, she ran up and cut the rope with her scythe. When she did this, her husband fell down from within the chimney. When the old woman came inside, she found him with his head in the porridge pot.[283]

The Mouse, the Bird, and the Sausage

Jacob and Wilhelm Grimm

Once upon a time a mouse, a bird, and a sausage formed a partnership. They kept house together, and for a long time they lived in peace and prosperity, acquiring many possessions. The bird's task was to fly into the forest every day to fetch wood. The mouse carried water, made the fire, and set the table. The sausage did the cooking.

Whoever is too well off always wants to try something different! Thus one day the bird chanced to meet another bird, who boasted to him of his own situation. This bird criticized him for working so hard while the other two enjoyed themselves at home. For after the mouse had made the fire and carried the water, she could sit in the parlor and rest until it was time for her to set the table. The sausage had only to stay by the hearth watching the food cook. When mealtime approached, she would slither through the stew or the vegetables, and thus everything was spiced and salted and ready to eat. The bird would bring his load of wood home. They would eat their meal, and then sleep soundly until the next morning. It was a great life.

---

[283]Type 1408. Source: Peter Christen Asbjørnsen and Jørgen Moe, *Norske Folkeeventyr* (Christiania [Oslo], 1842-1852), translated by George Webb Dasent (1859). Revised. It is surprising that this popular story was not included in the Grimms' collection, for it is told throughout Europe. A Russian version recorded by Aleksandr Afanasyev takes a particularly dramatic turn: The husband, while mismanaging his domestic duties loses his clothes. He covers his nakedness with a bundle of hay, but a horse eats the hay, depriving the househusband of his manhood at the same bite.

The next day, because of his friend's advice, the bird refused to go to the forest, saying that he had been their servant long enough. He was no longer going to be a fool for them. Everyone should try a different task for a change. The mouse and the sausage argued against this, but the bird was the master, and he insisted that they give it a try. The sausage was to fetch wood, the mouse became the cook, and the bird was to carry water.

And what was the result? The sausage trudged off toward the forest; the bird made the fire; and the mouse put on the pot and waited for the sausage to return with wood for the next day. However, the sausage stayed out so long that the other two feared that something bad had happened. The bird flew off to see if he could find her. A short distance away he came upon a dog that had seized the sausage as free booty and was making off with her. The bird complained bitterly to the dog about this brazen abduction, but he claimed that he had discovered forged letters on the sausage, and that she would thus have to forfeit her life to him.

Filled with sorrow, the bird carried the wood home himself and told the mouse what he had seen and heard. They were very sad, but were determined to stay together and make the best of it. The bird set the table while the mouse prepared the food. She jumped into the stew, as the sausage had always done, in order to flavor it, but before she reached the middle, her hair and skin were scalded off, and she perished.

When the bird wanted to eat, no cook was there. Beside himself, he threw the wood this way and that, called out, looked everywhere, but no cook was to be found. Because of his carelessness, the scattered wood caught fire, and the entire house was soon aflame. The bird rushed to fetch water, but the bucket fell into the well, carrying him with it, and he drowned.[284]

[284]Type 85. Source: *Kinder- und Hausmärchen*, 1st ed. (Berlin, 1812/1815), v. 1, no. 23.

Adultery

Of Adultery

Gesta Romanorum

A certain king had a lion, a lioness, and a leopard, whom he much delighted in. During the absence of the lion, the lioness was unfaithful, and colleagued with the leopard; and that she might prevent her mate's discovery of the crime, she used to wash herself in a fountain adjoining the king's castle. Now, the king, having often perceived what was going forward, commanded the fountain to be closed. This done, the lioness was unable to cleanse herself; and the lion returning, and ascertaining the injury that had been done him, assumed the place of a judge—sentenced her to death, and immediately executed the sentence.

> Application: My beloved, the king is our heavenly Father; the lion is Christ; and the lioness, the soul. The leopard is the devil, and the fountain is confession, which being closed, death presently follows.[285]

Of Judgment against Adulterers

Gesta Romanorum

A certain knight had a very beautiful castle, upon which two storks built their nest. At the foot of this castle was a clear fountain, in which the storks were wont to bathe themselves. It happened that the female stork brought forth young, and the male flew about to procure food. Now, while he was absent, the female admitted a gallant; and before the return of the male went down to the fountain to wash herself, in order that the other might perceive no disorder in her appearance. But the knight, often observing this with wonder, closed up the fountain, that the stork might no longer wash or bathe herself. In this dilemma, after meeting her lover, she was obliged to return to her nest; and when the male

---

[285]Source: *Gesta Romanorum*, translated by Charles Swan (London, 1877), no. 181.

446

came and saw by various signs that she had been unfaithful, he flew away, and brought back with him a great multitude of storks, who put the adulterous bird to death, in presence of the knight.

> Application: My beloved, the two storks are Christ and the soul, the spouse of Christ. The knight is the devil; and the fountain, that of confession and repentance. If Christ at the day of judgment find us unwashed, i.e. impenitent, He will come with a multitude of angels and put us to death.[286]

Potiphar's Wife and Joseph

The Book of Genesis

And it came to pass that Potiphar's wife cast her eyes upon Joseph, and she said, "Lie with me."

But Joseph refused, saying, "You are my master's wife. I cannot sin against him and against God."

Then Potiphar's wife caught Joseph by the shirt, but he fled, leaving his garment in her hands. She called for her guards, claiming that Joseph had attempted to force himself upon her, but that she had resisted. When Potiphar heard these charges, he had Joseph bound and cast into prison.[287]

The Himp-Hamp

Scandinavia

Once upon a time there was a king who had nothing better to do than to become friendly with a blacksmith's wife who lived in the vicinity of the castle. The king visited her often, but her husband was in his way, so he decided to get rid of him. Therefore one day the king commanded the poor fellow

---

[286]Source: *Gesta Romanorum*, translated by Charles Swan (London, 1877), no. 82. Although this tale has no Aarne-Thompson type number, it was a favorite among medieval storytellers, including Geoffrey Chaucer.

[287]Type 318. Source: Retold from Genesis 39:7-20.

to make him a magnificent castle standing on four pillars, and it had to be finished in three days, or else the blacksmith would lose his life.

The blacksmith saw that he was doomed, and in despair wandered into the woods.

At last he came to an old woman who asked what was troubling him. He told her of the king's hardheartedness and asked for advise. Then the old woman taught him the magic that he would need to finish the castle.

When the king saw the castle, he was amazed and angry, and now he commanded the blacksmith to dig a great moat around the new castle and to build four bridges over the moat, with a gate for each one, and all that within three days. The blacksmith, using the old woman's magic, completed this task in three days as well.

The king was even more amazed and more angry, because now he did not know what kind of a difficult and impossible task he would be able to give the blacksmith in order to find an excuse to take his life. Finally the king, quite beside himself, declared, "If you don't want to lose your life, you must make a himp-hamp for me in three days!" The smith did not even know what a himp-hamp was, so more desperate than ever, he walked away.

Once again he found the old woman, who said to him, "Make a chamber pot of iron and place it under your bed. Then hide, and when you see anyone touch it, just say 'hold fast' quietly to yourself, and you will soon see a himp-hamp!"

The blacksmith did what the old woman said.

One evening the king came, as usual, to visit the blacksmith's wife, and the smith hid himself where he could watch. The lovers got undressed, and the wife got into bed. Before following her, the king had to use the pot. As soon as he touched the iron pot, the smith whispered, "Hold fast," and the king, wearing only his nightshirt, stuck to the pot. The wife jumped out of bed and tried to tear the pot loose, but as soon as she touched it, the smith whispered "hold fast," and she too became stuck.

The king was enraged at this tomfoolery, and the smith's wife began to cry. Her maid heard the commotion and, half asleep and stark naked, came running to help them. But she too became stuck, just like the others.

Then the smith stepped forward and drove all three from the house with an iron club. It was almost daytime, and the embarrassed maid picked up a bundle of hay and tried to cover her shame with it. A cow came by and wanted to get at the hay, but the smith said "hold fast!" and it also became attached. Then a bull came by and mounted the cow, and the smith called out once more, "Hold fast!"

He drove them—all stuck to the iron pot—up one street and down another. The people were just beginning to stir, and they all laughed and jeered. A small boy looked out from his window and shouted, "What a himp-hamp!" The townspeople joined the smith, and together they drove the entire himp-hamp into the deep moat at the castle. Then they made the clever blacksmith their new king.[288]

---

[288]Type 571B. Retold from Scandinavian sources.

Old Hildebrand

Jacob and Wilhelm Grimm

Once upon a time there was a peasant whose wife appealed to the village priest. The priest wanted ever so much to spend an entire day alone with her, and the peasant's wife was quite willing. One day he said to her, "Listen, dear woman, I've thought it through, and I know how the two of us can spend an entire day together. On Wednesday tell your husband that you are sick and lie down in bed moaning and groaning. Carry on like that until Sunday, when in my sermon I will preach that if anyone has a sick child at home, a sick husband, a sick wife, a sick father, a sick mother, a sick sister, brother, or anyone else, then that person should make a pilgrimage to Mount Cuckoo in Italy. There, for a kreuzer, one can get a peck of laurel leaves, and this person's sick child, sick husband, sick wife, sick father, sick mother, sick sister, brother, or anyone else, will be healed on the spot."

"I'll do it," said the peasant's wife. So on Wednesday she went to bed, moaning and groaning. Her husband did everything for her that he could think of, but nothing helped. Sunday arrived, and the peasant's wife said, "I'm so miserable that I must be near death, but before I die, I would like to hear the sermon that the priest is going to give today."

The peasant answered, "Oh, my child, you can't go out. If you get up it might make you worse. Look, I'll go to church and pay close attention and tell you everything that the priest says.

"Okay," said the peasant's wife. "Go and pay close attention, and then tell me everything that you have heard. So the peasant went to church, and the priest began to preach, saying that if anyone had a sick child at home, a sick husband, a sick wife, a sick father, a sick mother, a sick sister, brother, or anyone else, then that person should make a pilgrimage to Mount Cuckoo in Italy, where a peck of laurel leaves costs one kreuzer, and this person's sick child, sick husband, sick wife, sick father, sick mother, sick sister, brother, or anyone else, will be healed on the spot, and that anyone who might want to undertake this trip should come to him after the mass, and he would give him a sack for the laurel leaves and a kreuzer.

No one was happier than the peasant, and immediately following the mass he went to the priest and asked for the laurel sack and the kreuzer. Then he went home, and even before going inside called out, "Hurrah! My dear wife, you are just as good as cured. The priest preached today that whoever has a sick child at home, a sick husband, a sick wife, a sick father, a sick mother, a sick sister, brother, or anyone else, then that person should make a pilgrimage to Mount Cuckoo in Italy, where a peck of laurel leaves costs one kreuzer, and this person's sick child, sick husband, sick wife, sick father, sick mother, sick sister, brother, or anyone else, will be healed on the spot, and I got the laurel sack and the kreuzer from the priest, and am going to take off immediately, so you can get better as soon as possible." And with that he set forth.

He had scarcely left before his wife got out of bed, and the priest arrived. But let's leave them for awhile and see what happened to the peasant. He was hurrying along in order to arrive at Mount Cuckoo as soon as possible, when he met a kinsman. Now this kinsman was an egg man, who was just returning from market, where he had sold his eggs.

"Bless you!" said the kinsman. "Where are you off to in such a hurry?"

"In all eternity!" said the peasant. "My wife has become sick, and today in the priest's sermon I heard that if anyone has a sick child at home, a sick husband, a sick wife, a sick father, a sick mother, a sick sister, brother, or anyone else, then that person should make a pilgrimage to Mount Cuckoo in Italy, where a peck of laurel leaves costs one kreuzer, and this person's sick child, sick husband, sick wife, sick father, sick mother, sick sister, brother, or anyone else, will be healed on the spot, and I got the laurel sack and the kreuzer from the priest, and now I am on my way.

"Listen, kinsman," said the peasant's kinsman. "Don't be so simple as to believe that. Do you know what? The priest wants to spend an entire day alone with your wife. He has given you this task just to get you out from under his feet."

"My!" the peasant said. "How I would like to know if that is true!"

"Do you know what?" said his kinsman, "Just climb into my egg basket, and I will carry you home, and you can see for yourself."

And that is just what happened. The peasant got into the egg basket, and his kinsman carried him home. When they arrived there, the good times had already started. The peasant's wife had slaughtered almost everything in the farmyard and had made pancakes, and the priest was there with his fiddle. The kinsman knocked at the door, and the peasant's wife asked who was there.

"It's me, kinswoman," said the kinsman. "Can you give me shelter for the night? I did not sell my eggs at the market, so now I have to carry them back home, but they are too heavy, and I can't make it. It is already dark."

"Well," said the peasant's wife, "you have come at a very inconvenient time, but it can't be helped. Just sit down over there on the bench by the stove." So the kinsman took a seat on the bench and set his pack basket down beside him. And the priest and the peasant's wife proceeded to carry on

After a while the priest said, "Listen, my dear woman, you are such a good singer. Sing something for me."

"No," said the peasant's wife, "I can't sing anymore. I could sing well when I was younger, but that's all behind me now."

"Oh," said the priest, "do sing just a little."

So the peasant's wife started to sing:

> I sent my husband out, you see,
> To Mount Cuckoo in Italy!

And the priest sang back:

> I wish he'd stay away a year
> The laurel leaves don't interest me
> Hallelujah!

Then the kinsman chimed in (oh, I have to tell you that the peasant's name was Hildebrand), and sang out:

> Hey, you my kinsman Hildebrand,
> What are you doing on that bench?
> Hallelujah!

The peasant, from inside the basket, sang forth:

> This singing I can bear no more,
> Here I come!
> Trala tralore!

With that he jumped from the basket, and with blows he drove the priest out of the house.[289]

An Adulteress's Punishment

Margaret of Navarre

King Charles VIII sent to Germany a gentleman named Bernage, Lord of Sivray, near Amboise. This gentleman, traveling day and night, arrived very late one evening at the house of a gentleman, where he asked for a night's lodging, and obtained it, but with difficulty. The owner of the house, nevertheless, learning in whose service he was, came to him and begged he would excuse the incivility of his servants, stating that certain of his wife's relations, who mean him mischief, obliged him to keep his doors thus closed. Bernage told him on what business he was traveling, and his host expressing his readiness to render the king his master all possible services, received his ambassador into his house, and lodged and treated him honorably.

Suppertime being come, he showed him into a richly tapestried hall, where, entering from behind the hangings, there appeared the most beautiful woman that ever was seen; but her hair was cropped close, and she was dressed in black garments of German cut. After the gentleman had washed with Bernage, water was set before this lady, who washed also, and took her seat at the end of the table without speaking to anyone, or anyone to her. Bernage often looked at her, and thought her one of the handsomest women he had ever seen except that her face was very pale, and her air extremely sad. After she had eaten a little, she asked for drink, which was given to her by a domestic in a very singular vessel. This was a death's head, the holes of which were stopped with silver; and out of this vessel she drank two or

---

[289]Type 1360C. Source: *Kinder- und Hausmärchen*, 2nd ed. (Berlin, 1819), no. 95.

three times. After she had supped and washed, she made a reverence to the master of the house, and retired again behind the tapestry without speaking to anyone.

Bernage was so surprised at this extraordinary spectacle that he became quite somber and pensive. His host perceived this, and said to him, "You are surprised, I see, at what you have beheld at table. Now, the courteous demeanor I have marked in you does not permit me to make a secret of the matter to you, but to explain it, in order that you may not suppose me capable of acting so cruelly without great reason. That lady whom you have seen is my wife, whom I loved more than man ever loved woman. I risked everything to marry her, and I brought her hither in spite of her relations. She, too, evinced so much love for me that I would have hazarded a thousand lives to obtain her. We lived long in such concord and pleasure that I esteemed myself the happiest gentleman in Christendom; but honor having obliged me to make a journey, she forgot hers, and the love she had for me, and conceived a passion for a young gentleman I had brought up in this house. I was near discovering the fact on my return home, but I loved her so ardently that I could not bring myself to doubt her. At last, however, experience opened my eyes, and I saw what I feared more than death. The love I had felt for her changed into fury and despair. Feigning one day to go into the country, I hid myself in the chamber which she at present occupies. Soon after my pretended departure, she retired to it, and sent for the young gentleman. I saw him enter the room and take liberties with her which should have been reserved for me alone. When I saw him about the enter the bed with her, I issued from my hiding place, seized him in her arms, and slew him. But as my wife's crime seemed to me so great that it would not have been a sufficient punishment for it had I killed her as I had killed her gallant, I imposed upon her one which I believe is more insupportable than death; which was, to shut her up in the chamber in which she used to enjoy her stolen pleasures. I have hung there in a press all the bones of her gallant, as one hangs up something precious in a cabinet; and that she may not forget them at her meals, I have her served, as she sits opposite to me at table, with the skull of that ingrate instead of a cup, in order that she may see living him whom she has made her mortal enemy by her crime, and dead, for her sake, him whose love she preferred to mine. In this way, when she dines and when she sups, she sees the two things which must afflict her most, namely, the living enemy and the dead friend; and all this through her guilt. In other respects, I treat her as I do myself, except that her hair is cropped; for the hair is an ornament no more appropriate to the adulteress than the veil to a harlot; therefore her cropped head denotes that she has lost honor and chastity. If you please to take the trouble to see her, I will take you into her room."

Bernage willingly accepted the offer, and going downstairs with his host, found the lady seated alone by an excellent fire in a very handsome chamber. The gentleman drew back a curtain which concealed a great press, and there he saw all the bones of a man suspended. Bernage had a great wish to speak to the lady, but durst not for fear of the husband, until the latter, guessing his thoughts, said to him, "If you like to say anything to her, you will see how she expresses herself."

"Your patience, madam," said Bernage, turning to her, "is equal to your torture; I regard you as the most unhappy woman in the world."

The lady, with eyes filled with tears, and with incomparable grace and humility, replied, "I confess, sir, that my fault is so great, that all the ills which the master of this house, whom I am not worthy to call husband, could inflict upon me, are nothing in comparison to the grief I feel for having offended him." So saying she wept profusely.

The gentleman took Bernage by the arm and led him away. Next morning he continued his journey upon the king's service; but on taking leave of the gentleman he could not help saying to him, "The esteem I entertain for you, sir, and the courtesies you have shown me in your house, oblige me to tell you that, in my opinion, considering the great repentance of your poor wife, you ought to forgive her; the more so as you are young and have no children. It would be a pity that a house like yours should fall, and that those who perhaps do not love you should become inheritors of your substance."

The gentleman, who had resolved never to forgive his wife, pondered long over what Bernage had said to him, and at last, owning that he had spoken the truth, promised that if she persevered in her present humility, he would forgive her after some time. Bernage, on his return to the court, related the whole story to the king, who directed inquiries to be made into the matter, and found that it was all just as Bernage had reported. The description he have of the lady's beauty so pleased the king that he sent his painter, Jean de Paris, to take her portrait exactly as she was, which he did with the husband's consent. After she had undergone a long penance, and always with the same humility, the gentleman, who longed much for children, took pity on his wife, reinstated her, and had by her several fine children.[290]

The One-Eyed Husband and His Faithless Wife

Margaret of Navarre

Charles, the last Duke of Alençon, had an old valet-de-chambre who was blind of an eye, and who was married to a woman much younger than himself. The duke and duchess liked this valet better than any other domestic of that order in their household, and the consequence was that he could not go and see his wife as often as he could have wished, whilst she, unable to accommodate herself to circumstances, so far forgot her honor and her conscience as to fall in love with a

---

[290]Type 992A. Source: *The Heptameron of the Tales of Margaret, Queen of Navarre,* edited by M. Le Roux de Lincy (Bibliophilist Library, 1902), day 4, novel 32. Margaret of Navarre (1492-1549) was the sister of King Francis I of France. Her *Heptameron* (1558) is a collection of 72 stories, many of which have parallels in folklore. It was written in the manner of Boccaccio's *Il Decamerone.*

young gentleman of the neighborhood. At last the affair got wind, and there was so much talk about it that it reached the ears of the husband, who could not believe it, so warm was the affection testified to him by his wife. One day, however, he made up his mind to know the truth of the matter, and to revenge himself, if he could, on the person who put this affront upon him. With this view he pretended to go for two or three days to a place at some little distance; and no sooner had he taken his departure than his wife sent for her gallant. They had hardly been half an hour together, when the husband came and knocked loudly at the door. The wife, knowing but too well who it was, told her lover, who was so astounded that he could have wished he was still in his mother's womb. But while he was swearing, and confounding her the intrigue which had brought him into such a perilous scrape, she told him not to be uneasy, for she would get him off without its costing him anything; and that all he had to do was to dress himself as quickly as possible.

Meanwhile, the husband kept knocking, and calling to his wife as loud as he could bawl, but she pretended not to know him. "Why don't you get up," she cried to the people of the house, "and go and silence those who are making such a noise? Is this a proper time to come to honest people's houses? If my husband were here he would make you know better." The husband hearing her voice, shouted louder than ever, "Let me in, wife; do you mean to keep me at the door until daylight?" At last, when she saw that her lover was ready to slip out, "Oh, is that you, husband?" she said; "I am so glad you are come! I was full of a dream I had that gave me the greatest pleasure I ever felt in my life. I thought you had recovered the sight of your eye." Here she opened the door, and catching her husband round the neck, kissed him, clapped one hand on his sound eye, and asked him if he did not see better than usual. Whilst the husband was thus blindfolded the gallant made his escape. The husband guessed how it was, but said, "I will watch you no more, wife. I thought to deceive you, but it is I who have been the dupe, and you have put the cunningest trick upon me that ever was invented. God mend you! for it passes the act of man to bring back a wicked woman from her evil ways by any means short of putting her to death. But since the regard I have had for you has not availed to make you behave better, perhaps the contempt with which I shall henceforth look upon you will touch you more, and have a more wholesome effect." Therefore he went away, leaving her in great confusion. At last, however, he was prevailed upon, by the solicitations of relations and friends, and by the tears and excuses of his wife, to cohabit with her again.[291]

---

[291]Type 1419C. Source: *The Heptameron of the Tales of Margaret, Queen of Navarre*, edited by M. Le Roux de Lincy (Bibliophilist Library, 1902), day 1, novel 6. This tale was a favorite among renaissance jest-book writers.

The Enchanted Pear Tree

Giovanni Boccaccio

Nicostratus, a wealthy patrician, married Lydia, a woman of great distinction and unsurpassed beauty. He was well advanced in years, while she was still a paragon of youth and vitality. Consequently, to state the matter delicately, their marriage did not leave the young wife entirely satisfied. Thus, it is quite understandable that Lydia found herself paying ever more attention to one of her husband's servants, Pyrrhus by name, who was elegant, handsome, young, and energetic. He was attracted to her as well, and gladly would have accepted her invitations to love, but the old man gave them no opportunity. What he lacked in vigor he made up with jealousy and perseverance, rarely leaving his beautiful young wife alone.

Their unrequited passion aglow, Lydia and Pyrrhus devised a daring scheme through which, even in the master's presence, they might satisfy their longing for one another. Accordingly, one day when the three were walking in the garden, as they often did, Lydia requested a pear from a certain tree. Pyrrhus climbed after the fruit, but once in the tree, he called to his master, "Have you no shame, making love like that in broad daylight?"

The master demanded an explanation for the strange remark, and Pyrrhus concluded that the pear tree was enchanted, giving the impression of unreal happenings below. To test the theory, he asked his master to climb the tree, and see if he too would behold impossible things below. His curiosity piqued, Nicostratus mustered enough strength to climb onto one of the pear tree's lower branches. Looking down, what did he behold but Pyrrhus and Lydia making fervent love. From his precarious perch, he shouted curses, threats, and insults at them; but they—engaged with other pursuits—quite ignored him.

Nicostratus climbed down from the tree, only to find Pyrrhus and Lydia seated discretely on a garden bench. Their innocent demeanor convinced him that nothing unseemly had happened. Fearing that only a bedeviled tree could be responsible for the vile images that he had perceived, he sent for an ax and had it cut down immediately.

From that time forth Nicostratus relaxed his watchful vigil over his young wife, and thus Pyrrhus and Lydia were able to pluck the fruits of their love at regular intervals, even without the help of their enchanted pear tree.[292]

---

[292]Type 1423. Source: *Il Decamerone*, day 7, tale 9. Retold and shortened. This tale is one of the great "dirty jokes" of all time. It is found from the Arabic world to northern Europe. Another famous literary treatment is Chaucer's "The Merchant's Tale." Boccaccio's *The Decameron* was written between 1350 and 1355.

The Priest Who Knew How to Make Heads

Georg Wickram

A priest, learning that a merchant had departed on a journey, leaving his pregnant wife at home, approached the woman with the sorrowful news that her baby, lacking the continuing presence of its father, would be born without a head. Beside herself with anxiety, the woman agreed to let the priest take her husband's place in bed, thus ensuring a complete baby. Two months later a son was born, and—just as the priest had promised—he had a head. The woman, in her husband's presence, naively thanked God for the priest's help in the completion of her child. The husband, sensing what had happened, went to the priest's pasture and cut off the heads of twelve of his sheep. When the priest complained of this evil deed, the merchant responded, "Priest, you know how to make heads, so now make some for your sheep."[293]

Virtuous Wives

Griselda

Giovanni Boccaccio

G ualtieri, the Marquis of Saluzzo, spent so much time at hunting and other sports that he gave no thought about marrying and establishing a family. His friends and subjects, fearing that old age would overtake him before he acquired an heir, pressured him to take a wife. Finally, more to silence his critics than to satisfy any desire that he might have for matrimony, he resolved to court a beautiful, but poor young woman from a neighboring village. Her family's low station in life would spite those who had so urgently insisted that he marry, and her beauty, he thought, would make living with her at least bearable.

---

[293]Type 1424. Retold from "Von einem pfaffen, der köpff kundt machen," *Das Rollwagenbüchlein* (1555). Similar stories are included in Boccaccio's *Il Decamerone* (day 7, tale 3) Poggio's *Facitiae* (no. 222), Straparola's, *Piacevoli notti* (night 6, tale 1), and Afanasyev's Russian *Erotic Tales*.

Gualtieri informed Griselda—that was the young woman's name—of his intention to marry her, and asked her if she would accept him as a husband, to love, honor, and obey, for better or for worse, and never criticize him nor question his authority. She readily agreed, and their wedding was celebrated forthwith.

Griselda appeared to be a worthy addition to Gualtieri's noble household, but the marquis, unsure of the depth of her character, decided to test her loyalty and her patience. Thus, soon after the birth of their first child—it was a beautiful girl—he informed her that his subjects were unhappy with the child and that it was to be put to death. Without hesitation she acceded to her husband's demands and surrendered the child. However, instead of killing the baby girl, Gualtieri had her spirited away and tended in a secret place.

Some time later Griselda gave birth to a son, and her husband, intent on carrying his test still further, berated her and insisted that her child be put to death. She again yielded to his demands without complaint, and as before, he took the child to a secret place where he was well cared for.

Still unsatisfied, Gualtieri devised a final test. He publicly denounced Griselda, claiming that the pope had granted him dispensation to divorce her and to take a more deserving wife. Griselda, wearing only a shift, was sent back to her father. All these indignities she bore without complaint.

As the day approached when Gualtieri was, as it was supposed, to take a new bride, he asked Griselda to return to his palace, for no one knew better how to prepare for guests than did she. Griselda returned to her former residence, now as a cleaning woman and servant, to make preparations for her former husband's wedding.

Gualtieri had his and Griselda's daughter, who was now twelve years old, dressed in bridal clothes, and he presented her to Griselda, who could not have known that this was her own child. "What do you think of my new bride?" he asked.

Griselda replied without guile, "If her wisdom matches her beauty, then the two of you will be very happy together."

At last recognizing Griselda's sincerity, faithfulness, and patience, Gualtieri revealed to her the trials that he had devised to test her loyalty. With tears of joy, she received her children and once again assumed her position as Gualtieri's ever patient and obedient wife.[294]

[294]Type 887. Source: *Il Decamerone*, day 10, tale 10. Retold and shortened. This terrible tale was among the most popular stories in renaissance Europe. Another famous literary treatment is Geoffrey Chaucer's "The Clerk's Tale" from the *Canterbury Tales* (written between ca. 1380 and 1400).

The Women of Weinsberg

Jacob and Wilhelm Grimm

When King Conrad III defeated the Duke of Welf (in the year 1140) and placed Weinsberg under siege, the wives of the besieged castle negotiated a surrender which granted them the right to leave with whatever they could carry on their shoulders. The king allowed them that much. Leaving everything else aside, each woman took her own husband on her shoulders and carried him out. When the king's people saw what was happening, many of them said that that was not what had been meant and wanted to put a stop to it. But the king laughed and accepted the women's clever trick. "A king " he said, "should always stand by his word."[295]

The Lute Player

Aleksandr Afanasyev

Once upon a time there was a king and queen who lived happily and comfortably together. They were very fond of each other and had nothing to worry them, but at last the king grew restless. He longed to go out into the world, to try his strength in battle against some enemy and to win all kinds of honor and glory.

So he called his army together and gave orders to start for a distant country where a heathen king ruled who ill treated or tormented everyone he could lay his hands on. The king then gave his parting orders and wise advice to his ministers, took a tender leave of his wife, and set off with his army across the seas.

I cannot say whether the voyage was short or long; but at last he reached the country of the heathen king and marched on, defeating all who came in his way. But this did not last long, for in time he came to a mountain pass, where a large army was waiting for him, who put his soldiers to flight, and took the king himself prisoner.

He was carried off to the prison where the heathen king kept his captives, and now our poor friend had a very bad time indeed. All night long the prisoners were

---

[295]Source: *Deutsche Sagen* (Berlin, 1816/1818), no. 493. Weinsberg is a town near Heilbronn in southwest Germany. The castle above Weinsberg is called "Burg Weibertreu," which translates roughly as "Castle Women's Faithfulness." Legends about similar rescues of besieged men by their courageous and clever wives are told about many other castles and fortified cities in Europe.

chained up, and in the morning they were yoked together like oxen and had to plow the land till it grew dark.

This state of things went on for three years before the king found any means of sending news of himself to his dear queen, but at last he contrived to send this letter: "Sell all our castles and palaces, and put all our treasures in pawn and come and deliver me out of this horrible prison."

The queen received the letter, read it, and wept bitterly as she said to herself, "How can I deliver my dearest husband? If I go myself and the heathen king sees me he will just take me to be one of his wives. If I were to send one of the ministers! — but I hardly know if I can depend on them."

She thought, and thought, and at last an idea came into her head. She cut off all her beautiful long brown hair and dressed herself in boy's clothes. Then she took her lute and, without saying anything to anyone, she went forth into the wide world.

She traveled through many lands and saw many cities, and went through many hardships before she got to the town where the heathen king lived. When she got there she walked all round the palace and at the back she saw the prison. Then she went into the great court in front of the palace, and taking her lute in her hand, she began to play so beautifully that one felt as though one could never hear enough.

After she had played for some time she began to sing, and her voice was sweeter than the lark's:

> I come from my own country far
> Into this foreign land,
> Of all I own I take alone
> My sweet lute in my hand.
>
> Oh! who will thank me for my song.
> Reward my simple lay?
> Like lover's sighs it still shall rise
> To greet thee day by day.
>
> I sing of blooming flowers
> Made sweet by sun and rain;
> Of all the bliss of love's first kiss,
> And parting's cruel pain,
>
> Of the sad captive's longing
> Within his prison wall,
> Of hearts that sigh when none are nigh
> To answer to their call.
>
> My song begs for your pity,
> And gifts from out your store,
> And as I play my gentle lay
> I linger near your door.

And if you hear my singing
Within your palace, sire,
Oh! give, I pray, this happy day
To me my heart's desire.

No sooner had the heathen king heard this touching song sung by such a lovely voice, than he had the singer brought before him. "Welcome, O lute player," said he. "Where do you come from?"

"My country, sire, is far away across many seas. For years I have been wandering about the world and gaining my living by my music."

"Stay here then a few days, and when you wish to leave I will give you what you ask for in your song—your heart's desire."

So the lute player stayed on in the palace and sang and played almost all day long to the king, who could never tire of listening and almost forgot to eat or drink or to torment people. He cared for nothing but the music, and nodded his head as he declared, "There's nothing like your playing and singing. It makes me feel as if some gentle hand had lifted every care and sorrow from me."

After three days the lute player came to take leave of the king.

"Well," said the king, "what do you desire as your reward?"

"Sire, give me one of your prisoners. You have so many in your prison, and I should be glad of a companion on my journeys. When I hear his happy voice as I travel along I shall think of you and thank you."

"Come along then," said the king, "choose whom you will." And he took the lute player through the prison himself.

The queen walked about amongst the prisoners, and at length she picked out her husband and took him with her on her journey. They were long on their way, but he never found out who she was, and she led him nearer and nearer to his own country.

When they reached the frontier the prisoner said, "Let me go now, kind lad; I am no common prisoner, but the king of this country. Let me go free and ask what you will as your reward."

"Do not speak of reward," answered the lute player. "Go in peace."

"Then come with me, dear boy, and be my guest."

"When the proper time comes I shall be at your palace," was the reply, and so they parted.

The queen took a short way home, got there before the king and changed her dress.

An hour later all the people in the palace were running to and fro and crying out, "Our king has come back! Our king has returned to us."

The king greeted every one very kindly, but he would not so much as look at the queen.

Then he called all his council and ministers together and said to them, "See what sort of a wife I have. Here she is falling on my neck, but when I was pining in prison and sent her word of it she did nothing to help me."

And his council answered with one voice, "Sire, when news was brought from you, the queen disappeared and no one knew where she went. She only returned today."

Then the king was very angry and cried, "Judge my faithless wife! Never would you have seen your king again, if a young lute player had not delivered him. I shall remember him with love and gratitude as long as I live."

Whilst the king was sitting with his council, the queen found time to disguise herself. She took her lute, and slipping into the court in front of the palace she sang, clear and sweet:

> I sing the captive's longing
> Within his prison wall,
> Of hearts that sigh when none are nigh
> To answer to their call.
>
> My song begs for your pity,
> And gifts from out your store
> And as I play my gentle lay
> I linger near your door.
>
> And if you hear my singing
> Within your palace, sire,
> Oh! give, I pray, this happy day
> To me my heart's desire.

As soon as the king heard this song he ran out to meet the lute player, took him by the hand and led him into the palace.

"Here," he cried, "is the boy who released me from my prison. And now, my true friend, I will indeed give you your heart's desire."

"I am sure you will not be less generous than the heathen king was, sire. I ask of you what I asked and obtained from him. But this time I don't mean to give up what I get. I want *you*—yourself!"

And as she spoke she threw off her long cloak and everyone saw it was the queen.

Who can tell how happy the king was? In the joy of his heart he gave a great feast to the whole world, and the whole world came and rejoiced with him for a whole week.

I was there too, and ate and drank many good things. I shan't forget that feast as long as I live.[296]

---

[296]Type 888. Source: Andrew Lang, *The Violet Fairy Book* (London, 1901), pp. 70-76. Variations on this tale are found throughout Europe. The story is typically set during the crusades, with the heathen captor being identified specifically as an Islamic sultan in Turkey or the Holy Land. In Aleksandr Afanasyev's version, almost certainly Lang's source, the plot gets underway when a Czar makes a pilgrimage "to the distant land where the Jews crucified Christ."

461

The Falsely Accused Wife

Europe

O nce there was a wealthy merchant who lived together in a great manor with his many servants and his beautiful and faithful wife. His trust in her loyalty was always a source of comfort to him on his long voyages to the great ports of the seven seas. But one fateful day a discussion with a friend and fellow merchant brought him cause for concern.

"Wives are faithful only until opportunity knocks," claimed the friend, who then added boastfully, "I can charm my way into any woman's bedroom!"

"Certainly not into my wife's chambers," replied the merchant. "Her virtue is beyond question."

"If you are so sure of her, then let us enter into a wager as to her real fidelity," returned the friend, if we may call him that, for in truth he was a deceitful villain and was setting a cruel trap for the merchant and his wife.

The merchant, ever sure of his wife's virtue, struck a wager with the friend. Each placed half his fortune at stake. The friend would win if he could bring evidence that he had seduced the merchant's wife. The merchant would win if the friend's attempts proved fruitless.

The bet having been made, the villain bribed one of the merchant's servants to carry a trunk into the mistress's bedroom for safekeeping. "It would need to be there for only one night," explained the devious schemer. He then procured a large trunk, drilled a peephole into one end, hid himself inside, and had his own servants deliver it to the merchant's manor.

That night he spied on the merchant's wife as she got ready for bed, observing through the peephole that she had a peculiar birthmark on her hip. When the good woman was sound asleep he lifted the trunk's lid and quietly stole the ring that was lying on the table beside her bed. The next morning his servants, as planned, returned for the trunk and carried him back to his own house.

Soon afterward he met with the unsuspecting merchant. "Such a night of lovemaking!" he boasted. "But tell me," doesn't the birthmark on your wife's hip annoy you? It's quite unbecoming of such an otherwise beautiful woman." The merchant was turning red with anger, but the worst was still to come. "As a token of our love," lied the villain further, "your good wife gave me this ring." The merchant, recognizing his wife's wedding ring, stormed from the place with rage.

He burst into his manor with fury, accosted his unsuspecting wife, and told her to prepare to die. Her pleas for an explanation went unheeded, nor did her supplications for mercy divert him from his cruel design.

The merchant charged his most loyal servant with the dreadful task. He was to take the accused woman into the forest and shoot her, then bring back her liver and lungs as evidence that vengeance had been served. With a heavy heart he led his mistress into the forest, but he could not force himself to perform the wicked deed. Instead, he gave her a set of his own clothes, provided her with what rations he could get together, wished her Godspeed, and let her escape into the woods. He

462

then killed a doe, cut out its liver and lungs, and returned to his heartless master with evidence that the terrible act had been performed.

The pitiful woman, dressed in men's clothes, made her way through the forest, arriving at last in the royal city. She applied for a position at the king's court. Her fine manners and elegant speech impressed the officials, and they hired her at once as a clerk.

Days turned to weeks and weeks to months. The falsely accused wife proved herself equal to every task that her new position presented. She quickly advanced from one post to the next until she, still disguised as a man, finally became the highest judge in the kingdom.

One day two merchants appeared before her bench. Embroiled in a dispute over a wager, they were bringing their case before the highest judge, whose justice and wisdom had rapidly found praise throughout the land. The judge recognized them immediately as her heartless husband and his deceitful friend. She listened carefully as her husband related how he had entered into the fateful wager, only to learn later from his servants about the delivery of the overnight trunk. Rightly sensing that he had been tricked, and was now attempting to recover the half of his fortune that he had lost.

The judge heard his story to its end, then arose. Standing proud and tall in her courtly robes she told her own story of cruel betrayal. Her hapless husband, now recognizing the injustice of his wrongful accusation, begged for mercy. The judge, seeking justice, but not revenge, solemnly pronounced her judgment: The two merchants were to be banished from the kingdom forever.

The king, in the meanwhile, had quietly entered the courtroom and had listened intently to the proceedings. The admiration and respect that he had felt toward his highest judge turned to love and devotion, now that he knew *he* was actually a *she*. Thus, the king gained not only a wise and prudent judge, but also a faithful and loving wife. And they ruled happily together until the end of their days.[297]

The Entrapped Suitors

Europe

An honest sculptor and his beautiful wife lived in a renowned city with a great cathedral. His work was always in demand, because there were many convents, monasteries, and churches in the city. The sculptor and his wife

---

[297]Type 882. Retold. This tale is found throughout Europe, both in literary and folkloristic versions. Most often the story concludes with the falsely accused wife returning to her now repentant husband, but I prefer the version given above.

463

would have been ever so happy, but for one problem. Her exquisite beauty caught the eye of many men, some of whom became increasingly bold in their attempts to gain her favor. Three men in particular—a bishop, a priest, and a sexton—were so open and so forceful in their solicitations that life became quite unbearable for the sculptor and his faithful wife. The sculptor, you see, feared that if any one of these three influential men would turn against him it could ruin his thriving trade. And his wife, an honorable and pious woman, was quite naturally offended by their overtures.

Finally the husband and wife devised a plan that would, they hoped, put an end to the unseemly advances and propositions.

The next time that the bishop approached the sculptor's wife, instead of giving her usual cool reply, she responded warmly, "Yes, it would be good if we could get to know one another better. My husband will be out this afternoon. Why don't you come by at three o'clock for tea?" The bishop, who could scarcely hide his eagerness and joy, accepted the invitation and left.

Then came the priest, and he too was delighted when his solicitation received an unexpectedly warm response. He too received an invitation for tea, but he was to come at half past three. The sexton came last, and he too was invited, but for four o'clock.

Three o'clock arrived and the bishop, true to his word, was as punctual as a church bell. "You must be very uncomfortable in that heavy, scratchy robe," purred the sculptor's wife, as they drank their tea. "Do make yourself at ease." He needed no further encouragement, and began to take off his clothes. Just as the last item fell, there came a knock at the door.

"Heaven help us!" cried the woman. "It's my husband! Quick, hide in the closet." The bishop, naked as a fish, fled to the closet.

The woman regained her composure and went to the door. It was, of course, the priest, as punctual as a church bell. A half hour later he too, having been encouraged by the sculptor's wife, had removed his clothes, just in time to hear a knock at the door. The previous scene repeated itself, and within seconds the naked priest had joined the naked bishop in the closet.

The sexton did not fare any better. He too, in grand anticipation, took off his clothes, only to be interrupted by a knock at the door. And he joined his two naked brethren in the closet.

This time it was indeed the husband returning home, and he had with him three nuns, worthy sisters from a nearby convent who had ordered statues of the three wise men for their sanctuary.

"I have just what you want," said the sculptor, leading the nuns to the closet holding the three entrapped suitors. "These will fit perfectly in the sanctuary," he added, opening the door with a flourish.

The three suitors stood breathless, as if made from stone as the nuns came closer to examine the workmanship.

First there was only silence, but then the senior sister said, hesitatingly, "Well, uh, we did have a somewhat different style in mind, perhaps something with a little less detail."

"No problem!" exclaimed the sculptor. I can remove the excess details at once!" He approached the three suitors, hammer in one hand, chisel in the other. And behold, the three statues suddenly came to life, bolted through the room, and disappeared out the door.

The three nuns returned to their convent without any statues. The good sisters there still give witness to the legend of the three stone saints that miraculously came to life.[298]

The Lady and Her Five Suitors

1001 Nights

A beautiful woman, whose husband had traveled abroad, fell in love with a handsome young man, who in turn came into difficulty with the law. Claiming that the young man was her brother, she asked the wali to support his case, and he acceded, but only if she would be his lover. She consented, giving him her address and setting a time for their tryst. She next petitioned a qadi. He too agreed to intercede on her brother's behalf, in return for her love, and she set the same time for his arrival that had been reserved for the wali. Then she went to a vizier, who, like the others, pledged his help, in exchange for her promise of intimacy, and his appointment was set for the same time as his predecessors. Next she took her petition to the king, and he too guaranteed a good outcome for her brother's case, if she would accept him as a lover. The arrangements were quickly made.

The woman then went to a carpenter and ordered from him a cabinet with four compartments, one above the other. "My price is four dinars or your affection" he said.

"Let it be the latter," she replied. "But only if you make a cabinet with five compartments, instead of four." The carpenter consented. The work was soon finished, and she told him when to return for his promised reward.

The appointed trysting day came. The qadi was the first to arrive, and she asked him to take off his clothes and put on a brightly colored, strangely cut robe. He had scarcely done so when there was a knock at the door. "It is my husband!" she cried. "Hide in the cabinet!" And she locked him in the lowermost compartment. So it went with the wali, the vizier, and the king.

---

[298]Type 1730. Retold. Concern about sexual harassment is not an invention of the twentieth century. This story, recorded in varying degrees of crudity, has been told for centuries throughout the world. The fear of getting caught with one's pants down, it would seem, is very nearly universal.

The carpenter was the last to arrive. She lured him into the cabinet's top compartment by complaining that, contrary to her instructions, it had been built too narrow to hold a man. "Not so," said the carpenter, and climbed inside to prove his claim. The woman locked the door on her final suitor, and then abandoned the place, departing with her young lover for another city.

Three days passed, and the carpenter, unable to hold his water any longer, relieved himself on the man beneath him. Each captive did the same, turning the cabinet into a sewer of filth. With time the neighbors entered the woman's lodgings and freed the befouled and strangely costumed suitors. Thus ends the story of the woman who tricked her five suitors.[299]

---

[299]Type 1730. Source: *The Book of the Thousand Nights and a Night*, translated by Richard F. Burton (Privately printed, 1885), v. 6, pp. 172-179. Revised and abridged.

Old Age

Man and His Years

Romania

When God had created the world, he called all his creatures together to grant them their span of life, and to tell them how long they would live and what manner of life they would lead.

The first to appear before God was man. And God said to him, "You, man, shall be king of the world, walking erect upon your feet and looking up to heaven. I give you a noble countenance; the power of thought and judgment shall be yours, and the capacity of disclosing your innermost thoughts by means of speech. All that lives and moves and goes about the earth shall be under your rule, the winged birds and the creeping things shall obey you, yours shall be all the fruits of the tree and land, and your life shall be thirty years."

Then man turned away dissatisfied and grumbling. "What is the good of living in pleasure and in might, if all the years of my life are to be thirty only?" So did man speak and grumble, especially when he heard of the years granted to other animals.

The turn came to the donkey. He stepped forward to hear what God had decreed for him. The Creator said, "You shall work hard; you shall carry heavy burdens and be constantly beaten. You shall always be scolded and have very little rest, your food shall be a poor one of thistles and thorns, and your life shall be fifty years." When the donkey heard what God had decreed for him he fell upon his knees and cried, "All merciful Creator, am I indeed to lead such a miserable life, and am I to have such poor food as thistles and thorns. Am I to work so hard and carry such heavy burdens and then live on for fifty years in such misery? Have pity on me and take off twenty years." Then man, greedy of long life, stepped forward and begged for himself these twenty years which the donkey had rejected. And the Lord granted them to him.

Then came the dog. To him the Creator said, "You shall guard the house and the property of your master; you shall cling to them as if you were afraid of losing them; you shall bark even at the shadow of the moon, and for all your trouble you shall gnaw bones and eat raw meat, and your life shall be forty years."

"All merciful Creator," cried the dog, "if my life is to be of worry and trouble, and if I am to live on bones and raw stuff, take off, I pray, twenty years."

Again man, greedy of life, stepped forward and begged the Creator to give him the twenty years rejected by the dog. And the Creator again granted his request.

Now it was the turn of the monkey. The creator said, "You shall only have the likeness of man, but not be man; you shall be stupid and childish. Your back shall be bent; you shall be an object of mockery to the children and a laughingstock of fools, and your life shall be sixty years."

When the monkey heard what was decreed for him, he fell upon his knees and said, "All merciful God, in your wisdom you have decided that I should be a man and not a man, that my back shall be bent, that I shall be a laughing stock for young and fools and I shall be stupid. Take, in mercy, thirty years off my life." And God, the all merciful, granted his request.

And again, man, whose greed can never be satisfied, stepped forward and asked also for these thirty years which the monkey had rejected. And again God gave them to him.

Then God dismissed all the animals and all his creatures, and each one went to his appointed station and to the life that has been granted to him.

And as man had asked, so has it come to pass.

Man lives as a king and ruler over all creatures for the thirty years which the Lord had given to him, in joy and in happiness, without care and without trouble.

Then come the years from thirty to fifty, which are the years of the donkey; they are full of hard work, heavy burdens, and little food, for man is anxious to gather and to lay up something for the years to come. It could not be otherwise, for were not these the years which he had taken over from the donkey? Then come the years from fifty to seventy, when man sits at home and guards with great trembling and fear the little that he possesses, fearful of every shadow, eating little, always keeping others away lest they rob him of that which he has gathered, and barking at everyone whom he suspects of wanting to take away what belongs to him. And no wonder that he behaves like that, for these are the dog's years, which man had asked for himself. And if a man lives beyond seventy, then his back gets bent, his face changes, his mind gets clouded, he becomes childish, a laughingstock for children, an amusement for the fool, and these are the years which man had taken over from the monkey.[300]

---

[300]Type 173. Source: M. Gaster, *Rumanian Bird and Beast Stories* (London, 1915), no. 116. Gaster's source: "some old Rumanian manuscripts." This widespread tale is also included in the Grimms' collection under the title "The Duration of Life" (no. 176).

The Bremen Town Musicians

Jacob and Wilhelm Grimm

A man had a donkey, who for long years had untiringly carried sacks to the mill, but whose strength was now failing, so that he was becoming less and less able to work. Then his master thought that he would no longer feed him, but the donkey noticed that it was not a good wind that was blowing and ran away, setting forth on the road to Bremen, where he thought he could become a town musician. When he had gone a little way he found a hunting dog lying in the road, who was panting like one who had run himself tired.

"Why are you panting so?" asked the donkey.

"Oh," said the dog, "because I am old and am getting weaker every day and can no longer go hunting, my master wanted to kill me, so I ran off; but now how should I earn my bread?"

"Do you know what," said the donkey, "I am going to Bremen and am going to become a town musician there. Come along and take up music too."

The dog was satisfied with that, and they went further. It didn't take long, before they came to a cat sitting by the side of the road and making the saddest face. "What has crossed you?" said the donkey.

"Oh," answered the cat, "who can be cheerful when his neck is at risk? I am getting on in years, and my teeth are getting dull, so I would rather sit behind the stove and purr than to chase around after mice. Therefore my mistress wanted to drown me, but I took off. Now good advice is scarce. Where should I go?"

"Come with us to Bremen. After all, you understand night music. You can become a town musician there." The cat agreed and went along.

The three refugees came to a farmyard, and the rooster of the house was sitting on the gate crying with all his might. "Your cries pierce one's marrow and bone," said the donkey. "What are you up to?"

"I just prophesied good weather," said the rooster, "because it is the day when Our Dear Lady washes the Christ child's shirts and wants to dry them; but because Sunday guests are coming tomorrow, the lady of the house has no mercy and told the cook that she wanted to eat me tomorrow in the soup, and I am supposed to let them cut my head this evening. So I am going to cry at the top of my voice as long as I can."

"Hey now, Redhead," said the donkey, "instead come away with us; we're going to Bremen. You can always find something better than death. You have a good voice, and when we make music together, it will be very pleasing."

The rooster was happy with the proposal, and all four went off together. However, they could not reach the city of Bremen in one day, and in the evening they came into a forest, where they would spend the night. The donkey and the dog lay down under a big tree, but the cat and the rooster took to the branches. The rooster flew right to the top, where it was safest for him. Before falling asleep he looked around once again in all four directions, and he thought that he saw a little spark burning in the distance. He hollered to his companions, that there must be a house not too far away, for a light was shining.

The donkey said, "Then we must get up and go there, because the lodging here is poor." The dog said that he could do well with a few bones with a little meat on them. Thus they set forth toward the place, where the light was, and they soon saw it glistening more brightly, and it became larger and larger, until they came to the front of a brightly lit robbers' house.

The donkey, the largest of them, approached the window and looked in.

"What do you see, Grayhorse?" asked the rooster.

"What do I see?" answered the donkey. "A table set with wonderful things to eat and drink, and robbers sitting there enjoying themselves."

"That would be something for us," said the rooster.

"Ee-ah, ee-ah, oh, if we were there!" said the donkey. Then the animals discussed how they might drive the robbers away, and at last they came upon a plan. The donkey was to stand with his front feet on the window, the dog to jump on the donkey's back, the cat to climb onto the dog, and finally the rooster would fly up and sit on the cat's head. When they had done that, at a signal they began to make their music all together. The donkey brayed, the dog barked, the cat meowed and the rooster crowed. Then they crashed through the window into the room, shattering the panes.

The robbers jumped up at the terrible bellowing, thinking that a ghost was coming in, and fled in great fear out into the forest. Then the four companions seated themselves at the table and freely partook of the leftovers, eating as if they would get nothing more for four weeks.

When the four minstrels were finished, they put out the light and looked for a place to sleep, each according to his nature and his customs. The donkey lay down on the manure pile, the dog behind the door, the cat on the hearth next to the warm ashes, and the rooster sat on the beam of the roof. Because they were tired from their long journey, they soon fell asleep.

When midnight had passed and the robbers saw from the distance that the light was no longer burning in the house, and everything appeared to be quiet, the captain said, "We shouldn't have let ourselves be chased off," and he told one to go back and investigate the house. The one they sent found everything still, and went into the kitchen to strike a light. He mistook the cat's glowing, fiery eyes for live coals, and held a sulfur match next to them, so that it would catch fire. But the cat didn't understand this game and jumped into his face, spitting, and scratching.

He was terribly frightened and ran toward the back door, but the dog, who was lying there, jumped up and bit him in the leg. When he ran across the yard past the manure pile, the donkey gave him a healthy blow with his rear foot, and the rooster, who had been awakened from his sleep by the noise and was now alert, cried down from the beam, "Cock-a-doodle-doo!"

Then the robber ran as fast as he could back to his captain and said, "Oh, there is a horrible witch sitting in the house, she blew at me and scratched my face with her long fingers. And there is a man with a knife standing in front of the door, and he stabbed me in the leg. And a black monster is lying in the yard, and it struck at me

470

with a wooden club. And the judge is sitting up there on the roof, and he was calling out, 'Bring the rascal here.' Then I did what I could to get away."

From that time forth, the robbers did not dare go back into the house. However, the four Bremen Musicians liked it so well there, that they never to left it again. And the person who just told that, his mouth is still warm.[301]

The Story of the White Pet

Scotland

There was a farmer before now who had a White Pet (sheep),[302] and when Christmas was drawing near, he thought that he would kill the White Pet. The White Pet heard that, and he thought he would run away; and that is what he did.

He had not gone far when a bull met him. Said the bull to him, "All hail! White Pet, where are you going?"

"I," said the White Pet, "am going to seek my fortune; they were going to kill me for Christmas, and I thought I had better run away."

"It is better for me," said the bull, "to go with you, for they were going to do the very same with me."

"I am willing," said the White Pet; "the larger the party the better the fun."

They went forward until they fell in with a dog. "All hail! White Pet," said the dog.

"All hail! dog."

"Where are you going?" said the dog.

"I am running away, for I heard that they were threatening to kill me for Christmas."

"They were going to do the very same to me," said the dog, "and I will go with you."

"Come, then," said the White Pet.

They went then, until a cat joined them. "All hail! White Pet," said the cat.

"All hail! oh cat."

"Where are you going?" said the cat.

"I am going to seek my fortune," said the White Pet, " because they were going to kill me at Christmas."

"They were talking about killing me too," said the cat," and I had better go with you."

---

[301]Type 130. Source: *Kinder- und Hausmärchen*, 2nd ed. (Berlin, 1819), no. 27.

[302]A "white pet" is a lamb brought up by hand.

471

"Come on then," said the White Pet.

Then they went forward until a cock met them. "All hail! White Pet," said the cock.

"All hail to yourself! oh cock," said the White Pet.

"Where," said the cock," are you going?"

"I," said the White Pet, "am going away, for they were threatening my death at Christmas."

"They were going to kill me at the very same time," said the cock, " and I will go with you."

"Come, then," said the White Pet.

They went forward until they fell in with a goose. "All hail! White Pet," said the goose. "All hail to yourself! oh goose," said the White Pet.

"Where are you going?" said the goose.

"I," said the White Pet, "am running away, because they were going to kill me at Christmas."

"They were going to do that to me too," said the goose, "and I will go with you."

The party went forward until the night was drawing on them, and they saw a little light far away; and though far off, they were not long getting there. When they reached the house they said to each other that they would look in at the window to see who was in the house, and they saw thieves counting money; and the White Pet said, "Let every one of us call his own call. I will call my own call; and let the bull call his own call; let the dog call his own call; and the cat her own call; and the cock his own call; and the goose his own call." With that they gave out one shout—GAIRE!

When the thieves heard the shouting outside, they thought the mischief was there; and they fled out, and they went to a wood that was near them. When the White Pet and his company saw that the house was empty, they went in and they got the money that the thieves had been counting, and they divided it among themselves; and then they thought that they would settle to rest. Said the White Pet, "Where will you sleep tonight, oh bull?"

"I will sleep," said the bull, "behind the door where I used to be."

"Where will you sleep, White Pet?"

"I will sleep," said the White Pet, "in the middle of the floor where I used to be."

"Where will you sleep, oh dog?" said the White Pet.

"I will sleep beside the fire where I used to be," said the dog.

"Where will you sleep, oh cat?"

"I will sleep," said the cat, "in the candle press, where I like to be."

"Where will you sleep, oh cock?" said the White Pet.

"I," said the cock, " will sleep on the rafters where I used to be."

"Where will you sleep, oh goose?"

"I will sleep," said the goose, "on the manure pile, where I was accustomed to be."

They were not long settled to rest, when one of the thieves returned to look in to see if he could perceive if any one at all was in the house. All things were still, and he went on forward to the candle press for a candle, that he might kindle to make him a light; but when he put his hand in the box the cat thrust her claws into his hand, but he took a candle with him, and he tried to light it. Then the dog got up, and he stuck his tail into a pot of water that was beside the fire; he shook his tail and put out the candle. Then the thief thought that the mischief was in the house, and he fled; but when he was passing the White Pet, he gave him a blow; before he got past the bull, he gave him a kick; and the cock began to crow; and when he went out, the goose began to belabor him with his wings about the shanks.

He went to the wood where his comrades were, as fast as was in his legs. They asked him how it had gone with him. "It went," said he, "but middling; when I went to the candle press, there was a man in it who thrust ten knives into my hand; and when I went to the fireside to light the candle, there was a big black man lying there, who was sprinkling water on it to put it out; and when I tried to go out, there was a big man in the middle of the floor, who gave me a shove; and another man behind the door who pushed me out; and there was a little brat on the loft calling out CUIR-ANEES-AN-SHAW-AY-S-FONI-MI-HAYN-DA—Send him up here and I'll do for him; and there was a shoemaker, out on the manure pile, belaboring me about the shanks with his apron."

When the thieves heard that, they did not return to seek their lot of money; and the White Pet and his comrades got it to themselves; and it kept them peaceably as long as they lived.[303]

The Old Husband and His Young Wife

The Panchatantra

In a certain place there once lived an old merchant by the name of Kâmâtura, which means "lovesick." His wife having died, he fell deeply in love with the daughter of a poor merchant, gave a large sum of money for her, and married her. She, however, was overcome by sorrow, and did not even want to look at the old man. For is it not right, that:

> The white field of hair on an old man's head attracts the greatest contempt. To avoid it, a girl will take the widest detour, like someone crossing a graveyard strewn with bones.

And further:

---

[303]Type 130. Source: J. F. Campbell, *Popular Tales of the West Highlands* (London, 1890), v. 1, pp. 199-202. Campbell's source was a Mrs. MacTavish, who collected the story in Gaelic from a servant maid in at Port Ellen, Isaly, in 1859.

The body is bent. The gait is broken. Teeth are lost. Vision is weak. Beauty is destroyed. The mouth is always filled with spit. Relatives do not follow his advice. His wife does not obey him. Alas! Alas! Even the son despises a man struck down by age!

One night they were lying in bed together, her face turned away from him, when a thief broke into their house. When she saw the thief, she was overcome by fear, and, in spite of his age, she clasped her husband tightly in her arms. The surprise embrace caused every hair on his body to stand on end. He said to himself, "Why is she holding me?" Then looking around, he too discovered the thief crouched in the corner, and he realized, "She is embracing me, because she is afraid of him," and said aloud, "The woman who has always despised me is embracing me tightly tonight. Praise be to you, you granter of desire! Take whatever of mine that you want!"

The thief answered, "I see nothing here that I would want to take. If in the future there is something worth taking, then I will return, but only when she is not embracing you so."[304]

The Partridge and Her Young

Romania

A partridge once built her nest in the furrows of a newly plowed cornfield, and hatched her young when the stalks of the corn had grown tall and the corn began to ripen. There was food in plenty and safety enough for them to play and to frolic about without fear of any danger.

But the good things in this world never stay long with us, and this the partridge was soon to find out. The time came when the corn was cut and hunters appeared followed by their dogs, whose barking they could hear drawing nearer and nearer. The partridge now began to be frightened for her young. She tried to cover them with her wings, but they could not help hearing the reports of the guns and the barking of the dogs.

One day, not being able to stand the strain any longer, she remembered a place of safety which she had known, in the cleft of a mountain beyond the seas. Tucking her eldest under her wing, she started one morning on her flight, intent on carrying it to the mountain beyond the sea. When she reached the border of the sea there stood a huge tree. Tired from her long flight, she settled on one of the branches of

---

[304]Source: *Pantschatantra: Fünf Bücher indischer Fabeln, Märchen und Erzählungen,* translated from the Sanskrit into German by Theodor Benfey (Leipzig, 1859), v. 2, book 3, story 8.

the tree overhanging the water. And she said to her young, "Little darling, see how great is the love of a mother and what trouble I am taking. Nay, I am putting my life in danger in order to save you."

"Never mind, mother," replied the little one, "Wait until we grow up and then we will take care of you when you grow old and weak." When the partridge heard these words she tilted her wing and let the young bird fall into the water of the sea, where it was drowned.

Distressed, weary, and lost in thought, she returned to her nest and took the middle one of her three young, and, putting it on the wing, she started again on her flight to the mountain beyond the sea. On the way she again alighted on the tree with the branches overhanging the sea. And she spoke to this one in the same manner as she had spoken to the first. And he replied, "Do not worry, mother, when you get old we shall take care of you and show you our love." The partridge, grieving at the words of this one, again dipped her wing and the young bird slid down into the bottom of the sea, where it was drowned.

Almost broken hearted, not knowing any more what to do with herself, and heavy with sorrow and anxiety, her only hope being the youngest one, she returned to her nest, and, taking the youngest—the mother's pet—she tucked it under her wing and flew again to the mountain beyond the sea. Tired from her continual flight hither and thither, she again alighted on the tree with the branches overhanging the sea, and with her heart trembling within her for fear and love, she said to the youngest, "See, my beloved little pet, how much trouble mother is taking to save her dear little ones, how willingly I am suffering pain and fatigue; see how exhausted I am and wearied, but nothing is too much for a mother if only she knows that her young will be safe."

"Do not worry, mother dear, for we when we grow up will also take care of our young children with the same love and devotion." At these words, the mother pressed the little one nearer to her heart, and, full of joy, carried him across the sea to a place of safety, for of all her children this alone had spoken the truth. And is it not so in the world?

This is the story of the partridge and her young.[305]

---

[305]Type 244C*. Source: M. Gaster, *Rumanian Bird and Beast Stories* (London, 1915), no. 95.

The Raven and His Young

Leo Tolstoy

A raven was carrying his chicks, one at a time, from an island to the mainland. In mid flight he asked the first, "Who will carry me when I am old and can no longer fly?"

"I will," answered the young raven, but the father did not believe him, and dropped him into the sea.

The same question was put to the second chick. He too replied, "I will carry you when you are old," and the father also let him fall into the sea.

The last chick received the same question, but he answered, "Father, you will have to fend for yourself when you are old, because by then I will have my own family to care for."

"You speak the truth," said the father raven, and carried the chick to safety.[306]

The Old Widow and Her Ungrateful Son

India

A man refused to support his mother, who was a widow and had no other son. So the poor old woman, not knowing what else to do, went to the governor, and falling on her knees before him, begged him to help her. "Oh my lord," she cried, "I am a widow, and have only one son, who declines to give me a little food and clothing, or even a corner in his house to lie down in. What shall I do? I cannot work. My eyes are failing and my strength is gone. Your honor is famous for wisdom and understanding. Please advise me."

On hearing her complaint the governor summoned the son of the old widow, and sharply upbraided him for not supporting her, to whom he was indebted beyond repayment.

"I do not owe her anything," replied the young man. "She never lent me a *pánsa*. On the contrary, she owes me very much. I have entirely supported her for the last three years. But now I cannot provide for her any longer. I have a wife and family of my own to feed and clothe and care for."

"For shame!" said the governor. "Is it necessary that I should tell you how much you owe your mother?—yea, even your life and health and strength? Who carried you about every moment for nine long weary months? Who suckled you

---

[306]Type 244C*. Retold from *Fourth Reader* (1872). This tale is especially well represented in Yiddish folklore.

476

for twice that time? Who taught you to walk? Who taught you to talk? Who fed you with food convenient for you? Who saved you from many a fall, from many a burn, and from many a scald? Who pounded the rice and prepared your food for several years, until you were able to marry and get a wife to do these things for you?"

"These are things that every mother has to do and likes to do," said the young man. "She would not wish to live if she could not perform them."

"True to a certain point, but" —— Here the governor stopped, and turning to one of the *wazírs* in attendance, ordered him to see that this young unthankful fellow pounded four *sers* of rice with a skin of water fastened round his stomach, and to beat him if he did not accomplish the task well and quickly.

The man soon got tired. The perspiration ran down over his face and neck. At last he could not lift the pestle any more; and the rice was not half pounded. Thwack, thwack, thwack, came down the whip on his bare shoulders, but it was no good, he could not pound another grain. He was then carried before the governor in a dead-alive condition.

"I need not say anything more to you," said the governor to him. "You have learned something of what your mother endured for you. Go and repay the debt with kind words and kind deeds."[307]

How the Wicked Sons Were Duped

India

A very wealthy old man, imagining that he was on the point of death, sent for his sons and divided his property among them. However, he did not die for several years afterwards; and miserable years many of them were. Besides the weariness of old age, the old fellow had to bear with much abuse and cruelty from his sons. Wretched, selfish ingrates! Previously they vied with one another in trying to please their father, hoping thus to receive more money, but now they had received their patrimony, they cared not how soon he left them—nay, the sooner the better, because he was only a needless trouble and expense. This, as we may suppose, was a great grief to the old man.

One day he met a friend and related to him all his troubles. The friend sympathized very much with him, and promised to think over the matter, and call in a little while and tell him what to do. He did so; in a few days he visited the old man and put down four bags full of stones and gravel before him.

---

[307]Type 926C. Source: J. Hinton Knowles, *Folk-Tales of Kashmir* (London, 1893), pp. 255-256. Knowles does not give this story a title.

477

"Look here, friend," said he. "Your sons will get to know of my coming here today, and will inquire about it. You must pretend that I came to discharge a long-standing debt with you, and that you are several thousands of rupees richer than you thought you were. Keep these bags in your own hands, and on no account let your sons get to them as long as you are alive. You will soon find them change their conduct towards you. *Salám.* I will come again soon to see how you are getting on."

When the young men got to hear of this further increase of wealth they began to be more attentive and pleasing to their father than ever before. And thus they continued to the day of the old man's demise, when the bags were greedily opened, and found to contain only stones and gravel![308]

The Ungrateful Son

Johann Pauli

The old man, it seemed, always visited his son just at mealtime. "You needn't fix anything for me," he would say, looking hungrily on as the others prepared to eat. Of course they had to give him something.

"This has to stop," said the old man's son on a day when they had killed a chicken for a special feast. "If the old man comes today, we will hide the pot."

As expected, the old man knocked at the door just before mealtime. Hurriedly they hid the pot with the chicken, then acted as if they knew nothing of a forthcoming meal. The old man sniffed in the air, said something about the good smell, looked about, then seeing nothing to eat, he took leave and returned to his own house.

"Now we can eat!" said the man, bringing the pot from its hiding place and taking off the lid. But to his terror, the chicken turned into a hideous toad before his very eyes. It jumped into his face, attaching itself firmly, and it did not come off as long as the man lived.[309]

---

[308]Type 982. Source: J. Hinton Knowles, *Folk-Tales of Kashmir* (London, 1893), pp. 241-242.

[309]Type 980D. Retold from *Schimpf und Ernst* (1522), no. 437. The Grimms also give a version of this tale in their *Kinder- und Hausmärchen* (no. 145).

The Stingy Daughter

India

Once a man went to visit his married daughter. He intended to arrive in time for dinner; so though he passed some edible herbs on the way he did not stop to eat them. When he arrived he was duly welcomed and after some conversation he told his daughter that he must return the same day; she said, "All right, but wait until it gets hot." (The father understood this to be a metaphorical way of saying "Wait until the dinner is cooked.) But the daughter was determined not to cook the rice while her father was there. So they sat talking and when the sun was high the daughter went into the yard and felt the ground with her foot and finding it scorching she said, "Now father, it is time for you to be going. It has got hot." Then the old man understood that she was not going to give him his dinner. So he took his stick and got up to go.

Now the son-in-law was a great hunter and that day he had killed and brought home a peacock; as he was leaving, the father said, "My daughter, if your husband ever brings home a peacock I advise you to cook it with mowah oil cake; that makes it taste very nice." So directly her father had gone, the woman set to work and cooked the peacock with mowah oil cake; but when her husband and children began to eat it they found it horribly bitter and she herself tasted it and found it uneatable; then she told them that her father had made fun of her and made her spoil all the meat. Her husband asked whether she had cooked rice for her father; and when she said "No" he said that this was the way in which he had punished her; he had had nothing to eat and so he had prevented their having any either; she should entertain all visitors and especially her father. So they threw away the meat and had no dinner.[310]

The Old Grandfather and His Grandson

Jacob and Wilhelm Grimm

Once upon a time there was an old man who could hardly walk. His knees shook. He could not hear or see very well, and he did not have any teeth left. When he sat at the table, he could scarcely hold a spoon. He spilled soup on the tablecloth, and, beside that, some of his soup would run back out of his mouth. His son and his son's wife were disgusted with this, so finally they

---

[310]Type 980. Source: Cecil Henry Bompas, *Folklore of the Santal Parganas* (London, 1909), no. 125.

made the old grandfather sit in the corner behind the stove, where they gave him his food in an earthenware bowl, and not enough at that. He sat there looking sadly at the table, and his eyes grew moist. One day his shaking hands could not hold the bowl, and it fell to the ground and broke. The young woman scolded, but he said not a word. He only sobbed. Then for a few hellers they bought him a wooden bowl and made him eat from it. Once when they were all sitting there, the little grandson of four years pushed some pieces of wood together on the floor.

"What are you making?" asked his father.

"Oh, I'm making a little trough for you and mother to eat from when I'm big."

The man and the woman looked at one another and then began to cry. They immediately brought the old grandfather to the table, and always let him eat there from then on. And if he spilled a little, they did not say a thing.[311]

A Wendish Legend

Germany

During heathen times the Sorbian Wends of Lausitz[312] practiced the shameful and gruesome custom of ridding themselves of their old people who were no longer able to contribute. A son would strike his own father dead when he became old and incompetent, or he would throw him into water, or he would push him over a high cliff. Indeed, there are many examples of this, even after the advent of Christianity.

For example: Herr Levin von Schulenburg, a high official in Altmark, was traveling among the Wends in about 1580 when he saw an old man being led away by several people. "Where are you going with the old man?" he asked, and received the answer, "To God!" They were going to sacrifice him to God, because he was no longer able to earn his own sustenance. When the official grasped what was happening, he forced them to turn the old man over to him. He took him home with him and hired him as a gatekeeper, a position that he held for twenty additional years.[313]

---

[311]Type 980B. Source: *Kinder- und Hausmärchen*, 1st ed. (Berlin, 1812/1815), v. 1, no. 78.

[312]In today's southeast Germany.

[313]Source: Karl Haupt, *Sagenbuch der Lausitz*, v. 2 (Leipzig, 1863), p. 9.

Why People Today Die their Own Death

Eastern Europe

In ancient days people did not die their own death. Instead, law and tradition required that they be taken into the mountains and pushed over a sacred cliff when they reached a certain age.

One family could not bring themselves to depart from their old grandfather, and so when his time came, they hid him in their cellar instead of taking him to the cliff of death. At this time there was a great famine in the land. The crops had failed, the food stores were exhausted, and indeed, no one even had grain left for seed.

The grandfather, from his hiding place in the cellar, told his kin to remove the thatched roofs from their houses and rethresh the straw for any kernels of grain that may have been missed the first time. They did as he suggested, and harvested a good measure of forgotten grain.

Acting again on the old man's advice, they sowed the newfound grain that very day. Miraculously their crop sprouted, matured, and was ready for harvest the next morning.

The king, who quickly learned of this miracle, demanded an explanation. Thus the family was forced to admit how they had violated law and tradition by sparing their old grandfather. The king, impressed by the family's courage and by the old man's wisdom, decreed that from that day forth old people would be allowed to live until they died their own death.[314]

---

[314]Type 981. Retold. Folktales depicting geronticide are too widespread to be dismissed as expressions of mere fantasy or unwarranted fear. This particular version is based on stories from Romania and the Ukraine. For further tales and commentary see *Folk-Lore: A Quarterly Review*, v. 29 (1918), p. 238; v. 30 (1919), pp. 136-139; v. 32 (1921), pp. 213-215.

Death

The Young

The Death of the Little Hen

Jacob and Wilhelm Grimm

The little hen and the little rooster once went to Nut Mountain, where they enjoyed themselves eating nuts together. One time, however, the little hen found such a large nut that she could not swallow its kernel. It got stuck in her throat, and, fearing that she would choke to death, she cried out, "Little Rooster, I beg you to run as fast as you can to the well and get me some water, or else I'll choke to death."

The little rooster ran to the well as fast as he could, and said, "Well, give me some water, for Little Hen is lying on Nut Mountain and is about to choke to death on a large nut kernel."

The well answered, "First run to the bride, and get some red silk from her."

The little rooster ran to the bride: "Bride, give me some red silk, and I'll give the red silk to the well, and the well will give me some water, and I'll take the water to the little hen who is lying on Nut Mountain and is about to choke to death on a large nut kernel."

The bride answered, "First run and get my wreath. It got caught on a willow branch."

So the little rooster ran to the willow and pulled the wreath from its branch and took it to the bride, and the bride gave him some red silk, which he took to the well, which gave him some water, and the little rooster took the water to the little hen, but when he arrived, she had already choked to death, and she lay there dead, and did not move at all.

The little rooster was so sad that he cried aloud, and all the animals came to mourn for the little hen. Six mice built a small carriage which was to carry the little hen to her grave. When the carriage was finished, they hitched themselves to it, and the little rooster drove. On the way they met Fox.

"Where are you going, Little Rooster?"

"I'm going to bury my little hen."

"May I ride along?"

"Yes, but you must sit at the rear, because my little horses don't like you too close to the front."

So he sat at the rear, and then the wolf, the bear, the elk, the lion, and all the animals in the forest. They rode on until they came to a brook. "How can we get across?" said the little rooster.

A straw was there, and he said, "I'll lay myself across, and you can drive over me." But just as the six mice got onto the straw, it slipped into the water, and the six mice all fell in and drowned.

They did not know what to do, until a coal came and said, "I am large enough. I will lay myself across and you can drive over me." So the coal laid himself across the water, but unfortunately he touched it, hissed, went out, and it was dead.

A stone saw this happen, and, wanting to help the little rooster, he laid himself across the water. The little rooster pulled the carriage himself. He nearly reached the other side with the dead little hen, but there were too many others seated on the back of the carriage, and the carriage tipped over, and they all fell into the water and drowned.

Now the little rooster was all alone with the dead little hen. He dug a grave for her and laid her inside. Then he made a mound on top, and sat on it, and grieved there so long that he too died. And then everyone was dead.[315]

Straw, Coal, and Bean Go Traveling

Jacob and Wilhelm Grimm

Astraw, a coal, and a bean formed a group in order to take a long trip together. They had already gone through many lands when they came to a brook with no bridge, and they could not get across. Finally Straw came upon a good idea. He would lay himself over the water, and the others would walk across him, first Coal and then Bean. Coal walked ahead, and Bean came tripping after. But when Coal reached the middle of the straw, it caught fire and burned through. Coal fell into the water hissing, and died. Straw floated away in two pieces. Bean, who had lagged behind, also slid in, but he managed to keep barely afloat by swimming. However, he swallowed so much water that he burst, and in this condition drifted ashore. Fortunately a tailor was sitting there, resting from his travels. He had needle and thread at hand, and he sewed Bean back together. And from that time forth, all beans have had a seam.

---

[315]Type 2021. Source: *Kinder- und Hausmärchen*, 1st ed. (Berlin, 1812/1815), v. 1, no. 80.

483

According to another story, it was the bean who first walked across the straw. He got across safely, and from the opposite bank watched the coal attempt to cross. Midway the coal burned the straw in two, and fell into the water hissing. When the bean saw this, he laughed so loudly that he burst. The tailor, who was sitting on the bank, sewed him back together, but he had only black thread, and for this reason all beans have a black seam.[316]

The Pancake

Norway

Once upon a time there was a good housewife, who had seven hungry children. One day she was busy frying pancakes for them, and this time she had used new milk in the making of them. One was lying in the pan, frizzling away—ah! so beautiful and thick—it was a pleasure to look at it. The children were standing round the fire, and the husband sat in the corner and looked on.

"Oh, give me a bit of pancake, mother, I am so hungry!" said one child.

"Ah, do! dear mother," said the second.

"Ah, do! dear, good mother," said the third.

"Ah, do! dear, good, kind mother," said the fourth.

"Ah, do! dear, good, kind, nice mother," said the fifth.

"Ah, do! dear, good, kind, nice, sweet mother," said the sixth.

"Ah, do! dear, good, kind, nice, sweet, darling mother," said the seventh. And thus they were all begging for pancakes, the one more prettily than the other, because they were so hungry, and such good little children.

"Yes, children dear, wait a bit until it turns itself," she answered—she ought to have said "until I turn it"— "and then you shall all have pancakes, beautiful pancakes, made of new milk—only look how thick and happy it lies there."

When the pancake heard this, it got frightened, and all of a sudden, it turned itself and wanted to get out of the pan, but it fell down in it again on the other side, and when it had been fried a little on that side too, it felt a little stronger in the back, jumped out on the floor, and rolled away, like a wheel, right through the door and down the road.

"Halloo!" cried the good wife, and away she ran after it, with the frying pan in one hand and the ladle in the other, as fast as she could, and the children behind her, while the husband came limping after, last of all.

---

[316]Type 295. Source: *Kinder- und Hausmärchen*, 1st ed. (Berlin, 1812/1815), v. 1, no. 18.

"Halloo, won't you stop? Catch it, stop it. Halloo there!" they all screamed, the one louder than the other, trying to catch it on the run, but the pancake rolled and rolled, and before long, it was so far ahead, that they could not see it, for the pancake was much smarter on its legs than any of them.

When it had rolled a time, it met a man.

"Good day, pancake!" said the man.

"Well met, Manny Panny," said the pancake.

"Dear pancake," said the man, "don't roll so fast, but wait a bit and let me eat you."

"When I have run away from Goody Poody and the husband and seven squalling children, I must run away from you too, Manny Panny," said the pancake, and rolled on and on, until it met a hen.

"Good day, pancake," said the hen.

"Good day, Henny Penny," said the pancake.

"My dear pancake, don't roll so fast, but wait a bit and let me eat you," said the hen.

"When I have run away from Goody Poody and the husband and seven squalling children, and from Manny Panny, I must run away from you too, Henny Penny," said the pancake, and rolled on like a wheel down the road. Then it met a cock.

"Good day, pancake," said the cock.

"Good day, Cocky Locky," said the pancake.

"My dear pancake, don't roll so fast, but wait a bit and let me eat you," said the cock.

"When I have run away from Goody Poody and the husband and seven squalling children, from Manny Panny, and Henny Penny, I must run away from you too, Cocky Locky," said the pancake, and rolled and rolled on as fast as it could. When it had rolled a long time, it met a duck.

"Good day, pancake," said the duck.

"Good day, Ducky Lucky," said the pancake.

"My dear pancake, don't roll so fast, but wait a bit and let me eat you," said the duck.

"When I have run away from Goody Poody and the husband and seven squalling children, from Manny Panny, and Henny Penny, and Cocky Locky, I must run away from you too, Ducky Lucky," said the pancake, and with that it fell to rolling and rolling as fast as ever it could. When it had rolled a long, long time, it met a goose.

Good day, pancake," said the goose.

"Good day, Goosey Poosey," said the pancake.

"My dear pancake, don't roll so fast, but wait a bit and let me eat you," said the goose.

"When I have run away from Goody Poody and the husband and seven squalling children, from Manny Panny, and Henny Penny, and Cocky Locky, and Ducky Lucky, I must run away from you too, Goosey Poosey," said the pancake, and away it rolled. So when it had rolled a long, very long time, it met a gander.

485

Good day, pancake," said the gander.

"Good day, Gander Pander," said the pancake.

"My dear pancake, don't roll so fast, but wait a bit and let me eat you," said the gander.

"When I have run away from Goody Poody and the husband and seven squalling children, from Manny Panny, and Henny Penny, and Cocky Locky, and Ducky Lucky, and Goosey Poosey, I must run away from you too, Gander Pander," said the pancake, and rolled and rolled as fast as it could. When it had rolled on a long, long time, it met a pig.

Good day, pancake," said the pig.

"Good day, Piggy Wiggy," said the pancake, and began to roll on faster than ever.

Nay, wait a bit," said the pig, "you needn't be in such a hurry-scurry; we two can walk quietly together and keep each other company through the wood, because they say it isn't very safe there."

The pancake thought there might be something in that, and so they walked together through the wood; but when they had gone some distance, they came to a brook.

The pig was so fat it wasn't much trouble for him to swim across, but the pancake couldn't get over.

"Sit on my snout," said the pig, "and I will ferry you over."

The pancake did so.

"Ouf, ouf," grunted the pig, and swallowed the pancake in one gulp, and as the pancake couldn't get any farther—well, you see we can't go on with this story any farther, either.[317]

The Starving Children

Jacob and Wilhelm Grimm

There was once a woman who came into such poverty with her two daughters that they did not have a bit of bread left to put into their mouths. When their hunger became so great that the mother had given up hope, she said to the oldest one, "I must kill you, so that I will have something to eat." The daughter said, "Oh, dear mother, spare me; I will go out and see that I get something to eat without begging." Then she went out and came back with a little piece of bread, which they ate together; but it was too little to still their hunger. Therefore the mother began speaking to her other daughter, "Then you must be the one." But she

---

[317]Type 2025. Source: H. L. Brækstad, *Round the Yule Log* (ca. 1890).

answered, "Oh, dear mother, spare me; I will go somewhere else and find something to eat without being noticed." Then she went forth and came back with two little pieces of bread, but it was too little to still their hunger. Therefore after a few hours the mother once again said to them, "You two must die after all, for otherwise we will suffer a slow death." To this they answered, "Mother dear, we want to lie down and sleep and not get up again until the Day of Judgment comes." Then they lay down and slept a deep sleep from which no one could awaken them; but the mother went away, and no one knows where she is.[318]

The Rose

Jacob and Wilhelm Grimm

Once there was a poor woman who had two children. The youngest one had to go into the forest every day to fetch wood. Once when he had gone a very long way to find wood, a child who was very little but very strong came to him and helped him gather the wood and carried it up to his house, but then in the wink of an eye he disappeared. The child told his mother about this, but she didn't believe him. Finally the child brought a rose and said that the beautiful child had given it to him and that when the rose was in full blossom he would come again. The mother placed the rose into water. One morning the child did not get up; the mother went to his bed and found him lying there dead. On that same morning the rose came into full blossom.[319]

---

[318]Grimm, *Kinder- und Hausmärchen*, 1st ed. (Berlin, 1812/1815), v. 2, no. 57. Because of its tragic outcome and its legendary quality, this tale was omitted from all succeeding editions.

[319]Source: *Kinder- und Hausmärchen*, 2nd ed. (Berlin, 1819), *Kinderlegenden*, no. 3. For similar accounts of foretold deaths, see the Grimms' *Deutsche Sagen*, nos. 263-267.

God's Food

Jacob and Wilhelm Grimm

Once there were two sisters; the one had no children and was rich; the other had five children, was a widow, and was so poor that she no longer had enough bread to feed herself and her children. In distress she went to her sister and said, "My children and I are starving. You are rich; give me a bite of bread." The rich but hard-hearted woman said, "I don't have anything in my house either," and with angry words she sent the poor woman away. Some time later the rich sister's husband came home and wanted to cut himself a piece of bread, but when he cut into the loaf, red blood gushed from it. When his wife saw this, she became horrified and told him what had happened. He hurried away and wanted to help. When he entered the poor widow's room, he found her there praying. She was holding the two youngest children in her arms; the three oldest ones were lying there dead. He offered her food, but she answered, "We no longer need earthly food; God has filled three already, and will hear our prayers as well." She had hardly uttered these words when the two small ones stopped breathing, whereupon her heart broke too, and she sank down dead.[320]

The Willful Child

Jacob and Wilhelm Grimm

Once upon a time there was a child that was stubborn and did not do what his mother wanted. For this reason God was displeased with him[321] and caused him to fall ill. No doctor could help him, and in a short time he lay on his deathbed. He was buried in a grave and covered with earth, but his little arm came forth and reached up, and it didn't help when they put it back in and put fresh earth over it, for the little arm always came out again. So the mother herself had to go to the grave and beat the little arm with a switch, and as soon as she had done that, it withdrew, and the child finally came to peace beneath the ground.[322]

---

[320]Source: *Kinder- und Hausmärchen*, 2nd ed. (Berlin, 1819), *Kinderlegenden*, no. 5.

[321]The Grimms refer to the child with the pronoun "it" throughout this short tale. It could, therefore, be either a boy or a girl.

[322]Type 779. Source: *Kinder- und Hausmärchen*, 1st ed. (Berlin, 1812/1815), v. 2, no. 31 (no. 117 in the final edition).

The Burial Shirt

Jacob and Wilhelm Grimm

A mother had a little boy of seven years who was so attractive and good-natured that no one could look at him without liking him, and he was dearer to her than anything else in the world. He suddenly died, and the mother could find no solace. She cried day and night. However, soon after his burial, the child began to appear every night at those places where he had sat and played while still alive. When the mother cried, he cried as well, but when morning came he had disappeared. The mother did not cease crying, and one night he appeared with the white shirt in which he had been laid into his coffin, and with the little wreath on his head. He sat down on the bed at her feet and said, "Oh, mother, please stop crying, or I will not be able to fall asleep in my coffin, because my burial shirt will not dry out from your tears that keep falling on it." This startled the mother, and she stopped crying. The next night the child came once again. He had a little light in his hand and said, "See, my shirt is almost dry, and I will be able to rest in my grave." Then the mother surrendered her grief to God and bore it with patience and peace, and the child did not come again, but slept in his little bed beneath the earth.[323]

The Parable of the Mustard Seed

India

Kisagotami is the name of a young girl, whose marriage with the only son of a wealthy man was brought about in true fairy-tale fashion. She had one child, but when the beautiful boy could run alone, it died. The young girl, in her love for it, carried the dead child clasped to her bosom, and went from house to house of her pitying friends asking them to give her medicine for it.

But a Buddhist mendicant, thinking "She does not understand," said to her, "My good girl, I myself have no such medicine as you ask for, but I think I know of one who has."

"O tell me who that is," said Kisagotami.

"The Buddha can give you medicine; go to him," was the answer.

She went to Gautama, and doing homage to him said, "Lord and master, do you know any medicine that will be good for my child?"

---

[323]Source: *Kinder- und Hausmärchen*, 1st ed. (Berlin, 1812/1815), v. 2, no. 23 (no. 109 in the final edition).

"Yes, I know of some," said the teacher.

Now it was the custom for patients or their friends to provide the herbs which the doctors required, so she asked what herbs he would want.

"I want some mustard seed," he said; and when the poor girl eagerly promised to bring some of so common a drug, he added, "You must get it from some house where no son, or husband, or parent, or slave has died."

"Very good," she said, and went to ask for it, still carrying her dead child with her.

The people said, "Here is mustard seed, take it."

But when she asked, "In my friend's house has any son died, or husband, or a parent or slave?" they answered, "Lady, what is this that you say; the living are few, but the dead are many."

Then she went to other houses, but one said, "I have lost a son"; another, "We have lost our parents"; another "I have lost my slave."

At last, not being able to find a single house where no one had died, her mind began to clear, and summoning up resolution, she left the dead body of her child in a forest, and returning to the Buddha paid him homage.

He said to her, "Have you the mustard seed?"

"My lord," she replied, "I have not; the people tell me that the living are few, but the dead are many."

Then he talked to her on that essential part of his system—the impermanence of all things, till her doubts were cleared away, and, accepting her lot, she became a disciple and entered the first path.[324]

The Old

The Sick Lion

Aesop

A lion had come to the end of his days and lay sick unto death at the mouth of his cave, gasping for breath. The animals, his subjects, came round him and drew nearer as he grew more and more helpless. When they saw him

---

[324]Source: T. W. Rhys Davids, *Buddhism: Being a Sketch of the Life and Teachings of Gautama, the Buddha* (London, 1907), pp. 133-134.

on the point of death they thought to themselves, "Now is the time to pay off old grudges." So the boar came up and drove at him with his tusks; then a bull gored him with his horns; still the lion lay helpless before them. So the donkey, feeling quite safe from danger, came up, and turning his tail to the old lion kicked up his heels into his face. "This is a double death," growled the lion.

Moral: Only cowards insult dying majesty.

Another moral: The bigger they are, the harder they fall.[325]

The Old Man and Death

Aesop

An old laborer, bent double with age and toil, was gathering sticks in a forest. At last he grew so tired and hopeless that he threw down the bundle of sticks, and cried out, "I cannot bear this life any longer. Ah, I wish Death would only come and take me!"

As he spoke, Death, a grisly skeleton, appeared and said to him, "What do you want, mortal? I heard you call me."

"Please, sir," replied the woodcutter, "would you kindly help me to lift this faggot of sticks onto my shoulder?"

Moral: We would often be sorry if our wishes were gratified.[326]

The Place Where There Were No Graves

Egypt

There was a man who married a wife of whom he was very fond. But after a while the wife died. Then the man wandered away in order to find a country in which no one died. So he went from place to place, looking for a town

---

[325]Type 50C. Source: Joseph Jacobs, *The Fables of Aesop* (London, 1894), no. 9.

[326]Type 845. Source: Joseph Jacobs, *The Fables of Aesop* (London, 1894), no. 69.

where there were no graves. At last he came to a town in the Sudan where there were no graves. So he remained here, in the house of the sheik. The sheik made a feast for him, and first offered him a piece of a roasted leg.

"Where is your father?" asked the man.

"This is his leg," said the sheik, "the rest of him is up there," pointing to a shelf.

Then the man learned that when anyone fell ill, he was killed and eaten, and that this was the reason there were no graves. So in the night he ran away back to his own country.[327]

Godfather Death

Europe

When, long ago and far away, a thirteenth child was born to a poor family, there was great concern that no one could be found who would serve as godfather. The father set forth to find a willing and appropriate person when he encountered Death, who volunteered to be the child's godfather.

"At least it must be said that you are just," said the man, "for you treat the rich and the poor alike." And the agreement was struck.

The thirteenth child grew and prospered. He became a famous physician. Prompted by his godfather, he refused to treat those whose fate it was to die, taking only those patients who were destined to recover. His fame and fortune grew.

One day the godfather offered to show the physician the place where the lights of the living were kept. The physician, eager to learn more about the mysteries of life and death, followed the godfather into an underground chamber, illuminated by thousands of lit candles, some long, some short, some burning brightly, some flickering and going out.

"Each candle is a life," said the godfather.

"And whose is this one?" asked the physician, pointing to a short candle threatening to go out.

"That candle belongs to you," answered the godfather.

The physician, seeing that his light was about to die, found a fresh, unlit candle and held it to the flickering flame. But in so doing, he pushed the short candle to the floor, and the flame went out.

That night the renowned physician died.[328]

---

[327]Source: A. H. Sayce, "Cairene and Upper Egyptian Folk-Lore," *Folk-Lore: Transactions of the Folk-Lore Society*, v. 31, no. 3 (September 1920), p. 178.

[328]Type 332. Retold from various European sources.

Death's Messengers

Europe

Death entered into a pact with a young man, agreeing not to come for him without first sending messengers in advance. Some years later Death appeared, saying, "Your time has come."

"But you did not send your messengers in advance," said the man. "You can't take me yet."

"Has your sight not dimmed?" asked Death. Is not your hair thin and gray? Your back hunched? Your arms weak? And your once long stride now a feeble shuffle?"

"That is true," admitted the man, then started to protest anew.

"Those were my messengers," said Death, interrupting him abruptly. "Your failure to recognize them changes nothing. Your time has come."[329]

The Stolen Corpse

Europe

A family that I met in Germany in 1964 told me about friends of theirs who had taken a vacation trip to Italy one or two years earlier. At first it seemed that one of them would have to stay home with their aging grandmother, who was too sickly to be left alone, but finally they decided to take her along, even though it would be crowded in their small car. About a week into their vacation, the old woman died. Not wanting to deal with the Italian and Austrian authorities, they packed the corpse into a large trunk and tied it on top of their car. However, at a meal stop someone stole the trunk. They were sorry that their grandmother could not be buried in her native country, but they could not help but laugh when they thought of the Italian thieves opening up their stolen goods.[330]

---

[329]Type 335. Retold from various European sources.

[330]Source: Personal recollection, Braunschweig, Germany, 1964. Jan Harold Brunvand gives numerous examples, with interpretations, of this and related urban legends in *The Vanishing Hitchhiker*, ch. 5. See also Katherine M. Briggs, *A Dictionary of British Folk-Tales* (London, 1971), part B, v. 2, pp. 769-771; and Alan Dundes, "On the Psychology of Legend," in *American Folk Legend; A Symposium*, Wayland D. Hand, ed. (Berkeley, 1971), pp. 33-36. The legend was built into the popular film *National Lampoon's Vacation* starring Chevy Chase.

Epilogue

The Golden Key

Jacob and Wilhelm Grimm

Once in the wintertime when the snow was very deep, a poor boy had to go out and fetch wood on a sled. After he had gathered it together and loaded it, he did not want to go straight home, because he was so frozen, but instead to make a fire and warm himself a little first. So he scraped the snow away, and while he was thus clearing the ground he found a small golden key. Now he believed that where there was a key, there must also be a lock, so he dug in the ground and found a little iron chest. "If only the key fits!" he thought. "Certainly there are valuable things in the chest." He looked, but there was no keyhole. Finally he found one, but so small that it could scarcely be seen. He tried the key, and fortunately it fitted. Then he turned it once, and now we must wait until he has finished unlocking it and has opened the lid. Then we shall find out what kind of wonderful things there were in the little chest.[331]

---

[331]Type 2260. Source: *Kinder- und Hausmärchen*, 2nd ed. (Berlin, 1819), no. 161 (no. 200 in the final edition). By closing their collection with this enigmatic tale without an end, the Grimms seem to be saying that folktales, too, are endless. There is no final word.